# TRANSPORTING DANGEROUS GOODS BY TRUCK

PUBLISHED BY

## THE CANADIAN TRUCKING ALLIANCE

in conjunction with:

British Columbia Trucking Association

Alberta Motor Transport Association

Saskatchewan Trucking Association

Manitoba Trucking Association

Ontario Trucking Association

Association du camionnage du Quebec
(Quebec Trucking Association)

Atlantic Provinces Trucking Association

Eleventh Printing

Revised December 2010

This Guide supersedes all previous versions. It contains editorial changes that reflect recent regulatory interpretations and amendments.

# PREFACE

The Transportation of Dangerous Goods Act and Regulations is a comprehensive body of legislation that governs the handling, offering for transport and transporting of dangerous goods in Canada. The Transportation of Dangerous Goods Act 1992 remains in effect. The Transportation of Dangerous Goods Regulations were substantially revised effective August 15, 2002. Since then there have been several revisions. This Guide contains all revisions that have been made up to the time of publication and provides information to assist in understanding and complying with these requirements. It is intended for employees of trucking companies and others as a reference and to supplement training provided by employers.

**This book is a guide only and carries no legal authority. In all cases, reference should be made to the full official text of the Act and Regulations.**

**Important notes to readers:**

This version of the Guide contains all the amendments made to the Transportation of Dangerous Goods Regulations until the time of publication. The reader is cautioned that there will be further amendments in the future, which may affect the explanations contained herein.

Determined efforts have been made to ensure the accuracy of the information in this Guide. However, it consists of interpretations and explanations that may not be complete, accurate or applicable in every situation. The Canadian Trucking Alliance assumes no responsibility for the interpretation or use of this Guide and/or any consequences whatsoever arising from its use.

The Canadian Trucking Alliance expressly disclaims the making of any representation, express or implied, with respect to the information published herein. **In all cases, persons involved with dangerous goods should refer to the full text of the Transportation of Dangerous Goods Act and its Regulations.***

*These may be found at: {http://www.tc.gc.ca/eng/acts-regulations/acts-1992c34.htm}

ISBN 0-920969-88-7

# CONTENTS

# Introduction

Many products, substances or organisms are dangerous to life, health, property or the environment. They may occur naturally or be manmade. These products pose immediate dangers such as toxicity, fire, explosion, asphyxiation, or burns, and long-term dangers such as polluting of the environment. They are classified in legislation as **dangerous goods**. They must be handled and transported properly according to the Transportation of Dangerous Goods Act and Regulations.

To ensure the safety of drivers, the public and the environment, the TDG Act and Regulations are in place to govern:

· The handling of dangerous goods.
· The offering of dangerous goods to a carrier for transportation.
· The transportation of dangerous goods.

## Overview of Dangerous Goods Regulations

The Transportation of Dangerous Goods Regulations are written to reduce the danger posed by these goods during their handling and transport. All handling, offering for transport or transporting of dangerous goods must be carried out in compliance with these Regulations. The Transportation of Dangerous Goods Regulations applicable in Canada are similar to Hazardous Materials Regulations in the United States but have distinctions that are specific to Canada and incorporate certain elements such as the unique numbers used to identify substances that have been developed by the United Nations.

The Transportation of Dangerous Goods Regulations have the following basic elements:

• The way goods are identified as being dangerous, how they are named and classified according to the specific danger(s) they represent
• The way dangerous goods are to be packaged and how that packaging is to be constructed
• The way dangerous goods are identified through the documentation that accompanies a shipment, the marks and labels on a package, and the placards on a vehicle
• The actions that must be taken in response to any accidental release or threat of accidental release of dangerous goods
• The need for all persons to have a sound knowledge of the applicable regulations though training
• Schedules identifying dangerous goods and the specific requirements for each of them.

# Presentation of the Material in this Guide

This guide is divided into several parts:

## Part I - TDG Regulations (Chapters 1 - 4)

This Part provides a basic understanding of TDG Regulations including interpretation of safety standards or requirements, definitions, general provisions, and special cases as well as documentation and safety marks for identification of dangerous goods during handling and transport.

## Part II - General Requirements (Chapters 5 - 8)

This Part describes the specific responsibilities of all persons involved in the handling and transportation of dangerous goods in specific means of containment, including consignors and consignees, carriers, and drivers. The duties and responsibilities of drivers are described, starting before pick up of a shipment and continuing through to the delivery of that shipment. Additional requirements for having an Emergency Response Plan in place - and the steps to take in response to an accidental or imminent release of dangerous goods - are also outlined.

## Part III - Specific Requirements (Chapters 9 - 12)

This Part provides additional information to drivers on issues related to particular types of movements such as when handling more than one shipment of dangerous goods, handling dangerous goods in bulk, exchanging dangerous goods with another carrier and when transporting dangerous goods between Canada and the United States.

## Part IV - Exemptions and Special Requirements (Chapters 13 & 14)

This Part provides information for drivers on particular dangerous goods having additional requirements or an exemption, or partial exemption from the Regulations.

## Appendices

The appendices include additional reference information that may be useful when transporting certain dangerous goods.

## Schedules

The schedules include detailed dangerous goods information in the form of reference tables, including: UN Numbers, Shipping Names & Descriptions, Class, Packing Group/Category, Special Provisions, Limited Quantity Index, Emergency Response Guides, Cross references, and other Dangerous Goods information.

**Note: Before using any Schedule, read and understand the proper use of the information it contains. This information is provided at the beginning of each Schedule.**

# Important Terms Used in this Guide

Certain terms and acronyms are used extensively throughout this Guide. It is important that the reader understands their meanings.

**'Means of containment' (MoC)**

All dangerous goods are transported within some means of containment. For simplicity, there are only two means of containing dangerous goods defined in the Regulations - small and large.

**'Small means of containment'**

A 'small means of containment' has a cargo capacity less than or equal to 450 litres. Examples of a small MoC include cartons, cylinders, boxes, packages, aerosols, etc.

**'Large means of containment'**

A 'large means of containment' has a capacity greater than 450 litres. Examples of a large MoC include semi-trailers, straight trucks, cargo tanks, totes, etc.

**'Means of Transport' (MoT)**

A 'means of transport' is a road vehicle, aircraft, ship, etc., which is used to transport dangerous goods.

This Guide also contains many *examples which are shown in italic type* and **key words and phrases are shown in bold text.**

# Transportation of Dangerous Goods Regulations

1.1 The original Transportation of Dangerous Goods (TDG) Act came into force in 1980, and the supporting Regulations in 1985. The TDG Act was revised in 1992, and remains in effect today. The Regulations have been completely rewritten in a version referred to as the **Clear Language Version. The revised Regulations became effective August 15, 2002**. Since that time there have been several revisions.

1.2 The aim of this latest revision was to make the Regulations easier to read, understand, and comply with. Better understanding and compliance minimizes the risks associated with the transportation of dangerous goods.

1.3 The TDG regulations apply:
- to all modes of transport: highway, rail, marine, pipeline and air.
- to all persons involved in the transportation process: consignors, carriers and consignees.
- in all jurisdictions: federal, provincial and municipal.

  The provincial governments have generally adopted the federal legislation to promote uniformity. Some differences remain.

  Many municipalities have implemented bylaws specifying routes to be used, or avoided, by vehicles transporting dangerous goods. The signs used to specify such routes are shown in the Driver's Reference.

1.4 The Regulations were written to be as simple as possible. However, a few simple rules can not satisfactorily deal with the many different situations and circumstances that may arise. Many products and classes of dangerous goods have special requirements and exemptions. Most drivers will not need to have a full understanding of the special requirements but for those that do, they are described in Chapter 14.

1.5 Many people besides drivers are involved in the process of preparing dangerous goods for transport and transporting them. Such as: those who manufacture, package, load, prepare shipping documents, and receive goods. Each person has specific responsibilities that he/she must thoroughly understand.

Drivers should have a basic understanding of the responsibilities of others. (A driver could be charged for non-compliance even if the consignor caused the violation). Employers are required to provide training to their employees and issue a Transportation of Dangerous Goods Act Training Certificate that ensures each person has all the necessary information.

1.6 The penalties for non-compliance can be severe. Fines of up to $100,000 and even imprisonment of less than two years can be imposed in the worst cases. To avoid such penalties, a person must be able to prove that he/she has taken all reasonable steps to comply with the legislation.

1.7 For shipments of dangerous goods between Canada and the United States, there are special requirements. Carriers transporting dangerous goods to the United States require a "Hazardous Materials Security Plan", according to the Pipeline and Hazardous Material Safety Administration Office of Hazardous Materials Safety.

1.8 Certain aspects of the transportation of explosives, infectious substances and radioactive materials may be covered by other legislation, such as the Explosives Act and the Packaging and Transport of Nuclear Substances Regulations. Carriers and drivers may be required to register with the federal government or a provincial government to handle these dangerous goods and drivers may need additional special training tailored to these specific dangerous goods.

1.9 The Regulations do not specify what precautions should be taken en route to minimize the risks associated with the transportation and handling of dangerous goods, for example, parking, the use of tunnels, etc., although some Provinces have done so.

1.10 Dangerous goods are shipped in either **small or large means of containment (MoC).** These terms are important. They are defined in Appendix 1. (The term MoC is used in this Guide to describe boxes, cartons, packages, totes, vans, straight trucks, tank trailers, etc.)

**Part 1**

2.1 A substance is classified as dangerous goods if it meets certain criteria set out in the Regulations, *for example, the criteria for toxicity, flammability or corrosiveness.* There are numerous substances that meet these criteria with more being created daily.

2.2 **It is the consignor's responsibility to classify dangerous goods.** The classification of dangerous goods includes its Shipping Name, Class(es), UN Number, and Packing Group. There is also a Compatibility Group for Explosives, a Category for Infectious Substances and a Category for Radioactive Materials.

2.3 **The Shipping Names of substances that are classified as dangerous goods are listed in Schedule 1 of the Regulations.** The names are arranged in UN Number sequence. **Only those Shipping Names shown in the list can be used.** The Shipping Names can be written in a different order as long as the full Shipping Name is used and the word order is that which is commonly used. **The description written in lower case letters following a shipping name must be used to determine the shipping name that most precisely describes the dangerous goods.** Schedule 3 of the Regulations lists the Shipping Names in alphabetical order.

UN Recommendations include UN Numbers and Shipping Names not shown in Schedule 1, which consignors are permitted to use. (If a UN number not shown in Schedule 1 is used, carriers must verify this information before proceeding).

2.4 **Dangerous goods are assigned a unique UN Number**, which is a 4-digit number preceded by the letters UN, *for example, UN1203.* (The use of NA Numbers is not allowed in Canada.)

2.5 All dangerous goods pose danger during transportation, but the dangers differ from one type goods to another. **Dangerous goods are separated into 9 Classes according to the type of danger** they represent. These Classes are:

- **Class 1,** Explosives
- **Class 2,** Gases (A gas, a mixture of gases, an article charged with a gas, or an aerosol.)
- **Class 3,** Flammable Liquids (Liquids that produce flammable vapors at temperatures below the maximum temperature that could be anticipated during transport.)
- **Class 4,** Flammable Solids; Substances Liable to Spontaneous Combustion; Substances That on Contact with Water Emit Flammable Gases
- **Class 5,** Oxidizing Substances and Organic Peroxides
- **Class 6,** Toxic and Infectious Substances (Substances that are liable to cause harm, disease, serious injury or death, if swallowed or inhaled, or contacts human skin.)
- **Class 7,** Radioactive Materials
- **Class 8,** Corrosives (Are known to cause full thickness destruction of human skin, or cause full thickness skin destruction.)
- **Class 9,** Miscellaneous Products, Substances or Organisms (Genetically modified micro-organism that would endanger public safety if released during transport.)

2.6 **Some of the Classes are further separated into Divisions**, which more clearly define specific dangers. A Class with no divisions is indicated by a single number, *for example, Class 3.* Two numbers separated by a decimal point indicate a Class that has been separated into Divisions. *For example, Class 2.1 denotes a product in Class 2, Division 1.*

2.7 **Many dangerous goods are also assigned a Packing Group number**, which identifies the degree of danger represented. Roman numerals are used to show Packing Groups, as follows:

**Packing Group I**:   Most Dangerous

**Packing Group II**:  Moderately Dangerous

**Packing Group III**: Least Dangerous

Class 2, Gases; Class 6.2, Infectious Substances; and Class 7, Radioactive Materials, do not have Packing Groups assigned to them. Class 9 Miscellaneous Products are generally in Packing Group III.

2.8 **Class 1, Explosives** are always in Packing Group II and have six divisions:

- **Class 1.1**, mass explosion hazard;
- **Class 1.2**, projection hazard but not a mass explosion hazard;
- **Class 1.3**, fire hazard and either a minor blast hazard or a minor projection hazard or both but not a mass explosion hazard;
- **Class 1.4**, no significant hazard beyond the package in the event of ignition or initiation during transport;
- **Class 1.5**, very insensitive substances with a mass explosion hazard; and
- **Class 1.6**, extremely insensitive articles with no mass explosion hazard

**Explosives are divided into 13 Compatibility Groups** identified by the letters A, B, C, D, E, F, G, H, J, K, L, N, and S, to indicate which products may be transported safely together. (Appendix 3.) For example, Gunpowder, Compressed, UN0028 is classified as 1.1D (i.e. Class 1, Division 1, Compatibility Group D).

2.9 **Class 6.2, Infectious Substances are divided into Category A or B.** Category A is identified by two UN numbers and shipping names, UN2814, Infectious Substance, Affecting Humans and UN2900, Infectious Substance, Affecting Animals. Category B is identified by one UN number and shipping name, UN3373, Biological Substance, Category B.

2.10 The classification of **Class 7, Radioactive Materials** is harmonized with the Packaging and Transport of Nuclear Substances Regulations. **Class 7, Radioactive Materials are assigned Categories** from I (lowest radiation level) to III (highest radiation level).

2.11 **A quantity of dangerous goods may present more than one type of danger**; it could be both toxic and flammable. When this occurs the Class that presents the greatest danger is the **Primary Class** and any others are **Subsidiary Classes** - shown in parentheses in Schedule 1. *For example, Anhydrous Ammonia, UN1005, is shown as 2.3 (8), which means that its Primary Class is 2.3, Toxic Gas, and its Subsidiary Class is 8, Corrosives.*

2.12 **Some Shipping Names describe more than one product and are listed with more than one Packing Group**. When this occurs, the consignor must determine the appropriate Packing Group according to the specific properties of the product in question. *For example, Butanols, Class 3, UN1120 can be in Packing Group II or in Packing Group III, depending on the degree of danger presented by the specific Butanol.*

2.13 There are approximately 2200 Shipping Names covering a host of different dangerous goods. It is not possible to have a simple set of rules to cover every product. To deal with this, **some dangerous goods are subject to one or more of about 90 Special Provisions** - listed in Schedule 2. The appropriate Special Provision(s) are shown in Column 5 of Schedule 1.

2.14 **Some dangerous goods are listed by a general name rather than by a specific name.** In these cases, the general name is usually followed by the letters N.O.S., meaning Not Otherwise Specified. These products will usually be subject to Special Provision 16, which requires that the technical name of the main component be indicated in parentheses immediately after the Shipping Name, *for example, Flammable Liquids, N.O.S., (Naptha) UN1993.* For each product, the most specific name available must be used.

2.15 Some dangerous goods in certain quantities are more dangerous than others. For those products the consignor must file an Emergency Response Assistance Plan (ERAP) with Transport Canada. Information on ERAPs is given in Chapter 3.

2.16 **Many products have dangerous properties but are not listed by specific product name in Schedule 1.** For such a product, the manufacturer or consignor of one of these products must classify it by determining its properties and level of danger.

2.17 **Some dangerous goods are forbidden to be transported**, *for example, Oxidizing Solid, Water Reactive, N.O.S., UN3121.*

2.18 It is the consignor's responsibility to determine the classification of the dangerous goods, not the carrier's. However, **if a driver notices an error or suspects there might be an error in classification** while the goods are being loaded or transported, he/she must advise the consignor and must not transport the dangerous goods until the classification has been verified.

2.19 **Dangerous goods shipments and/or MoC can and will be detained by an Inspector if the shipment does not comply with the regulations**. In such cases, the Inspector must deliver a Detention Notice to the person who has charge, management or control of the dangerous goods or of the means of containment at the time they are detained. An Inspector may also order a dangerous goods or MoC not be imported into Canada or, when already in Canada, that they be returned to their place of origin.

## Emergency Response Assistance Planning    Chapter 3

3.1 Some dangerous goods in certain quantities are considered more dangerous than others and need to have a suitable response to emergency situations immediately available. This is called an **Emergency Response Assistance Plan, or ERAP**.

3.2 The ERAP must be established by the person offering the goods for transport, or by the person importing them into Canada. (If the shipment is transported from a point in the US through Canada to a destination in the US, or vice versa, and no ERAP has been provided, then the carrier would be considered the importer and would have to provide the ERAP). Another person's ERAP may be used for dangerous goods that are being returned to the manufacturer or producer; or when the goods originate outside Canada and are being transported through Canada to a destination outside Canada. In all cases the person required to obtain the ERAP is still responsible.

3.3 The ERAP will describe the goods, the MoC for the shipment, the geographical area covered, and emergency response capabilities. Transport Canada must approve the Plan and assign a number to it before the dangerous goods can be transported in or through Canada.

3.4 Dangerous goods are often in more than one MoC. The dangerous goods are in the **minimum required MoC**, if, when all other MoC are removed, the dangerous goods are still in a MoC that meets the requirements of the TDG Regulations. *For example, a trailer containing many cylinders of propane would not be the minimum MoC, since, if the trailer were removed the propane would still be in cylinders that complied with the TDG Regulations. Each cylinder would be a minimum MoC.*

3.5 **An ERAP is required when the quantity of dangerous goods in the minimum MoC exceeds a certain limit** - the ERAP Index; shown in Column 7 of Schedule 1. When the dangerous goods are solid the ERAP Index is expressed in kilograms (kg); when liquid in litres (L); when a gas in litres (L); and when explosives either as the net explosive quantity in kilograms or as the number of articles (as explained in section 14.2). *For example, an ERAP is required for a shipment of 15,000L of SULPHURIC ACID, with more than 51% acid, Class 8, UN1830, PG II in a tank vehicle – the ERAP Index in 3000L. As a further example, UN1986 may require an ERAP for Packing Group I but not for Packing Group II or III.*

When the ERAP Index is 0 then any quantity of those dangerous goods requires an ERAP. *For example, an ERAP is required for any quantity of Nitrogen Dioxide, Class 2.3(5.1) (8), UN 1067.*

If no limit is shown in Column 7, then an ERAP is never required. *For example an ERAP is never required for Sodium Hydroxide, Class 8, PG II, UN1824.*

3.6 <u>When the dangerous goods are a gas and are in one minimum MoC</u> that has a capacity less than 100L, an ERAP is required when the capacity of the MoC is greater than the ERAP index. *For example, an ERAP is required for a quantity of Fluorine, Compressed, Class 2.3 (5.1) (8) UN 1045 if it is shipped in cylinders that have a capacity of 30L- the ERAP Index is 25L.*

<u>When the dangerous goods are a gas and are in one or more MoC</u> and at least one MoC has a capacity greater than 100L an ERAP is required when the total capacity of all the MoC is greater than the ERAP Index. *For example, an ERAP is required when 5 cylinders with a capacity of 200L of Sulphur Dioxide, Class 2.3 (8), UN 1079 are being transported, since the total capacity of shipment is 1000L - the ERAP Index is 500L.*

3.7 There are important exceptions when determining an ERAP is required. An ERAP is required when

- the dangerous goods are in **one or more MoC, each of which has a capacity greater than 10% of the ERAP Index, <u>and</u> the total quantity of dangerous goods exceeds the ERAP Limit.** *For example, 1500 kg of Toluene Diisocyanate, Class 6.1, UN2078, PG II in 6 MoC of 250 kg would require an ERAP. The ERAP Index is 1000 kg and the dangerous goods are in MoC greater than 100 kg.*

- **the <u>total quantity</u> of the dangerous goods exceeds the ERAP Index for the following:**
  - Class 1, Explosives. (for explosives not subject to Special Provision 86 when the Net Explosive Quantity is expressed in kilograms, and for explosives subject to Special Provision 86, the amount is expressed as the number of articles)
  - Class 3, Flammable Liquids, with a Subsidiary Class 6.1 Toxic Substances.
  - Class 4, Flammable Solids.
  - Class 5.2, Organic Peroxides that are Type B or Type C.
  - Class 6.1, Toxic Substances that are in Packing Group I.

  *For example, an ERAP is required for a shipment of Calcium Carbide, Class 4.3, UN 1402, PG I if the total weight exceeds 1000 kg.*

- **there is any quantity of some Class 6.2 Infectious Substances.**

3.8 The reference number of the ERAP issued by Transport Canada preceded or followed by the letters "ERP" or "ERAP" or "PIU", and the telephone number to activate the ERAP, must be shown on the Shipping Document.

3.9 Vehicles containing any quantity of dangerous goods that require an ERAP must display placards <u>and</u> UN Numbers on the outside of the MoC (see 4.22 and 9.7).

4.1 All **dangerous goods must be clearly identified** before being handled, offered for transport, or transported. (This ensures that everyone is aware of the potential dangers posed by the goods, and assists the emergency personnel to take the appropriate action in the event of an accidental release of the goods). This is accomplished by:

- having a properly completed Shipping Document accompanying the dangerous goods at all times;
- selecting the appropriate MoC for the dangerous goods;
- properly marking and labelling small MoC; and
- displaying the appropriate placards on the large MoC or MoT (the vehicle), when required.

There are exemptions from the general rules and there are specific requirements for each Class of dangerous goods and for some quantities of dangerous goods. These are described in Chapters 13 and 14.

## SHIPPING DOCUMENTATION

4.2 **All quantities of dangerous goods must be accompanied by a Shipping Document** containing specific information that is easy to identify, legible, and indelibly printed in English or French.

4.3 The consignor, with the carrier's permission, may provide an electronic copy of the Shipping Document. If the carrier allows this, then **the carrier must produce a paper copy of the Shipping Document** to accompany the dangerous goods. (There are some exceptions when a full Shipping Document is not required, as described in Sections 13 and 14).

4.4 **The Shipping Document must be prepared by the consignor**, and must include:

- the **name and address of the consignor's place of business in Canada.** (For imported shipments, the importer is deemed to be the consignor.)
- the **date** on which the Shipping Document was prepared, or given to the carrier.
- a **description for each dangerous goods in the following order**:
  - the **Shipping Name** of the product, from Schedule 1 and, if required by Special Provision 16, the technical name of the main component in parentheses, *for example, Flammable Liquids, N.O.S. (Naptha), 3, UN1993.* The Shipping Name may be in upper or lower case letters, but must be in upper case letters if the name contains descriptive text, *for example, ADHESIVES containing flammable liquid, UN1133.* The words in the Shipping Name may be written in a different order.
  - the **Primary Class** of the dangerous goods, which may be shown as a number only or with the word Class, *for example, Hydrochloric Acid, Class 8, UN1789 or Hydrochloric Acid, 8, UN1789.* For Class 1, Explosives, the Compatibility Group must also be shown, *for example, Cartridges, Signal, 1.3G, UN0054.*
  - the **Subsidiary Class(es),** when applicable, in parentheses, a number only or under the heading "subsidiary class" or following the words "subsidiary class" *for example, Oxygen, Compressed, 2.2 (5.1), UN1072.*
  - the **UN Number**, including the letters UN; *for example UN1072.*
  - the **Packing Group** (except for Class 2, Gases, for which Packing Groups are not assigned), which may be shown under the heading "PG" or following the letters "PG", or the words "Packing Group", *for example, Hydrochloric Acid, 8, UN1789, PG II, or Hydrochloric Acid, 8, UN1789, II;* or the **Category** for Class 6.2, Infectious Substances or for Class 7, Radioactive Materials.
- the **total quantity (weight or volume) of each dangerous goods** expressed in

metric units, except for Class 1, Explosives, which is expressed as the Net Explosive Quantity (NEQ) or number of articles.

- the **number** of labelled small MoC, except for Class 1, Explosives.
- the words "24-hour number" or an abbreviation of these words, followed by **a telephone number at which the consignor can be reached immediately** to provide technical information about the product without breaking the telephone connection made by the caller. With written permission, the telephone number of a competent authority such as CANUTEC may be used.
- if an ERAP is required, the **ERAP number** issued by Transport Canada, and **the telephone number to activate the ERAP**. (This number can be the same as the 24-hour number.)

4.5 If the Shipping Document shows both dangerous goods and other goods, **the dangerous goods must be identified by either:**

- listing them first; or
- highlighting them in a contrasting colour; or
- entering an "X" in front of the dangerous goods in a column headed "Dangerous Goods" or "DG", as shown on the sample Shipping Document below.

4.6 There is no prescribed format for the Shipping Document.

*Examples of the description of dangerous goods as it can appear on the Shipping Document are:*

*Gasoline, 3, UN1203, II; or Gasoline, Class 3, UN1203, PG II; or Gasoline, 3, UN1203, Packing Group II*

*Isobutylamine, Class 3, Subsidiary Class 8, UN1214, Packing Group II; or Isobutylamine, 3 (8), UN1214, PG II*

*Infectious Substance, Affecting Humans, Class 6.2, UN2814, Category A*

4.7 When the **quantity of dangerous goods or the number of means of containment changes during transportation**, such as for multiple deliveries to several different consignees, a single Shipping Document may be used. However, the driver must show each change on the Shipping Document or on an attachment to it.

4.8 If, at any time, **a MoC contains less than 10% of its maximum fill limit,** the quantity of dangerous goods may be described as "**Residue - Last Contained**", followed by the Shipping Name of the dangerous goods on the Shipping Document. This wording may never be used for Class 2, Gases in small MoC or for Class 7, Radioactive Materials.

### SHIPPING DOCUMENT

Initial Carrier: First Rate Trucking Inc.    DATE: 15/08/2002

| TO: ABC PRODUCTS | FROM: XYZ CHEMICALS INC. |
|---|---|
| Address: 31 Black Street | Address: 3620, St-Paul Avenue |
| City: Halifax, NS    Postal Code | CITY: Moncton, NB    Postal Code |

| Item No. | Qty. | DG | Shipping Name, Primary Class, Subsidiary Class(es), UN Number, Packing Group | Total Quantity |
|---|---|---|---|---|
| 1 | 7 Drums | X | SODIUM HYDROXIDE SOLUTION, Class 8, UN1824, PG II | 2000 kg |
| 2 | 20 Cyl. | X | PROPANE, Class 2.1, UN1978 | 900 L |
| 3 | 2 Cyl. | X | SULPHUR DIOXIDE, Classe 2.3 (8), UN1079 | 80 L |
| 4 | 10 Drums | X | SULPHURIC ACID, Class 8, UN1830, PG II | 3600 kg |
| 5 | 5 Rolls | | Paper | 9200 kg |

Carrier: First Rate Trucking    CONSIGNOR SIGNATURE: *Matt Dougas*

CARRIER SIGNATURE: *John Smith*

DATE: 21/08/2002    EMERGENCY RESPONSE ASSISTANCE PLAN #: 123456789

24-HOUR TELEPHONE NUMBER: (902) 555-6543    ERAP TELEPHONE #: (416) 555-0123

4.9 **During transportation, a copy of the Shipping Document must be located** as follows:

- when the driver is in the cab, either within the driver's reach or in a pocket in the driver's door;
- when the driver is not in the cab, either on the driver's seat, in a pocket in the driver's door, or in a location that is clearly visible to anyone entering the vehicle through the driver's door.

When a power unit is unhooked from a trailer (large MoC), the Shipping Document must accompany the load. This means:

- when the dangerous goods are left in a supervised area, the Shipping Document must be left with the person in charge of the supervised area or a designated person.
- when the person in charge of a supervised area leaves the area, the Shipping Document must be placed in a waterproof receptacle attached to the vehicle in a location that is easily identified and readily accessible.
- when there is no one available to take possession of the dangerous goods, the Shipping Document must be placed in a waterproof receptacle attached to the vehicle in a location that is easily identified and readily accessible, for example, when trailers are left at an unattended terminal at weekends.

4.10 Consignors and carriers must retain copies of Shipping Documents for 24 months. Some provincial authorities may require a longer retention period.

## PACKAGING REQUIREMENTS

4.11 It is the **consignor's responsibility** to ensure that dangerous goods are contained in a MoC that meets the performance standard specified in the TDG Regulations. A small MoC will have to be marked to show that it complies with an approved standard. For large MoC, such as a cargo tank, the carrier also has a responsibility to ensure that it meets an approved standard.

## MARKING AND LABELLING SMALL MoC

4.12 A small MoC must be marked by the consignor before it can be filled. It must be marked in a legible and clearly visible manner with:

- a **label** for the Primary Class and each Subsidiary Class of the dangerous goods. If there is more than one consignment of dangerous goods in the MoC, there must be labels for each of them. Labels are illustrated in the Driver's Reference.
- the **Shipping Name** of the goods as it appears in Schedule 1. For dangerous goods that are subject to Special Provision 16, the technical name of the most dangerous component must also be shown in parentheses following the shipping name.
- the **four-digit UN Number**, including the letters UN. This must be placed next to the Primary Class label, or it may be displayed, with the letters UN omitted, within a white rectangle on the Primary Class label. *For example, a small MoC containing Chloroacetic Acid Solution, 6.1 (8), UN1750, PG II would be marked as shown on page 14.*

4.13 **Labels and marks may be applied to any side of a small MoC except the bottom.** Labels must be visible on the small MoC when it is stacked. Labels should be on or near the shoulder of a cylinder.

4.14 When the required labels and marks cannot be displayed because of the irregular shape of the small MoC, the information may be reduced in size and displayed on a tag next to the primary class label that is securely attached to the small MoC.

4.15 **Labels are not required on a MoC that is inside another MoC,** as long as the outer MoC

- has mass less than 30kg;
- is marked with the words "Limited Quantity", or the abbreviation "Ltd Qty", or the words "Consumer Commodity", or the UN number and the letters UN in a diamond shaped label; and

- and is not opened during loading or unloading or while the dangerous goods are in transport. *For example, for small bottles inside a carton - the carton has to be labelled, but the bottles do not.*

4.16 **The labels must remain on the MoC until it has been emptied or unpacked.** The person who performs this duty must remove or cover the dangerous goods safety marks when there is no longer a danger present.

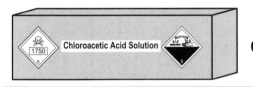 or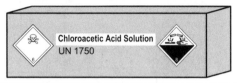

## PLACARDING LARGE MEANS OF CONTAINMENT AND MEANS OF TRANSPORT

4.17 Placards are usually the first identification seen by emergency responders. The information may be quite general (a) DANGER placard) or very specific (a Class placard with a UN Number).

4.18 **Before every large MoC or a MoT can be loaded or packed with dangerous goods, it must display all required placards and UN Numbers.** Examples of placards are shown in the Driver's Reference. When the UN Number is required, it is shown without the letters UN. It may be displayed within a white rectangle on the placard or on an orange panel beside the Primary Class placard, as shown.

4.19 Placarding requirements depend on:

- whether an **ERAP** is required for any of the dangerous goods;
- the primary Class of dangerous goods
- whether there is a **combination of different dangerous goods**; and
- the **quantity of dangerous goods** being shipped. (The weight must always be used to determine the placarding requirements, even if the quantity shown on the Shipping Document is expressed by volume.)

4.20 **When there is only one class of dangerous goods and the weight of those dangerous goods exceeds 500 kg, and an ERAP is not required,** then the large MoC must display the Primary Class placard but not the UN Number.

 or

4.21 **When the total weight of the dangerous goods does not exceed 500 kg,** the large MoC should not be placarded unless the dangerous goods require an ERAP.

4.22 When a quantity of dangerous goods requires an ERAP, the Primary Class placard for those dangerous goods and the UN number must be displayed on the large MoC.

4.23 **When all the dangerous goods have the same UN Number, no ERAP is required, the weight of those dangerous goods** exceeds 4000 kg, and they are shipped by one consignor, the Primary Class placard and UN Number may be displayed. (If other dangerous goods are subsequently placed in the large means of containment, the UN Number should be removed).

4.24 Placarding situations involving 2 or more dangerous goods are explained in Chapter 9. Placarding requirements are summarized on the next page, together with examples, and on the Driver's Reference inside the back cover.

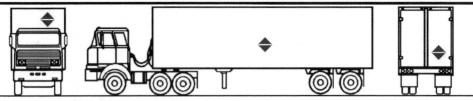

## LOCATION, MAINTENANCE AND REMOVAL OF PLACARDS

4.25 Placards and UN Numbers must be **displayed on all sides of the large MoC.**

4.26 The placard may be displayed on the front of the vehicle, instead of on the leading end of the cargo unit.

4.27 When the large MoC is permanently attached to the vehicle, placards and UN Numbers may be displayed on the frame if the resulting positions are equivalent to each side and end of a large MoC. This provision can not be used for such large MoC as totes and lugger buckets.

4.28 When the vehicle contains a quantity of dangerous goods for which a placard is required, but the placards and UN Numbers, when required, are not visible from outside the vehicle, *for example, a vehicle containing a tote larger than 450 litres,* the placards and UN Numbers, when required, must also be displayed on the outside of the vehicle. When totes or lugger buckets are on a chassis or flat deck they must be placarded, but if the placards are not visible on all four sides then additional placards must be displayed on the vehicle.

4.29 The driver must replace any placards that are lost or damaged while in transit.

4.30 **Placards and UN Numbers must remain on the large MoC.** But, when as a result of the delivery of some dangerous goods the total weight of the dangerous goods becomes less than 500 kg, the placards should be removed unless the quantity is still large enough that an ERAP is required. For example, 400 kg of Nitric Oxide, Compressed, 2.3 (5.1) (8), UN1660 would still require placards to be displayed (the ERAP Index is 0). When all the dangerous goods have been unloaded, the placards must be removed.

4.31 There are **special requirements for tank trailers** (This is described in Chapter 10).

4.32 There are other signs that must be applied in special circumstances. The **elevated temperature sign,** the **fumigation sign,** and the **marine pollutant sign** are described in Chapter 14. There are 3 new safety marks for the following goods: Anhydrous ammonia, Class 2.3 (8) gas; Category B Mark Infectious Substances, Class 6.2; and Radioactive Materials, Class 7. These special signs are illustrated in the Driver's Reference inside the back cover.

# Summary of Placarding Requirements

| Number of goods with different UN | Weight of dangerous goods being transported and ERAP requirements | Placard and UN Number Requirements | Examples | |
|---|---|---|---|---|
| | | | Dangerous Goods | Placard and UN Number Requirements |
| 1 | Greater than 500 kg, no ERAP | Primary Class placard | 1000 kg Acetone, Class 3, UN1090 | Class 3 without UN number |
| 1 | Any quantity, ERAP required | Primary Class placard wiht UN Number | 3500 kg Calcium, class 4.3, UN1401 | Class 4.3 with UN Number 1401 |
| 1 | More than 4000 kg from one consignor which are the only dangerous goods present | Primary Class placard with UN Number **OR** Primary Class placard | 5000 kg Sodium Hydroxide Solution, Class 8, UN1824 | Class 8 with UN Number 1824 **OR** Class 8 placard only |
| 1 or more | Total weight less than 500 kg, no ERAP | None | | |
| 2 or more | Dangerous goods are in different Primary Classes, the total weight is greater than 500 kg, and no ERAP | Primary Class placard for each Class **OR** DANGER* Placard | 400 kg Acetone, Class 3, UN1090 and 300 kg Sodium Hyrdroxide Solution, Class 8, UN1824 | Class 3 without UN Number and Class 8 without UN Number **OR** DANGER* |
| 2 or more | Total weight of all dangerous goods is more than 500 kg and dangerous goods are all in the same Primary Class, no ERAP | Primary Class placard | 400 kg Acetone, Class 3, UN1090 and 300 kg Kerosene, Class 3, UN1223 | DANGER* **OR** Class 3 without UN Number |
| 2 or more | Any Weight of dangerous goods with UN Numbers all of which require ERAP | Primary Class placard with UN Number for each dangerous goods | 2000 kg Methyl Iodide, Class 6.1, UN2644 and 3500 kg Calcium, Class 4.3, UN1401 | Class 6.1 with UN Number 2644 and Class 4.3 with UN Number 1401 |
| 2 or more | Total weight of dangerous goods more than 500 kg. ERAP required for at least one dangerous goods | Primary Class placard with UN Number for each ERAP product **AND** Placards are required for **OTHER** dangerous goods when considered as they were the only dangerous goods present | 2000 kg Methyl Iodide, Class 6.1, UN2644 and 3500 kg Calcium, Class 4.3, UN 1401 | Class 6.1 with UN Number 2644 and Class 4.3 with UN Number |
| | | | 3500 kg Calcium, Class 4.3, UN1401 and 1000 kg Sodium Hydroxide Solution, Class 8, UN1824 and 1000 kg Acetone, Class 3, UN1090 | Class 4.3 with UN Number 1401 and Class 8 without UN Number and Class 3 without UN Number **OR** Class 4.3 with UN Number 1401 and DANGER* |
| | | | 3500 kg Calcium, Class 4.3, UN1401 and 200 kg Acetone, Class 3, UN1090 | Class 4.3 with UN Number 1401 |
| All | Shipments including Class 1, Explosives and Class 7 Radioactive Materials | See Section 14 | | |
| All | Any Quantity in bulk | See Section 10 | | |

*Note:* The UN number is always required for dangerous goods in a liquid or gas form that are in direct contact with the large means of containment. * Carriers are strongly urged to consult the recently issued Transport Canada Alert 4.15(2) regarding placards and UN numbers that must be displayed on a large means of containment {http://www.tc.gc.ca/eng/tdg/publications-alerts-alert415-236.htm}. Carriers may also wish to verify with the relevant provincial enforcement agency that they are in compliance with the regulation.

Also see the flowchart on the Driver's Reference inside the back cover of this book.

Part 1

**Part 2**

5.1 Everyone involved in the transportation of dangerous goods: consignors, carriers and their drivers, and consignees, has specific responsibilities.

5.2 While it is not the responsibility of the carrier or its drivers to identify dangerous goods, prepare the documentation, or label the packages, it is important for them to have an understanding of those tasks and the responsibilities of the consignors and consignees. An error by anyone involved in the transportation of dangerous goods can result in enforcement actions at roadside or truck inspection station along with creating problems for others that may potentially be life-threatening.

## CONSIGNORS

5.3 The consignor's employees must be properly trained so that they have a sound knowledge of those aspects of the Regulations that relate to their duties. This may include, but is not limited to, classification and naming of dangerous goods; documentation; labels, placards and other markings; specification, selection and use of the MoC; Emergency Response Assistance Planning (ERAP); safe handling practices; reporting accidental releases; and reasonable emergency procedures that must be taken to reduce or eliminate the danger to the public in the event of an accidental release.

5.4 The consignor must ensure that:

- the dangerous goods are properly classified, packaged, and labelled.
- each MoC is of an appropriate specification or type for the dangerous goods being transported, and displays all the required certification, test and inspection information.

- the Shipping Document is correctly filled out and dated.

- a complete set of placards and UN Numbers (if applicable) is provided and affixed <u>before</u> the dangerous goods are loaded. (The consignor does not have to provide placards if they would be incorrect due to the presence of other dangerous goods already on board.)

- the dangerous goods are properly secured in the MoT and there are no leaks.

5.5 The consignor may, with the carrier's permission, provide an electronic version of the Shipping Document rather than a paper version.

5.6 The consignor must retain the Shipping Document for 24 months. It may be stored electronically.

## CARRIERS

5.7 The carrier's employees must be properly trained so that they have a sound knowledge of those aspects of the Regulations that relate to their duties. This includes, but is not limited to, the classification and naming of dangerous goods; documentation; labels, placards and other markings; specification, selection and use of a large MoC; Emergency Response Assistance Planning (ERAP); reporting accidental releases; safe handling practices; and reasonable emergency procedures that must be taken to reduce or eliminate the danger to the public in the event of an accidental release. Once a carrier has reasonable grounds to believe that an employee is adequately trained and will perform duties to which the training relates, the carrier must issue a training certificate to the employee, which remains valid for a period of 3 years provided the employee remains employed with the carrier.

5.8 **Before the vehicle is dispatched**, the carrier should establish whether the shipment contains dangerous goods, and obtain the necessary information about it. (For bulk tankers the carrier should ensure that the MoT is of an appropriate specification for the dangerous goods to be transported, is mechanically fit according to equipment regulatory standards and displays all the required certification, test and inspection information.)

5.9 When the consignor has provided an electronic copy of the Shipping Record, the carrier must provide a paper version to accompany the dangerous goods.

5.10 The carrier must retain the Shipping Document for 24 months. It may be stored electronically.

5.11 If the dangerous goods were transported through Canada between two US points, the carrier does not have to retain the Shipping Document.

5.12 If the carrier was involved only in handling the dangerous goods, including storing them during the course of transportation, but not in the transportation of those dangerous goods, the carrier does not have to retain the Shipping Document.

## CONSIGNEES

5.13 The consignee's employees must be properly trained so that they have a sound knowledge of those aspects of the Regulations that relate to their duties. This may include, but is not limited to, the use and removal of labels and placards; safe handling practices; reporting accidental releases; and reasonable emergency procedures that must be taken to reduce or eliminate the danger to the public in the event of an accidental release.

5.14 The consignee must ensure that:
- the shipment is promptly and completely unloaded;
- the appropriate placards are removed from the MoT;
- when the MoT has been fumigated or filled with an inert gas, the appropriate warning signs are affixed to all openings;

5.15 The labels must remain on a small MoC until it has been emptied, purged or unpacked. The person who performs this duty must remove or cover the dangerous goods safety marks when a danger is no longer present.

Part 2

**Part 2**

**6.1 A driver must be properly trained so that he/she has a sound knowledge of those aspects of the transportation of dangerous goods that relate to his/her duties.** This may include, but is not limited to, classification and naming of dangerous goods; documentation; labels and placards and other markings; Emergency Response Assistance Planning (ERAP); reporting accidental releases; safe handling practices; and reasonable emergency procedures to be taken to reduce or eliminate the danger to the public in the event of an accidental release.

Drivers should have an understanding of the duties of consignors.

6.2 It can be difficult to remember all of the requirements of the TDG Regulations. Drivers should be in the habit of asking themselves the following questions to ensure they are in compliance:

*Does the shipment contain dangerous goods?*

*Is this shipment consistent with the instructions I received from my dispatcher?*

*Do I have the necessary documentation?*

*Are the means of containment labelled properly?*

*Is the vehicle placarded properly?*

*What do I do if there is a spill?*

*Am I handling these products safely?*

*Do I know of all route restrictions during the transportation of the dangerous goods?*

**Driver Responsibility Checklists**

The following check lists identify specific driver responsibilities at each stage of transport.

6.3 Before leaving the terminal, the driver should:

- be aware that he/she is going to be transporting dangerous goods.
- be carrying his/her training valid TDG certificate.
- check that the vehicle is equipped with the necessary emergency equipment - fire extinguisher, reflective triangles or equivalent devices, and any necessary personal protective equipment; although these requirements are not specified in the Regulations.
- have a paper copy of the Shipping Document if the carrier has permitted the consignor to provide an electronic version of it.

6.4 Before taking possession of the dangerous goods, the driver should take all reasonable precautions to ensure that:

- the pick-up of the shipment has been approved and planned by the carrier.
- when the Shipping Document was prepared by the consignor, it is correctly filled out and dated by the consignor.
- the Shipping Document (as described in detail in 4.4) includes:
  - the name and address of the consignor.
  - the date the Shipping Document or an electronic copy of it was prepared or given to the carrier.
  - a description of each quantiity of dangerous goods in the following order - the Shipping Name; the technical name, in parentheses, of the most dangerous substance related to the primary class, if required, in parentheses; the Primary Class; the Subsidiary Class(es), if applicable, in parentheses; the UN Number; and the Packing Group.
  - the total gross weight or volume of each dangerous goods expressed in metric units, except Class 1, Explosives.

- the number of labelled small MoCs, except for Class 1, Explosives.

- a 24-hour telephone number at which the consignor or another approved body such as Canutec can be reached immediately to provide technical information about the product. (Note: The consignor must receive Canutec's permission before using their telephone number.)

- when an ERAP is required, the Emergency Response Assistance Plan reference number, and a telephone number to activate the ERAP.

• there are no discrepancies between the instructions received from the carrier, the information on the Shipping Document, and the physical shipment itself.

• correct labels, placards and UN Numbers, if required, are affixed before the dangerous goods are loaded.

• in those situations when the MoC already contains dangerous goods, the labeling and placarding is correct.

6.5 <u>During loading</u> (if loading takes place in the presence of the driver) the driver should ensure that:

• the shipment is labelled and marked.

• there is no leakage - packages, drums, or pails should not be accepted if they are leaking, dented, rusted, punctured, crushed, or show wet marks.

• the dangerous goods are securely blocked or braced to prevent movement during transportation.

6.6 <u>During transportation</u>, the driver must ensure that:

• the correct placards are maintained - any lost or damaged placards must be replaced immediately.

• the placards are changed or removed when the requirements change during transport.

• a copy of the Shipping Document is:

- located within reach, either on the passenger seat or in a pocket in the driver's door, when the driver is in the cab.

- located either on the driver's seat, in a pocket in the driver's door, or in a location easily seen by anyone entering the cab through the driver's door, when the driver is not in the cab; (it is a good practice to place dangerous goods Shipping Documents on top of any other shipping documents).

- given to the person in charge of a supervised area, or placed in a waterproof container on the outside of the large MoC or vehicle if the power unit is uncoupled from the trailer.

• changes to the shipment during transportation are noted on the Shipping Document.

• he/she is carrying the valid training certificate issued by the employer.

6.7 <u>At the delivery site</u> the driver must ensure that all the placards are removed, unless the MoC still contains other dangerous goods, in which case, the driver must ensure that the correct placards remain on the MoC or MoT.

6.8 When a driver notices or suspects an error in classification, he/she must stop loading or transporting the dangerous goods immediately, and not resume until the consignor verifies or corrects the classification. The consignor must do so immediately upon a request by the driver, and ensure the driver is provided with the verified or corrected information.

**General Driver Duties**

6.9 Although not part of the current DG Regulations, precautions should be taken to ensure that dangers associated with the movement are minimized. With the increased concern regarding terrorism additional precautions should be taken. The following safe operating practices and general rules for handling freight are recommended for drivers:

- Treat containers with care to avoid damage that could release dangerous goods.

- Protect containers from moisture, as wet packages break will more easily, and moisture can react with certain dangerous goods.

- Do not discuss information related to their load, route, or delivery schedule with any person(s) other than authorized company officials.

- Report any suspicious activity (including load-related inquiries from strangers) to their supervisors immediately and prior to transporting any load of dangerous goods.

- Be alert while driving and when stopped for possible surveillance by following vehicles or anyone approaching the vehicle.

- Carry out the freight movements with a minimum of delay and reduce the need for unnecessary or unplanned stops.

- Understand special routing instructions and designated dangerous goods routes established by municipalities. If no specific routes are designated, then whenever practical, and with the agreement of the consignor, the route should avoid tunnels, heavily populated areas, schools and hospitals.

- Do not leave the vehicle unattended unnecessarily or parked where it presents a danger.

- Shut off the engine and lock the vehicle whenever it is left unattended. Never leave the vehicle with the engine running or the keys in it.

- Park in safe, well lit, designated truck parking locations only (such as reputable truck stops or high-traffic, major rest areas). When possible, trailers loaded with hazardous materials should be parked against a wall, fence, or other stationary/fixed object to enhance cargo security

- Do not park in any unsecured area on or close to the travelled portion of the highway unless absolutely necessary. Keep the vehicle within view.

- Take special precautions at railroad crossings. In the U.S. vehicles displaying placards must stop at railroad crossings. In most Canadian provinces, vehicles carrying Class 1, Explosives must stop at railroad crossings. In Quebec vehicles displaying placards must stop at railroad crossings and the transportation of dangerous goods through certain tunnels is prohibited, as described in 14.56.

- Check the vehicle and load regularly to ensure placards are in place, there are no leaks, the vehicle has no apparent problems and seals have not been tampered with.

- Inspect their vehicle and trailer for evidence of tampering after each stop.

- Check that tires are properly inflated and are not overheating.

- Have a copy of the latest edition of the Emergency Response Guide (the latest edition reproduced in Schedule 4).

- Do not smoke close to a vehicle transporting any dangerous goods, in particular those in Classes 1, 2.1, 3, 4 and 5. Smoking can be an offence under different legislation, such as the Explosives Act.

- Park the vehicle in a controlled area; and have appropriate protective equipment available.

- Do not pick up and transport any unauthorized person.

6.10 In the event that there is an accidental release or an imminent accidental release of the dangerous goods, the driver:

  - must report the incident immediately (as explained in Chapter 7).

  - should not enter the immediate hazard area, and should keep people away from the scene.

**Do not attempt anything unless you are trained by your employer and have the appropriate protective equipment available. Protect yourself, and then others if it will not jeopardize your safety. Resist the urge to rush in; you cannot help others until you know what you are facing. Do not move the injured if it could cause additional injury.**

## EMERGENCY REPORTING REQUIREMENTS

7.1 An **Accidental Release** is an unplanned or accidental discharge, emission, explosion, outgassing or other escape of dangerous goods, or of any component or compound evolving from dangerous goods from any MoC, that exceeds a certain quantity depending on the Class of dangerous goods. These quantities are shown in the Driver's Reference.

7.2 An **Imminent Accidental Release** applies only to large MoC, and is an incident in which:

- there is likely to be a need to transfer or remove all or a portion of the dangerous goods from one large MoC to another; or
- there is damage to the MoC which could result in an accidental release in a quantity or emission level exceeding those listed in the Driver's Reference.

7.3 An **accidental release must be reported** when the dangerous goods that have been released exceed the quantities shown in the Driver's Reference.

7.4 **The person in charge of the dangerous goods at the time of an occurrence** must immediately notify, or cause to be notified, the following:

- the local police and/or other local authorities, these are listed in the Driver's Reference;
- his/her employer;
- the consignor of the dangerous goods; &
- the owner or lessee of the vehicle.

For Class 1, Explosives and Class 6.2, Infectious Substances, or major failures of cylinders CANUTEC must also be called at (613) 996-6666.

7.5 There is no prescribed format for the report. However it must contain the following information:

- Shipping Name or UN Number of the dangerous goods;
- original quantity of dangerous goods in the MoC, and the amount known or suspected to have been released;
- the condition of the MoC (damage, etc);
- the conditions of transportation when event occurred (weather, traffic, etc);
- location of the event;
- number of deaths and/or injuries;
- number of people evacuated.

## 30-DAY INCIDENT REPORTING

7.6 If an immediate report was made, then a follow-up report in writing must be made by the employer of the person who had possession of the dangerous goods at the time of the accidental release within 30 days to the Transport Dangerous Goods Director General. The report must contain all the details that were included in the immediate report. There is no prescribed format for this report. When an ERAP is activated, the name of the person who responded to the emergency in accordance with the ERAP must be included in the report.

### Emergency Procedures

**When an incident occurs: Secure the site and ensure that there is no smoking in the incident area. While maintaining a safe distance from the spill, prevent access to individuals not familiar with the dangers of the material released. If the incident involves vehicles, erect safety reflectors (as required by Canadian Federal or Provincial Transportation Regulations or U.S. Department of Transportation (DOT).**

**Assess the situation only if and when it is safe to do so. Review the shipping papers, manifests, placards, to identify the material(s) released and their potential dangers. Estimate the quantity of material(s) released and identify the source and location of the release. Evaluate the extent of property damage or injuries, and determine whether it is safe to approach the injured. For incidents in Canada and the U.S., consult the Emergency Response Guidebook (ERG).**

## EMERGENCY RESPONSE GUIDELINES

7.7 The driver is responsible to report an incident to the authorities, their employer, and the owner of the dangerous goods.

The immediate hazard area should not be entered, and people should be kept away from the scene.

7.8 There are **62 Emergency Response Guides** that assist emergency response personnel to quickly identify and respond to the specific hazards of dangerous goods involved in an incident. Drivers transporting dangerous goods (hazardous materials) in the U.S. must have this emergency response information immediately accessible to them (49CFR 172.602). **All the information that is necessary for drivers to carry is provided in Schedules 3 & 4.**

(The Emergency Response Guides are part of the more extensive 2008 Emergency Response Guidebook developed by Transport Canada and the US Department of Transportation and designed for use primarily by emergency response personnel that includes other general emergency response information.)

7.9 The **Emergency Response Guides** are numbered from 111 to 172 and include safety recommendations for each hazard, provided in three sections - the potential hazard(s) listed in order of risk; suggested public safety measures; and emergency response actions. (See Schedule 4.)

7.10 **The Emergency Response Guide Number** applicable for each of the dangerous goods is shown in Schedule 3. *For example, the hazard properties and appropriate emergency response for Propane, Flammable Gas 2.1, UN1978 are shown in Emergency Response Guide #115.*

## 7.11 REPORTING DANGEROUS GOODS THAT ARE LOST OR STOLEN

Transport Canada has issued an Interim Order which was effective on August 9, 2009. (The order may be replaced by a permanent amendment to the Regulations at a later date).

When during the course of handling or transporting dangerous goods, (other than dangerous goods in Class 9), it is discovered that ANY of the dangerous goods, however small, have been lost, stolen or unlawfully interfered with; it must be reported immediately to:

- the local police;
- CANUTEC at 613 996-6666; and
- for dangerous goods in Class 7 to the Canadian Nuclear Safety Commission at 613 995-0479.

Note: This requirement is different from the normal incident reporting requirements described in Chapter 7 (page 23) and in the Driver's Reference.

The report must contain the following information

- name of the person reporting, employer's name and contact information;
- name and addresses of the consignor and consignee;
- classification of the dangerous, including Shipping Name, Primary Class, Compatibility Group, Subsidiary Class, UN Number, Packing Group, and Infectious Substance Category;
- quantity of dangerous goods;
- description of the means of containment (package, drum, tote, cylinder, etc.);
- location where the dangerous goods were lost, stolen or unlawfully interfered with; and
- the last time the dangerous goods were seen or were in the possession of the person reporting.

Reports are to be made to:
Transport Dangerous Goods (TDG), Place de Ville, Tower C, 9th Floor, 330 Sparks St., Ottawa, Ontario K1A 0N5

8.1 The employer must ensure that all employees have a sound knowledge of those aspects of handling dangerous goods, offering dangerous goods for transport and transporting dangerous goods that <u>relate directly to their duties</u>, and to the dangerous goods they are expected to handle, offer for transport or transport. **The employer must ensure that training is given** to provide each employee with this required knowledge.

Everyone who handles, offers for transport, or transports dangerous goods must:
- be adequately trained and hold a valid training certificate, or
- be working in the presence of, and under the direct supervision of a trained person.

As drivers are deemed to be unsupervised when in their vehicles, all drivers who transport dangerous goods must be trained.

8.2 A person must be able to identify a dangerous goods shipment, understand safe handling procedures and know what to do in an emergency. **Training may include**, but is not limited to:
- classification, nature and characteristics of the dangerous goods, the Shipping Names and the use of Schedules 1, 2 and 3 of the Regulations
- documentation
- labels, placards, and other safety signs and markings
- specification, selection and use of the MoC (e.g. drum, aerosol container, box, or tank vehicle)
- Emergency Response Assistance Plan (ERAP) requirements
- reporting accidental and imminent releases
- safe handling and transportation practices
- proper use of equipment used to handle and transport dangerous goods

- reasonable emergency procedures that must be taken to reduce or eliminate danger to the public that may result from an accidental and imminent release of goods.

8.3 Upon completion of adequate training, the **employer must provide the employee with a training certificate** that shows:
- the name and address of the employer's place of business.
- the name of the employee.
- the date on which the training certificate expires, preceded by the words "Expires on" (36 months after the training certificate is issued).
- the aspects of handling, offering to a carrier for transport or transporting dangerous goods for which the employee has been trained.

*Example 1, the certificate could show that an employee is trained to handle and transport all dangerous goods;*

*Example 2, the certificate could show that an employee is trained to handle and transport only Class 3, Flammable Liquids;*

*Example 3, the certificate could show that an employee is trained to handle and transport only a single product, for example, Chlorine;*

- the signatures of both the employee and the employer (or employer's designate).

8.4 A **self-employed person**, and in particular, an independent contractor, must issue to himself/herself a training certificate as outlined above, which contains his/her signature. A carrier utilizing the services of an independent contractor (owner/operator) may provide the training.

Part 2

8.5 A driver must produce his/her certificate of training immediately upon request by an inspector or peace officer. If a trained person is directly supervising an untrained person, the trained person must produce his/her certificate immediately upon a similar request.

8.6 An employer (or the self-employed person) must keep a record of the training provided, a description of the training material and a copy of the training certificate. These must be retained for 24 months after their expiry date. The employer (or self-employed person) must produce proof of training within 15 days after the date of a written request by an inspector.

8.7 **A certificate is valid for 36 months after the training certificate is issued.** Before renewing a certificate or issuing a new certificate, the employer must be satisfied that the employee still has the necessary knowledge. At the employer's discretion, an employee may have to undergo retraining before a new certificate is issued.

8.8 Both the driver and employer must ensure that training is up to date. Employees must be kept informed of all changes to the Regulations that relate to their duties. **Additional training may be required during the valid term of the certificate** if an employee's duties change, or if the Regulations change and the employee's duties are affected.

8.9 A **certificate is not transferable** to a new employer. When a person changes employment, the new employer must issue a new certificate of training, after ensuring he/she is adequately knowledgeable to perform the duties of the new position.

8.10 There are additional training requirements for those drivers who transport dangerous goods into the US. Drivers are required to receive training with respect to the employer's security plan, including specific security procedures, employee responsibilities, actions to be taken in the event of a security breach, the company security objectives and organizational security structure.

Specific emergency response information includes measures to protect employees from the hazards associated with hazardous materials to which they may be exposed in the work place. This training must also include specific measures the employer has implemented to protect employees from exposure, as well as methods and procedures for avoiding accidents, such as the proper procedures for handling packages containing hazardous materials.

In addition, the employee must receive training that provides awareness of general security risks associated with the movement of dangerous goods and how to recognize and respond to possible security threats.

**9.1** The requirements for less-than-truckload shipments that contain either dangerous goods combined with non-dangerous goods, or are mixed loads of dangerous goods, or are dangerous goods in quantities not exceeding 500 kg, are summarized in this chapter.

## DOCUMENTATION

**9.2 When a shipment contains both dangerous goods and other goods**, the dangerous goods must be highlighted on the Shipping Document by:

- listing them first; or
- highlighting them in a colour which contrasts with the colour of the information relating to the non-dangerous goods; or
- entering an "X" in front of the dangerous goods in a column headed "Dangerous Goods", or "DG".

## LABELLING

**9.3** Packages containing dangerous goods must be clearly marked with:

- a label indicating the Primary Class;
- the proper Shipping Name;
- the UN Number; and
- label(s) indicating any Subsidiary Class(es), if applicable.

**9.4** Packages that do not contain dangerous goods must not have any markings that might cause them to be mistaken for dangerous goods. However, the packages may contain WHMIS labels (as described in Appendix 4).

## PLACARDING THE VEHICLE

**9.5 When there are two or more dangerous goods with different UN Numbers present, <u>and</u> the total weight of the dangerous goods exceeds 500 kg <u>and</u> none of the dangerous goods requires an ERAP and are not dangerous goods**

**included in Classes 1 or 7,** DANGER placards may be displayed instead of the individual placards for each Class of dangerous goods being transported. However, it is permissible to display Primary Class placards for each of the dangerous goods present.

**9.6 When the total weight of dangerous goods, whether there more than one or not, does not exceed 500 kg, the large MoC should not be placarded unless the dangerous goods require an ERAP.**

When the total weight of dangerous goods becomes less than 500 kg during delivery, the placards should be removed unless the dangerous goods still remaining require an ERAP and are not exempt from the Regulations.

**9.7 When more than one dangerous goods are in the same Primary Class and do not require an ERAP**, then that Primary Class placard must be used.

**9.8 When there are dangerous goods requiring an ERAP present, the Primary Class placard(s) and UN Number(s) for each of those dangerous goods** must be displayed in addition to any placards required by the other products present. The dangerous goods that do not require an ERAP are treated as if they were the only dangerous goods present and the placarding requirements for them are determined accordingly, using DANGER or Primary Class placards without UN Numbers. *For example, a shipment of 3500 kg of Calcium, Class 4.3, UN1401 and 400 kg of Sodium Hydroxide Solution, Class 8, UN1824 and 400 kg of Acetone, Class 3, UN1090, the 3500 kg of Calcium requires an ERAP and therefore Class 4.3 placards with UN Number.*

9.9 Specific examples of placarding when atleast two dangerous goods are present are shown on page 16.

9.10 When placards are displayed on a large MoC and the conditions that required the placards to be displayed are changed, the driver under direction from the carrier is responsible to determine if the placards should be changed or removed.

9.11 When the DANGER placard is displayed to be used on a large MoC, the DANGER placard may continue to be displayed until the large MoC no longer contains a quantity of dangerous that requires any placard to be displayed, either a Class placard or a DANGER placard.

9.12 There are special placarding requirements for Class 1, Explosives and Class 7, Radioactive Materials which are described in Chapter 14.

## SEGREGATION

9.13 There are no specific requirements in the TDG Regulations to segregate different dangerous goods in a large MoC. However, it is common practice that different types of goods being transported together are "effectively segregated." This means they should be separated so that under normal conditions of transport, in the event of a leakage, mixing of products or cross contamination would not occur.

9.14 Segregation of dangerous goods from other products or materials may be required by other regulations, for example those of Health Canada.

9.15 There are US regulations governing which products can be shipped together and under what conditions. These are described in Appendix 2, and can be used for further guidance.

Part 3

10.1 There are special requirements for shipment of dangerous goods in bulk (that is, in large MoC, without any intermediate packaging), *for example, tank trucks or totes*. (The term "bulk" is used here for ease of reference; it is not a term used in the Regulations.)

10.2 Drivers transporting dangerous goods in bulk should **receive special training in safe operating practices**. These should be observed at all times.

## DOCUMENTATION

10.3 When a MoC has been emptied so that it **contains less than 10% of its capacity**, a copy of the original Shipping Document may be marked "Residue - Last Contained", followed by the Shipping Name of the dangerous goods.

10.4 This Shipping Document must accompany the MoC until it has been cleaned and purged of all residues so that no hazard remains.

## PLACARDING

10.5 **When the UN Number is required to be displayed,** it must be shown either:
- within the Primary Class placard, or
- on an orange rectangular panel located immediately adjacent to the Primary Class placard without the prefix "UN".

10.6 When **different dangerous goods** are being transported in a **multi-compartment tank**, the Primary Class placard and the UN Number must be displayed on both sides of each compartment containing dangerous goods, and on the front and rear of the large MoC. When a Primary Class placard and UN Number is displayed more than once on the side of a multi-compartment tank (that is, the same dangerous goods are in more than one compartment) that Primary Class placard with UN Number need only be displayed once on the front and rear of the large MoC.

10.7 When **different Class 3 products** are being transported in a multi-compartment tank, only the UN Number of the dangerous goods with the lowest flash point is required. *For example, when transporting Diesel, UN1202, 3, PG III and Gasoline, UN1203, 3, PG II, only a placard showing UN1203 need be used.*

10.8 The **placards must remain on the unloaded MoC** until it has been cleaned and purged of all residues so that no hazard remains. The person in charge of cleaning or purging the tank must remove the placards.

**Part 3**

11.1 Interlined freight is freight that is transported by more than one carrier from its point of origin to its final destination. Interlining may involve the transfer of unopened trailers, or the transfer of packages or containers from one vehicle to another.

11.2 Before accepting an interline shipment or vehicle, the receiving carrier should take reasonable steps to ensure that:

- the packages are properly marked and labelled;
- the container or vehicle is properly placarded; and
- the Shipping Document(s) contain all the necessary information.

All drivers involved in an interline movement must have copies of the Shipping Document(s).

11.3 If dangerous goods are to be transported to a port or airport for furtherance by sea or air it may be transported for the road portion of the movement using the documentation and labelling provisions of the International Maritime Dangerous Goods (IMDG) Code or the International Civil Aviation Organization (ICAO) Technical Instructions. When An ERAP is required the ERAP number and the telephone number to activate the ERAP must be included on the documentation. In all cases the placards required by the TDG Regulations must to be displayed.

Part 3

12.1 The United States has different rules governing the transportation of dangerous goods. **Drivers who transport dangerous goods cross-border must understand the differences.** (In particular, the Shipping Document is referred to as Shipping Papers, and a small MoC is referred to as a package). The purpose of this chapter is to identify the primary differences. There may be others, and consignors must be fully aware of all differences that apply.

12.2 Dangerous goods are called **hazardous materials** in the US. Canadian TDG and US Hazardous Materials (HazMat) Regulations are similar, and there is considerable **reciprocity between the two countries,** so that most shipments can be transported under the rules of the country of origin. However, reciprocity does not extend to all shipments. Some differences must be observed when transporting certain cross-border shipments. This may require additional training.

12.3 In the US, the regulations are contained within **US Code of Federal Regulations, Title 49** (49CFR), Parts 100 to 185. In particular, the hazardous materials are identified in Part 172.101, which contains a table similar to Schedule 1 of the Regulations, but is arranged in alphabetical order by Shipping Name.

12.4 If a product is regulated in Canada but not in the US, it must be shipped according to the TDG Regulations. If a product is regulated in the US but not in Canada, it must be shipped according to 49CFR.

**SHIPMENTS ENTERING CANADA FROM THE UNITED STATES**

12.5 For shipments originating in the US and entering Canada:

- the **Shipping Document must show the name of the consignee or importer**, since that person is considered to be the consignor for imported consignments. In the absence of this information, the carrier will be considered the importer, and will have the duties and responsibilities of the consignor.

- the **Shipping Document must include a declaration** that the hazardous materials have been properly classified, packaged, marked, and labelled for transportation.

- in the US, some products have a NA Number instead of a UN Number. For these products, the Shipping Name and UN Number from the TDG Regulations must be used. For example, Compounds, Cleaning Liquid, NA1760, Class 8, PG I, would be shipped in Canada as Corrosive Liquid, N.O.S., UN1760, Class 8, PG I.

- when an ERAP is required, the Shipping Document must show the ERAP reference number and the telephone number to activate the plan.

- for shipments travelling **from a point in the US through Canada to a destination in the US,** the carrier is considered to be the importer and may be required to have an ERAP if the manufacturer or consignor does not already have one, or does not give the carrier permission to use it.

- an additional placarding requirement applies when more than 1000 kg (2200 pounds) of one type of dangerous goods is being shipped by one consignor. The Primary Class Placards must be displayed even if there are other dangerous goods present. - it is not sufficient to just display a DANGEROUS placard. *For example, a mixed shipment of 2000 kg of Sodium Hydroxide Solution, Class 8, UN1824, PG II, and 1500 kg of Acetone, Class 3, UN1090, PG II, must display Class 8 and Class 3 placards, not DANGEROUS placards.*

Note: placards are not required on a transport vehicle or freight container which contains less than 454 kg (1001 pounds) aggregate gross weight of hazardous materials.

Note: Dangerous goods which are exempt from displaying safety marks or from a packaging requirement in the US, where these

Part 3

exceptions are not permitted in Canada, they must be transported in accordance with Canadian TDG Regulations.

12.6 The placards used in the US are slightly different - the words describing the hazard appear on the placard, whereas in Canada no words appear (except for Class 6.2, Infectious Substances and Class 7, Radioactive Materials). The words that appear on US placards are shown in the following table:

| Class | Wording on US Placard |
|---|---|
| Explosives, 1.1, 1.2 and 1.3 | EXPLOSIVES |
| Explosives, 1.4 | 1.4 EXPLOSIVES |
| Explosives, 1.5 | 1.5 BLASTING AGENTS |
| Explosives, 1.6 | 1.6 EXPLOSIVES |
| Flammable Gases, 2.1 | FLAMMABLE GAS |
| Non-flammable and Non-toxic Gases, 2.2 | NON-FLAMMABLE GAS |
| Oxygen, 2.2 | OXYGEN |
| Toxic Gases, 2.3 | INHALATION HAZARD |
| Flammable Liquids, 3 | FLAMMABLE or COMBUSTIBLE |
| Flammable Solids, 4.1 | FLAMMABLE SOLID |
| Substances liable to spontaneous combustion, 4.2 | SPONTANEOUSLY COMBUSTIBLE |
| Water Reactive Substances, 4.3 | DANGEROUS WHEN WET |
| Oxidizing Substances, 5.1 | OXIDIZER |
| Organic Peroxides, 5.2 | ORGANIC PEROXIDE |
| Toxic Substances, 6.1 | POISON, INHALATION HAZARD |
| Radioactive, 7 | RADIOACTIVE |
| Corrosives, 8 | CORROSIVE |
| DANGER | DANGEROUS |

Note: When the dangerous goods are Class 2.3, Toxic Gases, or Class 6.1, Toxic Substances, the placards required by the TDG Regulations must be displayed.

## SHIPMENTS ENTERING THE UNITED STATES FROM CANADA

12.7 The carrier should make every reasonable effort to ensure that Canadian consignors are aware of and have complied with the special requirements, before accepting a shipment destined for the US.

12.8 **Most carriers hauling hazardous materials must register** with and pay a fee to the US Department of Transportation. A copy of the Carrier's Certificate of Registration must be carried in the vehicle. Carriers must register to transport hazardous materials in Ohio, Nevada, West Virginia and Minnesota.

12.9 All documentation must be in English. It is not necessary for the Shipping Document to contain the declaration that the dangerous goods have been properly classified, packaged, marked, and labelled for transportation, as is the case for shipments originating in the US.

12.10 **Combustible liquids** have a flash point between 61°C (141°F) and 93.3°C (200°F). These are not regulated in Canada, but are in the US when being transported in bulk. They must be transported according to 49CFR. Documentation is required. Either a Combustible Liquid placard or a Flammable Liquids placard may be used. In addition, a flammable liquid with a flash point at or above 38°C (100°F) that does not meet the definition of any other hazard class, may be also reclassed as a combustible liquid.

12.11 The US Environmental Protection Agency (EPA) has classified some products to be environmentally hazardous substances.

Each of these products has been assigned a Reportable Quantity and are divided into two tables, with table 1 referring to hazardous substances other than radionuclides, and table 2 for hazardous substances that are radionuclides. *For example, the Reportable Quantity for Sodium Hydroxide Solution, Class 8, UN1824, PG II is 1000 lbs (454 kg); and the Reportable Quantity for Benzene, Class 3, UN1114, PG II is 10 lbs (4.54 kg).*

Some products are listed as Environmentally Hazardous Substances, Liquid, N.O.S. UN3082 or Environmentally Hazardous Substances, Solid, N. O. S. UN3077; in these cases the technical name must be shown in parentheses after the shipping name; *for example, Environmentally Hazardous Substance, Solid, N.O.S., Class 9, UN3077, PG III (Adipic Acid).*

When a shipment consists of a Reportable Quantity, the Shipping Document and small MoC must be marked with the letters RQ, either before or after the product description, *for example, Sodium Hydroxide Solution, Class 8, UN1824, PG II, RQ.*

12.12 Some products have been designated as **Poisonous by Inhalation**. In Canada these products have a Primary or Subsidiary Class 6.1 and are identified in Special Provision 23. The Shipping Document must include the words "Toxic by Inhalation," but there are no other requirements.

In the US products that are designated as Poisonous by Inhalation are included in both Class 2.3 and Class 6.1 and are subject to Special Provisions 1 to 6 as listed in 49CFR, Part 172.102. Class 2.3 have 4 hazard zones (A,B,C,D) whereas, Class 6.1 have 3 hazard zones (A,B,C) depending on the packing group.

For shipments to the U.S., the Shipping Name must include the words "Poison - Inhalation Hazard" or "Inhalation Hazard". The small MoC can display a 6.1 or 2.3 label that conforms to the TDG Regulations, but it must also be marked "Inhalation Hazard". The large MoC can display a 6.1

or 2.3 placard that conforms to the TDG Regulations. (Anhydrous Ammonia, Class 2.3(8), UN1005, which is classified as poisonous by inhalation in the U.S., is exempt from the requirements for cross-border movements, provided the Shipping Document indicates that the markings and placards comply with TDG Regulations).

(For shipments originating in the U.S., the Shipping Document must contain the words "Toxic - Inhalation Hazard" or "Poison - Inhalation Hazard", together with the words "Zone A", "Zone B", "Zone C", or "Zone D", depending on the level of toxicity. A large MoC containing packages of material that have the same Shipping Name and UN Number, are poisonous by inhalation (Zone A or Zone B), and are being shipped from one facility in a quantity greater than 1000 kg, must be marked with the UN Number).

12.13 **Marine Pollutants** are designated in 49CFR. A marine pollutant is a material identified as environmentally hazardous when in a solution or mixture of one or more marine pollutants that is packaged in a concentration that equals or exceeds 10% by weight of the solution or mixture, or 1% by weight of the solution or mixture for materials identified as severe marine pollutants (PP). The words "Marine Pollutant" must be entered on the Shipping Document. For bulk shipments of marine pollutants transported on land the large MoC must be marked with the "Marine Pollutant" sign.

12.14 There are some **other special requirements that must be observed** while the hazardous materials are being transported:

- **the driver must carry the proper shipping paper.** The shipping paper must include the identification number for the material, the proper shipping name, the hazard class or division number, the words "Class" or "Division" may be included preceding class or division numbers, the packing group in Roman numerals, the total quantity of hazardous materials by mass or volume, for example, "200 kg" (440 pounds) or "50 L"

(13 gallons). There are also additional provisions that apply for specific types of hazardous materials. Please consult the U.S. Hazardous Materials regulations for more information. The document should also contain precautions to be taken in the event of an accident or incident, firefighting information, the initial method for handling spills or leaks, and preliminary first aid measures. This information must be immediately accessible to the driver. Schedule 4 when used in conjunction with Schedule 3 satisfies this requirement. The information may be shown on the Shipping Document or on a separate document such as a Material Safety Data Sheet (MSDS) provided by the consignor.

- placarded vehicles **must stop at rail crossings.**
- drivers of placarded vehicles **must conduct routine inspections**, to ensure that the placards are still in place, there are no leaks and that the vehicle has no apparent problems.
- there must be **no misleading placards** displayed, such as "Drive Safely".
- in the U.S. there are **segregation requirements** restricting the transportation of some combinations of dangerous goods. These restrictions are shown in Appendix 2.

12.15 An **incident occurring in the US** must be reported promptly by telephone when there is:

- a death of any person.
- an injury requiring hospitalization.
- damage estimated to exceed $50,000.
- an evacuation, or a major transportation artery or facility closed down for more than one hour.
- an incident involving Class 7, Radioactive Materials.
- an incident involving infectious substances (Report to the Centre for Disease Control - (800) 232-0124).
- a release of a marine pollutant, a situation exists of such a nature (e.g., a continuing

danger to life exists at the scene of the incident) that, in the judgment of the person in possession of the hazardous material, it should be reported.

12.16 A **follow-up report** is required within 30 days using form F-5800.1. Furthermore all incidents, whether reported by telephone or not, must be reported in writing within 30 days using form F-5800.1.

12.17 The **telephone report** should be made to US DOT National Response Centre - (800) 424-8802, or online at http://www.nrc.uscg.mil and should include:

- name of carrier, address, and phone number where person making the report can be contacted;
- date, time, and location of incident.
- extent of injuries, if any;
- class or division, proper shipping name, and quantity of hazardous materials;
- quantity of hazardous materials involved;
- type of incident and nature of hazardous material involvement and whether a continuing danger to life exists at the scene.

12.18 If there is an incident of a hazardous substance which **exceeds the Reportable Quantity (RQ),** it must be reported to National Response Centre - (800) 424-8802, and to the local police.

12.19 Other contact information that could assist in the event of an incident is given in the Driver's Reference.

12.20 A shipment originating in the US that is being reshipped in Canada may continue to retain the US marks and labels on the small MoC. However, the Shipping Document and placarding must meet the requirements of the Transportation of Dangerous Goods Regulations. Furthermore, the Shipping Document must contain a notation stating that the MoC are marked in accordance with US Regulations.

# Exemptions from the Regulations  Chapter 13

13.1 Many products classified as dangerous goods are used and transported in everyday life in relatively small quantities, and pose minimal risk. Some other dangerous goods are transported in quantities and circumstances that also pose minimal risk. Some exemptions are provided to cover those situations.

## LIMITED QUANTITIES EXEMPTION

13.2 **A quantity of dangerous goods, other than explosives, is a limited quantity when shipped in a small means of containment.** Since these are considered to be less dangerous, parts 3 to 8 of the Regulations do not apply. A quantity of dangerous goods is considered to be a Limited Quantity if:

- the **innermost containers** do not exceed the quantity specified in Column 6 of Schedule 1, (if the number in Column 6 is a zero, then that product cannot be shipped as a Limited Quantity, *for example, Sulphuric Acid, Fuming, Class 8 (6.1), UN1831, PG I* can not be shipped as a Limited Quatity); and
- the weight of each small MoC and its contents does not exceed 30 kg.
- the inner means of containment is not required to be marked, when the outer means of containment is not intended to be opened during transport.

*For example, Sodium Hydroxide Solution, Class 8, UN 1824, PG II can be shipped as a Limited Quantity if the inner containers weigh less than 1 kg, and are in a small MoC that weighs less than 30 kg.*

13.3 **Limited Quantities are exempt** from most of the requirements of the Regulations except that the MoC must be marked with the words "Limited Quantity" or the abbreviation "Ltd. Qty." or the words "Consumer Commodity" and be visible and legible and displayed on a contrasting background, or the UN number and the letters UN within a diamond-shaped mark.

When an **accumulation of limited quantities offered by one consignor to one destination exceeds 500 kg**, the consignor must prepare a Shipping Document which includes the words "Limited Quantity" or its abbreviation. For an accumulation of Limited Quantities the incident reporting requirements apply (as described in Chapter 7).

## 500 kg EXEMPTION

13.4 **The Regulations provide an exemption** for dangerous goods when:

- total weight does not exceed 500 kg.; and
- no MoC exceeds 30 kg; or for Class 2, Gases are in small MoC that comply with the TDG Regulations; or for a drum that complies with the TDG Regulations; and
- the person handling or transporting these consignments is trained, and
- each MoC has displayed on one side a label required by the TDG regulations or other Acts, which is visible when the MoC is stacked.

The dangerous goods must be accompanied by a Shipping Document, properly located (as described in 4.9), that shows only the Primary Class and the number of MoC for each dangerous goods, *for example, Class 3, Class 8, number of means of containment 10 (i.e. there is a total of 10 MoC, some of which contain Class 3 dangerous goods and some contain Class 8 dangerous goods).*

Note: When the gross mass of an accumulation of limited quantities of dangerous goods by one consignor to one destination is greater than 500 kg, the Accidental Release and Imminent Accidental Release Report Requirements must be complied with.

13.5 The 500 kg exemption does not apply to:
- Class 1, Explosives (except Class 1.4S and UN0191, UN0197, UN0276,

Part 4

UN0312, UN0336, UN0403, UN0431, UN0453, and UN0493).

- Class 2.1, Flammable Gases, in cylinders with a capacity greater than 46 litres.
- Class 2.3, Toxic Gases.
- Class 4, Flammable Solids in Packing Group I.
- Class 5.2, Organic Peroxides, unless they are limited quantities.
- Liquids in Class 6.1, Toxic Substances in Packing Group I.
- Class 6.2, Infectious Substances.
- Class 7, Radioactive Materials and are required to be licenced by the Canadian Nuclear Safety Commission.
- dangerous goods that require an ERAP.
- dangerous goods that require a control or emergency temperature.
- dangerous goods that are forbidden to be transported.

This means that for these classes and quantities the dangerous goods must be accompanied by a Shipping Document that meets all the requirements. **This exemption should not be confused with the placarding exception when the total weight of the dangerous goods present is less than 500 kg.**

## GENERAL EXEMPTIONS

13.6 The Regulations do not apply to dangerous goods that are:

- **less than 150 kg** and are in a small MoC designed so that there will be no accidental leak; and that does not exceed 30kg or in the case of gases that are in a small MoC which meets the requirements of the TDG Regulations; and being transported by the user, purchaser, or retailer to or from a user or purchaser. (This exemption does not apply to dangerous goods that require an ERAP and to certain Classes of dangerous goods as described in section 14.) When more than one shipment of dangerous goods that qualify for the 150kg exemption are transported together and the combined weight is greater than 150 kg but less than 500 kg, the 500 kg exemption will apply.

(The goods will have to be labelled and the person transporting the goods would have to be trained.)

**Please note that this exemption is no longer restricted to personal use.** If all conditions are met, anyone transporting dangerous goods can use this exemption. In fact, many services vehicles or other vehicles transporting small amounts of dangerous goods may choose to use this exemption. For dangerous goods included in Class 2, Gases, if they are in one or more small MoC they must comply with the requirements for transporting gases

- **being transported exclusively within a facility** to which public access is controlled, normally one that is a fenced and gated chemical plant.
- **being transported between two properties**, both owned or leased by the user, producer or manufacturer, travelling on a public highway for a distance less than 3 km. The Primary Class placard or the DANGER placard must be shown, the local police must be advised, in writing, of the nature of the dangerous goods no more than 12 months in advance of the transport, and the goods must be in one or more MoC designed, constructed and filled so that there will be no accidental release of dangerous goods from it. (This exemption does not apply to Class1, Explosives and Class 7, Radioactive Materials.)
- **in an Instrument or in Equipment** Documentation, safety marks and MoC requirements do not apply to dangerous goods contained in, and are not intended to be discharged from an instrument or equipment that is not dangerous goods itself. In the case of explosives, a paragraph has been added to specify what net explosives quantity is permitted to be transported when using this exemption. As well, two new special provisions that state the permitted quantity of articles that can be transported using this exemption have also been added.
- **There are two farming exemptions that can be used for quantities not exceeding 1,500 kg, or 3,000 kg.** The

fundamental difference is that a valid training certificate is required in those instances where the 3,000 kg exemption is being used. Otherwise, Part 3 (Documentation), Part 4 (Dangerous Goods Safety Marks), Part 5 (Means of Containment), Part 6 (Training) do not apply to the handling, offering for transport or transporting of dangerous goods on a road vehicle licensed as a farm vehicle provided the goods are being transported for a distance of no more than 100 km; are in a MoC designed, constructed and filled so that there will be no accidental leak or in the case of gases that are in a MoC which meets the requirements of the TDG Regulations, and the driver is trained. (This exemption does not apply to dangerous goods that require an ERAP, in which case a Shipping Document is required, nor to certain Classes of dangerous goods as described in section 14.) Any accidental release must be reported. Class 2, Gases, must be in a MoC which meets the requirements of the regulations. For dangerous goods other than those included in Class 2, Gases, they must be transported in a MoC that is designed, constructed, filled, closed, secured and maintained so that under normal conditions of transport, including handling, there will be no accidental release of the dangerous goods that could endanger public safety. Finally, the dangerous goods are to be or have been used by a farmer for farming purposes.

There is also a farming pesticide and anhydrous ammonia exemption contained in the TDG regulation.

- necessary for many aspects of **the operation of a vehicle**, for example, gasoline in an automobile, batteries, refrigeration units used in a vehicle, shock absorbers, and fire extinguishers.
- **Class 3, Flammable Liquids in small containers** (not exceeding 450L) with a Flash Point greater than 35°C, do not sustain combustion, have a fire point greater than 100°C, or are water-miscible solutions with a water content greater than

90 percent by mass, included in Packing Group III, and with no Subsidiary Class.

- **Samples** in a means of containment that are less than or equal to 10 kg of goods that the consignor reasonably believes to be dangerous goods, but the classification or the exact chemical composition of the goods is unknown and cannot be readily determined. This includes samples that are reasonably believed to be a gas, including a gas in a liquefied form, they are in one or more means of containment in compliance with the requirements for transporting gases. In addition, samples that are reasonably believed not to be a gas, in one or more means of containment where there will be no accidental release of the dangerous goods that could endanger public safety. Further, samples are in transport for the purposes of classifying, analysing or testing, provided they do not to contain explosives, infectious substances or radioactive materials. The samples must be accompanied by a document that includes the name and address of the consignor and the words "test samples", and each means of containment has marked on it the words "test samples" and the words are legible and displayed on a contrasting background. There is also a samples demonstration exemption to documentation and safety marks that can be used provided they are not for sale.
- **Emergency Response Exemption -** There is also an emergency response exemption for dangerous goods that are in quantities necessary to respond to an emergency that endangers public safety and that are in transport in a means of transport that is dedicated to emergency response, unless the dangerous goods are forbidden for transport in Schedule 1, Schedule 3.
- **Operation of a Means of Transport or a Means of Containment Exemption.** Dangerous goods on a means of transport used for the propulsion of the means of transport, the safety of individuals, the operation or safety of the means of transport (i.e. air bags, shock absorbers,

fire extinguishers), or ventilation, refrigeration or heating units that are necessary to maintain the environmental conditions within a means of containment in transport on the means of transport are exempt from the regulation. It is important to note this exemption does not apply to ammunition or dangerous goods being delivered to a destination and from which a portion is drawn off during transport for propulsion of the means of transport.

## OTHER EXEMPTIONS

13.7 There are many other specific exemptions for certain dangerous goods. Refer to the Regulations for further details.

Note: The regulation does not apply to the handling, offering for transport or transporting of MoCs of FIRE EXTINGUISHERS, UN1044 for FIRE EXTINGUISHERS, UN1044 on a road vehicle on a domestic voyage provided the fire extinguishers are not included in Class 2.3, Class 6.1 or Class 8, are contained in an outer MoC. The fire extinguisher must have a capacity less than 18 L or, if they contain liquefied gas, a capacity less than 0.6 L, and have an internal pressure less than or equal to 1 650 kPa at 21°C. Finally, the fire extinguisher must be manufactured, tested, maintained, marked and used in accordance with ULC Standards.

14.1 The Regulations were written to be as simple as possible. However, a few simple rules can not satisfactorily deal with the many different situations and circumstances that may arise. Many products and Classes of dangerous goods have special requirements and exemptions, in addition to the general rules already described. These special requirements are described below. (When there is a special provision in Schedule 2 for dangerous goods, that special provision applies. When there is a conflict between a special provision in Schedule 2 and other provisions in these Regulations, the special provision applies.)

When the word "Forbidden" is shown for dangerous goods in column 3 of Schedule 1 or column 4 of Schedule 3, a person must not handle, offer for transport or transport the dangerous goods. In addition, when the word "Forbidden" is shown for dangerous goods in column 8 or 9 of Schedule 1, a person must not offer for transport or transport the dangerous goods by the means of transport set out in the heading of that column.

## CLASS 1, EXPLOSIVES

14.2 The weight of explosives is expressed as the Net Explosive Quantity (NEQ). When the Shipping Document shows the number of articles, 100 articles must be counted as 1 kg.

14.3 The following exemptions do not apply to Class 1, Explosives:
- the limited quantity exemption;
- the 500 kg exemption, except for Class 1.4S;
- the exemption for transportation between two properties owned by the same manufacturer;
- the farm vehicle and agricultural use exemptions, except for Class 1.4S;
- the 150 kg exemption, except for UN0012, UN0014, UN044, UN0055 UN0131, UN0161, UN0173, UN0186, UN0191, UN0197, UN0276, UN0312, UN0323, UN0335, UN0336, UN0337, UN0351, UN0373, UN0404, UN0405, UN0431, UN0432, UN0454, UN0499;
- the empty drum exemption (see 14.51).

14.4 The documentation, labelling, and training requirements do not apply under some conditions:
- when the total NEQ of all the Class 1, Explosives is less than the Explosive Limit shown in Column 6 of Schedule 1 for any one of the explosives; and
- each small MoC displays the Class, Compatibility Group and UN Number ; and
- when a placard is displayed and the explosives are in class 1.1, 1.2, 1.3 1.5 and in a quantity that exceeds 10kg, a placard is displayed.

Note: Special provisions 85 and 86 of Schedule 2, Special Provisions, must be taken into account when determining if this exemption can be applied to the explosives being transported.

*For example, the Explosive Limit for Explosive, Blasting, Type E, Class 1.1D, UN0241, PG II is 25 kg, and for Rocket Motors, Class 1.3C, UN0186, PG II is 10 kg. If the total NEQ of a consignment of these two products does not exceed 10 kg, then the Regulations do not apply.*

14.5 The documentation, labelling, and training requirements do not apply to
- UN0044, when it is in a quantity of less than 15,000 articles; and
- UN0029, UN0030, UN0121, UN0131, UN0255, UN0267, UN0315, UN0325, UN0349, UN0360, UN0361, UN0367, UN0368, UN0454, UN0455, UN0456, and UN0500 when it is a quantity of less than 100 articles.

This exemption only applies when
- each small MoC displays the Class, Compatibility Group and UN Number; and
- when the explosives are in Class 1.1, 1.2, 1.3 1.5 and in a quantity that

Part 4

exceeds exceeding 10 kg net explosives quantity, or in any number of articles exceeding 1 000 for explosives subject to special provision 85 or 86, a placard is displayed.

14.6 When a Shipping Document is needed there are additional requirements:

- the Compatibility Group letter be shown immediately after the Primary Class, for example, Cord, Igniter, Class 1.4G, UN0066, PG II; and
- the number of small MoC not be shown.

14.7 The following **special placarding requirements** apply:

- placards are not required for Class 1.4; except UN0301, Ammunition, Tear-producing, in quantities less than 1000 kg, and for any quantity of Class 1.4S.
- when **Class 1, Explosives in different divisions** are transported together, only the placard for the explosive with the lowest division number need be displayed. *For example, if Explosives, Class 1.1 and Class 1.2 are being transported together, only the Class 1.1 placard is needed.* Exceptions to this provision are:
  - when Class 1.2 and Class 1.5 are transported together, the placard for Class 1.1 must be displayed; or
  - when Class 1.4 and Class 1.5 are transported together, the placard for Class 1.5 must be displayed.
- the **UN Number** need not be displayed.
- when Class 1, Explosives are part of a mixed load, the Primary Class placard must always be used - a **DANGER placard can never replace the Primary Class placard.**
- when the **dangerous goods has a Subsidiary Class 1, and an ERAP is required**, then a Subsidiary Class placard is required. Use a placard for Class 1.1 without the Class number. *For example, Self Reactive Liquid Type B, UN3221, Class 4.1 (1), PG II in a quantity greater than 75 kg would require a Class 4.1 placard with UN Number, and a Class 1.1 placard without the Division1.1 or Compatibility Group Letter shown.*

14.8 Some examples of applying the special placarding rules for Class 1, Explosives are given below:

- *400 kg of Cartridges Flash, Class 1.3G, UN0050: No placards required*
- *600 kg of Cartridges Flash, Class 1.3G, UN0050: Class 1.3 without UN Number*
- *400 kg of Charges, Depth, Class 1.1D, UN0056: Class 1.1 without UN Number (Note: ERAP required if transporting 75 kilograms of net explosives quantity)*
- *600 kg of cartridges Flash, Class 1.3G, UN0050 and 200kg Acetone, Class 3, UN1090: (1) Class 1.3 without UN Number **AND** DANGER **OR** (2) Class 1.3 without UN Number **AND** Class 3.*
- *600 kg of cartridges Flash, Class 1.3G UN0050 and 2000kg Methyl Iodide, Class 6.1, UN2644: Class 1.3 without UN Number **AND** Class 6.1 with UN Number 2644.*

14.9 The **maximum net quantity of explosives** that can be transported together is the least of

- 25 kg that are Samples, Explosives, UN0190 (*For example, if you had two explosives, with one being UN0190, the total of the two explosives when added together could not exceed 25 kg.*)
- 2,000 kg of any explosives in Class 1.1A
- 20,000 kg

14.10 **Shipments of Class 1, Explosives into the US** must conform to the requirements of 49CFR. In particular, for shipments of Class 1.1, 1.2 and 1.3, Explosives, a written security plan must be filed. The security plan must include an assessment of possible transportation security risks for shipments of the hazardous materials and appropriate measures to address the assessed risks. Specific measures put into place by the plan may vary depending on the level of threat at a particular time. At a minimum, a security plan must include personnel security, unauthorized access, and enroute security.

14.11 **Shipments of Class 1, Explosives in different Compatibility Groups** cannot be shipped together unless permitted in the Compatibility Table. (See Appendix 3).

14.12 Class 1, Explosives should never be left unattended while being transported.

## CLASS 2, GASES

14.13 The Regulations do not apply to a Class 2.2, Non-flammable, Non-toxic Gas used in refrigerating machine components **in a quantity of less than 12 kg.**

14.14 The documentation and training requirements do not apply to UN1001, UN1002, UN1006, UN1013, UN1060, UN1066, UN1072 and UN1978 when the dangerous goods:

- are in 5 or fewer small MoC; and
- gross mass is less than 500 kg; and
- the labels can be seen from outside the vehicle.

14.15 The **500 kg and 150 kg exemptions, the farming exemptions do not apply** to Class 2.1 Flammable Gases in cylinders with a capacity exceeding 46 litres or to Class 2.3 Toxic Gases.

14.16 The documentation requirements **do not apply to Anhydrous Ammonia**, Class 2.3(8), UN1005 when transported solely on land and the distance on public roads is less than or equal to 100 km and when shipped in a container with a capacity not exceeding 10,000 L and intended to be used for field applications.

14.17 There are some **special documentation requirements:**

- for a liquefied petroleum gas that has not been odorized, the words **"Not Odorized"** must be shown on the Shipping Document after the Shipping Name;
- the wording **"Residue - Last Contained"** cannot be used to describe the quantity of Class 2, Gases in small MoC.
- The shipping name of the dangerous goods subject to this exemption may be shown on the shipping document following the words LIQUEFIED PETROLEUM GAS. If either, PROPYLENE, UN1077 or PROPANE, UN1978, is being transported and is identified as LIQUEFIED PETROLEUM GAS on the shipping document, the shipping name PROPYLENE or PROPANE must be shown on the shipping document, in parentheses, following the words LIQUEFIED PETROLEUM GAS.

- Gases that have an absolute pressure between 101.3 kPa and 280 kPa at 20°C, other than gases included in Class 2.1 or Class 2.3, may be transported on a road vehicle as Class 2.2, Non-flammable, Non-toxic gas. In this case, the requirements of the Regulations relating to gases included in Class 2.2 must be complied with.

14.18 **When Class 2, Gases in different divisions** (see Section 2.6) are being transported together, there are some placarding options. Instead of having a Primary Class placard and UN Number for each gas, the DANGER placard may be used together with the Primary Class placard and UN Number for the most dangerous gas on board. The most dangerous gas is determined by the following order - Class 2.3, Toxic Gas; Class 2.1 Flammable Gas; Class 2.2 (5.1), Oxidizing Gas; and then any other gas. When any gas requires an ERAP, or is being transported by ship, the Primary Class placard and UN Number must be displayed.

14.19 Class 2, Gases UN1011, UN1012, UN1055, UN1077, UN1969, and UN1978 may be identified as UN1075, Liquefied Petroleum Gases. The shipping name for those dangerous goods may be shown in parentheses after the words Liquefied Petroleum Gases.

14.20 When Class 2.2 (5.1) oxidizing gases (UN1072, UN1073, UN3156, and UN3157) are being transported, the oxidizing gas label and placard must be displayed. When an ERAP is required for any of these products, the UN Number, if required, must also be displayed.

14.21 When Anhydrous Ammonia, UN1005, is in a large MoC it must display either Class 2.3 placards or Anhydrous Ammonia placards. When Anhydrous Ammonia placards are displayed, the large MoC must also have displayed the words "Anhydrous Ammonia, Inhalation Hazard" on at least two sides.

14.22 When cylinders with a capacity greater than 225L are interconnected and have total capacity greater than 450L, the combination may be placarded as one large MoC. An ERAP is required when the total quantity of the interconnected dangerous goods exceeds the ERAP Index shown in Column 7 of Schedule 1.

## CLASS 3, FLAMMABLE LIQUIDS

14.23   With the exception of an accidental release and imminent accidental release reporting requirements, the Regulations do not apply to Class 3, Flammable Liquids if they:

- have no Subsidiary Class, and are included in Packing Group III;
- flash point is greater than 37.8 C; and
- are securely contained in small MoC.

14.24 The regulations do not apply to the shipment of **alcoholic beverages that contains less than or equal to 24 per cent of alcohol by volume** that is included in Packing Group II and is in a means of containment with a capacity that is less than or equal to 5 L, or that is included in Packing Group III and is in a means of containment with a capacity that is less than or equal to 250 L. The regulation also does not apply to an aqueous solution of alcohol having a flash point greater than 23°C, and contains alcohol that is less than or equal to 50 per cent by volume, and is contained in a small MoC.

14.25 This regulation, with the exception of classification, does not apply to the handling, offering for transport or transporting of a **polyester resin kit** that consists of a substance included in Class 3, Packing Group II or III and a substance included in Class 5.2, Type D, E or F that does not require temperature control. The kit must be in transport on a road vehicle on a domestic voyage, be less than or equal to 30 kg gross mass. The quantity of Class 3 Packing Group II substances is less than or equal to 1 L, and 5 L for Packing Group III substances. For Class 5.2 substances, the kit must be less than or equal to 125 ML for liquids, and 500 g for solids.

14.26 The documentation, UN Number, safety marks, MoC, and training requirements do not apply to Diesel, UN1202 and Gasoline, UN1203 when the total capacity of all containers in the shipment does not exceed 2000 litres.    The containers, commonly known as slip tanks or totes must display labels, be in an open vehicle so labels are visible from outside the vehicle, and be properly secured. Placards and UN Numbers are not required to be displayed on the vehicle.

14.27 **When 2 or more different dangerous goods in Class 3** are in different compartments of a compartmentalized large MoC, only the UN Number of the product with the lowest flash point need be displayed.

14.28 A liquid with a flash point greater than 60° and less than or equal to 93° may be transported as a Class 3, Flammable Liquids, PG III.

## CLASS 4, FLAMMABLE SOLIDS; SUBSTANCES LIABLE TO SPONTANEOUS COMBUSTION; SUBSTANCES THAT ON CONTACT WITH WATER EMIT FLAMMABLE GASES

14.29 **The 500 kg and the 150 kg exemptions do not apply** to dangerous goods in Class 4, Packing Group I.

14.30 When dangerous goods require an ERAP and have a Subsidiary Class of 4.3, Water Reactive Substance, then Subsidiary Class placards are required. The placard for Class 4.3 is used. *For example, for 4000 kg of Corrosive Solid, Self-Heating, N.O.S., Class 8 (4.3), UN3094, PG I, requires a Class 8 placard with UN Number and a Class 4.3 placard*

14.31 The **empty drum exemption** does not apply to dangerous goods in Class 4.3 (see 14.51).

## CLASS 5, OXIDIZING SUBSTANCES AND ORGANIC PEROXIDES

14.32 **The 500 kg and 150 kg exemptions do not apply** to dangerous goods Class 5.2, Organic Peroxides unless the dangerous goods is a limited quantity.

14.33 The labelling, placarding, and training requirements do not apply to **Ammonium Nitrate** products UN1942, UN2067, UN2068, UN2069, UN2070, and UN2072, in Class 5.1, PG III, if they are:

- in a quantity not exceeding 13.6 tonnes (30,000 lbs);
- being transported from a retail outlet and transported for consumption; and
- accompanied by a Shipping Document showing the Shipping Name, UN Number and quantity.

## CLASS 6.1, TOXIC SUBSTANCES

14.34 The **500 kg and 150 kg exemptions do not apply** to Class 6.1, Toxic Substances, Packing Group I.

14.35 When dangerous goods **require an ERAP and have a Subsidiary Class of 6.1, Packing Group I due to inhalation toxicity (Special Provision 23)**, then Subsidiary Class placards are required. The placard for Class 6.1 is used. *For example, a shipment of 2000 kg of ORGANOPHOSPHOROUS PESTICIDE, LIQUID, FLAMMABLE, TOXIC, flash point less than 23° C, Class 3 (6.1), UN 2784, PG I requires an ERAP (see 3.5) and therefore requires a Class 3 placard with UN Number and a Class 6.1 placard*

## CLASS 6.2, INFECTIOUS SUBSTANCES

14.36 The documentation and ERAP requirements do not apply to Class 6.2, Infectious Substances, Category B, when

- the MoC complies with the requirements of the regulations; and
- the required safety mark, the Shipping Name, and the required 24-hour number is displayed on the MoC.

14.37 The Category B mark must be displayed for Biological Substance, Category B, UN3373.

14.38 The **500 kg and 150 kg exemptions, the exemptions for farming, and the exemption for empty drums do not apply** to dangerous goods in Class 6.2.

14.39 Biological Products are exempt from documentation, safety marks, MoC, training, emergency response assistance plans, and release reporting requirements if they are prepared in accordance with the requirements set out under the "Food and Drugs Act". The MoC must be a Type 1B to prevent an accidental release of the dangerous goods that could endanger public safety. The MoC must be marked with the words "Biological Product" in black letters at least 6 mm high on a contrasting background.

14.40 **Tissues or Organs for Transplant** are exempt in the regulation for handling, offering for transport or transporting.

14.41 **Blood or Blood Components** are exempt in the regulation for handling, offering for transport or transporting, when they are intended for transfusion or for the preparation of blood products and are reasonably believed not to contain infectious substances. The only requirement is that the blood or blood components must be in MoC that meets the requirements of the regulation.

## CLASS 7, RADIOACTIVE MATERIALS

14.42 With the exception of the Accidental Release and Imminent Accidental Release Report, the Regulations **do not apply** when the radioactive materials satisfy the conditions for an **excepted package** in the Packaging and Transport of Nuclear Substances Regulations, are in an excepted package, and are accompanied by a Shipping Document that includes the Shipping Name and UN Number.

14.43 The labels and placards required to be displayed are determined in accordance with the Packaging and Transport of Nuclear Substances Regulations. Those regulations may require that the goods display a Fissile label.

14.44 For Class 7, Radioactive Materials:

- the **500 kg and 150 kg exemptions, the exemptions related to farming, and the empty drum exemption** (see 14.51) do not apply.
- the wording **"Residue - Last Contained"** cannot be applied.
- **two labels** are required on opposite sides of a small MoC.

- the Primary Class and UN number placard must be displayed for any quantity of Radioactive Materials for which a Category III - Yellow label is required.
- the name or symbol of the radioactive material, except that if there is a mixture of radioactive materials, the name or symbol of the most restrictive of the radioactive material in the mixture, and the activity and the transport index of the dangerous goods.

## CLASS 8, CORROSIVES

14.45 When **dangerous goods UN2977 or UN2978, Class 7, Subsidiary Class 8 require an ERAP**, the Subsidiary Class 8 Placard without UN number must be used, in addition to the Primary Class 7 placard with UN Number.

## CLASS 9, MISCELLANEOUS

14.46 The labelling, placarding, and training requirements do not apply to **Ammonium Nitrate Fertilizer, UN2071, Class 9, PG III**, if it is:
- in a quantity not exceeding 13.6 tonnes (30,000 lbs);
- being transported from a retail outlet to the place of use or consumption; and
- accompanied by a Shipping Document showing the Shipping Name, UN Number and quantity.

Substances included in Class 9, Miscellaneous Products, Substances and Organisms, are included in Packing Group III unless they are specifically included in a different packing group shown for them in the regulations.

## OTHER SPECIAL CONDITIONS:
## FUMIGATION

14.47 When a MoC has been **fumigated** with dangerous goods, and the fumigant is the only dangerous goods present, the Regulations do not apply, if the MoC is accompanied by a Shipping Document that includes only the following information:
- the shipping name: FUMIGATED UNIT
- the Class: Class 9
- the UN Number: UN3359

- the quantity of the fumigant
- the date of fumigation
- instructions for disposal of residues of the fumigant or fumigation device.

14.48 When the large MoC contains **dangerous goods that are being fumigated with other dangerous goods**, the Shipping Document that accompanied the other dangerous goods must also include:
- the name of the fumigant
- the quantity of the fumigant
- the date of fumigation, and
- instructions for the disposal of residues of the fumigant or fumigation device.

14.49 **Fumigation sign** must be displayed next to or at each entryway through which a person can enter. The sign must be displayed by the person in charge of the fumigation process, and must have on it the name of the fumigant and the date and time it was applied. The sign is shown in the Driver's Reference.

## MARINE POLLUTANTS

14.50 Some dangerous goods are classified as marine pollutants. They are identified in column 10 of **Schedule 1** as follows:
- **marine pollutants** are indicated by the letter **P**;
- **severe marine pollutants** are indicated by the letters **PP**; and
- **potential marine pollutants** are indicated by this symbol (•). The consignor must determine if the substance to be transported under the shipping name is a marine pollutant or a severe marine pollutant.

14.51 The words **"Marine Pollutant"** must be shown on the Shipping Document. Further, if the pollutant is a pesticide, the name and concentration of the most active substance in the pesticide must be shown.

14.52 The Marine Pollutant must be displayed for dangerous goods that are being transported by ship, except when in a road vehicle on a roll-on/roll-off ship. The sign is shown in the Driver's Reference. The sign must be placed next to the

Primary Class label or the Subsidiary Class label if one is present.

14.53 For Marine Pollutants in a MoC that are to be transported by ship and are travelling into the US, the Marine Pollutant sign must be displayed.

## RESIDUES and DRUMS

14.54 When the quantity of dangerous goods in a MoC is **less than 10% of its maximum fill limit**, the description "Residue - Last Contained" may be used to describe the quantity. This wording cannot be used for dangerous goods in Class 2 in small MoC, or Class 7.

14.55 A **drum containing residue** being transported on a road vehicle is exempt from the classification, documentation, labelling, placarding and ERAP requirements if the drum:

- has been emptied to the maximum extent possible and is **less than 10%** full; and
- is being transported for the purpose of **reconditioning or refilling.**

This exemption can not be used for drums that have contained dangerous goods in Packing Group I, or in Class 1, Class 4.3, Class 6.2 or Class 7.

The Regulations covering standards for means of containment, training and accidental release still apply.

14.56 The drum(s) must be accompanied by document that shows the Primary Class, and the total number of drums, *for example, 14 Class 3 Residue Drums.* If the Primary Class is not known, the document may state "Residue Drum(s) – Content(s) Unknown", followed by the number of drums, *for example, 3 Residue Drums – Contents Unknown.*

When the quantity of dangerous goods or the number of small means of containment changes during transport, the carrier must show on the shipping document or on a document attached to the shipping document the change in the quantity of dangerous goods or the number of small means of containment.

14.57 If there are more than 10 empty drums on the road vehicle, the DANGER placard must be displayed.

## ELEVATED TEMPERATURES

14.58 For Elevated Temperature Liquid, Flammable N.O.S. Class 3, UN3256; Elevated Temperature Liquid, Flammable N.O.S. Class 9, UN3257; and Elevated Temperature Solid, Flammable N.O.S. Class 9, UN3258 the **Elevated Temperature sign** must be displayed on each side and each end of the large means of containment next to each primary class placard for the dangerous goods or, if there is a subsidiary class placard, next to the subsidiary class placard.

14.59 For **Molten Sulphur**, Class 4.1, UN2448, PG III, the MoC must be marked with the words MOLTEN SULPHUR, UN2448 (Special Provision 32).

## SPECIAL REQUIREMENTS FOR QUEBEC
### Level crossings

14.60 Placarded vehicles must stop at all level crossings, except those on:

- Highway 20 in Saint-Hyacinthe,
- Route 132 in Rimouski-East, and
- Route 170, at the junction of the railway branch line used by the Bagotville military base.

 **When stopping at a level crossing the driver must:**

- use the lane farthest to the right on multi-lane highways;
- activate the hazard lights far enough from the level crossing to indicate the intention to stop;
- stop 5 metres from the level crossing;
- check that there are no on-coming trains, and if the visibility is reduced, lower the window and listen for any on-coming trains;
- if there is no on-coming train, move forward in the lowest gear and cross without changing gears

- after crossing, deactivate the hazard lights.

**Tunnels**

14.61 In the following tunnels:
- the Louis-Hippolyte-Lafontaine Tunnel;
- Viger tunnel in Montréal,
- the tunnel sections of the Ville-Marie Highway;
- the Joseph-Samson Bridge-Tunnel; or
- the part of the approach to Melocheville Tunnel controlled by traffic lights and hold lanes that is parallel to the lane reserved for vehicles carrying dangerous goods,

Travel is prohibited for:
- a vehicle on which placards must be displayed;
- a service truck exempted from displaying placards;
- a vehicle which has a permit providing an exemption from displaying placards;
- a vehicle transporting Class 3 dangerous goods, unless the total quantity of dangerous goods does not exceed 30 litres and is being transported in MoC that meet the safety standards and the capacity of each does not exceed 30 litres;

- a vehicle transporting dangerous goods that have a Primary Class 2.1 or a Subsidiary Class 5.1 unless
- the dangerous goods are 2.3 (2.1), 2.2 (5.1) and 2.3 (5.1) gases in more than two cylinders or the water capacity of a cylinder exceeds 46 L; and
- no more than 2 cylinders are on the vehicle;
- a vehicle equipped with a functioning accessory that produces an open flame.

These regulations do not apply to dangerous goods that are necessary for the operation of the vehicle nor to emergency vehicles and cranes equipped with a second diesel fuel tank installed by the crane manufacturer, as well as maintenance vehicles used inside tunnels or at the entrances to and exits from the tunnels.

**REPORTING REQUIREMENTS FOR MANITOBA**

14.62 In the case of an accidental release, Manitoba has established different thresholds for reporting the release. These are shown in the Driver's Reference.

Part 4

# Definitions

**The definitions shown below are taken from the Transportation of Dangerous Goods Regulations.**

**Capacity**  For a means of containment used to contain a liquid or a gas, the maximum volume of water, normally expressed in litres, that the means of containment can hold at 15°C and at an absolute pressure of 101.325 kPa; and  dangerous goods other than a liquid or a gas, the maximum volume, normally expressed in cubic metres, that the means of containment can hold.

**Carrier**  A person (an individual, corporation or any other entity carrying on a business) who, whether or not for hire or reward, has possession of goods while they are in transport.

**Category A**  An infectious substance that is transported in a form such that, when it is released outside of its means of containment and there is physical contact with humans or animals, it is capable of causing permanent disability or life-threatening or fatal disease to humans or animals.

**Category B**  An infectious substance that does not meet the criteria for inclusion in Category A.

**Class**  The Class of dangerous goods listed in Schedule 1, or the Class of dangerous goods including its division, if applicable.

**Classification**  The Shipping Name, Primary Class, Subsidiary Class(es), UN Number of dangerous goods.  It may also include Packing Group, Compatibility Group or Risk Group and the infectious substance category, as applicable. (Dangerous goods can have more than one Class - a Primary Class and Subsidiary Class(es).)

**Consignment**  A quantity of dangerous goods in transport from one consignor at one location to one consignee at another location and the means of containment required for transport. *(The size of a consignment is determined by the smallest innermost means of containment for which performance standards are specified in the TDG Regulations. Consignments packed together in a larger means of containment such as a carton, box or other container are called an acculumation of consignments.)*

**Compatibility group**  One of the 13 groups of Class 1 explosives.

**Consignor**  The person in Canada who is named in the Shipping Document as consignor, imports or will import the goods into Canada, or has possession of the dangerous goods immediately before they are in transport. *(This term is always used in this Guide and not  terms such as shipper).*

**Culture**  The result of a process by which pathogens in a specimen are intentionally propagated. This definition does not include specimens taken from a human or animal patient and that are intended to be processed in a laboratory. Often, a specimen taken from a human or animal patient in a doctor's office, a clinic, a hospital or a lab is referred to by the health care professional as a "culture". In fact, such a specimen is usually intended to be sent to a laboratory where it will be manipulated or "cultured". It is packaged in such a way that the specimen itself will not deteriorate but any pathogens it contains will not "grow" during transport

**Dangerous Goods**  A product, substance or organism included by its nature or by the regulations in any of the Classes listed in Schedule 1 of the Regulations.

**Drum** A flat-ended or convex-ended cylindrical means of containment made of metal, fibreboard, plastic or other similar material, with a maximum capacity of 450 L, or for a drum made of plywood, a maximum capacity of 250 L. This definition includes means of containment of other shapes such as pail-shaped or round with a tapered neck, but does not include a wood barrel or jerrican.

**Emergency** An immediate danger to public safety requiring the use of dangerous goods to avert or mitigate the danger, or arising directly or indirectly from dangerous goods.

**Emergency response assistance plan or ERAP** A plan that outlines what is to be done if there is an accident involving certain dangerous goods

**Farmer** A person engaged in farming in Canada for commercial purposes.

**Farming** The production of field-grown crops, cultivated and uncultivated and horticultural crops, the raising of livestock, poultry and fur-bearing animals, the production of eggs, milk, honey, maple syrup, tobacco, fibre and fodder crops, but does not include aquaculture.

**Flash point** The lowest temperature at which the application of an ignition source causes the vapours of a liquid to ignite near the surface of the liquid or within a test vessel.

**Handling** Loading, unloading, packing or unpacking dangerous goods in a means of containment or transport for the purpose of, in the course of, or following transportation, and includes storing them in the course of transportation.

**Imminent accidental release** For dangerous goods in transport in a large MoC that there has been an incident and that there is likely a need to remove or transfer all or a portion of the dangerous goods to another large MoC, or there is damage to the MoC which, if not corrected, could result in an accidental release of the dangerous goods.

**In Transport** A person has possession of dangerous goods for the purpose of transportation or for the purpose of storing them in the course of transportation.

**Label** A safety mark that is visible and legible, made of a durable and weather-resistant material, and is of a specified colour. It's shape is a square on point with each side measuring at least 100 mm (4 inches) in length, with a line running 5 mm inside the edge. *Usually applied to a small means of containment.*

**Means of Containment (MoC)** A container or packaging, or any part of a means of transport that is or may be used to contain goods.

A large means of containment has a capacity greater than 450 L. (Examples of large MoC are tanks, containers, etc.)

A small means of containment has a capacity less than or equal to 450 L. (Examples of small MoC are cartons, cylinders, packages, boxes, aerosols, etc.)

*(450 litres is equivalent to 0.45 cubic metres, or 15.9 cubic feet.)*

*(The term MoC is always used in this Guide to describe boxes, cartons, packages, vans, tank trailers, totes, etc.)*

**Type 1A means of containment** is a means of containment that is in compliance with the requirements of CGSB-43.125 for Type 1A means of containment or, if it is manufactured outside Canada, is in compliance with the requirements of Chapter 6.3 of the UN Recommendations and the national regulations of the country of manufacture.

**Type 1B means of containment** is a means of containment that is in compliance with the requirements of CGSB-43.125 for Type 1B means of containment and with the additional requirements of section 5.16.1 of Part 5, Means of Containment.

**Appendices**

**Type 1C means of containment** is a means of containment that is in compliance with the requirements of CGSB-43.125 for Type 1C means of containment.

**Means of Transport (MoT)** A road or railway vehicle, aircraft, ship, pipeline or any other contrivance that is or may be used to transport persons or goods. (Examples of means of transport are trailers, vans, trucks, etc.) *(The term MoT may be used in this Guide to describe the various vehicles used to transport dangerous goods.)*

**Offer for Transport** Selecting a carrier to transport dangerous goods, preparing dangerous goods so that a carrier can take possession of them for transport, or allowing any of these functions to be performed.

**Packing group** A group in which dangerous goods are included based on the inherent danger of the dangerous goods; Packing Group I indicates great danger, Packing Group II indicates medium danger and Packing Group III indicates minor danger.

**Placard** A safety mark that is visible and legible, made of a durable and weather-resistant material, and is of a specified colour. It's shape is a square on point with each side measuring at least 250 mm (10 inches) in length, with a line running 12.5 mm inside the edge. *(Usually applied to means of transport or large means of containment.)*

**Primary class** The first class shown in column 3 of Schedule 1 of the regulation.

**Safety Mark** A label, placard, orange panel, sign, mark, number or word that is used to identify dangerous goods and to show the nature of the danger posed by them.

**Shipping Document** A document that relates to dangerous goods being handled, offered for transport or transported, and that contains the required information relating to the dangerous goods. It does not include an electronic record.

**Shipping Name** An entry in upper-case letters in Column 2 of Schedule 1, not including any lower-case descriptive text. Only those names that appear in Schedule 1 may be used to describe dangerous goods.

**Shipping Record** A record that relates to dangerous goods being handled, offered for transport or transported, and that contains information relating to the goods, including an electronic record.

**Subsidiary class** A class shown in parentheses in column 3 of Schedule 1.

**Appendices**

# US Segregation Table for Hazardous Materials    Appendix 2

US Hazardous Materials Regulations contain segregation requirements that indicate which hazardous materials may not be loaded, transported or stored together. Materials which are in packages (small MoC) that require labels, in a compartment within a multi-compartment cargo tank, or in a portable tank loaded on a vehicle (MoT) are subject to the segregation requirements shown in the following table:

| Class | | 1.1 1.2 | 1.3 | 1.4 | 1.5 | 1.6 | 2.1 | 2.2 | 2.3 Zone A | 2.3 Zone B | 3 | 4.1 | 4.2 | 4.3 | 5.1 | 5.2 | 6.1 Liquids PG 1 Zone A | 7 | 8 liquids only |
|---|---|---|---|---|---|---|---|---|---|---|---|---|---|---|---|---|---|---|---|
| Explosives | 1.1, 1.2 | * | * | * | * | * | X | X | X | X | X | X | X | X | X | X | X | X | X |
| Explosives | 1.3 | * | * | * | * | * | X | | X | X | X | | X | X | X | X | X | | X |
| Explosives | 1.4 | * | * | * | * | * | O | | O | O | O | | O | | | | | O | | O |
| Explosives | 1.5 | * | * | * | * | * | X | X | X | X | X | X | X | X | X | X | X | X | X |
| Explosives | 1.6 | * | * | * | * | * | | | | | X | | | | | | | | |
| Flammable Gas | 2.1 | X | X | O | X | | | | X | O | | | | | | | O | O | |
| Non-toxic Gas | 2.2 | X | | | X | | | | | | | | | | | | | | |
| Toxic Gas (Zone A) | 2.3 | X | X | O | X | | X | | | | X | X | X | X | X | X | | | X |
| Toxic Gas (Zone B) | 2.3 | X | X | O | X | | O | | | | O | O | O | O | O | O | | | O |
| Flammable Liquids | 3 | X | X | O | X | | | | X | O | | | | | O | | X | | |
| Flammable Solids | 4.1 | X | | | X | | | | X | O | | | | | | | X | | O |
| Spontaneously Combustible | 4.2 | X | X | O | X | | | | X | O | | | | | | | X | | X |
| Water reactive materials | 4.3 | X | X | | X | | | | X | O | | | | | | | X | | O |
| Oxidizers | 5.1 | X | X | | X | | | | X | O | O | | | | | | X | | O |
| Organic Peroxides | 5.2 | X | X | | X | | | | X | O | | | | | | | X | | O |
| Poisonous liquids, PG1, Zone A | 6.1 | X | X | O | X | | O | | | | X | X | X | X | X | X | | | X |
| Radioactive materials | 7 | X | | | X | | O | | | | | | | | | | | | |
| Corrosives (liquids only) | 8 | X | X | O | X | | | | X | O | | O | X | O | O | O | X | | |

## Legend

1.  A blank space means there are no segregation restrictions.

2.  The letter "X" indicates that these hazardous materials cannot be loaded, transported or stored together.

3.  The letter "O" indicates that these materials may not be loaded, transported or stored together unless separated in such a way that mixing of the products would not occur.

4.  The symbol * indicates that segregation between explosives is determined by the Compatibility Groups.

5.  When a hazardous material has a Subsidiary Class, the segregation appropriate to the Subsidiary Class must be applied when the segregation requirement is more restrictive than that required by the Primary Class.

Appendices

Explosives with the Compatibility Group letter shown in Column 1 can only be loaded in the same MoC with explosives that have a Compatibility Group letter shown in Column 2. *Example: Detonators for Ammunition, Class 1.1B, UN0073 can be loaded with Fuzes, Detonating, Class 1.1B, UN0106, but not with Igniters, Class 1.1G, UN0121. Example 2:ROCKETS, with expelling charge, Class 1.3C, UN0437 can be loaded with ROCKETS with bursting charge, Class 1.1E, UN0181.*

| Column 1 | Column 2 |
|----------|----------|
| A | A |
| B | B, S |
| C | C, D, E, N, S |
| D | C, D, E, N, S |
| E | C, D, E, N, S |
| F | F, S |
| G | G, S |
| H | H, S |
| J | J, S |
| K | K, S |
| L | L |
| N | C, D, E, N, S |
| S | B, C, D, E, F, G, H, J, K, N, S |

Appendices

# Workplace Hazardous Materials Information System (WHMIS)

Although a driver may not be transporting dangerous goods, he/she will still be exposed to hazardous materials. For example, the maintenance garage may have gasoline, antifreeze, paints, compressed gases and solvents. Although these materials are common, they do have safety and health hazards associated with their use. WHMIS was developed to protect employees from these hazards.

WHMIS legislation is a Canada-wide system to provide employers and workers with information about the hazardous material they work with on the job to protect their health and safety. Federally regulated companies are governed by WHMIS Regulations under the Canada Labour Code Part II. Provincially regulated companies are governed by WHMIS legislation contained in the provincial Occupational Health & Safety Acts (OHSA). All provinces have adopted WHMIS legislation in a similar way.

**The WHMIS and TDG regulations provide complementary information systems**. TDG regulations set out information requirements for products being shipped to and from workplaces. WHMIS applies to products inside workplaces. One system takes over where the other leaves off - no overlap is intended. Worker exposure to dangerous goods that are in transit is most likely to occur in the event of a spill or an accident.

WHMIS uses labels that are different from TDG labels. There are two types of labels. **Supplier labels** are required on controlled products that arrive from a supplier and contain 7 separate items of information: a product identifier; supplier identifier; MSDS statement (material safety data sheets); hazard symbol; risk phrases; precautionary measures; first aid measures. (There is a distinctive broken border around supplier labels.) **Workplace labels** are required on controlled products that are produced in the workplace or on material decanted from its original container into another container at the workplace. The workplace label gives only 3 kinds of information: product identifier; safe handling instructions; MSDS statement. The consignor will provide the MSDS with the Shipping Document. It is possible to have a product that is covered by WHMIS Regulations and not TDG Regulations.

WHMIS has only 6 Classes as shown. If a product meets the criteria for one of the 6 Classes it is referred to as a **controlled product**.

## Hazard Classification & Symbols

| | | | |
|---|---|---|---|
| **Class A - Compressed Gases** |  | **Class D (Cont.)** | |
| **Class B - Flammable and Combustible Materials** |  | Division 2 Materials Causing Other Toxic Effects |  |
| **Class C - Oxidizing Materials** |  | Division 3 Biohazardous Infectious Materials |  |
| **Class D - Poisonous and Infectious Materials** | | **Class E - Corrosive Materials** |  |
| Division 1 Materials Causing Immediate and Serious Toxic Effects |  | **Class F - Dangerously Reactive Materials** |  |

Appendices

# SCHEDULE 1

## Dangerous Goods by UN Number

Schedule 1 contains all the information required to correctly identify, label and placard any dangerous goods.

| Column | Description |
|:---:|:---|
| 1 | **UN Number.** This column gives the UN Numbers for the Shipping Names of dangerous goods. An alphabetic index of the Shipping Names is provided in Schedule 3. |
| 2 | **Shipping Name and Description.** This column gives the Shipping Names for dangerous goods. Each Shipping Name is written in upper case letters (capitals) and any descriptive text is written in lower case letters. The word "or" between Shipping Names indicates that there is more than one Shipping Name for the dangerous goods and that each Shipping Name given is correct. Any one of the Shipping Names may be used, for example, to complete a Shipping Document. |
| 3 | **Class.** This column gives the Primary Class for dangerous goods. Subsidiary Class, or classes, are shown in parentheses under the Primary Class. There is no priority between or among Subsidiary Classes. <br><br> The word "F" in this column means that the dangerous goods must not be transported. Schedule 3 includes some dangerous goods that must not be transported and do not have a UN Number. A person may apply for a permit for equivalent level of safety to transport these dangerous goods. |
| 4 | **Packing Group/Category.** This column gives the Packing Groups or Category for dangerous goods |
| 5 | **Special Provisions.** This column refers to the Special Provisions that apply to dangerous goods. The text of the Special Provisions is in Schedule 2. |
| 6 | **Explosive Limit and Limited Quantity Index**. This column gives the quantity of dangerous goods at or below which the dangerous goods may be handled, offered for transport or transported as Limited Quantities. For Class 1, Explosives, it gives the net explosive quantity below which the product qualifies for the exemption described in 14.3. |
| 7 | **ERAP Index.** This column gives the ERAP (emergency response assistance plan) quantity limit above which the dangerous goods must have an ERAP. The ERAP quantity limit applies to the row on which it appears so that, for example, UN1986 may require an ERAP for Packing Group I but not for Packing Groups II or III. <br><br> If no index number is shown, no ERAP is needed. |
| 8 | Omitted |
| 9 | Omitted |
| 10 | **Marine Pollutant.** This column indicates the dangerous goods that are marine pollutants. The letter "P" indicates a marine pollutant. The letters "PP" indicate a severe marine pollutant. The symbol "•" indicates a potential marine pollutant. |

# HOW TO USE THIS SCHEDULE

UN1660 is used to illustrate the way information is presented in Schedule 1 and how to use it.

| | |
|---|---|
| **Column 1** **and** **Column 2** | UN1660 is the UN Number for the Shipping Name NITRIC OXIDE, COMPRESSED. The Shipping Names are allowed to be written in a different order from the order in Schedule 1 when written in English as long as the full Shipping Name is used and the word order is a commonly used one. For example, this substance can be written as COMPRESSED NITRIC OXIDE. |
| **Column 3** | The Primary Class is Class 2.3 and the two Subsidiary Classes are Class 5.1 and Class 8. Note that no priority is to be assumed between or among Subsidiary Classes. |
| **Column 4** | There is no Packing Group, which is true for all gases. |
| **Column 5** | There is one Special Provision that applies. It is Special Provision 38, the text of which is in Schedule 2. |
| **Column 6** | NITRIC OXIDE, COMPRESSED, cannot be transported as a limited quantity because a "0" is shown for it. |
| **Column 7** | Any quantity of NITRIC OXIDE, COMPRESSED, in a consignment requires an Emergency Response Assistance Plan because a "0" is shown for it. |
| **Column 10** | There is no "P", "PP" or symbol "•" shown, so NITRIC OXIDE, COMPRESSED, is not a marine pollutant, a severe marine pollutant or a potential marine pollutant. |

When completing Shipping Documents, the data in each row must be used exactly as it is presented.

When two rows have the same UN Number (e.g., an entry for a solid and an entry for a liquid) or one row has more than one sub-row in columns 4 to 10 (e.g., there is more than one Packing Group), the data used for that UN Number must be taken entirely from the same row and the same one of its subs-rows, if there are sub-rows.

| 1 | 2 | 3 | 4 | 5 | 6 | 7 | 10 |
|---|---|---|---|---|---|---|---|
| UN Number | Shipping Name and Description | Class | Packing Group/Category | Special Provisions | Explosive Limit & Limited Quantity Index | ERAP Index | Marine Pollut. |
| UN0004 | AMMONIUM PICRATE dry or wetted with less than 10 per cent water, by mass | 1.1D | II | | 5 | 75 | |
| UN0005 | CARTRIDGES FOR WEAPONS with bursting charge | 1.1F | II | | 0 | 75 | |
| UN0006 | CARTRIDGES FOR WEAPONS with bursting charge | 1.1E | II | | 0 | 75 | |
| UN0007 | CARTRIDGES FOR WEAPONS with bursting charge | 1.2F | II | | 0 | 75 | |
| UN0009 | AMMUNITION, INCENDIARY with or without burster, expelling charge or propelling charge | 1.2G | II | | 0 | 75 | |
| UN0010 | AMMUNITION, INCENDIARY with or without burster, expelling charge or propelling charge | 1.3G | II | | 0 | | |
| UN0012 | CARTRIDGES FOR WEAPONS, INERT PROJECTILE; or CARTRIDGES, SMALL ARMS | 1.4S | II | | 25 | | |
| UN0014 | CARTRIDGES FOR WEAPONS, BLANK; or CARTRIDGES, SMALL ARMS, BLANK | 1.4S | II | | 25 | | |
| UN0015 | AMMUNITION, SMOKE with or without burster, expelling charge or propelling charge | 1.2G (8) | II | | 0 | 75 | |
| UN0016 | AMMUNITION, SMOKE with or without burster, expelling charge or propelling charge | 1.3G (8) | II | | 0 | | |
| UN0018 | AMMUNITION, TEAR-PRODUCING with burster, expelling charge or propelling charge | 1.2G (6.1) (8) | II | | 0 | 75 | |
| UN0019 | AMMUNITION, TEAR-PRODUCING with burster, expelling charge or propelling charge | 1.3G (6.1) (8) | II | | 10 | 75 | |
| UN0020 | AMMUNITION, TOXIC with burster, expelling charge or propelling charge | 1.2K (6.1) | II | 16 | 0 | 75 | |
| UN0021 | AMMUNITION, TOXIC with burster, expelling charge or propelling charge | 1.3K (6.1) | II | 16 | 0 | 75 | |
| UN0027 | BLACK POWDER granular or as a meal; or GUNPOWDER granular or as a meal | 1.1D | II | 76 | 10 | 75 | |
| UN0028 | BLACK POWDER, COMPRESSED; BLACK POWDER, IN PELLETS; GUNPOWDER, COMPRESSED; or GUNPOWDER, IN PELLETS | 1.1D | II | | 10 | 75 | |
| UN0029 | DETONATORS, NON-ELECTRIC for blasting | 1.1B | II | 86 | 0 | 5000 | |
| UN0030 | DETONATORS, ELECTRIC for blasting | 1.1B | II | 86 | 0 | 5000 | |
| UN0033 | BOMBS with bursting charge | 1.1F | II | | 0 | 75 | |
| UN0034 | BOMBS with bursting charge | 1.1D | II | | 0 | 75 | |
| UN0035 | BOMBS with bursting charge | 1.2D | II | | 0 | 75 | |
| UN0037 | BOMBS, PHOTO-FLASH | 1.1F | II | | 0 | 75 | |
| UN0038 | BOMBS, PHOTO-FLASH | 1.1D | II | | 0 | 75 | |
| UN0039 | BOMBS, PHOTO-FLASH | 1.2G | II | | 0 | 75 | |
| UN0042 | BOOSTERS without detonator | 1.1D | II | | 0 | 75 | |
| UN0043 | BURSTERS, explosive | 1.1D | II | | 0 | 75 | |
| UN0044 | PRIMERS, CAP TYPE | 1.4S | II | 85 | 0 | | |
| UN0048 | CHARGES, DEMOLITION | 1.1D | II | | 0 | 75 | |
| UN0049 | CARTRIDGES, FLASH | 1.1G | II | | 0 | 75 | |
| UN0050 | CARTRIDGES, FLASH | 1.3G | II | | 0 | | |
| UN0054 | CARTRIDGES, SIGNAL | 1.3G | II | | 25 | | |
| UN0055 | CASES, CARTRIDGE, EMPTY, WITH PRIMER | 1.4S | II | | 25 | | |
| UN0056 | CHARGES, DEPTH | 1.1D | II | | 0 | 75 | |
| UN0059 | CHARGES, SHAPED without detonator | 1.1D | II | | 25 | 75 | |
| UN0060 | CHARGES, SUPPLEMENTARY, EXPLOSIVE | 1.1D | II | | 0 | 75 | |
| UN0065 | CORD, DETONATING, flexible | 1.1D | II | | 25 | 75 | |
| UN0066 | CORD, IGNITER | 1.4G | II | 76 | 25 | | |
| UN0070 | CUTTERS, CABLE, EXPLOSIVE | 1.4S | II | | 25 | | |

| 1<br>UN Number | 2<br>Shipping Name and Description | 3<br>Class | 4<br>Packing Group/Category | 5<br>Special Provisions | 6<br>Explosive Limit & Limited Quantity Index | 7<br>ERAP Index | 10<br>Marine Pollut. |
|---|---|---|---|---|---|---|---|
| UN0072 | CYCLONITE WETTED with not less than 15 per cent water, by mass; CYCLOTRIMETHYLENETRINITRAMINE WETTED with not less than 15 per cent water, by mass; HEXOGEN WETTED with not less than 15 per cent water, by mass; or RDX WETTED with not less than 15 per cent water, by mass | 1.1D | II | 79 | 0 | 75 | |
| UN0073 | DETONATORS FOR AMMUNITION | 1.1B | II | | 0 | 75 | |
| UN0074 | DIAZODINITROPHENOL, WETTED with not less than 40 per cent water, or mixture of alcohol and water, by mass | 1.1A | II | 79 | 0 | 75 | |
| UN0075 | DIETHYLENEGLYCOL DINITRATE, DESENSITIZED with not less than 25 per cent non-volatile, water-insoluble phlegmatizer, by mass | 1.1D | II | 79 | 0 | 75 | |
| UN0076 | DINITROPHENOL, dry or wetted with less than 15 per cent water, by mass | 1.1D (6.1) | II | | 5 | 75 | P |
| UN0077 | DINITROPHENOLATES, alkali metals, dry or wetted with less than 15 per cent water, by mass | 1.3C (6.1) | II | | 10 | 75 | P |
| UN0078 | DINITRORESORCINOL, dry or wetted with less than 15 per cent water, by mass | 1.1D | II | | 5 | 75 | |
| UN0079 | HEXANITRODIPHENYLAMINE; DIPICRYLAMINE; or HEXYL | 1.1D | II | | 0 | 75 | |
| UN0081 | EXPLOSIVE, BLASTING, TYPE A | 1.1D | II | | 25 | 75 | |
| UN0082 | EXPLOSIVE, BLASTING, TYPE B | 1.1D | II | | 25 | 75 | |
| UN0083 | EXPLOSIVE, BLASTING, TYPE C | 1.1D | II | | 25 | 75 | |
| UN0084 | EXPLOSIVE, BLASTING, TYPE D | 1.1D | II | | 25 | 75 | |
| UN0092 | FLARES, SURFACE | 1.3G | II | | 25 | | |
| UN0093 | FLARES, AERIAL | 1.3G | II | | 10 | | |
| UN0094 | FLASH POWDER | 1.1G | II | 76 | 5 | 75 | |
| UN0099 | FRACTURING DEVICES, EXPLOSIVE without detonator, for oil wells | 1.1D | II | | 25 | 75 | |
| UN0101 | FUSE, NON-DETONATING | 1.3G | II | 76 | 25 | | |
| UN0102 | CORD DETONATING, metal clad; or FUSE DETONATING, metal clad | 1.2D | II | | 5 | 75 | |
| UN0103 | FUSE, IGNITER, tubular, metal clad | 1.4G | II | | 0 | | |
| UN0104 | CORD DETONATING, MILD EFFECT, metal clad; or FUSE DETONATING, MILD EFFECT, metal clad | 1.4D | II | | 5 | | |
| UN0105 | FUSE, SAFETY | 1.4S | II | 76 | 25 | | |
| UN0106 | FUZES, DETONATING | 1.1B | II | | 0 | 75 | |
| UN0107 | FUZES, DETONATING | 1.2B | II | | 0 | 75 | |
| UN0110 | GRENADES, PRACTICE, hand or rifle | 1.4S | II | | 0 | | |
| UN0113 | GUANYL NITROSAMINOGUANYLIDENE HYDRAZINE, WETTED with not less than 30 per cent water, by mass | 1.1A | II | 79 | 0 | 75 | |
| UN0114 | GUANYL NITROSAMINOGUANYLTETRAZENE WETTED with not less than 30 per cent water, or mixture of alcohol and water, by mass; or TETRAZENE, WETTED with not less than 30 per cent water, or mixture of alcohol and water, by mass | 1.1A | II | 79 | 0 | 75 | |
| UN0118 | HEXOLITE, dry or wetted with less than 15 per cent water, by mass; or HEXOTOL, dry or wetted with less than 15 per cent water, by mass | 1.1D | II | | 0 | 75 | |
| UN0121 | IGNITERS | 1.1G | II | 86 | 0 | 5000 | |
| UN0124 | JET PERFORATING GUNS, CHARGED, oil well, without detonator | 1.1D | II | | 0 | 75 | |
| UN0129 | LEAD AZIDE, WETTED with not less than 20 per cent water, or mixture of alcohol and water, by mass | 1.1A | II | 79 | 0 | 75 | |
| UN0130 | LEAD STYPHNATE, WETTED with not less than 20 per cent water, or mixture of alcohol and water, by mass; or LEAD TRINITRORESORCINATE, WETTED with not less than 20 per cent water, or mixture of alcohol and water, by mass | 1.1A | II | 79 | 0 | 75 | |
| UN0131 | LIGHTERS, FUSE | 1.4S | II | 86 | 0 | | |
| UN0132 | DEFLAGRATING METAL SALTS OF AROMATIC NITRO DERIVATIVES, N.O.S. | 1.3C | II | | 0 | | |

| 1 UN Number | 2 Shipping Name and Description | 3 Class | 4 Packing Group/Category | 5 Special Provisions | 6 Explosive Limit & Limited Quantity Index | 7 ERAP Index | 10 Marine Pollut. |
|---|---|---|---|---|---|---|---|
| UN0133 | MANNITOL HEXANITRATE, WETTED with not less than 40 per cent water, or mixture of alcohol and water, by mass; or NITROMANNITE, WETTED with not less than 40 per cent water, or mixture of alcohol and water, by mass | 1.1D | II | 79 | 0 | 75 | |
| UN0135 | MERCURY FULMINATE, WETTED with not less than 20 per cent water, or mixture of alcohol and water, by mass | 1.1A | II | 79 | 0 | 75 | |
| UN0136 | MINES with bursting charge | 1.1F | II | | 0 | 75 | |
| UN0137 | MINES with bursting charge | 1.1D | II | | 0 | 75 | |
| UN0138 | MINES with bursting charge | 1.2D | II | | 0 | 75 | |
| UN0143 | NITROGLYCERIN, DESENSITIZED with not less than 40 per cent non-volatile water-insoluble phlegmatizer, by mass | 1.1D (6.1) | II | 79 | 0 | 75 | |
| UN0144 | NITROGLYCERIN SOLUTION IN ALCOHOL with more than 1 per cent but not more than 10 per cent nitroglycerin | 1.1D | II | | 0 | 75 | |
| UN0146 | NITROSTARCH, dry or wetted with less than 20 per cent water, by mass | 1.1D | II | | 0 | 75 | |
| UN0147 | NITRO UREA | 1.1D | II | | 0 | 75 | |
| UN0150 | PENTAERYTHRITE TETRANITRATE, DESENSITIZED with not less than 15 per cent phlegmatizer, by mass; PENTAERYTHRITE TETRANITRATE, WETTED with not less than 25 per cent water, by mass; PENTAERYTHRITOL TETRANITRATE, DESENSITIZED with not less than 15 per cent phlegmatizer, by mass; PENTAERYTHRITOL TETRANITRATE, WETTED with not less than 25 per cent water, by mass; PETN, DESENSITIZED with not less than 15 per cent phlegmatizer, by mass; or PETN, WETTED with not less than 25 per cent water, by mass | 1.1D | II | 79 | 0 | 75 | |
| UN0151 | PENTOLITE, dry or wetted with less than 15 per cent water, by mass | 1.1D | II | | 0 | 75 | |
| UN0153 | PICRAMIDE; or TRINITROANILINE | 1.1D | II | | 0 | 75 | |
| UN0154 | PICRIC ACID, dry or wetted with less than 30 per cent water, by mass; or TRINITROPHENOL, dry or wetted with less than 30 per cent water, by mass | 1.1D | II | 10 | 0 | 75 | |
| UN0155 | PICRYL CHLORIDE; or TRINITROCHLOROBENZENE | 1.1D | II | 10 | 0 | 75 | |
| UN0159 | POWDER CAKE, WETTED with not less than 25 per cent water, by mass; or POWDER PASTE, WETTED with not less than 25 per cent water, by mass | 1.3C | II | 79 | 0 | | |
| UN0160 | POWDER, SMOKELESS | 1.1C | II | | 0 | 75 | |
| UN0161 | POWDER, SMOKELESS | 1.3C | II | 76 | 25 | | |
| UN0167 | PROJECTILES with bursting charge | 1.1F | II | | 0 | 75 | |
| UN0168 | PROJECTILES with bursting charge | 1.1D | II | | 0 | 75 | |
| UN0169 | PROJECTILES with bursting charge | 1.2D | II | | 0 | 75 | |
| UN0171 | AMMUNITION, ILLUMINATING with or without burster, expelling charge or propelling charge | 1.2G | II | | 0 | 75 | |
| UN0173 | RELEASE DEVICES, EXPLOSIVE | 1.4S | II | | 25 | | |
| UN0174 | RIVETS, EXPLOSIVE | 1.4S | II | | 25 | | |
| UN0180 | ROCKETS with bursting charge | 1.1F | II | | 0 | 75 | |
| UN0181 | ROCKETS with bursting charge | 1.1E | II | | 0 | 75 | |
| UN0182 | ROCKETS with bursting charge | 1.2E | II | | 0 | 75 | |
| UN0183 | ROCKETS with inert head | 1.3C | II | | 0 | | |
| UN0186 | ROCKET MOTORS | 1.3C | II | | 10 | | |
| UN0190 | SAMPLES, EXPLOSIVE, other than initiating explosive | | II | 16 | 0 | 75 | |
| UN0191 | SIGNAL DEVICES, HAND | 1.4G | II | | 25 | | |
| UN0192 | SIGNALS, RAILWAY TRACK, EXPLOSIVE | 1.1G | II | | 5 | 75 | |
| UN0193 | SIGNALS, RAILWAY TRACK, EXPLOSIVE | 1.4S | II | | 25 | | |

| 1 | 2 | 3 | 4 | 5 | 6 | 7 | 10 |
|---|---|---|---|---|---|---|---|
| UN Number | Shipping Name and Description | Class | Packing Group/Category | Special Provisions | Explosive Limit & Limited Quantity Index | ERAP Index | Marine Pollut |
| UN0194 | SIGNALS, DISTRESS, ship | 1.1G | II | | 25 | 75 | |
| UN0195 | SIGNALS, DISTRESS, ship | 1.3G | II | | 10 | | |
| UN0196 | SIGNALS, SMOKE | 1.1G | II | | 0 | 75 | |
| UN0197 | SIGNALS, SMOKE | 1.4G | II | 76 | 25 | | |
| UN0204 | SOUNDING DEVICES, EXPLOSIVE | 1.2F | II | | 0 | 75 | |
| UN0207 | TETRANITROANILINE | 1.1D | II | | 0 | 75 | |
| UN0208 | TETRYL; or TRINITROPHENYLMETHYLNITRAMINE | 1.1D | II | | 0 | 75 | |
| UN0209 | TNT, dry or wetted with less than 30 per cent water, by mass; or TRINITROTOLUENE, dry or wetted with less than 30 per cent water, by mass | 1.1D | II | 10 | 25 | 75 | |
| UN0212 | TRACERS FOR AMMUNITION | 1.3G | II | | 0 | | |
| UN0213 | TRINITROANISOLE | 1.1D | II | | 0 | 75 | |
| UN0214 | TRINITROBENZENE, dry or wetted with less than 30 per cent water, by mass | 1.1D | II | 10 | 0 | 75 | |
| UN0215 | TRINITROBENZOIC ACID, dry or wetted with less than 30 per cent water, by mass | 1.1D | II | 10 | 0 | 75 | |
| UN0216 | TRINITRO-m-CRESOL | 1.1D | II | | 0 | 75 | |
| UN0217 | TRINITRONAPHTHALENE | 1.1D | II | | 0 | 75 | |
| UN0218 | TRINITROPHENETOLE | 1.1D | II | | 0 | 75 | |
| UN0219 | STYPHNIC ACID, dry or wetted with less than 20 per cent water, or mixture of alcohol and water, by mass; or TRINITRORESORCINOL, dry or wetted with less than 20 per cent water, or mixture of alcohol and water, by mass | 1.1D | II | | 0 | 75 | |
| UN0220 | UREA NITRATE, dry or wetted with less than 20 per cent water, by mass | 1.1D | II | 60 | 0 | 75 | |
| UN0221 | WARHEADS, TORPEDO with bursting charge | 1.1D | II | | 0 | 75 | |
| UN0222 | AMMONIUM NITRATE with more than 0.2 per cent combustible substances, including any organic substance calculated as carbon, to the exclusion of any other added substance | 1.1D | II | | 0 | 75 | |
| UN0223 | AMMONIUM NITRATE FERTILIZER which is more liable to explode than ammonium nitrate with 0.2 per cent combustible substances, including any organic substance calculated as carbon, to the exclusion of any other added substance | 1.1D | II | | 0 | 75 | |
| UN0224 | BARIUM AZIDE, dry or wetted with less than 50 per cent water, by mass | 1.1A (6.1) | II | | 0 | 75 | |
| UN0225 | BOOSTERS WITH DETONATOR | 1.1B | II | | 0 | 75 | |
| UN0226 | CYCLOTETRAMETHYLENETETRANITRAMINE WETTED with not less than 15 per cent water, by mass; HMX WETTED with not less than 15 per cent water, by mass; or OCTOGEN WETTED with not less than 15 per cent water, by mass | 1.1D | II | 79 | 0 | 75 | |
| UN0234 | SODIUM DINITRO-o-CRESOLATE, dry or wetted with less than 15 per cent water, by mass | 1.3C | II | 10 | 0 | | P |
| UN0235 | SODIUM PICRAMATE, dry or wetted with less than 20 per cent water, by mass | 1.3C | II | | 0 | | |
| UN0236 | ZIRCONIUM PICRAMATE, dry or wetted with less than 20 per cent water, by mass | 1.3C | II | | 0 | | |
| UN0237 | CHARGES, SHAPED, FLEXIBLE, LINEAR | 1.4D | II | | 25 | | |
| UN0238 | ROCKETS, LINE-THROWING | 1.2G | II | | 5 | 75 | |
| UN0240 | ROCKETS, LINE-THROWING | 1.3G | II | | 10 | 75 | |
| UN0241 | EXPLOSIVE, BLASTING, TYPE E | 1.1D | II | | 25 | 75 | |
| UN0242 | CHARGES, PROPELLING, FOR CANNON | 1.3C | II | | 0 | | |
| UN0243 | AMMUNITION, INCENDIARY, WHITE PHOSPHORUS with burster, expelling charge or propelling charge | 1.2H | II | | 0 | 75 | |
| UN0244 | AMMUNITION, INCENDIARY, WHITE PHOSPHORUS with burster, expelling charge or propelling charge | 1.3H | II | | 0 | | |

| 1 | 2 | 3 | 4 | 5 | 6 | 7 | 10 |
|---|---|---|---|---|---|---|---|
| UN Number | Shipping Name and Description | Class | Packing Group/Category | Special Provisions | Explosive Limit & Limited Quantity Index | ERAP Index | Marine Pollut. |
| UN0245 | AMMUNITION, SMOKE, WHITE PHOSPHORUS with burster, expelling charge or propelling charge | 1.2H | II | | 0 | 75 | |
| UN0246 | AMMUNITION, SMOKE, WHITE PHOSPHORUS with burster, expelling charge or propelling charge | 1.3H | II | | 0 | | |
| UN0247 | AMMUNITION, INCENDIARY, liquid or gel, with burster, expelling charge or propelling charge | 1.3J | II | | 0 | | |
| UN0248 | CONTRIVANCES, WATER-ACTIVATED with burster, expelling charge or propelling charge | 1.2L | II | 16 | 0 | 75 | |
| UN0249 | CONTRIVANCES, WATER-ACTIVATED with burster, expelling charge or propelling charge | 1.3L | II | 16 | 0 | | |
| UN0250 | ROCKET MOTORS WITH HYPERGOLIC LIQUIDS with or without expelling charge | 1.3L | II | | 0 | | |
| UN0254 | AMMUNITION, ILLUMINATING with or without burster, expelling charge or propelling charge | 1.3G | II | | 0 | | |
| UN0255 | DETONATORS, ELECTRIC for blasting | 1.4B | II | 76,86 | 0 | | |
| UN0257 | FUZES, DETONATING | 1.4B | II | | 0 | | |
| UN0266 | OCTOL, dry or wetted with less than 15 per cent water, by mass; or OCTOLITE, dry or wetted with less than 15 per cent water, by mass | 1.1D | II | | 0 | 75 | |
| UN0267 | DETONATORS, NON-ELECTRIC for blasting | 1.4B | II | 86 | 0 | | |
| UN0268 | BOOSTERS WITH DETONATOR | 1.2B | II | | 0 | 75 | |
| UN0271 | CHARGES, PROPELLING | 1.1C | II | | 0 | 75 | |
| UN0272 | CHARGES, PROPELLING | 1.3C | II | | 0 | | |
| UN0275 | CARTRIDGES, POWER DEVICE | 1.3C | II | | 25 | | |
| UN0276 | CARTRIDGES, POWER DEVICE | 1.4C | II | | 25 | | |
| UN0277 | CARTRIDGES, OIL WELL | 1.3C | II | | 25 | | |
| UN0278 | CARTRIDGES, OIL WELL | 1.4C | II | | 25 | | |
| UN0279 | CHARGES, PROPELLING, FOR CANNON | 1.1C | II | | 0 | 75 | |
| UN0280 | ROCKET MOTORS | 1.1C | II | | 0 | 75 | |
| UN0281 | ROCKET MOTORS | 1.2C | II | | 0 | 75 | |
| UN0282 | NITROGUANIDINE, dry or wetted with less than 20 per cent water, by mass; or PICRITE, dry or wetted with less than 20 per cent water, by mass | 1.1D | II | | 0 | 75 | |
| UN0283 | BOOSTERS without detonator | 1.2D | II | | 0 | 75 | |
| UN0284 | GRENADES, hand or rifle, with bursting charge | 1.1D | II | | 0 | 75 | |
| UN0285 | GRENADES, hand or rifle, with bursting charge | 1.2D | II | | 0 | 75 | |
| UN0286 | WARHEADS, ROCKET with bursting charge | 1.1D | II | | 0 | 75 | |
| UN0287 | WARHEADS, ROCKET with bursting charge | 1.2D | II | | 0 | 75 | |
| UN0288 | CHARGES, SHAPED, FLEXIBLE, LINEAR | 1.1D | II | | 25 | 75 | |
| UN0289 | CORD, DETONATING, flexible | 1.4D | II | | 25 | | |
| UN0290 | CORD, DETONATING, metal clad; or FUSE, DETONATING, metal clad | 1.1D | II | | 5 | 75 | |
| UN0291 | BOMBS with bursting charge | 1.2F | II | | 0 | 75 | |
| UN0292 | GRENADES, hand or rifle, with bursting charge | 1.1F | II | | 0 | 75 | |
| UN0293 | GRENADES, hand or rifle, with bursting charge | 1.2F | II | | 0 | 75 | |
| UN0294 | MINES with bursting charge | 1.2F | II | | 0 | 75 | |
| UN0295 | ROCKETS with bursting charge | 1.2F | II | | 0 | 75 | |
| UN0296 | SOUNDING DEVICES, EXPLOSIVE | 1.1F | II | | 0 | 75 | |
| UN0297 | AMMUNITION, ILLUMINATING with or without burster, expelling charge or propelling charge | 1.4G | II | | 0 | | |
| UN0299 | BOMBS, PHOTO-FLASH | 1.3G | II | | 0 | | |
| UN0300 | AMMUNITION, INCENDIARY with or without burster, expelling charge or propelling charge | 1.4G | II | | 0 | | |
| UN0301 | AMMUNITION, TEAR-PRODUCING with burster, expelling charge or propelling charge | 1.4G (6.1) (8) | II | | 10 | 75 | |

| 1<br>UN Number | 2<br>Shipping Name and Description | 3<br>Class | 4<br>Packing Group/Category | 5<br>Special Provisions | 6<br>Explosive Limit & Limited Quantity Index | 7<br>ERAP Index | 10<br>Marine Pollut. |
|---|---|---|---|---|---|---|---|
| UN0303 | AMMUNITION, SMOKE with or without burster, expelling charge or propelling charge | 1.4G (8) | II | | 0 | | |
| UN0305 | FLASH POWDER | 1.3G | II | 76 | 5 | 75 | |
| UN0306 | TRACERS FOR AMMUNITION | 1.4G | II | | 0 | | |
| UN0312 | CARTRIDGES, SIGNAL | 1.4G | II | | 25 | | |
| UN0313 | SIGNALS, SMOKE | 1.2G | II | | 0 | 75 | |
| UN0314 | IGNITERS | 1.2G | II | | 0 | 75 | |
| UN0315 | IGNITERS | 1.3G | II | 86 | 0 | 5 000 | |
| UN0316 | FUZES, IGNITING | 1.3G | II | | 0 | | |
| UN0317 | FUZES, IGNITING | 1.4G | II | | 0 | | |
| UN0318 | GRENADES, PRACTICE, hand or rifle | 1.3G | II | | 0 | | |
| UN0319 | PRIMERS, TUBULAR | 1.3G | II | | 0 | | |
| UN0320 | PRIMERS, TUBULAR | 1.4G | II | | 0 | | |
| UN0321 | CARTRIDGES FOR WEAPONS with bursting charge | 1.2E | II | | 0 | 75 | |
| UN0322 | ROCKET MOTORS WITH HYPERGOLIC LIQUIDS with or without expelling charge | 1.2L | II | | 0 | 75 | |
| UN0323 | CARTRIDGES, POWER DEVICE | 1.4S | II | | 25 | | |
| UN0324 | PROJECTILES with bursting charge | 1.2F | II | | 0 | 75 | |
| UN0325 | IGNITERS | 1.4G | II | 76,86 | 0 | | |
| UN0326 | CARTRIDGES FOR WEAPONS, BLANK | 1.1C | II | | 0 | 75 | |
| UN0327 | CARTRIDGES FOR WEAPONS, BLANK; or CARTRIDGES, SMALL ARMS, BLANK | 1.3C | II | | 0 | | |
| UN0328 | CARTRIDGES FOR WEAPONS, INERT PROJECTILE | 1.2C | II | | 0 | 75 | |
| UN0329 | TORPEDOES with bursting charge | 1.1E | II | | 0 | 75 | |
| UN0330 | TORPEDOES with bursting charge | 1.1F | II | | 0 | 75 | |
| UN0331 | EXPLOSIVE, BLASTING, TYPE B | 1.5D | II | | 25 | 1 000 | |
| UN0332 | EXPLOSIVE, BLASTING, TYPE E | 1.5D | II | | 25 | 1 000 | |
| UN0333 | FIREWORKS | 1.1G | II | 4 | 0 | 75 | |
| UN0334 | FIREWORKS | 1.2G | II | 4 | 0 | 75 | |
| UN0335 | FIREWORKS | 1.3G | II | 4,76 | 25 | | |
| UN0336 | FIREWORKS | 1.4G | II | 5,76 | 25 | | |
| UN0337 | FIREWORKS | 1.4S | II | 3,5,76 | 25 | | |
| UN0338 | CARTRIDGES FOR WEAPONS, BLANK; or CARTRIDGES, SMALL ARMS, BLANK | 1.4C | II | | 25 | | |
| UN0339 | CARTRIDGES FOR WEAPONS, INERT PROJECTILE; or CARTRIDGES, SMALL ARMS | 1.4C | II | | 0 | | |
| UN0340 | NITROCELLULOSE, dry or wetted with less than 25 per cent water (or alcohol), by mass | 1.1D | II | | 0 | 75 | |
| UN0341 | NITROCELLULOSE, unmodified or plasticized with less than 18 per cent plasticizing substance, by mass | 1.1D | II | | 0 | 75 | |
| UN0342 | NITROCELLULOSE, WETTED with not less than 25 per cent alcohol, by mass | 1.3C | II | | 0 | | |
| UN0343 | NITROCELLULOSE, PLASTICIZED with not less than 18 per cent plasticizing substance, by mass | 1.3C | II | | 0 | | |
| UN0344 | PROJECTILES with bursting charge | 1.4D | II | | 0 | | |
| UN0345 | PROJECTILES, inert with tracer | 1.4S | II | | 0 | | |
| UN0346 | PROJECTILES with burster or expelling charge | 1.2D | II | | 0 | 75 | |
| UN0347 | PROJECTILES with burster or expelling charge | 1.4D | II | | 0 | | |
| UN0348 | CARTRIDGES FOR WEAPONS with bursting charge | 1.4F | II | | 0 | | |
| UN0349 | ARTICLES, EXPLOSIVE, N.O.S. | 1.4S | II | 16,76,86 | 0 | | |
| UN0350 | ARTICLES, EXPLOSIVE, N.O.S. | 1.4B | II | 16 | 0 | | |
| UN0351 | ARTICLES, EXPLOSIVE, N.O.S. | 1.4C | II | 16 | 0 | | |
| UN0352 | ARTICLES, EXPLOSIVE, N.O.S. | 1.4D | II | 16 | 0 | | |

| 1 UN Number | 2 Shipping Name and Description | 3 Class | 4 Packing Group/Category | 5 Special Provisions | 6 Explosive Limit & Limited Quantity Index | 7 ERAP Index | 10 Marine Pollut. |
|---|---|---|---|---|---|---|---|
| UN0353 | ARTICLES, EXPLOSIVE, N.O.S. | 1.4G | II | 16 | 0 | | |
| UN0354 | ARTICLES, EXPLOSIVE, N.O.S. | 1.1L | II | 16 | 0 | 75 | |
| UN0355 | ARTICLES, EXPLOSIVE, N.O.S. | 1.2L | II | 16 | 0 | 75 | |
| UN0356 | ARTICLES, EXPLOSIVE, N.O.S. | 1.3L | II | 16 | 0 | | |
| UN0357 | SUBSTANCES, EXPLOSIVE, N.O.S. | 1.1L | II | 16 | 0 | 75 | |
| UN0358 | SUBSTANCES, EXPLOSIVE, N.O.S. | 1.2L | II | 16 | 0 | 75 | |
| UN0359 | SUBSTANCES, EXPLOSIVE, N.O.S. | 1.3L | II | 16 | 0 | | |
| UN0360 | DETONATOR ASSEMBLIES, NON-ELECTRIC for blasting | 1.1B | II | 86 | 0 | 5 000 | |
| UN0361 | DETONATOR ASSEMBLIES, NON-ELECTRIC for blasting | 1.4B | II | 86 | 0 | | |
| UN0362 | AMMUNITION, PRACTICE | 1.4G | II | | 0 | | |
| UN0363 | AMMUNITION, PROOF | 1.4G | II | | 0 | | |
| UN0364 | DETONATORS FOR AMMUNITION | 1.2B | II | | 0 | 75 | |
| UN0365 | DETONATORS FOR AMMUNITION | 1.4B | II | | 0 | | |
| UN0366 | DETONATORS FOR AMMUNITION | 1.4S | II | | 0 | | |
| UN0367 | FUZES, DETONATING | 1.4S | II | 86 | 0 | | |
| UN0368 | FUZES, IGNITING | 1.4S | II | 86 | 0 | | |
| UN0369 | WARHEADS, ROCKET with bursting charge | 1.1F | II | | 0 | 75 | |
| UN0370 | WARHEADS, ROCKET with burster or expelling charge | 1.4D | II | | 0 | | |
| UN0371 | WARHEADS, ROCKET with burster or expelling charge | 1.4F | II | | 0 | | |
| UN0372 | GRENADES, PRACTICE, hand or rifle | 1.2G | II | | 0 | 75 | |
| UN0373 | SIGNAL DEVICES, HAND | 1.4S | II | | 25 | | |
| UN0374 | SOUNDING DEVICES, EXPLOSIVE | 1.1D | II | | 0 | 75 | |
| UN0375 | SOUNDING DEVICES, EXPLOSIVE | 1.2D | II | | 0 | 75 | |
| UN0376 | PRIMERS, TUBULAR | 1.4S | II | | 0 | | |
| UN0377 | PRIMERS, CAP TYPE | 1.1B | II | | 0 | 75 | |
| UN0378 | PRIMERS, CAP TYPE | 1.4B | II | | 0 | | |
| UN0379 | CASES, CARTRIDGE, EMPTY, WITH PRIMER | 1.4C | II | | 25 | | |
| UN0380 | ARTICLES, PYROPHORIC | 1.2L | II | | 0 | 75 | |
| UN0381 | CARTRIDGES, POWER DEVICE | 1.2C | II | | 25 | 75 | |
| UN0382 | COMPONENTS, EXPLOSIVE TRAIN, N.O.S. | 1.2B | II | 16 | 0 | 75 | |
| UN0383 | COMPONENTS, EXPLOSIVE TRAIN, N.O.S. | 1.4B | II | 16 | 0 | | |
| UN0384 | COMPONENTS, EXPLOSIVE TRAIN, N.O.S. | 1.4S | II | 16 | 0 | | |
| UN0385 | 5-NITROBENZOTRIAZOL | 1.1D | II | | 0 | 75 | |
| UN0386 | TRINITROBENZENESULFONIC ACID; or TRINITROBENZENESULPHONIC ACID | 1.1D | II | | 0 | 75 | |
| UN0387 | TRINITROFLUORENONE | 1.1D | II | | 0 | 75 | |
| UN0388 | TNT AND HEXANITROSTILBENE MIXTURE; TNT AND TRINITROBENZENE MIXTURE; TRINITROTOLUENE AND HEXANITROSTILBENE MIXTURE; or TRINITROTOLUENE AND TRINITROBENZENE MIXTURE | 1.1D | II | | 0 | 75 | |
| UN0389 | TNT MIXTURE CONTAINING TRINITROBENZENE AND HEXANITROSTILBENE; or TRINITROTOLUENE MIXTURE CONTAINING TRINITROBENZENE AND HEXANITROSTILBENE | 1.1D | II | | 0 | 75 | |
| UN0390 | TRITONAL | 1.1D | II | | 0 | 75 | |

| 1 UN Number | 2 Shipping Name and Description | 3 Class | 4 Packing Group/Category | 5 Special Provisions | 6 Explosive Limit & Limited Quantity Index | 7 ERAP Index | 10 Marine Pollut. |
|---|---|---|---|---|---|---|---|
| UN0391 | CYCLONITE and CYCLOTETRAMETHYLENETETRANITRAMINE MIXTURE, DESENSITIZED with not less than 10 per cent phelgmatizer, by mass;<br>CYCLONITE and CYCLOTETRAMETHYLENETETRANITRAMINE MIXTURE, WETTED with not less than 15 per cent water, by mass;<br>CYCLONITE and HMX MIXTURE, DESENSITIZED with not less than 10 per cent phelgmatizer, by mass;<br>CYCLONITE and HMX MIXTURE, WETTED with not less than 15 per cent water, by mass;<br>CYCLONITE and OCTOGEN MIXTURE, DESENSITIZED with not less than 10 per cent phelgmatizer, by mass;<br>CYCLONITE and OCTOGEN MIXTURE, WETTED with not less than 15 per cent water, by mass;<br>CYCLOTRIMETHYLENETRINITRAMINE AND CYCLOTETRAMETHYLENETETRANITRAMINE MIXTURE, DESENSITIZED with not less than 10 per cent phlegmatizer, by mass;<br>CYCLOTRIMETHYLENETRINITRAMINE AND CYCLOTETRAMETHYLENETETRANITRAMINE MIXTURE, WETTED with not less than 15 per cent water, by mass;<br>CYCLOTRIMETHYLENETRINITRAMINE AND HMX MIXTURE, DESENSITIZED with not less than 10 per cent phlegmatizer, by mass;<br>CYCLOTRIMETHYLENETRINITRAMINE AND HMX MIXTURE, WETTED with not less than 15 per cent water, by mass;<br>CYCLOTRIMETHYLENETRINITRAMINE AND OCTOGEN MIXTURE, DESENSITIZED with not less than 10 per cent phlegmatizer, by mass;<br>CYCLOTRIMETHYLENETRINITRAMINE AND OCTOGEN MIXTURE, WETTED with not less than 15 per cent water, by mass;<br>HEXOGEN AND CYCLOTETRAMETHYLENETETRANITRAMINE MIXTURE, DESENSITIZED with not less than 10 per cent phelgmatizer, by mass;<br>HEXOGEN AND CYCLOTETRAMETHYLENETETRANITRAMINE MIXTURE, WETTED with not less than 15 per cent water, by mass;<br>HEXOGEN AND HMX MIXTURE, DESENSITIZED with not less than 10 per cent phelgmatizer, by mass;<br>HEXOGEN AND HMX MIXTURE, WETTED with not less than 15 per cent water, by mass;<br>HEXOGEN AND OCTOGEN MIXTURE, DESENSITIZED with not less than 10 per cent phelgmatizer, by mass;<br>HEXOGEN AND OCTOGEN MIXTURE, WETTED with not less than 15 per cent water, by mass;<br>RDX AND CYCLOTETRAMETHYLENETETRANITRAMINE MIXTURE, DESENSITIZED with not less than 10 per cent phelgmatizer, by mass;<br>RDX AND CYCLOTETRAMETHYLENETETRANITRAMINE MIXTURE, WETTED with not less than 15 per cent water, by mass;<br>RDX AND HMX MIXTURE, DESENSITIZED with not less than 10 per cent phelgmatizer, by mass;<br>RDX AND HMX MIXTURE, WETTED with not less than 15 per cent water, by mass;<br>RDX AND OCTOGEN MIXTURE, DESENSITIZED with not less than 10 per cent phelgmatizer, by mass; or<br>RDX AND OCTOGEN MIXTURE, WETTED with not less than 15 per cent water, by mass | 1.1D | II | 79 | 0 | 75 | |
| UN0392 | HEXANITROSTILBENE | 1.1D | II | | 0 | 75 | |
| UN0393 | HEXOTONAL | 1.1D | II | | 0 | 75 | |
| UN0394 | STYPHNIC ACID, WETTED with not less than 20 per cent water, or mixture of alcohol and water, by mass; or<br>TRINITRORESORCINOL, WETTED with not less than 20 per cent water, or mixture of alcohol and water, by mass | 1.1D | II | | 0 | 75 | |
| UN0395 | ROCKET MOTORS, LIQUID FUELLED | 1.2J | II | | 0 | 75 | |

| 1 | 2 | 3 | 4 | 5 | 6 | 7 | 10 |
|---|---|---|---|---|---|---|---|
| UN Number | Shipping Name and Description | Class | Packing Group/Category | Special Provisions | Explosive Limit & Limited Quantity Index | ERAP Index | Marine Pollut. |
| UN0396 | ROCKET MOTORS, LIQUID FUELLED | 1.3J | II | | 0 | | |
| UN0397 | ROCKETS, LIQUID FUELLED with bursting charge | 1.1J | II | | 0 | 75 | |
| UN0398 | ROCKETS, LIQUID FUELLED with bursting charge | 1.2J | II | | 0 | 75 | |
| UN0399 | BOMBS WITH FLAMMABLE LIQUID with bursting charge | 1.1J | II | | 0 | 75 | |
| UN0400 | BOMBS WITH FLAMMABLE LIQUID with bursting charge | 1.2J | II | | 0 | 75 | |
| UN0401 | DIPICRYL SULFIDE, dry or wetted with less than 10 per cent water, by mass; or DIPICRYL SULPHIDE, dry or wetted with less than 10 per cent water, by mass | 1.1D | II | 10 | 5 | 75 | |
| UN0402 | AMMONIUM PERCHLORATE | 1.1D | II | | 5 | 75 | |
| UN0403 | FLARES, AERIAL | 1.4G | II | | 25 | | |
| UN0404 | FLARES, AERIAL | 1.4S | II | | 25 | | |
| UN0405 | CARTRIDGES, SIGNAL | 1.4S | II | | 25 | | |
| UN0406 | DINITROSOBENZENE | 1.3C | II | | 10 | | |
| UN0407 | TETRAZOL-1-ACETIC ACID | 1.4C | II | | 0 | | |
| UN0408 | FUZES, DETONATING with protective features | 1.1D | II | | 0 | 75 | |
| UN0409 | FUZES, DETONATING with protective features | 1.2D | II | | 0 | 75 | |
| UN0410 | FUZES, DETONATING with protective features | 1.4D | II | | 0 | | |
| UN0411 | PENTAERYTHRITE TETRANITRATE with not less than 7 per cent wax, by mass; PENTAERYTHRITOL TETRANITRATE with not less than 7 per cent wax, by mass; or PETN with not less than 7 per cent wax, by mass | 1.1D | II | | 0 | 75 | |
| UN0412 | CARTRIDGES FOR WEAPONS with bursting charge | 1.4E | II | | 0 | | |
| UN0413 | CARTRIDGES FOR WEAPONS, BLANK | 1.2C | II | | 0 | 75 | |
| UN0414 | CHARGES, PROPELLING, FOR CANNON | 1.2C | II | | 0 | 75 | |
| UN0415 | CHARGES, PROPELLING | 1.2C | II | | 0 | 75 | |
| UN0417 | CARTRIDGES FOR WEAPONS, INERT PROJECTILE; or CARTRIDGES, SMALL ARMS | 1.3C | II | | 0 | | |
| UN0418 | FLARES, SURFACE | 1.1G | II | | 0 | 75 | |
| UN0419 | FLARES, SURFACE | 1.2G | II | | 0 | 75 | |
| UN0420 | FLARES, AERIAL | 1.1G | II | | 0 | 75 | |
| UN0421 | FLARES, AERIAL | 1.2G | II | | 0 | 75 | |
| UN0424 | PROJECTILES, inert with tracer | 1.3G | II | | 0 | | |
| UN0425 | PROJECTILES, inert with tracer | 1.4G | II | | 0 | | |
| UN0426 | PROJECTILES with burster or expelling charge | 1.2F | II | | 0 | 75 | |
| UN0427 | PROJECTILES with burster or expelling charge | 1.4F | II | | 0 | | |
| UN0428 | ARTICLES, PYROTECHNIC for technical purposes | 1.1G | II | 4 | 0 | 75 | |
| UN0429 | ARTICLES, PYROTECHNIC for technical purposes | 1.2G | II | 4 | 0 | 75 | |
| UN0430 | ARTICLES, PYROTECHNIC for technical purposes | 1.3G | II | 4,76 | 25 | | |
| UN0431 | ARTICLES, PYROTECHNIC for technical purposes | 1.4G | II | 5,76 | 25 | | |
| UN0432 | ARTICLES, PYROTECHNIC for technical purposes | 1.4S | II | 5,76 | 25 | | |
| UN0433 | POWDER CAKE, WETTED with not less than 17 per cent alcohol, by mass; or POWDER PASTE, WETTED with not less than 17 per cent alcohol, by mass | 1.1C | II | 79 | 0 | 75 | |
| UN0434 | PROJECTILES with burster or expelling charge | 1.2G | II | | 0 | 75 | |
| UN0435 | PROJECTILES with burster or expelling charge | 1.4G | II | | 0 | | |
| UN0436 | ROCKETS with expelling charge | 1.2C | II | | 0 | 75 | |
| UN0437 | ROCKETS with expelling charge | 1.3C | II | | 0 | | |
| UN0438 | ROCKETS with expelling charge | 1.4C | II | | 0 | | |
| UN0439 | CHARGES, SHAPED, without detonator | 1.2D | II | | 25 | 75 | |
| UN0440 | CHARGES, SHAPED, without detonator | 1.4D | II | | 25 | | |

| 1 UN Number | 2 Shipping Name and Description | 3 Class | 4 Packing Group/Category | 5 Special Provisions | 6 Explosive Limit & Limited Quantity Index | 7 ERAP Index | 10 Marine Pollut. |
|---|---|---|---|---|---|---|---|
| UN0441 | CHARGES, SHAPED, without detonator | 1.4S | II | | 25 | | |
| UN0442 | CHARGES, EXPLOSIVE, COMMERCIAL without detonator | 1.1D | II | | 25 | 75 | |
| UN0443 | CHARGES, EXPLOSIVE, COMMERCIAL without detonator | 1.2D | II | | 25 | 75 | |
| UN0444 | CHARGES, EXPLOSIVE, COMMERCIAL without detonator | 1.4D | II | | 25 | | |
| UN0445 | CHARGES, EXPLOSIVE, COMMERCIAL without detonator | 1.4S | II | | 25 | | |
| UN0446 | CASES, COMBUSTIBLE, EMPTY, WITHOUT PRIMER | 1.4C | II | | 0 | | |
| UN0447 | CASES, COMBUSTIBLE, EMPTY, WITHOUT PRIMER | 1.3C | II | | 0 | | |
| UN0448 | 5-MERCAPTOTETRAZOL-1-ACETIC ACID | 1.4C | II | | 0 | | |
| UN0449 | TORPEDOES, LIQUID FUELLED with or without bursting charge | 1.1J | II | | 0 | 75 | |
| UN0450 | TORPEDOES, LIQUID FUELLED with inert head | 1.3J | II | | 0 | | |
| UN0451 | TORPEDOES with bursting charge | 1.1D | II | | 0 | 75 | |
| UN0452 | GRENADES, PRACTICE, hand or rifle | 1.4G | II | | 0 | | |
| UN0453 | ROCKETS, LINE-THROWING | 1.4G | II | | 25 | | |
| UN0454 | IGNITERS | 1.4S | II | 76,86 | 0 | | |
| UN0455 | DETONATORS, NON-ELECTRIC for blasting | 1.4S | II | 86 | 0 | | |
| UN0456 | DETONATORS, ELECTRIC for blasting | 1.4S | II | 86 | 0 | | |
| UN0457 | CHARGES, BURSTING, PLASTICS BONDED | 1.1D | II | | 0 | 75 | |
| UN0458 | CHARGES, BURSTING, PLASTICS BONDED | 1.2D | II | | 0 | 75 | |
| UN0459 | CHARGES, BURSTING, PLASTICS BONDED | 1.4D | II | | 0 | | |
| UN0460 | CHARGES, BURSTING, PLASTICS BONDED | 1.4S | II | | 0 | | |
| UN0461 | COMPONENTS, EXPLOSIVE TRAIN, N.O.S. | 1.1B | II | 16 | 0 | 75 | |
| UN0462 | ARTICLES, EXPLOSIVE, N.O.S. | 1.1C | II | 16 | 0 | 75 | |
| UN0463 | ARTICLES, EXPLOSIVE, N.O.S. | 1.1D | II | 16 | 0 | 75 | |
| UN0464 | ARTICLES, EXPLOSIVE, N.O.S. | 1.1E | II | 16 | 0 | 75 | |
| UN0465 | ARTICLES, EXPLOSIVE, N.O.S. | 1.1F | II | 16 | 0 | 75 | |
| UN0466 | ARTICLES, EXPLOSIVE, N.O.S. | 1.2C | II | 16 | 0 | 75 | |
| UN0467 | ARTICLES, EXPLOSIVE, N.O.S. | 1.2D | II | 16 | 0 | 75 | |
| UN0468 | ARTICLES, EXPLOSIVE, N.O.S. | 1.2E | II | 16 | 0 | 75 | |
| UN0469 | ARTICLES, EXPLOSIVE, N.O.S. | 1.2F | II | 16 | 0 | 75 | |
| UN0470 | ARTICLES, EXPLOSIVE, N.O.S. | 1.3C | II | 16 | 0 | | |
| UN0471 | ARTICLES, EXPLOSIVE, N.O.S. | 1.4E | II | 16 | 0 | | |
| UN0472 | ARTICLES, EXPLOSIVE, N.O.S. | 1.4F | II | 16 | 0 | | |
| UN0473 | SUBSTANCES, EXPLOSIVE, N.O.S. | 1.1A | II | 16 | 0 | 75 | |
| UN0474 | SUBSTANCES, EXPLOSIVE, N.O.S. | 1.1C | II | 16 | 0 | 75 | |
| UN0475 | SUBSTANCES, EXPLOSIVE, N.O.S. | 1.1D | II | 16 | 0 | 75 | |
| UN0476 | SUBSTANCES, EXPLOSIVE, N.O.S. | 1.1G | II | 16 | 0 | 75 | |
| UN0477 | SUBSTANCES, EXPLOSIVE, N.O.S. | 1.3C | II | 16 | 0 | | |
| UN0478 | SUBSTANCES, EXPLOSIVE, N.O.S. | 1.3G | II | 16 | 0 | | |
| UN0479 | SUBSTANCES, EXPLOSIVE, N.O.S. | 1.4C | II | 16 | 0 | | |
| UN0480 | SUBSTANCES, EXPLOSIVE, N.O.S. | 1.4D | II | 16 | 0 | | |
| UN0481 | SUBSTANCES, EXPLOSIVE, N.O.S. | 1.4S | II | 16 | 0 | | |
| UN0482 | SUBSTANCES, EVI, N.O.S.; or SUBSTANCES, EXPLOSIVE, VERY INSENSITIVE, N.O.S. | 1.5D | II | 16 | 0 | 1 000 | |

| 1 | 2 | 3 | 4 | 5 | 6 | 7 | 10 |
|---|---|---|---|---|---|---|---|
| UN Number | Shipping Name and Description | Class | Packing Group/Category | Special Provisions | Explosive Limit & Limited Quantity Index | ERAP Index | Marine Pollut. |
| UN0483 | CYCLONITE, DESENSITIZED; CYCLOTRIMETHYLENETRINITRAMINE, DESENSITIZED; HEXOGEN, DESENSITIZED; or RDX, DESENSITIZED | 1.1D | II | | 0 | 75 | |
| UN0484 | CYCLOTETRAMETHYLENETETRANITRAMINE, DESENSITIZED; HMX, DESENSITIZED; or OCTOGEN, DESENSITIZED | 1.1D | II | | 0 | 75 | |
| UN0485 | SUBSTANCES, EXPLOSIVE, N.O.S. | 1.4G | II | 16 | 0 | | |
| UN0486 | ARTICLES, EEI; or ARTICLES, EXPLOSIVE, EXTREMELY INSENSITIVE | 1.6N | II | | 0 | | |
| UN0487 | SIGNALS, SMOKE | 1.3G | II | | 10 | | |
| UN0488 | AMMUNITION, PRACTICE | 1.3G | II | | 0 | | |
| UN0489 | DINGU; or DINITROGLYCOLURIL | 1.1D | II | | 0 | 75 | |
| UN0490 | NITROTRIAZOLONE; or NTO | 1.1D | II | | 0 | 75 | |
| UN0491 | CHARGES, PROPELLING | 1.4C | II | | 0 | | |
| UN0492 | SIGNALS, RAILWAY TRACK, EXPLOSIVE | 1.3G | II | | 10 | | |
| UN0493 | SIGNALS, RAILWAY TRACK, EXPLOSIVE | 1.4G | II | | 25 | | |
| UN0494 | JET PERFORATING GUNS, CHARGED, oil well, without detonator | 1.4D | II | | 0 | | |
| UN0495 | PROPELLANT, LIQUID | 1.3C | II | | 0 | | |
| UN0496 | OCTONAL | 1.1D | II | | 0 | 75 | |
| UN0497 | PROPELLANT, LIQUID | 1.1C | II | | 0 | 75 | |
| UN0498 | PROPELLANT, SOLID | 1.1C | II | | 0 | 75 | |
| UN0499 | PROPELLANT, SOLID | 1.3C | II | 76 | 25 | | |
| UN0500 | DETONATOR ASSEMBLIES, NON-ELECTRIC, for blasting | 1.4S | II | 86 | 0 | | |
| UN0501 | PROPELLANT, SOLID | 1.4C | II | 11 | 0 | | |
| UN0502 | ROCKETS with inert head | 1.2C | II | 12 | 0 | 75 | |
| UN0503 | AIR BAG INFLATORS, pyrotechnic; AIR BAG MODULES, pyrotechnic; or SEAT-BELT PRETENSIONERS, pyrotechnic | 1.4G | II | 13 | 25 | | |
| UN0504 | 1H-TETRAZOLE | 1.1D | II | 14 | 0 | 75 | |
| UN1001 | ACETYLENE, DISSOLVED | 2.1 | | 38 | 0 | | |
| UN1002 | AIR, COMPRESSED, with not more than 23.5 per cent oxygen, by volume | 2.2 | | | 0.125 | | |
| UN1003 | AIR, REFRIGERATED LIQUID | 2.2 (5.1) | | | 0.125 | 3 000 | |
| UN1005 | AMMONIA, ANHYDROUS; or ANHYDROUS AMMONIA | 2.3 (8) | | | 0 | 3 000 | |
| UN1006 | ARGON, COMPRESSED | 2.2 | | | 0.125 | | |
| UN1008 | BORON TRIFLUORIDE, COMPRESSED | 2.3 (8) | | | 0 | 50 | |
| UN1009 | BROMOTRIFLUOROMETHANE; or REFRIGERANT GAS R 13B1 | 2.2 | | | 0.125 | | |
| UN1010 | BUTADIENES, STABILIZED | 2.1 | | | 0.125 | 3 000 | |
| UN1011 | BUTANE | 2.1 | | | 0.125 | 3 000 | |
| UN1012 | BUTYLENE | 2.1 | | | 0.125 | 3 000 | |
| UN1013 | CARBON DIOXIDE | 2.2 | | | 0.125 | | |
| UN1014 | CARBON DIOXIDE AND OXYGEN MIXTURE, COMPRESSED | 2.2 (5.1) | | | 0.125 | 3 000 | |
| UN1015 | CARBON DIOXIDE AND NITROUS OXIDE MIXTURE | 2.2 | | | 0.125 | | |
| UN1016 | CARBON MONOXIDE, COMPRESSED | 2.3 (2.1) | | | 0 | 500 | |

| 1 | 2 | 3 | 4 | 5 | 6 | 7 | 10 |
|---|---|---|---|---|---|---|---|
| UN Number | Shipping Name and Description | Class | Packing Group/Category | Special Provisions | Explosive Limit & Limited Quantity Index | ERAP Index | Marine Pollut. |
| UN1017 | CHLORINE | 2.3 (8) | | | 0 | 500 | P |
| UN1018 | CHLORODIFLUOROMETHANE; or REFRIGERANT GAS R 22 | 2.2 | | | 0.125 | | |
| UN1020 | CHLOROPENTAFLUOROETHANE; or REFRIGERANT GAS R 115 | 2.2 | | | 0.125 | | |
| UN1021 | 1-CHLORO-1,2,2,2-TETRAFLUOROETHANE; or REFRIGERANT GAS R 124 | 2.2 | | | 0.125 | | |
| UN1022 | CHLOROTRIFLUOROMETHANE; or REFRIGERANT GAS R 13 | 2.2 | | | 0.125 | | |
| UN1023 | COAL GAS, COMPRESSED | 2.3 (2.1) | | | 0 | 500 | |
| UN1026 | CYANOGEN | 2.3 (2.1) | | 28 | 0 | 25 | |
| UN1027 | CYCLOPROPANE | 2.1 | | | 0.125 | 3 000 | |
| UN1028 | DICHLORODIFLUOROMETHANE; or REFRIGERANT GAS R 12 | 2.2 | | | 0.125 | | |
| UN1029 | DICHLOROFLUOROMETHANE; or REFRIGERANT GAS R 21 | 2.2 | | | 0.125 | | |
| UN1030 | 1,1-DIFLUOROETHANE; or REFRIGERANT GAS R 152a | 2.1 | | | 0.125 | 3 000 | |
| UN1032 | DIMETHYLAMINE, ANHYDROUS | 2.1 (8) | | | 0 | 3 000 | |
| UN1033 | DIMETHYL ETHER | 2.1 | | | 0.125 | 3 000 | |
| UN1035 | ETHANE | 2.1 | | | 0.125 | 3 000 | |
| UN1036 | ETHYLAMINE | 2.1 | | | 0.125 | 3 000 | |
| UN1037 | ETHYL CHLORIDE | 2.1 | | | 0.125 | 3 000 | |
| UN1038 | ETHYLENE, REFRIGERATED LIQUID | 2.1 | | | 0 | 3 000 | |
| UN1039 | ETHYL METHYL ETHER | 2.1 | | | 0.125 | 3 000 | |
| UN1040 | ETHYLENE OXIDE; or ETHYLENE OXIDE WITH NITROGEN up to a total pressure of 1 MPa (10 bar) at 50 °C | 2.3 (2.1) | | | 0 | 500 | |
| UN1041 | ETHYLENE OXIDE AND CARBON DIOXIDE MIXTURE with more than 9 per cent but not more than 87 per cent ethylene oxide | 2.1 | | | 0 | 3 000 | |
| UN1043 | FERTILIZER AMMONIATING SOLUTION with free ammonia | 2.2 | | | 0.125 | | |
| UN1044 | FIRE EXTINGUISHERS with compressed or liquefied gas | 2.2 | | | 0.125 | | |
| UN1045 | FLUORINE, COMPRESSED | 2.3 (5.1) (8) | | 38 | 0 | 25 | |
| UN1046 | HELIUM, COMPRESSED | 2.2 | | | 0.125 | | |
| UN1048 | HYDROGEN BROMIDE, ANHYDROUS | 2.3 (8) | | | 0 | 500 | |
| UN1049 | HYDROGEN, COMPRESSED | 2.1 | | | 0.125 | 3 000 | |
| UN1050 | HYDROGEN CHLORIDE, ANHYDROUS | 2.3 (8) | | | 0 | 500 | |
| UN1051 | HYDROGEN CYANIDE, STABILIZED, containing less than 3 per cent water | 6.1 (3) | I | | 0 | 1 000 | P |
| UN1052 | HYDROGEN FLUORIDE, ANHYDROUS | 8 (6.1) | I | | 0 | 1 000 | |
| UN1053 | HYDROGEN SULFIDE; or HYDROGEN SULPHIDE | 2.3 (2.1) | | | 0 | 500 | |
| UN1055 | ISOBUTYLENE | 2.1 | | | 0.125 | 3 000 | |
| UN1056 | KRYPTON, COMPRESSED | 2.2 | | | 0.125 | | |
| UN1057 | LIGHTER REFILLS (cigarettes) containing flammable gas and capable of passing the tests specified in the Hazardous Products (Lighters) Regulations; or LIGHTERS (cigarettes) containing flammable gas and capable of passing the tests specified in the Hazardous Products (Lighters) Regulations | 2.1 | | | 0.125 | | |

| 1 | 2 | 3 | 4 | 5 | 6 | 7 | 10 |
|---|---|---|---|---|---|---|---|
| UN Number | Shipping Name and Description | Class | Packing Group/Category | Special Provisions | Explosive Limit & Limited Quantity Index | ERAP Index | Marine Pollut. |
| UN1058 | LIQUEFIED GASES, non-flammable, charged with nitrogen, carbon dioxide or air | 2.2 | | 38 | 0.125 | | |
| UN1060 | METHYLACETYLENE AND PROPADIENE MIXTURE, STABILIZED | 2.1 | | | 0.125 | 3 000 | |
| UN1061 | METHYLAMINE, ANHYDROUS | 2.1 | | | 0.125 | 3 000 | |
| UN1062 | METHYL BROMIDE | 2.3 | | | 0 | 50 | |
| UN1063 | METHYL CHLORIDE; or REFRIGERANT GAS R 40 | 2.1 | | | 0.125 | 3 000 | |
| UN1064 | METHYL MERCAPTAN | 2.3 (2.1) | | | 0 | 500 | P |
| UN1065 | NEON, COMPRESSED | 2.2 | | | 0.125 | | |
| UN1066 | NITROGEN, COMPRESSED | 2.2 | | | 0.125 | | |
| UN1067 | DINITROGEN TETROXIDE; or NITROGEN DIOXIDE | 2.3 (5.1) (8) | | | 0 | 0 | |
| UN1069 | NITROSYL CHLORIDE | 2.3 (8) | | | 0 | 25 | |
| UN1070 | NITROUS OXIDE | 2.2 (5.1) | | | 0 | 3 000 | |
| UN1071 | OIL GAS, COMPRESSED | 2.3 (2.1) | | | 0 | 25 | |
| UN1072 | OXYGEN, COMPRESSED | 2.2 (5.1) | | | 0.125 | 3 000 | |
| UN1073 | OXYGEN, REFRIGERATED LIQUID | 2.2 (5.1) | | 87 | 0.125 | 3 000 | |
| UN1075 | LIQUEFIED PETROLEUM GASES; or PETROLEUM GASES, LIQUEFIED | 2.1 | | | 0.125 | 3 000 | • |
| UN1076 | PHOSGENE | 2.3 (8) | | | 0 | 0 | |
| UN1077 | PROPYLENE | 2.1 | | | 0.125 | 3 000 | |
| UN1078 | REFRIGERANT GAS, N.O.S. | 2.2 | | 16 | 0.125 | | • |
| UN1079 | SULFUR DIOXIDE; or SULPHUR DIOXIDE | 2.3 (8) | | | 0 | 500 | |
| UN1080 | SULFUR HEXAFLUORIDE; or SULPHUR HEXAFLUORIDE | 2.2 | | | 0.125 | | |
| UN1081 | TETRAFLUOROETHYLENE, STABILIZED | 2.1 | | 38 | 0.125 | 3 000 | |
| UN1082 | TRIFLUOROCHLOROETHYLENE, STABILIZED | 2.3 (2.1) | | | 0 | 500 | |
| UN1083 | TRIMETHYLAMINE, ANHYDROUS | 2.1 | | | 0.125 | 3 000 | |
| UN1085 | VINYL BROMIDE, STABILIZED | 2.1 | | | 0.125 | 3 000 | |
| UN1086 | VINYL CHLORIDE, STABILIZED | 2.1 | | | 0.125 | 3 000 | |
| UN1087 | VINYL METHYL ETHER, STABILIZED | 2.1 | | | 0.125 | 3 000 | |
| UN1088 | ACETAL | 3 | II | | 1 | | |
| UN1089 | ACETALDEHYDE | 3 | I | | 0 | 3 000 | |
| UN1090 | ACETONE | 3 ✓ | II ✓ | | 1 | | |
| UN1091 | ACETONE OILS | 3 | II | | 1 | | |
| UN1092 | ACROLEIN, STABILIZED | 6.1 (3) | I | | 0 | 1 000 | P |
| UN1093 | ACRYLONITRILE, STABILIZED | 3 (6.1) | I | | 0 | 1 000 | |
| UN1098 | ALLYL ALCOHOL | 6.1 (3) | I | | 0 | 1 000 | |
| UN1099 | ALLYL BROMIDE | 3 (6.1) | I | | 0 | 1 000 | P |
| UN1100 | ALLYL CHLORIDE | 3 (6.1) | I | | 0 | 1 000 | |
| UN1104 | AMYL ACETATES | 3 | III | | 5 | | |
| UN1105 | PENTANOLS | 3 | II / III | | 1 / 5 | | |

| 1 | 2 | 3 | 4 | 5 | 6 | 7 | 10 |
|---|---|---|---|---|---|---|---|
| UN Number | Shipping Name and Description | Class | Packing Group/Category | Special Provisions | Explosive Limit & Limited Quantity Index | ERAP Index | Marine Pollut. |
| UN1106 | AMYLAMINE | 3 (8) | II III | | 1 5 | | |
| UN1107 | AMYL CHLORIDE | 3 | II | | 1 | | |
| UN1108 | n-AMYLENE; or 1-PENTENE | 3 | I | | 0 | | |
| UN1109 | AMYL FORMATES | 3 | III | | 5 | | |
| UN1110 | n-AMYL METHYL KETONE | 3 | III | | 5 | | |
| UN1111 | AMYL MERCAPTAN | 3 | II | | 1 | | P |
| UN1112 | AMYL NITRATE | 3 | III | | 5 | | |
| UN1113 | AMYL NITRITE | 3 | II | | 1 | | |
| UN1114 | BENZENE | 3 | II | | 1 | | |
| UN1120 | BUTANOLS | 3 | II III | | 1 5 | | |
| UN1123 | BUTYL ACETATES | 3 | II III | | 1 5 | | |
| UN1125 | n-BUTYLAMINE | 3 (8) | II | | 1 | | |
| UN1126 | 1-BROMOBUTANE | 3 | II | | 1 | | |
| UN1127 | CHLOROBUTANES | 3 | II | | 1 | | |
| UN1128 | n-BUTYL FORMATE | 3 | II | | 1 | | |
| UN1129 | BUTYRALDEHYDE | 3 | II | | 1 | | P |
| UN1130 | CAMPHOR OIL | 3 | III | | 5 | | P |
| UN1131 | CARBON DISULFIDE; or CARBON DISULPHIDE | 3 (6.1) | I | | 0 | 1 000 | |
| UN1133 | ADHESIVES containing flammable liquid | 3 | I II III | 83 83 | 0.5 5 5 | | • |
| UN1134 | CHLOROBENZENE | 3 | III | | 5 | | |
| UN1135 | ETHYLENE CHLOROHYDRIN | 6.1 (3) | I | | 0 | 1 000 | |
| UN1136 | COAL TAR DISTILLATES, FLAMMABLE | 3 | II III | | 1 5 | | |
| UN1139 | COATING SOLUTION (includes surface treatments or coatings used for industrial or other purposes such as vehicle undercoating, drum or barrel lining) | 3 | I II III | | 0.5 5 5 | | • |
| UN1143 | CROTONALDEHYDE, STABILIZED | 6.1 (3) | I | | 0 | 1 000 | P |
| UN1144 | CROTONYLENE | 3 | I | | 0 | | |
| UN1145 | CYCLOHEXANE | 3 | II | | 1 | | |
| UN1146 | CYCLOPENTANE | 3 | II | | 1 | | |
| UN1147 | DECAHYDRONAPHTHALENE | 3 | III | | 5 | | |
| UN1148 | DIACETONE ALCOHOL | 3 | II III | | 1 5 | | |
| UN1149 | DIBUTYL ETHERS | 3 | III | | 5 | | |
| UN1150 | 1,2-DICHLOROETHYLENE | 3 | II | | 1 | | |
| UN1152 | DICHLOROPENTANES | 3 | III | | 5 | | |
| UN1153 | ETHYLENE GLYCOL DIETHYL ETHER | 3 | III | | 5 | | |
| UN1154 | DIETHYLAMINE | 3 (8) | II | | 1 | | |
| UN1155 | DIETHYL ETHER; or ETHYL ETHER | 3 | I | | 0 | | |
| UN1156 | DIETHYL KETONE | 3 | II | | 1 | | |
| UN1157 | DIISOBUTYL KETONE | 3 | III | | 5 | | |
| UN1158 | DIISOPROPYLAMINE | 3 (8) | II | | 1 | | |

| 1 | 2 | 3 | 4 | 5 | 6 | 7 | 10 |
|---|---|---|---|---|---|---|---|
| UN Number | Shipping Name and Description | Class | Packing Group/Category | Special Provisions | Explosive Limit & Limited Quantity Index | ERAP Index | Marine Pollut. |
| UN1159 | DIISOPROPYL ETHER | 3 | II | | 1 | | |
| UN1160 | DIMETHYLAMINE, AQUEOUS SOLUTION | 3 (8) | II | | 1 | | |
| UN1161 | DIMETHYL CARBONATE | 3 | II | | 1 | | |
| UN1162 | DIMETHYLDICHLOROSILANE | 3 (8) | II | | 0 | 1 000 | |
| UN1163 | DIMETHYLHYDRAZINE, UNSYMMETRICAL | 6.1 (3) (8) | I | | 0 | 1 000 | P |
| UN1164 | DIMETHYL SULFIDE; or DIMETHYL SULPHIDE | 3 | II | | 1 | | |
| UN1165 | DIOXANE | 3 | II | | 1 | | |
| UN1166 | DIOXOLANE | 3 | II | | 1 | | |
| UN1167 | DIVINYL ETHER, STABILIZED | 3 | I | | 0 | | |
| UN1169 | EXTRACTS, AROMATIC, LIQUID | 3 | II III | | 5 5 | | • |
| UN1170 | ETHANOL more than 24 per cent ethanol, by volume; ETHANOL SOLUTION more than 24 per cent ethanol, by volume; ETHYL ALCOHOL more than 24 per cent ethanol, by volume; or ETHYL ALCOHOL SOLUTION more than 24 per cent ethanol, by volume | 3 | II III | | 1 5 | | |
| UN1171 | ETHYLENE GLYCOL MONOETHYL ETHER | 3 | III | | 5 | | |
| UN1172 | ETHYLENE GLYCOL MONOETHYL ETHER ACETATE | 3 | III | | 5 | | |
| UN1173 | ETHYL ACETATE | 3 | II | | 1 | | |
| UN1175 | ETHYLBENZENE | 3 | II | | 1 | | |
| UN1176 | ETHYL BORATE | 3 | II | | 1 | | |
| UN1177 | ETHYLBUTYL ACETATE | 3 | III | | 5 | | |
| UN1178 | 2-ETHYLBUTYRALDEHYDE | 3 | II | | 1 | | |
| UN1179 | ETHYL BUTYL ETHER | 3 | II | | 1 | | |
| UN1180 | ETHYL BUTYRATE | 3 | III | | 5 | | |
| UN1181 | ETHYL CHLOROACETATE | 6.1 (3) | II | | 0.1 | 1 000 | |
| UN1182 | ETHYL CHLOROFORMATE | 6.1 (3) (8) | I | | 0 | 1 000 | |
| UN1183 | ETHYLDICHLOROSILANE | 4.3 (3) (8) | I | | 0 | 1 000 | |
| UN1184 | ETHYLENE DICHLORIDE | 3 (6.1) | II | | 1 | | |
| UN1185 | ETHYLENEIMINE, STABILIZED | 6.1 (3) | I | | 0 | 1 000 | |
| UN1188 | ETHYLENE GLYCOL MONOMETHYL ETHER | 3 | III | | 5 | | |
| UN1189 | ETHYLENE GLYCOL MONOMETHYL ETHER ACETATE | 3 | III | | 5 | | |
| UN1190 | ETHYL FORMATE | 3 | II | | 1 | | |
| UN1191 | OCTYL ALDEHYDES | 3 | III | | 5 | | |
| UN1192 | ETHYL LACTATE | 3 | III | | 5 | | |
| UN1193 | ETHYL METHYL KETONE; or METHYL ETHYL KETONE | 3 | II | | 1 | | |
| UN1194 | ETHYL NITRITE SOLUTION | 3 (6.1) | I | 38, 68 | 0 | 1 000 | |
| UN1195 | ETHYL PROPIONATE | 3 | II | | 1 | | |
| UN1196 | ETHYLTRICHLOROSILANE | 3 (8) | II | | 0 | 3 000 | |
| UN1197 | EXTRACTS, FLAVOURING, LIQUID | 3 | II III | | 1 5 | | • |

| 1<br>UN Number | 2<br>Shipping Name and Description | 3<br>Class | 4<br>Packing Group/Category | 5<br>Special Provisions | 6<br>Explosive Limit & Limited Quantity Index | 7<br>ERAP Index | 10<br>Marine Pollut. |
|---|---|---|---|---|---|---|---|
| UN1198 | FORMALDEHYDE SOLUTION, FLAMMABLE | 3 (8) | III | | 5 | | |
| UN1199 | FURALDEHYDES | 6.1 (3) | II | | 0.1 | 1 000 | |
| UN1201 | FUSEL OIL | 3 | II<br>III | | 1<br>5 | | |
| UN1202 | DIESEL FUEL;<br>FUEL OIL;<br>GAS OIL; or<br>HEATING OIL LIGHT | 3 | III | 82,88 | 30 | SP82 | |
| UN1203 | GASOLINE; (North America)<br>MOTOR SPIRIT; or<br>PETROL | 3 | II ✓ | 17,82,88 | 30 | SP82 | P |
| UN1204 | NITROGLYCERIN SOLUTION IN ALCOHOL with not more than 1 per cent nitroglycerin | 3 | II | 38 | 1 | | |
| UN1206 | HEPTANES | 3 | II | | 1 | | |
| UN1207 | HEXALDEHYDE | 3 | III | | 5 | | |
| UN1208 | HEXANES | 3 | II | | 1 | | |
| UN1210 | PRINTING INK, flammable, with not more than 20 per cent nitrocellulose by mass if the nitrogen content of the nitrocellulose is not more than 12.6 per cent by mass; or<br>PRINTING INK RELATED MATERIAL (including printing ink thinning or reducting compound) flammable, with not more than 20 per cent nitrocellulose by mass if the nitrogen content of the nitrocellulose is not more than 12.6 per cent by mass | 3 | I<br>II<br>III | 59<br>59,83<br>59,83 | 0.5<br>5<br>5 | | |
| UN1212 | ISOBUTANOL; or<br>ISOBUTYL ALCOHOL | 3 | III | | 5 | | |
| UN1213 | ISOBUTYL ACETATE | 3 | II | | 1 | | |
| UN1214 | ISOBUTYLAMINE | 3 (8) | II | | 1 | | |
| UN1216 | ISOOCTENE | 3 | II | | 1 | | |
| UN1218 | ISOPRENE, STABILIZED | 3 | I | | 0 | | |
| UN1219 | ISOPROPANOL; or<br>ISOPROPYL ALCOHOL | 3 | II | | 1 | | |
| UN1220 | ISOPROPYL ACETATE | 3 | II | | 1 | | |
| UN1221 | ISOPROPYLAMINE | 3 (8) | I | | 0 | | |
| UN1222 | ISOPROPYL NITRATE | 3 | II | 38 | 1 | | |
| UN1223 | KEROSENE | 3 | III | | 5 | | |
| UN1224 | KETONES, LIQUID, N.O.S. | 3 | II<br>III | 16<br>16 | 1<br>5 | | • |
| UN1228 | MERCAPTAN MIXTURE, LIQUID, FLAMMABLE, TOXIC, N.O.S; or<br>MERCAPTANS, LIQUID, FLAMMABLE, TOXIC, N.O.S. | 3 (6.1) | II<br>III | 16<br>16 | 1<br>5 | 1 000 | • |
| UN1229 | MESITYL OXIDE | 3 | III | | 5 | | |
| UN1230 | METHANOL | 3 (6.1) | II | 43 | 1 | | |
| UN1231 | METHYL ACETATE | 3 | II | | 1 | | |
| UN1233 | METHYLAMYL ACETATE | 3 | III | | 5 | | |
| UN1234 | METHYLAL | 3 | II | | 1 | | |
| UN1235 | METHYLAMINE, AQUEOUS SOLUTION | 3 (8) | II | | 1 | | |
| UN1237 | METHYL BUTYRATE | 3 | II | | 1 | | |
| UN1238 | METHYL CHLOROFORMATE | 6.1 (3) (8) | I | | 0 | 1 000 | |
| UN1239 | METHYL CHLOROMETHYL ETHER | 6.1 (3) | I | | 0 | 1 000 | |

| 1 UN Number | 2 Shipping Name and Description | 3 Class | 4 Packing Group/Category | 5 Special Provisions | 6 Explosive Limit & Limited Quantity Index | 7 ERAP Index | 10 Marine Pollut. |
|---|---|---|---|---|---|---|---|
| UN1242 | METHYLDICHLOROSILANE | 4.3 (3) (8) | I | | 0 | 1 000 | |
| UN1243 | METHYL FORMATE | 3 | I | | 0 | | |
| UN1244 | METHYLHYDRAZINE | 6.1 (3) (8) | I | | 0 | 1 000 | |
| UN1245 | METHYL ISOBUTYL KETONE | 3 | II | | 1 | | |
| UN1246 | METHYL ISOPROPENYL KETONE, STABILIZED | 3 | II | | 1 | | |
| UN1247 | METHYL METHACRYLATE MONOMER, STABILIZED | 3 | II | | 1 | | |
| UN1248 | METHYL PROPIONATE | 3 | II | | 1 | | |
| UN1249 | METHYL PROPYL KETONE | 3 | II | | 1 | | |
| UN1250 | METHYLTRICHLOROSILANE | 3 (8) | I | | 0 | 1 000 | |
| UN1251 | METHYL VINYL KETONE, STABILIZED | 6.1 (3) (8) | I | | 0 | 1 000 | |
| UN1259 | NICKEL CARBONYL | 6.1 (3) | I | 38 | 0 | 1 000 | PP |
| UN1261 | NITROMETHANE | 3 | II | 38 | 1 | | |
| UN1262 | OCTANES | 3 | II | | 1 | | |
| UN1263 | PAINT (including paint, lacquer, enamel, stain, shellac, varnish, polish, liquid filler and liquid lacquer base) with not more than 20 per cent nitrocellulose by mass if the nitrogen content of the nitrocellulose is not more than 12.6 per cent by mass; or PAINT RELATED MATERIAL (including paint thinning or reducing compound) with not more than 20 per cent nitrocellulose by mass if the nitrogen content of the nitrocellulose is not more than 12.6 per cent by mass | 3 | I II III | 59 59,83 59,83 | 0.5 5 5 | | • |
| UN1264 | PARALDEHYDE | 3 | III | | 5 | | |
| UN1265 | PENTANES, liquid | 3 | I II | | 0 1 | | |
| UN1266 | PERFUMERY PRODUCTS with flammable solvents | 3 | II III | | 5 5 | | • |
| UN1267 | PETROLEUM CRUDE OIL | 3 | I II III | | 0.5 1 5 | | |
| UN1268 | PETROLEUM DISTILLATES, N.O.S.; or PETROLEUM PRODUCTS, N.O.S. | 3 | I II III | | 0.5 1 5 | | • |
| UN1272 | PINE OIL | 3 | III | | 5 | | |
| UN1274 | n-PROPANOL; or PROPYL ALCOHOL, NORMAL | 3 | II III | | 1 5 | | |
| UN1275 | PROPIONALDEHYDE | 3 | II | | 1 | | |
| UN1276 | n-PROPYL ACETATE | 3 | II | | 1 | | |
| UN1277 | PROPYLAMINE | 3 (8) | II | | 1 | | |
| UN1278 | PROPYL CHLORIDE | 3 | II | | 1 | | |
| UN1279 | 1,2-DICHLOROPROPANE | 3 | II | | 1 | | |
| UN1280 | PROPYLENE OXIDE | 3 | I | | 0 | | |
| UN1281 | PROPYL FORMATES | 3 | II | | 1 | | |
| UN1282 | PYRIDINE | 3 | II | | 1 | | |
| UN1286 | ROSIN OIL | 3 | II III | | 1 5 | | |
| UN1287 | RUBBER SOLUTION | 3 | II III | | 5 5 | | • |
| UN1288 | SHALE OIL | 3 | II III | | 1 5 | | |

| 1<br>UN Number | 2<br>Shipping Name and Description | 3<br>Class | 4<br>Packing Group/Category | 5<br>Special Provisions | 6<br>Explosive Limit & Limited Quantity Index | 7<br>ERAP Index | 10<br>Marine Pollut. |
|---|---|---|---|---|---|---|---|
| UN1289 | SODIUM METHYLATE SOLUTION in alcohol | 3<br>(8) | II<br>III | | 1<br>5 | | |
| UN1292 | TETRAETHYL SILICATE | 3 | III | | 5 | | |
| UN1293 | TINCTURES, MEDICINAL | 3 | II<br>III | | 1<br>5 | | • |
| UN1294 | TOLUENE | 3 | II | | 1 | | |
| UN1295 | TRICHLOROSILANE | 4.3<br>(3)<br>(8) | I | | 0 | 1 000 | |
| UN1296 | TRIETHYLAMINE | 3<br>(8) | II | | 1 | | |
| UN1297 | TRIMETHYLAMINE, AQUEOUS SOLUTION, not more than 50 per cent trimethylamine, by mass | 3<br>(8) | I<br>II<br>III | | 0<br>1<br>5 | | |
| UN1298 | TRIMETHYLCHLOROSILANE | 3<br>(8) | II | | 0 | 1 000 | |
| UN1299 | TURPENTINE | 3 | III | | 5 | | |
| UN1300 | TURPENTINE SUBSTITUTE | 3 | II<br>III | | 1<br>5 | | |
| UN1301 | VINYL ACETATE, STABILIZED | 3 | II | | 1 | | |
| UN1302 | VINYL ETHYL ETHER, STABILIZED | 3 | I | | 0 | | |
| UN1303 | VINYLIDENE CHLORIDE, STABILIZED | 3 | I | | 0 | | P |
| UN1304 | VINYL ISOBUTYL ETHER, STABILIZED | 3 | II | | 1 | | |
| UN1305 | VINYLTRICHLOROSILANE, STABILIZED | 3<br>(8) | I | | 0 | | |
| UN1306 | WOOD PRESERVATIVES, LIQUID | 3 | II<br>III | | 5<br>5 | | • |
| UN1307 | XYLENES | 3 | II<br>III | | 1<br>5 | | |
| UN1308 | ZIRCONIUM SUSPENDED IN A FLAMMABLE LIQUID | 3 | I<br>II<br>III | 38<br>38 | 0<br>1<br>5 | | |
| UN1309 | ALUMINUM POWDER, COATED | 4.1 | II<br>III | | 1<br>5 | | |
| UN1310 | AMMONIUM PICRATE, WETTED with not less than 10 per cent water, by mass | 4.1 | I | 38, 62 | 0 | 75 | |
| UN1312 | BORNEOL | 4.1 | III | | 5 | | |
| UN1313 | CALCIUM RESINATE | 4.1 | III | | 5 | | |
| UN1314 | CALCIUM RESINATE, FUSED | 4.1 | III | | 5 | | |
| UN1318 | COBALT RESINATE, PRECIPITATED | 4.1 | III | | 5 | | |
| UN1320 | DINITROPHENOL, WETTED with not less than 15 per cent water, by mass | 4.1<br>(6.1) | I | 38, 62 | 0 | 75 | P |
| UN1321 | DINITROPHENOLATES, WETTED with not less than 15 per cent water, by mass | 4.1<br>(6.1) | I | 38, 62 | 0 | 75 | P |
| UN1322 | DINITRORESORCINOL, WETTED with not less than 15 per cent water, by mass | 4.1 | I | 38, 62 | 0 | 75 | |
| UN1323 | FERROCERIUM, unstabilized against corrosion or with less than 10 per cent iron content | 4.1 | II | | 1 | 3 000 | |
| UN1324 | FILMS, NITROCELLULOSE BASE, gelatin coated, except scrap | 4.1 | III | 38 | 5 | | |
| UN1325 | FLAMMABLE SOLID, ORGANIC, N.O.S. | 4.1 | II<br>III | 16<br>16 | 1<br>5 | 1 000 | • |
| UN1326 | HAFNIUM POWDER, WETTED with not less than 25 per cent water (a visible excess of water must be present) (a) mechanically produced, particle size less than 53 microns; (b) chemically produced, particle size less than 840 microns | 4.1 | II | | 1 | | |
| UN1327 | BHUSA, regulated by ship only;<br>HAY, regulated by ship only; or<br>STRAW, regulated by ship only | 4.1 | III | 64 | 5 | | |

| 1 UN Number | 2 Shipping Name and Description | 3 Class | 4 Packing Group/Category | 5 Special Provisions | 6 Explosive Limit & Limited Quantity Index | 7 ERAP Index | 10 Marine Pollut |
|---|---|---|---|---|---|---|---|
| UN1328 | HEXAMETHYLENETETRAMINE | 4.1 | III | | 5 | | |
| UN1330 | MANGANESE RESINATE | 4.1 | III | | 5 | | |
| UN1331 | MATCHES, "STRIKE ANYWHERE" | 4.1 | III | 69 | 5 | | |
| UN1332 | METALDEHYDE | 4.1 | III | | 5 | | |
| UN1333 | CERIUM, slabs, ingots or rods | 4.1 | II | | 1 | | |
| UN1334 | NAPHTHALENE, CRUDE; or NAPHTHALENE, REFINED | 4.1 | III | | 5 | | |
| UN1336 | NITROGUANIDINE, WETTED with not less than 20 per cent water, by mass; or PICRITE, WETTED with not less than 20 per cent water, by mass | 4.1 | I | 38, 62 | 0 | 75 | |
| UN1337 | NITROSTARCH, WETTED with not less than 20 per cent water, by mass | 4.1 | I | 38, 62 | 0 | 75 | |
| UN1338 | PHOSPHORUS, AMORPHOUS | 4.1 | III | | 5 | | |
| UN1339 | PHOSPHORUS HEPTASULFIDE, free from yellow and white phosphorus; or PHOSPHORUS HEPTASULPHIDE, free from yellow and white phosphorus | 4.1 | II | | 1 | 1 000 | |
| UN1340 | PHOSPHORUS PENTASULFIDE, free from yellow and white phosphorus; or PHOSPHORUS PENTASULPHIDE, free from yellow and white phosphorus | 4.3 (4.1) | II | | 0.5 | 1 000 | |
| UN1341 | PHOSPHORUS SESQUISULFIDE, free from yellow and white phosphorus; or PHOSPHORUS SESQUISULPHIDE, free from yellow and white phosphorus | 4.1 | II | | 1 | 1 000 | |
| UN1343 | PHOSPHORUS TRISULFIDE, free from yellow and white phosphorus; or PHOSPHORUS TRISULPHIDE, free from yellow and white phosphorus | 4.1 | II | | 1 | 1 000 | |
| UN1344 | TRINITROPHENOL, WETTED with not less than 30 per cent water, by mass | 4.1 | I | 10, 38, 62 | 0 | 75 | |
| UN1345 | RUBBER SCRAP powdered or granulated, not exceeding 840 microns and rubber content exceeding 45 per cent; or RUBBER SHODDY powdered or granulated, not exceeding 840 microns and rubber content exceeding 45 per cent | 4.1 | II | | 1 | | |
| UN1346 | SILICON POWDER, AMORPHOUS | 4.1 | III | | 5 | | |
| UN1347 | SILVER PICRATE, WETTED with not less than 30 per cent water, by mass | 4.1 | I | 38, 66, 68 | 0 | 75 | |
| UN1348 | SODIUM DINITRO-o-CRESOLATE, WETTED with not less than 15 per cent water, by mass | 4.1 (6.1) | I | 38, 62 | 0 | 75 | P |
| UN1349 | SODIUM PICRAMATE, WETTED with not less than 20 per cent water, by mass | 4.1 | I | 38, 62 | 0 | 75 | |
| UN1350 | SULFUR; or SULPHUR | 4.1 | III | 33 | 5 | | |
| UN1352 | TITANIUM POWDER, WETTED with not less than 25 per cent water (a visible excess of water must be present) (a) mechanically produced, particle size less than 53 microns; (b) chemically produced, particle size less than 840 microns | 4.1 | II | | 1 | | |
| UN1353 | FABRICS IMPREGNATED WITH WEAKLY NITRATED NITROCELLULOSE, N.O.S.; or FIBRES IMPREGNATED WITH WEAKLY NITRATED NITROCELLULOSE, N.O.S. | 4.1 | III | | 5 | | • |
| UN1354 | TRINITROBENZENE, WETTED with not less than 30 per cent water, by mass | 4.1 | I | 10, 38, 62 | 0 | 75 | |
| UN1355 | TRINITROBENZOIC ACID, WETTED with not less than 30 per cent water, by mass | 4.1 | I | 10, 38, 62 | 0 | 75 | |
| UN1356 | TRINITROTOLUENE, WETTED with not less than 30 per cent water, by mass | 4.1 | I | 10, 38, 62 | 0 | 75 | |
| UN1357 | UREA NITRATE, WETTED with not less than 20 per cent water, by mass | 4.1 | I | 38, 60, 61 | 0 | 75 | |
| UN1358 | ZIRCONIUM POWDER, WETTED with not less than 25 per cent water (a visible excess of water must be present) (a) mechanically produced, particle size less than 53 microns; (b) chemically produced, particle size less than 840 microns | 4.1 | II | | 1 | | |

| 1 | 2 | 3 | 4 | 5 | 6 | 7 | 10 |
|---|---|---|---|---|---|---|---|
| UN Number | Shipping Name and Description | Class | Packing Group/Category | Special Provisions | Explosive Limit & Limited Quantity Index | ERAP Index | Marine Pollut. |
| UN1360 | CALCIUM PHOSPHIDE | 4.3 (6.1) | I | 38 | 0 | 1 000 | |
| UN1361 | CARBON, animal or vegetable origin | 4.2 | II<br>III | | 0<br>0 | | |
| UN1362 | CARBON, ACTIVATED | 4.2 | III | | 0 | | |
| UN1363 | COPRA | 4.2 | III | | 0 | | |
| UN1364 | COTTON WASTE, OILY | 4.2 | III | | 0 | | |
| UN1365 | COTTON, WET | 4.2 | III | | 0 | | |
| UN1366 | DIETHYLZINC | 4.2 (4.3) | I | | 0 | 1 000 | |
| UN1369 | p-NITROSODIMETHYLANILINE | 4.2 | II | | 0 | | |
| UN1370 | DIMETHYLZINC | 4.2 (4.3) | I | | 0 | 1 000 | |
| UN1373 | FABRICS, ANIMAL or VEGETABLE or SYNTHETIC, N.O.S. with oil; or<br>FIBRES, ANIMAL or VEGETABLE or SYNTHETIC, N.O.S. with oil | 4.2 | III | | 0 | | • |
| UN1374 | FISH MEAL, UNSTABILIZED; or<br>FISH SCRAP, UNSTABILIZED | 4.2 | II | | 0 | | |
| UN1376 | IRON OXIDE, SPENT obtained from hydrocarbon gas purification; or<br>IRON SPONGE, SPENT obtained from hydrocarbon gas purification | 4.2 | III | | 0 | | |
| UN1378 | METAL CATALYST, WETTED, with a visible excess of liquid | 4.2 | II | 38 | 0 | 1 000 | |
| UN1379 | PAPER, UNSATURATED OIL TREATED, incompletely dried (including carbon paper) | 4.2 | III | | 0 | | |
| UN1380 | PENTABORANE | 4.2 (6.1) | I | 38 | 0 | 1 000 | |
| UN1381 | PHOSPHORUS, WHITE, DRY;<br>PHOSPHORUS, WHITE, IN SOLUTION;<br>PHOSPHORUS, WHITE, UNDER WATER;<br>PHOSPHORUS, YELLOW, DRY;<br>PHOSPHORUS, YELLOW, IN SOLUTION; or<br>PHOSPHORUS, YELLOW, UNDER WATER | 4.2 (6.1) | I | | 0 | 1 000 | PP |
| UN1382 | POTASSIUM SULFIDE, ANHYDROUS;<br>POTASSIUM SULFIDE with less than 30 per cent water of crystallization;<br>POTASSIUM SULPHIDE, ANHYDROUS; or<br>POTASSIUM SULPHIDE with less than 30 per cent water of crystallization | 4.2 | II | | 0 | 1 000 | |
| UN1383 | PYROPHORIC ALLOY, N.O.S.; or<br>PYROPHORIC METAL, N.O.S. | 4.2 | I | 16, 38 | 0 | 1 000 | • |
| UN1384 | SODIUM DITHIONITE;<br>SODIUM HYDROSULFITE; or<br>SODIUM HYDROSULPHITE | 4.2 | II | | 0 | 3 000 | |
| UN1385 | SODIUM SULFIDE, ANHYDROUS;<br>SODIUM SULFIDE with less than 30 per cent water of crystallization;<br>SODIUM SULPHIDE, ANHYDROUS; or<br>SODIUM SULPHIDE with less than 30 per cent water of crystallization | 4.2 | II | | 0 | 1 000 | |
| UN1386 | SEED CAKE with more than 1.5 per cent oil and not more than 11 per cent moisture | 4.2 | III | 36 | 0 | | |
| UN1389 | ALKALI METAL AMALGAM, liquid; or<br>ALKALI METAL AMALGAM, LIQUID<br>(ICAO/IMO terminology) | 4.3 | I | 38 | 0 | 1 000 | • |
| UN1389 | ALKALI METAL AMALGAM, solid; or<br>ALKALI METAL AMALGAM, SOLID<br>(ICAO/IMO terminology) | 4.3 | I | 38 | 0 | 1 000 | • |
| UN1390 | ALKALI METAL AMIDES | 4.3 | II | | 0.5 | | |

| UN Number | Shipping Name and Description | Class | Packing Group/Category | Special Provisions | Explosive Limit & Limited Quantity Index | ERAP Index | Marine Pollut. |
|---|---|---|---|---|---|---|---|
| UN1391 | ALKALI METAL DISPERSION; or ALKALINE EARTH METAL DISPERSION | 4.3 | I | 38 | 0 | 1 000 | |
| UN1391 | ALKALI METAL DISPERSION in a liquid with a flash point that is equal to or less than 60.5 °C; or ALKALINE EARTH METAL DISPERSION in a liquid with a flash point that is equal to or less than 60.5 °C | 4.3 (3) | I | 38 | 0 | 1 000 | |
| UN1392 | ALKALINE EARTH METAL AMALGAM | 4.3 | I | 38 | 0 | 1 000 | • |
| UN1393 | ALKALINE EARTH METAL ALLOY, N.O.S. | 4.3 | II | | 0.5 | 1 000 | • |
| UN1394 | ALUMINUM CARBIDE | 4.3 | II | | 0.5 | 1 000 | |
| UN1395 | ALUMINUM FERROSILICON POWDER | 4.3 (6.1) | II | | 0.5 | 1 000 | |
| UN1396 | ALUMINUM POWDER, UNCOATED | 4.3 | II III | 38 | 0.5 1 | | |
| UN1397 | ALUMINUM PHOSPHIDE | 4.3 (6.1) | I | | 0 | 1 000 | |
| UN1398 | ALUMINUM SILICON POWDER, UNCOATED | 4.3 | III | | 1 | | |
| UN1400 | BARIUM | 4.3 | II | | 0.5 | 1 000 | |
| UN1401 | CALCIUM | 4.3 | II | | 0.5 | 3 000 | |
| UN1402 | CALCIUM CARBIDE | 4.3 | I II | | 0 0.5 | 1 000 1 000 | |
| UN1403 | CALCIUM CYANAMIDE with more than 0.1 per cent calcium carbide | 4.3 | III | | 1 | | |
| UN1404 | CALCIUM HYDRIDE | 4.3 | I | 38 | 0 | 1 000 | |
| UN1405 | CALCIUM SILICIDE | 4.3 | II III | | 0.5 1 | | |
| UN1407 | CAESIUM | 4.3 | I | 38 | 0 | 1 000 | |
| UN1408 | FERROSILICON with 30 per cent or more but less than 90 per cent silicon | 4.3 (6.1) | III | | 1 | | |
| UN1409 | METAL HYDRIDES, WATER-REACTIVE, N.O.S. | 4.3 | I II | 16, 38 16 | 0 0.5 | 1 000 | • |
| UN1410 | LITHIUM ALUMINUM HYDRIDE | 4.3 | I | 38 | 0 | 1 000 | |
| UN1411 | LITHIUM ALUMINUM HYDRIDE, ETHEREAL | 4.3 (3) | I | 38 | 0 | 1 000 | |
| UN1413 | LITHIUM BOROHYDRIDE | 4.3 | I | 38 | 0 | 1 000 | |
| UN1414 | LITHIUM HYDRIDE | 4.3 | I | 38 | 0 | 1 000 | |
| UN1415 | LITHIUM | 4.3 | I | 38 | 0 | 1 000 | |
| UN1417 | LITHIUM SILICON | 4.3 | II | | 0.5 | | |
| UN1418 | MAGNESIUM ALLOYS, POWDER; or MAGNESIUM POWDER | 4.3 (4.2) | I II III | 38 | 0 0 0 | 1 000 | |
| UN1419 | MAGNESIUM ALUMINUM PHOSPHIDE | 4.3 (6.1) | I | 38 | 0 | 1 000 | |
| UN1420 | POTASSIUM METAL ALLOYS | 4.3 | I | | 0 | 1 000 | |
| UN1421 | ALKALI METAL ALLOY, LIQUID, N.O.S. | 4.3 | I | 38 | 0 | 1 000 | • |
| UN1422 | POTASSIUM SODIUM ALLOYS | 4.3 | I | | 0 | 1 000 | |
| UN1423 | RUBIDIUM | 4.3 | I | | 0 | 1 000 | |
| UN1426 | SODIUM BOROHYDRIDE | 4.3 | I | 38 | 0 | 1 000 | |
| UN1427 | SODIUM HYDRIDE | 4.3 | I | 38 | 0 | 1 000 | |
| UN1428 | SODIUM | 4.3 | I | | 0 | 1 000 | |
| UN1431 | SODIUM METHYLATE | 4.2 (8) | II | | 0 | 1 000 | |
| UN1432 | SODIUM PHOSPHIDE | 4.3 (6.1) | I | 38 | 0 | 1 000 | |
| UN1433 | STANNIC PHOSPHIDES | 4.3 (6.1) | I | 38 | 0 | 1 000 | |
| UN1435 | ZINC ASHES | 4.3 | III | | 1 | | |

| 1<br>UN Number | 2<br>Shipping Name and Description | 3<br>Class | 4<br>Packing Group/Category | 5<br>Special Provisions | 6<br>Explosive Limit & Limited Quantity Index | 7<br>ERAP Index | 10<br>Marine Pollut. |
|---|---|---|---|---|---|---|---|
| UN1436 | ZINC DUST; or<br>ZINC POWDER | 4.3<br>(4.2) | I<br>II<br>III | 38 | 0<br>0<br>0 | 1 000 | |
| UN1437 | ZIRCONIUM HYDRIDE | 4.1 | II | | 1 | | |
| UN1438 | ALUMINUM NITRATE | 5.1 | III | | 5 | | |
| UN1439 | AMMONIUM DICHROMATE | 5.1 | II | | 1 | | |
| UN1442 | AMMONIUM PERCHLORATE for substances that are not ammonium perchlorate, Class 1.1D, UN0402 | 5.1 | II | | 1 | 1 000 | |
| UN1444 | AMMONIUM PERSULFATE; or<br>AMMONIUM PERSULPHATE | 5.1 | III | | 5 | | |
| UN1445 | BARIUM CHLORATE | 5.1<br>(6.1) | II | | 0.5 | | |
| UN1446 | BARIUM NITRATE | 5.1<br>(6.1) | II | | 0.5 | | |
| UN1447 | BARIUM PERCHLORATE | 5.1<br>(6.1) | II | | 0.5 | | |
| UN1448 | BARIUM PERMANGANATE | 5.1<br>(6.1) | II | | 0.5 | | |
| UN1449 | BARIUM PEROXIDE | 5.1<br>(6.1) | II | | 0.5 | | |
| UN1450 | BROMATES, INORGANIC, N.O.S. | 5.1 | II | 68 | 1 | | • |
| UN1451 | CAESIUM NITRATE | 5.1 | III | | 5 | | |
| UN1452 | CALCIUM CHLORATE | 5.1 | II | | 1 | | |
| UN1453 | CALCIUM CHLORITE | 5.1 | II | | 1 | | |
| UN1454 | CALCIUM NITRATE | 5.1 | III | 31 | 5 | | |
| UN1455 | CALCIUM PERCHLORATE | 5.1 | II | | 1 | | |
| UN1456 | CALCIUM PERMANGANATE | 5.1 | II | | 1 | | |
| UN1457 | CALCIUM PEROXIDE | 5.1 | II | | 1 | | |
| UN1458 | CHLORATE AND BORATE MIXTURE | 5.1 | II<br>III | | 1<br>5 | | • |
| UN1459 | CHLORATE AND MAGNESIUM CHLORIDE MIXTURE | 5.1 | II<br>III | | 1<br>5 | | • |
| UN1461 | CHLORATES, INORGANIC, N.O.S. | 5.1 | II | 68 | 1 | | • |
| UN1462 | CHLORITES, INORGANIC, N.O.S. | 5.1 | II | 68 | 1 | | • |
| UN1463 | CHROMIUM TRIOXIDE, ANHYDROUS | 5.1<br>(8) | II | | 0.5 | | |
| UN1465 | DIDYMIUM NITRATE | 5.1 | III | | 5 | | |
| UN1466 | FERRIC NITRATE | 5.1 | III | | 5 | | |
| UN1467 | GUANIDINE NITRATE | 5.1 | III | | 5 | | |
| UN1469 | LEAD NITRATE | 5.1<br>(6.1) | II | | 0.5 | | P |
| UN1470 | LEAD PERCHLORATE | 5.1<br>(6.1) | II | | 0.5 | | P |
| UN1471 | LITHIUM HYPOCHLORITE, DRY; or<br>LITHIUM HYPOCHLORITE MIXTURE | 5.1 | II | | 1 | | |
| UN1472 | LITHIUM PEROXIDE | 5.1 | II | | 1 | | |
| UN1473 | MAGNESIUM BROMATE | 5.1 | II | | 1 | | |
| UN1474 | MAGNESIUM NITRATE | 5.1 | III | | 5 | | |
| UN1475 | MAGNESIUM PERCHLORATE | 5.1 | II | | 1 | | |
| UN1476 | MAGNESIUM PEROXIDE | 5.1 | II | | 1 | | |
| UN1477 | NITRATES, INORGANIC, N.O.S. | 5.1 | II<br>III | | 1<br>5 | | • |
| UN1479 | OXIDIZING SOLID, N.O.S. | 5.1 | I<br>II<br>III | 16<br>16<br>16 | 0<br>1<br>5 | 1 000 | • |
| UN1481 | PERCHLORATES, INORGANIC, N.O.S. | 5.1 | II<br>III | | 1<br>5 | | • |

| 1 | 2 | 3 | 4 | 5 | 6 | 7 | 10 |
|---|---|---|---|---|---|---|---|
| UN Number | Shipping Name and Description | Class | Packing Group/Category | Special Provisions | Explosive Limit & Limited Quantity Index | ERAP Index | Marine Pollut. |
| UN1482 | PERMANGANATES, INORGANIC, N.O.S. | 5.1 | II<br>III | 68, 78 | 1<br>5 | | • |
| UN1483 | PEROXIDES, INORGANIC, N.O.S. | 5.1 | II<br>III | | 1<br>5 | | • |
| UN1484 | POTASSIUM BROMATE | 5.1 | II | | 1 | | |
| UN1485 | POTASSIUM CHLORATE | 5.1 | II | | 1 | | |
| UN1486 | POTASSIUM NITRATE | 5.1 | III | | 5 | | |
| UN1487 | POTASSIUM NITRATE AND SODIUM NITRITE MIXTURE | 5.1 | II | | 1 | | |
| UN1488 | POTASSIUM NITRITE | 5.1 | II | | 1 | | |
| UN1489 | POTASSIUM PERCHLORATE | 5.1 | II | | 1 | | |
| UN1490 | POTASSIUM PERMANGANATE | 5.1 | II | | 1 | | |
| UN1491 | POTASSIUM PEROXIDE | 5.1 | I | 38 | 0 | 1 000 | |
| UN1492 | POTASSIUM PERSULFATE; or POTASSIUM PERSULPHATE | 5.1 | III | | 5 | | |
| UN1493 | SILVER NITRATE | 5.1 | II | | 1 | | |
| UN1494 | SODIUM BROMATE | 5.1 | II | | 1 | | |
| UN1495 | SODIUM CHLORATE | 5.1 | II | | 1 | | |
| UN1496 | SODIUM CHLORITE more than 7 per cent available chlorine | 5.1 | II | | 1 | | |
| UN1498 | SODIUM NITRATE | 5.1 | III | | 5 | | |
| UN1499 | SODIUM NITRATE AND POTASSIUM NITRATE MIXTURE | 5.1 | III | | 5 | | |
| UN1500 | SODIUM NITRITE | 5.1 (6.1) | III | | 1 | | |
| UN1502 | SODIUM PERCHLORATE | 5.1 | II | | 1 | | |
| UN1503 | SODIUM PERMANGANATE | 5.1 | II | | 1 | | |
| UN1504 | SODIUM PEROXIDE | 5.1 | I | 38 | 0 | 1 000 | |
| UN1505 | SODIUM PERSULFATE; or SODIUM PERSULPHATE | 5.1 | III | | 5 | | |
| UN1506 | STRONTIUM CHLORATE | 5.1 | II | | 1 | 1 000 | |
| UN1507 | STRONTIUM NITRATE | 5.1 | III | | 5 | | |
| UN1508 | STRONTIUM PERCHLORATE | 5.1 | II | | 1 | 1 000 | |
| UN1509 | STRONTIUM PEROXIDE | 5.1 | II | | 1 | 1 000 | |
| UN1510 | TETRANITROMETHANE | 5.1 (6.1) | I | 38 | 0 | 1 000 | |
| UN1511 | UREA HYDROGEN PEROXIDE | 5.1 (8) | III | | 1 | | |
| UN1512 | ZINC AMMONIUM NITRITE | 5.1 | II | 66, 68 | 1 | | |
| UN1513 | ZINC CHLORATE | 5.1 | II | | 1 | | |
| UN1514 | ZINC NITRATE | 5.1 | II | | 1 | | |
| UN1515 | ZINC PERMANGANATE | 5.1 | II | | 1 | | |
| UN1516 | ZINC PEROXIDE | 5.1 | II | | 1 | 1 000 | |
| UN1517 | ZIRCONIUM PICRAMATE, WETTED with not less than 20 per cent water, by mass | 4.1 | I | 38, 62 | 0 | 75 | |
| UN1541 | ACETONE CYANOHYDRIN, STABILIZED | 6.1 | I | | 0 | 1 000 | P |
| UN1544 | ALKALOID SALTS, SOLID, N.O.S.; or ALKALOIDS, SOLID, N.O.S. | 6.1 | I<br>II<br>III | 16<br>16<br>16 | 0<br>0.5<br>5 | 1 000 | •  |
| UN1545 | ALLYL ISOTHIOCYANATE, STABILIZED | 6.1 (3) | II | | 0.1 | 1 000 | |
| UN1546 | AMMONIUM ARSENATE | 6.1 | II | | 0.5 | | |
| UN1547 | ANILINE | 6.1 | II | 43 | 0.1 | | |
| UN1548 | ANILINE HYDROCHLORIDE | 6.1 | III | | 5 | | |
| UN1549 | ANTIMONY COMPOUND, INORGANIC, SOLID, N.O.S. except antimony oxides and sulphides containing less than 0.5 per cent arsenic, by mass | 6.1 | III | | 5 | | |

| 1 | 2 | 3 | 4 | 5 | 6 | 7 | 10 |
|---|---|---|---|---|---|---|---|
| UN Number | Shipping Name and Description | Class | Packing Group/Category | Special Provisions | Explosive Limit & Limited Quantity Index | ERAP Index | Marine Pollut. |
| UN1550 | ANTIMONY LACTATE | 6.1 | III | | 5 | | |
| UN1551 | ANTIMONY POTASSIUM TARTRATE | 6.1 | III | | 5 | | |
| UN1553 | ARSENIC ACID, LIQUID | 6.1 | I | | 0 | 1 000 | |
| UN1554 | ARSENIC ACID, SOLID | 6.1 | II | | 0.5 | | |
| UN1555 | ARSENIC BROMIDE | 6.1 | II | | 0.5 | | |
| UN1556 | ARSENIC COMPOUND, LIQUID, N.O.S., inorganic, including: Arsenates, n.o.s.; Arsenites, n.o.s.; and Arsenic sulphides, n.o.s. | 6.1 | I / II / III | 23, 38 | 0 / 0.1 / 5 | 1 000 | • |
| UN1557 | ARSENIC COMPOUND, SOLID, N.O.S., inorganic, including: Arsenates, n.o.s.; Arsenites, n.o.s.; and Arsenic sulphides, n.o.s. | 6.1 | I / II / III | 38 | 0 / 0.5 / 5 | 1 000 | • |
| UN1558 | ARSENIC | 6.1 | II | | 0.5 | | |
| UN1559 | ARSENIC PENTOXIDE | 6.1 | II | | 0.5 | | |
| UN1560 | ARSENIC TRICHLORIDE | 6.1 | I | | 0 | 1 000 | |
| UN1561 | ARSENIC TRIOXIDE | 6.1 | II | | 0.5 | | |
| UN1562 | ARSENICAL DUST | 6.1 | II | | 0.5 | | |
| UN1564 | BARIUM COMPOUND, N.O.S. other than barium sulphate | 6.1 | II / III | | 0.5 / 5 | | • |
| UN1565 | BARIUM CYANIDE | 6.1 | I | | 0 | 1 000 | P |
| UN1566 | BERYLLIUM COMPOUND, N.O.S. | 6.1 | II / III | | 0.5 / 5 | | |
| UN1567 | BERYLLIUM POWDER | 6.1 (4.1) | II | | 0.5 | | |
| UN1569 | BROMOACETONE | 6.1 (3) | II | 38 | 0 | 1 000 | P |
| UN1570 | BRUCINE | 6.1 | I | | 0 | 1 000 | |
| UN1571 | BARIUM AZIDE, WETTED with not less than 50 per cent water, by mass | 4.1 (6.1) | I | 38 | 0 | 75 | |
| UN1572 | CACODYLIC ACID | 6.1 | II | | 0.5 | | |
| UN1573 | CALCIUM ARSENATE | 6.1 | II | | 0.5 | | P |
| UN1574 | CALCIUM ARSENATE AND CALCIUM ARSENITE MIXTURE, SOLID | 6.1 | II | | 0.5 | | P |
| UN1575 | CALCIUM CYANIDE | 6.1 | I | 38 | 0 | 1 000 | P |
| UN1577 | CHLORODINITROBENZENES, LIQUID | 6.1 | II | 43 | 0.1 | | P |
| UN1577 | CHLORODINITROBENZENES, SOLID | 6.1 | II | 43 | 0.5 | | P |
| UN1578 | CHLORONITROBENZENES | 6.1 | II | 43 | 0.5 | | |
| UN1579 | 4-CHLORO-o-TOLUIDINE HYDROCHLORIDE | 6.1 | III | | 5 | | |
| UN1580 | CHLOROPICRIN | 6.1 | I | | 0 | 1 000 | |
| UN1581 | CHLOROPICRIN AND METHYL BROMIDE MIXTURE | 2.3 | | | 0 | 25 | |
| UN1582 | CHLOROPICRIN AND METHYL CHLORIDE MIXTURE | 2.3 | | 38 | 0 | 25 | |
| UN1583 | CHLOROPICRIN MIXTURE, N.O.S. | 6.1 | I / II / III | | 0 / 0.1 / 5 | 1 000 | • |
| UN1585 | COPPER ACETOARSENITE | 6.1 | II | | 0.5 | | P |
| UN1586 | COPPER ARSENITE | 6.1 | II | | 0.5 | | P |
| UN1587 | COPPER CYANIDE | 6.1 | II | | 0.5 | | PP |
| UN1588 | CYANIDES, INORGANIC, SOLID, N.O.S., excluding ferricyanides and ferrocyanides | 6.1 | I / II / III | 16 / 16 / 16 | 0 / 0.5 / 5 | 1 000 | P |
| UN1589 | CYANOGEN CHLORIDE, STABILIZED | 2.3 (8) | | 38 | 0 | 0 | P |
| UN1590 | DICHLOROANILINES, LIQUID | 6.1 | II | 43 | 0.1 | | P |
| UN1590 | DICHLOROANILINES, SOLID | 6.1 | II | 43 | 0.5 | | P |
| UN1591 | o-DICHLOROBENZENE | 6.1 | III | 43 | 5 | | |

| 1 | 2 | 3 | 4 | 5 | 6 | 7 | 10 |
|---|---|---|---|---|---|---|---|
| UN Number | Shipping Name and Description | Class | Packing Group/Category | Special Provisions | Explosive Limit & Limited Quantity Index | ERAP Index | Marine Pollut. |
| UN1593 | DICHLOROMETHANE | 6.1 | III | | 5 | | |
| UN1594 | DIETHYL SULFATE; or<br>DIETHYL SULPHATE | 6.1 | II | | 0.1 | 1 000 | |
| UN1595 | DIMETHYL SULFATE; or<br>DIMETHYL SULPHATE | 6.1 (8) | I | | 0 | 1 000 | |
| UN1596 | DINITROANILINES | 6.1 | II | | 0.5 | | |
| UN1597 | DINITROBENZENES, LIQUID | 6.1 | II | | 0.1 | | |
| UN1597 | DINITROBENZENES, SOLID | 6.1 | II | | 0.5 | | |
| UN1598 | DINITRO-o-CRESOL, solution; or<br>DINITRO-o-CRESOL, SOLUTION<br>(ICAO terminology) | 6.1 | II | | 0.1 | | P |
| UN1598 | DINITRO-o-CRESOL, solid; or<br>DINITRO-o-CRESOL, SOLID<br>(ICAO terminology) | 6.1 | II | | 0.5 | | P |
| UN1599 | DINITROPHENOL SOLUTION | 6.1 | II<br>III | | 0.1<br>5 | | P |
| UN1600 | DINITROTOLUENES, MOLTEN | 6.1 | II | | 0 | | |
| UN1601 | DISINFECTANT, SOLID, TOXIC, N.O.S. | 6.1 | I<br>II<br>III | 16<br>16<br>16 | 0<br>0.5<br>5 | 1 000 | • |
| UN1602 | DYE INTERMEDIATE, LIQUID, TOXIC, N.O.S.; or<br>DYE, LIQUID, TOXIC, N.O.S. | 6.1 | I<br>II<br>III | 16, 23<br>16<br>16 | 0<br>0.1<br>5 | 1 000 | • |
| UN1603 | ETHYL BROMOACETATE | 6.1 (3) | II | | 0.1 | 1 000 | |
| UN1604 | ETHYLENEDIAMINE | 8 (3) | II | | 0.5 | 1 000 | |
| UN1605 | ETHYLENE DIBROMIDE | 6.1 | I | | 0 | 1 000 | |
| UN1606 | FERRIC ARSENATE | 6.1 | II | | 0.5 | | P |
| UN1607 | FERRIC ARSENITE | 6.1 | II | | 0.5 | | P |
| UN1608 | FERROUS ARSENATE | 6.1 | II | | 0.5 | | P |
| UN1611 | HEXAETHYL TETRAPHOSPHATE | 6.1 | II | | 0.5 | | P |
| UN1612 | HEXAETHYL TETRAPHOSPHATE AND COMPRESSED GAS MIXTURE | 2.3 | | 38 | 0 | 25 | |
| UN1613 | HYDROCYANIC ACID, AQUEOUS SOLUTION with not more than 20 per cent hydrogen cyanide; or<br>HYDROGEN CYANIDE, AQUEOUS SOLUTION with not more than 20 per cent hydrogen cyanide | 6.1 | I | 68 | 0 | 1 000 | P |
| UN1614 | HYDROGEN CYANIDE, STABILIZED, containing less than 3 per cent water and absorbed in a porous inert material | 6.1 | I | 38 | 0 | 1 000 | P |
| UN1616 | LEAD ACETATE | 6.1 | III | | 5 | | P |
| UN1617 | LEAD ARSENATES | 6.1 | II | | 0.5 | | P |
| UN1618 | LEAD ARSENITES | 6.1 | II | | 0.5 | | P |
| UN1620 | LEAD CYANIDE | 6.1 | II | | 0.5 | | P |
| UN1621 | LONDON PURPLE | 6.1 | II | | 0.5 | | P |
| UN1622 | MAGNESIUM ARSENATE | 6.1 | II | | 0.5 | | P |
| UN1623 | MERCURIC ARSENATE | 6.1 | II | | 0.5 | | PP |
| UN1624 | MERCURIC CHLORIDE | 6.1 | II | | 0.5 | | PP |
| UN1625 | MERCURIC NITRATE | 6.1 | II | | 0.5 | | PP |
| UN1626 | MERCURIC POTASSIUM CYANIDE | 6.1 | I | | 0 | 1 000 | PP |
| UN1627 | MERCUROUS NITRATE | 6.1 | II | | 0.5 | 1 000 | PP |
| UN1629 | MERCURY ACETATE | 6.1 | II | | 0.5 | | PP |
| UN1630 | MERCURY AMMONIUM CHLORIDE | 6.1 | II | | 0.5 | | PP |
| UN1631 | MERCURY BENZOATE | 6.1 | II | | 0.5 | | PP |
| UN1634 | MERCURY BROMIDES | 6.1 | II | | 0.5 | | PP |

| 1 | 2 | 3 | 4 | 5 | 6 | 7 | 10 |
|---|---|---|---|---|---|---|---|
| UN Number | Shipping Name and Description | Class | Packing Group/Category | Special Provisions | Explosive Limit & Limited Quantity Index | ERAP Index | Marine Pollut |
| UN1636 | MERCURY CYANIDE | 6.1 | II | | 0.5 | | PP |
| UN1637 | MERCURY GLUCONATE | 6.1 | II | | 0.5 | | PP |
| UN1638 | MERCURY IODIDE, solution; or MERCURY IODIDE, SOLUTION (ICAO terminology) | 6.1 | II | | 0.1 | | P |
| UN1638 | MERCURY IODIDE, solid; or MERCURY IODIDE, SOLID (ICAO terminology) | 6.1 | II | | 0.5 | | P |
| UN1639 | MERCURY NUCLEATE | 6.1 | II | | 0.5 | | PP |
| UN1640 | MERCURY OLEATE | 6.1 | II | | 0.5 | | PP |
| UN1641 | MERCURY OXIDE | 6.1 | II | | 0.5 | | PP |
| UN1642 | MERCURY OXYCYANIDE, DESENSITIZED | 6.1 | II | 68 | 0.5 | | PP |
| UN1643 | MERCURY POTASSIUM IODIDE | 6.1 | II | | 0.5 | | PP |
| UN1644 | MERCURY SALICYLATE | 6.1 | II | | 0.5 | | PP |
| UN1645 | MERCURY SULFATE; or MERCURY SULPHATE | 6.1 | II | | 0.5 | | PP |
| UN1646 | MERCURY THIOCYANATE | 6.1 | II | | 0.5 | | PP |
| UN1647 | METHYL BROMIDE AND ETHYLENE DIBROMIDE MIXTURE, LIQUID | 6.1 | I | | 0 | 1 000 | P |
| UN1648 | ACETONITRILE | 3 | II | | 1 | | |
| UN1649 | MOTOR FUEL ANTI-KNOCK MIXTURE | 6.1 | I | 52 | 0 | 1 000 | P |
| UN1649 | MOTOR FUEL ANTI-KNOCK MIXTURE with a flash point that is equal to or less than 60.5 °C | 6.1 (3) | I | 52 | 0 | 1 000 | P |
| UN1650 | beta-NAPHTHYLAMINE | 6.1 | II | | 0.5 | | |
| UN1651 | NAPHTHYLTHIOUREA | 6.1 | II | | 0.5 | | |
| UN1652 | NAPHTHYLUREA | 6.1 | II | | 0.5 | | |
| UN1653 | NICKEL CYANIDE | 6.1 | II | | 0.5 | | PP |
| UN1654 | NICOTINE | 6.1 | II | | 0.1 | | |
| UN1655 | NICOTINE COMPOUND, SOLID, N.O.S.; or NICOTINE PREPARATION, SOLID, N.O.S. | 6.1 | I II III | | 0 0.5 5 | 1 000 | |
| UN1656 | NICOTINE HYDROCHLORIDE, liquid; or NICOTINE HYDROCHLORIDE SOLUTION | 6.1 | II | | 0.1 | | |
| UN1656 | NICOTINE HYDROCHLORIDE, solid | 6.1 | II | | 0.5 | | |
| UN1657 | NICOTINE SALICYLATE | 6.1 | II | | 0.5 | | |
| UN1658 | NICOTINE SULFATE, SOLUTION; or NICOTINE SULPHATE, SOLUTION | 6.1 | II | | 0.1 | | |
| UN1658 | NICOTINE SULFATE, SOLID; or NICOTINE SULPHATE, SOLID | 6.1 | II | | 0.5 | | |
| UN1659 | NICOTINE TARTRATE | 6.1 | II | | 0.5 | | |
| UN1660 | NITRIC OXIDE, COMPRESSED | 2.3 (5.1) (8) | | 38 | 0 | 0 | |
| UN1661 | NITROANILINES, (o-,m-,p-) | 6.1 | II | 43 | 0.5 | | |
| UN1662 | NITROBENZENE | 6.1 | II | 43 | 0.1 | | |
| UN1663 | NITROPHENOLS (o-,m-,p-) | 6.1 | III | 43 | 5 | | |
| UN1664 | NITROTOLUENES, LIQUID | 6.1 | II | | 0.1 | | |
| UN1664 | NITROTOLUENES, SOLID | 6.1 | II | | 0.5 | | |
| UN1665 | NITROXYLENES, LIQUID | 6.1 | II | | 0.1 | | |
| UN1665 | NITROXYLENES, SOLID | 6.1 | II | | 0.5 | | |
| UN1669 | PENTACHLOROETHANE | 6.1 | II | | 0.1 | | P |
| UN1670 | PERCHLOROMETHYL MERCAPTAN | 6.1 | I | | 0 | 1 000 | P |
| UN1671 | PHENOL, SOLID | 6.1 | II | 43 | 0.5 | 1 000 | |
| UN1672 | PHENYLCARBYLAMINE CHLORIDE | 6.1 | I | | 0 | 1 000 | |

| 1 UN Number | 2 Shipping Name and Description | 3 Class | 4 Packing Group/Category | 5 Special Provisions | 6 Explosive Limit & Limited Quantity Index | 7 ERAP Index | 10 Marine Pollut. |
|---|---|---|---|---|---|---|---|
| UN1673 | PHENYLENEDIAMINES (o-,m-,p-) | 6.1 | III | 43 | 5 | | |
| UN1674 | PHENYLMERCURIC ACETATE | 6.1 | II | | 0.5 | | PP |
| UN1677 | POTASSIUM ARSENATE | 6.1 | II | | 0.5 | | |
| UN1678 | POTASSIUM ARSENITE | 6.1 | II | | 0.5 | | |
| UN1679 | POTASSIUM CUPROCYANIDE | 6.1 | II | | 0.5 | | PP |
| UN1680 | POTASSIUM CYANIDE | 6.1 | I | | 0 | 1 000 | P |
| UN1683 | SILVER ARSENITE | 6.1 | II | | 0.5 | | P |
| UN1684 | SILVER CYANIDE | 6.1 | II | | 0.5 | | P |
| UN1685 | SODIUM ARSENATE | 6.1 | II | | 0.5 | | |
| UN1686 | SODIUM ARSENITE, AQUEOUS SOLUTION | 6.1 | II<br>III | | 0.1<br>5 | | |
| UN1687 | SODIUM AZIDE | 6.1 | II | | 0.5 | 1 000 | |
| UN1688 | SODIUM CACODYLATE | 6.1 | II | | 0.5 | | |
| UN1689 | SODIUM CYANIDE | 6.1 | I | | 0 | 1 000 | P |
| UN1690 | SODIUM FLUORIDE | 6.1 | III | | 5 | | P |
| UN1691 | STRONTIUM ARSENITE | 6.1 | II | | 0.5 | | |
| UN1692 | STRYCHNINE; or STRYCHNINE SALTS | 6.1 | I | | 0 | 1 000 | P |
| UN1693 | TEAR GAS SUBSTANCE, LIQUID, N.O.S. | 6.1 | I<br>II | 16, 38<br>16, 38 | 0<br>0 | 1 000 | • |
| UN1693 | TEAR GAS SUBSTANCE, SOLID, N.O.S. | 6.1 | I<br>II | 16, 38<br>16, 38 | 0<br>0 | 1 000 | • |
| UN1694 | BROMOBENZYL CYANIDES, LIQUID | 6.1 | I | | 0 | 1 000 | • |
| UN1694 | BROMOBENZYL CYANIDES, SOLID | 6.1 | I | | 0 | 1 000 | • |
| UN1695 | CHLOROACETONE, STABILIZED | 6.1 (3) (8) | I | | 0 | 1 000 | P |
| UN1697 | CHLOROACETOPHENONE, liquid; or CHLOROACETOPHENONE, LIQUID (ICAO terminology) | 6.1 | II | | 0 | | |
| UN1697 | CHLOROACETOPHENONE, solid; or CHLOROACETOPHENONE, SOLID (ICAO terminology) | 6.1 | II | 38 | 0 | | |
| UN1698 | DIPHENYLAMINE CHLOROARSINE | 6.1 | I | 38 | 0 | 1 000 | PP |
| UN1699 | DIPHENYLCHLOROARSINE, LIQUID | 6.1 | I | 38 | 0 | 1 000 | PP |
| UN1699 | DIPHENYLCHLOROARSINE, SOLID | 6.1 | I | 38 | 0 | 1 000 | PP |
| UN1700 | TEAR GAS CANDLES | 6.1 (4.1) | II | 38 | 0 | | |
| UN1701 | XYLYL BROMIDE | 6.1 | II | 38 | 0 | | |
| UN1702 | TETRACHLOROETHANE | 6.1 | II | | 0.1 | | |
| UN1704 | TETRAETHYL DITHIOPYROPHOSPHATE | 6.1 | II | | 0.5 | | P |
| UN1707 | THALLIUM COMPOUND, N.O.S. | 6.1 | II | | 0.5 | 1 000 | P |
| UN1708 | TOLUIDINES, LIQUID | 6.1 | II | | 0.1 | | P |
| UN1708 | TOLUIDINES, SOLID | 6.1 | II | 43 | 0.5 | | |
| UN1709 | 2,4-TOLUYLENEDIAMINE | 6.1 | II | 43 | 0.5 | | |
| UN1710 | TRICHLOROETHYLENE | 6.1 | III | | 5 | | |
| UN1711 | XYLIDINES, LIQUID | 6.1 | III | | 5 | | |
| UN1711 | XYLIDINES, SOLID | 6.1 | II | | 0.1 | | |
| UN1712 | ZINC ARSENATE; ZINC ARSENATE AND ZINC ARSENITE MIXTURES; or ZINC ARSENITE | 6.1 | II | | 0.5 | | |
| UN1713 | ZINC CYANIDE | 6.1 | I | | 0 | 1 000 | P |

| 1<br>UN Number | 2<br>Shipping Name and Description | 3<br>Class | 4<br>Packing Group/Category | 5<br>Special Provisions | 6<br>Explosive Limit & Limited Quantity Index | 7<br>ERAP Index | 10<br>Marine Pollut. |
|---|---|---|---|---|---|---|---|
| UN1714 | ZINC PHOSPHIDE | 4.3 (6.1) | I | 38 | 0 | 1 000 | |
| UN1715 | ACETIC ANHYDRIDE | 8 (3) | II | | 0.5 | 3 000 | |
| UN1716 | ACETYL BROMIDE | 8 | II | | 1 | | |
| UN1717 | ACETYL CHLORIDE | 3 (8) | II | | 1 | 3 000 | |
| UN1718 | BUTYL ACID PHOSPHATE | 8 | III | | 5 | | |
| UN1719 | CAUSTIC ALKALI LIQUID, N.O.S. | 8 | II<br>III | 16<br>16 | 1<br>5 | | • |
| UN1722 | ALLYL CHLOROFORMATE | 6.1 (3) (8) | I | | 0 | 1 000 | |
| UN1723 | ALLYL IODIDE | 3 (8) | II | | 1 | 3 000 | |
| UN1724 | ALLYLTRICHLOROSILANE, STABILIZED | 8 (3) | II | | 0 | 3 000 | |
| UN1725 | ALUMINUM BROMIDE, ANHYDROUS | 8 | II | | 1 | | |
| UN1726 | ALUMINUM CHLORIDE, ANHYDROUS | 8 | II | | 1 | | |
| UN1727 | AMMONIUM HYDROGENDIFLUORIDE, SOLID | 8 | II | | 1 | | |
| UN1728 | AMYLTRICHLOROSILANE | 8 | II | | 0 | | |
| UN1729 | ANISOYL CHLORIDE | 8 | II | | 1 | | |
| UN1730 | ANTIMONY PENTACHLORIDE, LIQUID | 8 | II | | 1 | | |
| UN1731 | ANTIMONY PENTACHLORIDE SOLUTION | 8 | II<br>III | | 1<br>5 | | |
| UN1732 | ANTIMONY PENTAFLUORIDE | 8 (6.1) | II | | 0.5 | | |
| UN1733 | ANTIMONY TRICHLORIDE, liquid; or ANTIMONY TRICHLORIDE, LIQUID (ICAO terminology) | 8 | II | | 1 | | |
| UN1733 | ANTIMONY TRICHLORIDE, solid; or ANTIMONY TRICHLORIDE, SOLID (ICAO terminology) | 8 | II | | 1 | | |
| UN1736 | BENZOYL CHLORIDE | 8 | II | | 1 | | |
| UN1737 | BENZYL BROMIDE | 6.1 (8) | II | | 0 | 3 000 | |
| UN1738 | BENZYL CHLORIDE | 6.1 (8) | II | | 0 | 1 000 | |
| UN1739 | BENZYL CHLOROFORMATE | 8 | I | | 0 | 1 000 | P |
| UN1740 | HYDROGENDIFLUORIDES, N.O.S., solution; or HYDROGENDIFLUORIDES, N.O.S., SOLUTION (ICAO terminology) | 8 | II<br>III | | 1<br>5 | | • |
| UN1740 | HYDROGENDIFLUORIDES, N.O.S., solid; or HYDROGENDIFLUORIDES, N.O.S., SOLID (ICAO terminology) | 8 | II<br>III | | 1<br>5 | | • |
| UN1741 | BORON TRICHLORIDE | 2.3 (8) | | | 0 | 500 | |
| UN1742 | BORON TRIFLUORIDE ACETIC ACID COMPLEX | 8 | II | | 1 | | |
| UN1743 | BORON TRIFLUORIDE PROPIONIC ACID COMPLEX | 8 | II | | 1 | | |
| UN1744 | BROMINE; or BROMINE SOLUTION | 8 (6.1) | I | | 0 | 3 000 | |
| UN1745 | BROMINE PENTAFLUORIDE | 5.1 (6.1) (8) | I | | 0 | 1 000 | |
| UN1746 | BROMINE TRIFLUORIDE | 5.1 (6.1) (8) | I | | 0 | 1 000 | |
| UN1747 | BUTYLTRICHLOROSILANE | 8 (3) | II | | 0 | | |

| 1 UN Number | 2 Shipping Name and Description | 3 Class | 4 Packing Group/Category | 5 Special Provisions | 6 Explosive Limit & Limited Quantity Index | 7 ERAP Index | 10 Marine Pollut. |
|---|---|---|---|---|---|---|---|
| UN1748 | CALCIUM HYPOCHLORITE, DRY with more than 39 per cent available chlorine (8.8 per cent available oxygen); or CALCIUM HYPOCHLORITE MIXTURE, DRY with more than 39 per cent available chlorine (8.8 per cent available oxygen) | 5.1 | II | 38 | 1 | | |
| UN1749 | CHLORINE TRIFLUORIDE | 2.3 (5.1) (8) | | 38 | 0 | 25 | |
| UN1750 | CHLOROACETIC ACID SOLUTION | 6.1 (8) | II | | 0.1 | 1 000 | |
| UN1751 | CHLOROACETIC ACID, SOLID | 6.1 (8) | II | | 0.5 | 1 000 | |
| UN1752 | CHLOROACETYL CHLORIDE | 6.1 (8) | I | | 0 | 1 000 | |
| UN1753 | CHLOROPHENYLTRICHLOROSILANE | 8 | II | | 1 | | P |
| UN1754 | CHLOROSULFONIC ACID with or without sulfur trioxide; or CHLOROSULPHONIC ACID with or without sulphur trioxide | 8 | I | | 0 | 1 000 | |
| UN1755 | CHROMIC ACID SOLUTION | 8 | II III | | 1 5 | | |
| UN1756 | CHROMIC FLUORIDE, SOLID | 8 | II | | 1 | | |
| UN1757 | CHROMIC FLUORIDE SOLUTION | 8 | II III | | 1 5 | | |
| UN1758 | CHROMIUM OXYCHLORIDE | 8 | I | | 0 | 1 000 | |
| UN1759 | CORROSIVE SOLID, N.O.S. | 8 | I II III | 16 16 16 | 0 1 5 | 3 000 | • |
| UN1760 | CORROSIVE LIQUID, N.O.S. | 8 | I II III | 16 16 16 | 0 1 5 | 3 000 | • |
| UN1761 | CUPRIETHYLENEDIAMINE SOLUTION | 8 (6.1) | II III | | 0.5 1 | | P |
| UN1762 | CYCLOHEXENYLTRICHLOROSILANE | 8 | II | | 1 | | |
| UN1763 | CYCLOHEXYLTRICHLOROSILANE | 8 | II | | 1 | | |
| UN1764 | DICHLOROACETIC ACID | 8 | II | | 1 | | |
| UN1765 | DICHLOROACETYL CHLORIDE | 8 | II | | 1 | | |
| UN1766 | DICHLOROPHENYLTRICHLOROSILANE | 8 | II | | 1 | | P |
| UN1767 | DIETHYLDICHLOROSILANE | 8 (3) | II | | 0 | | |
| UN1768 | DIFLUOROPHOSPHORIC ACID, ANHYDROUS | 8 | II | | 1 | | |
| UN1769 | DIPHENYLDICHLOROSILANE | 8 | II | | 1 | | |
| UN1770 | DIPHENYLMETHYL BROMIDE | 8 | II | | 1 | | |
| UN1771 | DODECYLTRICHLOROSILANE | 8 | II | | 1 | | |
| UN1773 | FERRIC CHLORIDE, ANHYDROUS | 8 | III | | 5 | | |
| UN1774 | FIRE EXTINGUISHER CHARGES, corrosive liquid | 8 | II | | 1 | | |
| UN1775 | FLUOROBORIC ACID | 8 | II | | 1 | | |
| UN1776 | FLUOROPHOSPHORIC ACID, ANHYDROUS | 8 | II | | 1 | | |
| UN1777 | FLUOROSULFONIC ACID; or FLUOROSULPHONIC ACID | 8 | I | | 0 | 1 000 | |
| UN1778 | FLUOROSILICIC ACID | 8 | II | | 1 | | |
| UN1779 | FORMIC ACID | 8 | II | | 1 | | |
| UN1780 | FUMARYL CHLORIDE | 8 | II | | 1 | | |
| UN1781 | HEXADECYLTRICHLOROSILANE | 8 | II | | 1 | | |
| UN1782 | HEXAFLUOROPHOSPHORIC ACID | 8 | II | | 1 | | |
| UN1783 | HEXAMETHYLENEDIAMINE SOLUTION | 8 | II III | | 1 5 | | |
| UN1784 | HEXYLTRICHLOROSILANE | 8 | II | | 1 | | |

| 1 | 2 | 3 | 4 | 5 | 6 | 7 | 10 |
|---|---|---|---|---|---|---|---|
| UN Number | Shipping Name and Description | Class | Packing Group/Category | Special Provisions | Explosive Limit & Limited Quantity Index | ERAP Index | Marine Pollut. |
| UN1786 | HYDROFLUORIC ACID AND SULFURIC ACID MIXTURE; or HYDROFLUORIC ACID AND SULPHURIC ACID MIXTURE | 8 (6.1) | I | | 0 | 1 000 | |
| UN1787 | HYDRIODIC ACID | 8 | II III | | 1 5 | | |
| UN1788 | HYDROBROMIC ACID | 8 | II III | | 1 5 | 3 000 | |
| UN1789 | HYDROCHLORIC ACID | 8 | II III | | 1 5 | 3 000 | |
| UN1790 | HYDROFLUORIC ACID, solution, with more than 60 per cent hydrofluoric acid | 8 (6.1) | I | | 0 | 1 000 | |
| UN1790 | HYDROFLUORIC ACID, solution, with not more than 60 per cent hydrofluoric acid | 8 (6.1) | II | | 0.5 | | |
| UN1791 | HYPOCHLORITE SOLUTION, more than 7 per cent available chlorine | 8 | II III | | 1 5 | | |
| UN1792 | IODINE MONOCHLORIDE | 8 | II | | 1 | | |
| UN1793 | ISOPROPYL ACID PHOSPHATE | 8 | III | | 5 | | |
| UN1794 | LEAD SULFATE with more than 3 per cent free acid; or LEAD SULPHATE with more than 3 per cent free acid | 8 | II | | 1 | | |
| UN1796 | NITRATING ACID MIXTURE with more than 50 per cent nitric acid | 8 (5.1) | I | | 0 | 3 000 | |
| UN1796 | NITRATING ACID MIXTURE with not more than 50 per cent nitric acid | 8 | II | | 1 | | |
| UN1798 | NITROHYDROCHLORIC ACID | 8 | I | | 0 | 1 000 | |
| UN1799 | NONYLTRICHLOROSILANE | 8 | II | | 1 | | |
| UN1800 | OCTADECYLTRICHLOROSILANE | 8 | II | | 1 | | |
| UN1801 | OCTYLTRICHLOROSILANE | 8 | II | | 1 | | |
| UN1802 | PERCHLORIC ACID with not more than 50 per cent acid, by mass | 8 (5.1) | II | 68 | 0.5 | 3 000 | |
| UN1803 | PHENOLSULFONIC ACID, LIQUID; or PHENOLSULPHONIC ACID, LIQUID | 8 | II | | 1 | | |
| UN1804 | PHENYLTRICHLOROSILANE | 8 | II | | 1 | | |
| UN1805 | PHOSPHORIC ACID, LIQUID | 8 | III | | 5 | | |
| UN1805 | PHOSPHORIC ACID, SOLID | 8 | III | | 5 | | |
| UN1806 | PHOSPHORUS PENTACHLORIDE | 8 | II | | 1 | 1 000 | |
| UN1807 | PHOSPHORUS PENTOXIDE | 8 | II | | 1 | 1 000 | |
| UN1808 | PHOSPHORUS TRIBROMIDE | 8 | II | | 1 | | |
| UN1809 | PHOSPHORUS TRICHLORIDE | 6.1 (8) | I | | 0 | 1 000 | |
| UN1810 | PHOSPHORUS OXYCHLORIDE | 8 | II | | 1 | 1 000 | |
| UN1811 | POTASSIUM HYDROGENDIFLUORIDE, LIQUID (IMO terminology); POTASSIUM HYDROGENDIFLUORIDE, solution; or POTASSIUM HYDROGENDIFLUORIDE, SOLUTION (ICAO/IMO terminology) | 8 (6.1) | II | | 0 | 1 000 | |
| UN1811 | POTASSIUM HYDROGENDIFLUORIDE, solid; or POTASSIUM HYDROGENDIFLUORIDE, SOLID (ICAO/IMO terminology) | 8 (6.1) | II | | 1 | | |
| UN1812 | POTASSIUM FLUORIDE | 6.1 | III | | 5 | | |
| UN1813 | POTASSIUM HYDROXIDE, SOLID | 8 | II | | 1 | | |
| UN1814 | POTASSIUM HYDROXIDE, SOLUTION | 8 | II III | | 1 5 | | |
| UN1815 | PROPIONYL CHLORIDE | 3 (8) | II | | 1 | | |
| UN1816 | PROPYLTRICHLOROSILANE | 8 (3) | II | | 0 | 3 000 | |
| UN1817 | PYROSULFURYL CHLORIDE; or PYROSULPHURYL CHLORIDE | 8 | II | | 1 | 1 000 | |
| UN1818 | SILICON TETRACHLORIDE | 8 | II | | 1 | | |

| 1 UN Number | 2 Shipping Name and Description | 3 Class | 4 Packing Group/Category | 5 Special Provisions | 6 Explosive Limit & Limited Quantity Index | 7 ERAP Index | 10 Marine Pollut. |
|---|---|---|---|---|---|---|---|
| UN1819 | SODIUM ALUMINATE SOLUTION | 8 | II III | | 1 5 | | |
| UN1823 | SODIUM HYDROXIDE, SOLID | 8 | II | | 1 | | |
| UN1824 | SODIUM HYDROXIDE SOLUTION | 8 | II III | | 1 5 | | |
| UN1825 | SODIUM MONOXIDE | 8 | II | | 1 | | |
| UN1826 | NITRATING ACID MIXTURE, SPENT, with more than 50 per cent nitric acid | 8 (5.1) | I | 19 | 0 | 3 000 | |
| UN1826 | NITRATING ACID MIXTURE, SPENT, with not more than 50 per cent nitric acid | 8 | II | 19 | 1 | | |
| UN1827 | STANNIC CHLORIDE, ANHYDROUS | 8 | II | | 1 | | |
| UN1828 | SULFUR CHLORIDES; or SULPHUR CHLORIDES | 8 | I | | 0 | 3 000 | |
| UN1829 | SULFUR TRIOXIDE, STABILIZED; or SULPHUR TRIOXIDE, STABILIZED | 8 | I | | 0 | 3 000 | |
| UN1830 | SULFURIC ACID with more than 51 per cent acid; or SULPHURIC ACID with more than 51 per cent acid | 8 | II | | 1 | 3 000 | |
| UN1831 | SULFURIC ACID, FUMING; or SULPHURIC ACID, FUMING | 8 (6.1) | I | | 0 | 1 000 | |
| UN1832 | SULFURIC ACID, SPENT; or SULPHURIC ACID, SPENT | 8 | II | 19 | 1 | | |
| UN1833 | SULFUROUS ACID; or SULPHUROUS ACID | 8 | II | | 1 | | |
| UN1834 | SULFURYL CHLORIDE; or SULPHURYL CHLORIDE | 8 | I | | 0 | 3 000 | |
| UN1835 | TETRAMETHYLAMMONIUM HYDROXIDE | 8 | II | | 1 | | |
| UN1836 | THIONYL CHLORIDE | 8 | I | | 0 | 3 000 | |
| UN1837 | THIOPHOSPHORYL CHLORIDE | 8 | II | | 1 | | |
| UN1838 | TITANIUM TETRACHLORIDE | 8 | II | | 1 | | |
| UN1839 | TRICHLOROACETIC ACID | 8 | II | | 1 | | |
| UN1840 | ZINC CHLORIDE SOLUTION | 8 | III | | 5 | | |
| UN1841 | ACETALDEHYDE AMMONIA | 9 | III | 81 | 5 | | |
| UN1843 | AMMONIUM DINITRO-o-CRESOLATE | 6.1 | II | | 0.5 | | P |
| UN1845 | CARBON DIOXIDE, SOLID; or DRY ICE | 9 | III | 18,81 | 5 | | |
| UN1846 | CARBON TETRACHLORIDE | 6.1 | II | | 0.1 | | P |
| UN1847 | POTASSIUM SULFIDE, HYDRATED with not less than 30 per cent water of crystallization; or POTASSIUM SULPHIDE, HYDRATED with not less than 30 per cent water of crystallization | 8 | II | | 1 | | |
| UN1848 | PROPIONIC ACID | 8 | III | | 5 | | |
| UN1849 | SODIUM SULFIDE, HYDRATED with not less than 30 per cent water; or SODIUM SULPHIDE, HYDRATED with not less than 30 per cent water | 8 | II | | 1 | | |
| UN1851 | MEDICINE, LIQUID, TOXIC, N.O.S. | 6.1 | II III | 16 16 | 0.1 5 | | • |
| UN1854 | BARIUM ALLOYS, PYROPHORIC | 4.2 | I | 38 | 0 | 1 000 | |
| UN1855 | CALCIUM ALLOYS, PYROPHORIC; or CALCIUM, PYROPHORIC | 4.2 | I | 38 | 0 | 1 000 | |
| UN1858 | HEXAFLUOROPROPYLENE; or REFRIGERANT GAS R 1216 | 2.2 | | | 0.125 | | |
| UN1859 | SILICON TETRAFLUORIDE, COMPRESSED | 2.3 (8) | | 38 | 0 | 25 | |
| UN1860 | VINYL FLUORIDE, STABILIZED | 2.1 | | | 0.125 | 3 000 | |
| UN1862 | ETHYL CROTONATE | 3 | II | | 1 | | |

| 1 UN Number | 2 Shipping Name and Description | 3 Class | 4 Packing Group/Category | 5 Special Provisions | 6 Explosive Limit & Limited Quantity Index | 7 ERAP Index | 10 Marine Pollut. |
|---|---|---|---|---|---|---|---|
| UN1863 | FUEL, AVIATION, TURBINE ENGINE | 3 | I | 17,82 | 0.5 | SP82 | |
| | | | II | 17,82 | 1 | SP82 | |
| | | | III | 17,82 | 5 | SP82 | |
| UN1865 | n-PROPYL NITRATE | 3 | II | 38 | 1 | | |
| UN1866 | RESIN SOLUTION, flammable | 3 | I | | 0.5 | | |
| | | | II | 83 | 5 | | • |
| | | | III | 83 | 5 | | |
| UN1868 | DECABORANE | 4.1 (6.1) | II | 38 | 0.5 | 75 | |
| UN1869 | MAGNESIUM in pellets, turnings or ribbons; or MAGNESIUM ALLOYS with more than 50 per cent magnesium in pellets, turnings or ribbons | 4.1 | III | | 5 | | |
| UN1870 | POTASSIUM BOROHYDRIDE | 4.3 | I | 38 | 0 | 1 000 | |
| UN1871 | TITANIUM HYDRIDE | 4.1 | II | | 1 | | |
| UN1872 | LEAD DIOXIDE | 5.1 | III | | 5 | | |
| UN1873 | PERCHLORIC ACID with more than 50 per cent but not more than 72 per cent acid, by mass | 5.1 (8) | I | 68 | 0 | 1 000 | |
| UN1884 | BARIUM OXIDE | 6.1 | III | | 5 | | |
| UN1885 | BENZIDINE | 6.1 | II | | 0.5 | | |
| UN1886 | BENZYLIDENE CHLORIDE | 6.1 | II | | 0.1 | | |
| UN1887 | BROMOCHLOROMETHANE | 6.1 | III | | 5 | | |
| UN1888 | CHLOROFORM | 6.1 | III | | 5 | | |
| UN1889 | CYANOGEN BROMIDE | 6.1 (8) | I | 38 | 0 | 1 000 | P |
| UN1891 | ETHYL BROMIDE | 6.1 | II | | 0.1 | | |
| UN1892 | ETHYLDICHLOROARSINE | 6.1 | I | | 0 | 1 000 | P |
| UN1894 | PHENYLMERCURIC HYDROXIDE | 6.1 | II | | 0.5 | | PP |
| UN1895 | PHENYLMERCURIC NITRATE | 6.1 | II | | 0.5 | | PP |
| UN1897 | TETRACHLOROETHYLENE | 6.1 | III | | 5 | | P |
| UN1898 | ACETYL IODIDE | 8 | II | | 1 | | |
| UN1902 | DIISOOCTYL ACID PHOSPHATE | 8 | III | | 5 | | |
| UN1903 | DISINFECTANT, LIQUID, CORROSIVE, N.O.S. | 8 | I | 16 | 0 | 3 000 | |
| | | | II | 16 | 1 | | • |
| | | | III | 16 | 5 | | |
| UN1905 | SELENIC ACID | 8 | I | | 0 | 3 000 | |
| UN1906 | SLUDGE ACID | 8 | II | | 1 | | |
| UN1907 | SODA LIME with more than 4 per cent sodium hydroxide | 8 | III | | 5 | | |
| UN1908 | CHLORITE SOLUTION | 8 | II | | 1 | | • |
| | | | II | | 5 | | |
| UN1910 | CALCIUM OXIDE, regulated by aircraft only | 8 | III | 63 | 5 | | |
| UN1911 | DIBORANE, COMPRESSED | 2.3 (2.1) | | 38 | 0 | 50 | |
| UN1912 | METHYL CHLORIDE AND METHYLENE CHLORIDE MIXTURE | 2.1 | | | 0.125 | 3 000 | |
| UN1913 | NEON, REFRIGERATED LIQUID | 2.2 | | | 0.125 | | |
| UN1914 | BUTYL PROPIONATES | 3 | III | | 5 | | |
| UN1915 | CYCLOHEXANONE | 3 | III | | 5 | | |
| UN1916 | 2,2'-DICHLORODIETHYL ETHER | 6.1 (3) | II | | 0.1 | 1 000 | |
| UN1917 | ETHYL ACRYLATE, STABILIZED | 3 | II | | 1 | | |
| UN1918 | ISOPROPYLBENZENE | 3 | III | | 5 | | |
| UN1919 | METHYL ACRYLATE, STABILIZED | 3 | II | | 1 | | |
| UN1920 | NONANES | 3 | III | | 5 | | |
| UN1921 | PROPYLENEIMINE, STABILIZED | 3 (6.1) | I | 81 | 0 | 1 000 | |

| 1 UN Number | 2 Shipping Name and Description | 3 Class | 4 Packing Group/Category | 5 Special Provisions | 6 Explosive Limit & Limited Quantity Index | 7 ERAP Index | 10 Marine Pollut. |
|---|---|---|---|---|---|---|---|
| UN1922 | PYRROLIDINE | 3 (8) | II | | 1 | | |
| UN1923 | CALCIUM DITHIONITE; CALCIUM HYDROSULFITE; or CALCIUM HYDROSULPHITE | 4.2 | II | | 0 | 3 000 | |
| UN1928 | METHYL MAGNESIUM BROMIDE IN ETHYL ETHER | 4.3 (3) | I | | 0 | 1 000 | |
| UN1929 | POTASSIUM DITHIONITE; POTASSIUM HYDROSULFITE; or POTASSIUM HYDROSULPHITE | 4.2 | II | | 0 | 3 000 | |
| UN1931 | ZINC DITHIONITE; ZINC HYDROSULFITE; or ZINC HYDROSULPHITE | 9 | III | 81 | 5 | | |
| UN1932 | ZIRCONIUM SCRAP | 4.2 | III | | 0 | | |
| UN1935 | CYANIDE SOLUTION, N.O.S. | 6.1 | I II III | 23 | 0 0.1 5 | 1 000 | P |
| UN1938 | BROMOACETIC ACID | 8 | II | | 1 | | |
| UN1939 | PHOSPHORUS OXYBROMIDE | 8 | II | | 1 | | |
| UN1940 | THIOGLYCOLIC ACID | 8 | II | | 1 | | |
| UN1941 | DIBROMODIFLUOROMETHANE | 9 | III | | 5 | | |
| UN1942 | AMMONIUM NITRATE with not more than 0.2 per cent combustible substances, including any organic substance calculated as carbon, to the exclusion of any other added substance | 5.1 | III | 37 | 5 | | |
| UN1944 | MATCHES, SAFETY (book, card or strike on box) | 4.1 | III | | 5 | | |
| UN1945 | MATCHES, WAX "VESTA" | 4.1 | III | | 5 | | |
| UN1950 | AEROSOLS, containing compressed oxygen | 2.2 (5.1) | | 80 | 0.125 | | • |
| UN1950 | AEROSOLS, flammable | 2.1 | | 80 | 1 | | • |
| UN1950 | AEROSOLS, flammable, containing substances in Class 6.1, packing group II | 2.1 (6.1) | | 80 | 0.125 | | • |
| UN1950 | AEROSOLS, flammable, containing substances in Class 6.1, packing group III | 2.1 (6.1) | | 80 | 1 | | • |
| UN1950 | AEROSOLS, flammable, containing substances in Class 6.1, packing group III and in Class 8, packing group II | 2.1 (8) (6.1) | | 80 | 0.125 | | • |
| UN1950 | AEROSOLS, flammable, containing substances in Class 6.1, packing group III and in Class 8, packing group III | 2.1 (6.1) (8) | | 80 | 1 | | • |
| UN1950 | AEROSOLS, flammable, containing substances in Class 8, packing group II | 2.1 (8) | | 80 | 0.125 | | • |
| UN1950 | AEROSOLS, flammable, containing substances in Class 8, packing group III | 2.1 (8) | | 80 | 1 | | • |
| UN1950 | AEROSOLS, non-flammable | 2.2 | | 80 | 1 | | • |
| UN1950 | AEROSOLS, non-flammable, containing substances in Class 6.1, packing group II | 2.2 (6.1) | | 80 | 0.125 | | • |
| UN1950 | AEROSOLS, non-flammable, containing substances in Class 6.1, packing group III | 2.2 (6.1) | | 80 | 1 | | • |
| UN1950 | AEROSOLS, non-flammable, containing substances in Class 6.1, packing group III and in Class 8, packing group II | 2.2 (8) (6.1) | | 80 | 0.125 | | • |
| UN1950 | AEROSOLS, non-flammable, containing substances in Class 6.1, packing group III and in Class 8, packing group III | 2.2 (6.1) (8) | | 80 | 1 | | • |
| UN1950 | AEROSOLS, non-flammable, containing substances in Class 8, packing group II | 2.2 (8) | | 80 | 0.125 | | • |
| UN1950 | AEROSOLS, non-flammable, containing substances in Class 8, packing group III | 2.2 (8) | | 80 | 1 | | • |
| UN1951 | ARGON, REFRIGERATED LIQUID | 2.2 | | | 0.125 | | |
| UN1952 | ETHYLENE OXIDE AND CARBON DIOXIDE MIXTURE with not more than 9 per cent ethylene oxide | 2.2 | | | 0.125 | | |

| 1 | 2 | 3 | 4 | 5 | 6 | 7 | 10 |
|---|---|---|---|---|---|---|---|
| UN Number | Shipping Name and Description | Class | Packing Group/Category | Special Provisions | Explosive Limit & Limited Quantity Index | ERAP Index | Marine Pollut. |
| UN1953 | COMPRESSED GAS, TOXIC, FLAMMABLE, N.O.S. | 2.3 (2.1) | | 16, 38 | 0 | 50 | • |
| UN1954 | COMPRESSED GAS, FLAMMABLE, N.O.S. | 2.1 | | 16 | 0.125 | 3 000 | • |
| UN1955 | COMPRESSED GAS, TOXIC, N.O.S. | 2.3 | | 16, 38 | 0 | 50 | • |
| UN1956 | COMPRESSED GAS, N.O.S. | 2.2 | | | 0.125 | | • |
| UN1957 | DEUTERIUM, COMPRESSED | 2.1 | | 38 | 0.125 | 3 000 | |
| UN1958 | 1,2-DICHLORO-1,1,2,2-TETRAFLUOROETHANE; or REFRIGERANT GAS R 114 | 2.2 | | | 0.125 | | |
| UN1959 | 1,1-DIFLUOROETHYLENE; or REFRIGERANT GAS R 1132a | 2.1 | | 38 | 0.125 | 3 000 | |
| UN1961 | ETHANE, REFRIGERATED LIQUID | 2.1 | | | 0.125 | 3 000 | |
| UN1962 | ETHYLENE, COMPRESSED | 2.1 | | | 0.125 | 3 000 | |
| UN1963 | HELIUM, REFRIGERATED LIQUID | 2.2 | | | 0.125 | | |
| UN1964 | HYDROCARBON GAS MIXTURE, COMPRESSED, N.O.S. | 2.1 | | 16 | 0.125 | 3 000 | • |
| UN1965 | HYDROCARBON GAS MIXTURE, LIQUEFIED, N.O.S. | 2.1 | | 16 | 0.125 | 3 000 | • |
| UN1966 | HYDROGEN, REFRIGERATED LIQUID | 2.1 | | | 0.125 | 3 000 | |
| UN1967 | INSECTICIDE GAS, TOXIC, N.O.S. | 2.3 | | 16, 38 | 0 | 0 | • |
| UN1968 | INSECTICIDE GAS, N.O.S. | 2.2 | | 16 | 0.125 | | |
| UN1969 | ISOBUTANE | 2.1 | | 29 | 0.125 | 3 000 | |
| UN1970 | KRYPTON, REFRIGERATED LIQUID | 2.2 | | | 0.125 | | |
| UN1971 | METHANE, COMPRESSED; or NATURAL GAS, COMPRESSED with high methane content | 2.1 | | | 0.125 | 3 000 | |
| UN1972 | METHANE, REFRIGERATED LIQUID; or NATURAL GAS, REFRIGERATED LIQUID with high methane content | 2.1 | | | 0.125 | 3 000 | |
| UN1973 | CHLORODIFLUOROMETHANE AND CHLOROPENTAFLUOROETHANE MIXTURE with fixed boiling point, with approximately 49 per cent chlorodifluoromethane; or REFRIGERANT GAS R 502 | 2.2 | | | 0.125 | | |
| UN1974 | CHLORODIFLUOROBROMOMETHANE; or REFRIGERANT GAS R 12B1 | 2.2 | | | 0.125 | | |
| UN1975 | NITRIC OXIDE AND DINITROGEN TETROXIDE MIXTURE; or NITRIC OXIDE AND NITROGEN DIOXIDE MIXTURE | 2.3 (5.1) (8) | | 38 | 0 | 0 | |
| UN1976 | OCTAFLUOROCYCLOBUTANE; or REFRIGERANT GAS RC 318 | 2.2 | | | 0.125 | | |
| UN1977 | NITROGEN, REFRIGERATED LIQUID | 2.2 | | | 0.125 | | |
| UN1978 | PROPANE | 2.1 | | | 0.125 | 3 000 | |
| UN1979 | RARE GASES MIXTURE, COMPRESSED | 2.2 | | | 0.125 | | |
| UN1980 | RARE GASES AND OXYGEN MIXTURE, COMPRESSED | 2.2 | | | 0.125 | | |
| UN1981 | RARE GASES AND NITROGEN MIXTURE, COMPRESSED | 2.2 | | | 0.125 | | |
| UN1982 | REFRIGERANT GAS R 14, COMPRESSED; or TETRAFLUOROMETHANE, COMPRESSED | 2.2 | | 38 | 0.125 | | |
| UN1983 | 1-CHLORO-2,2,2-TRIFLUOROETHANE; or REFRIGERANT GAS R 133a | 2.2 | | | 0.125 | | |
| UN1984 | REFRIGERANT GAS R 23; or TRIFLUOROMETHANE | 2.2 | | | 0.125 | | |
| UN1986 | ALCOHOLS, FLAMMABLE, TOXIC, N.O.S. | 3 (6.1) | I<br>II<br>III | 16<br>16<br>16 | 0<br>1<br>5 | 1 000 | • |
| UN1987 | ALCOHOLS, N.O.S. | 3 | II<br>III | 16<br>16 | 1<br>5 | | • |
| UN1988 | ALDEHYDES, FLAMMABLE, TOXIC, N.O.S. | 3 (6.1) | I<br>II<br>III | 16<br>16<br>16 | 0<br>1<br>5 | 1 000 | • |

| 1 | 2 | 3 | 4 | 5 | 6 | 7 | 10 |
|---|---|---|---|---|---|---|---|
| UN Number | Shipping Name and Description | Class | Packing Group/Category | Special Provisions | Explosive Limit & Limited Quantity Index | ERAP Index | Marine Pollut. |
| UN1989 | ALDEHYDES, N.O.S. | 3 | I | 16 | 0 | | |
| | | | II | 16 | 1 | | • |
| | | | III | 16 | 5 | | |
| UN1990 | BENZALDEHYDE | 9 | III | | 5 | | |
| UN1991 | CHLOROPRENE, STABILIZED | 3 (6.1) | I | | 0 | 1 000 | |
| UN1992 | FLAMMABLE LIQUID, TOXIC, N.O.S. | 3 (6.1) | I | 16 | 0 | 1 000 | |
| | | | II | 16 | 1 | | • |
| | | | III | 16 | 5 | | |
| UN1993 | FLAMMABLE LIQUID, N.O.S. | 3 | I | 16 | 0 | | |
| | | | II | 16 | 1 | | • |
| | | | III | 16 | 5 | | |
| UN1994 | IRON PENTACARBONYL | 6.1 (3) | I | 38 | 0 | 1 000 | |
| UN1999 | TARS, LIQUID, including road asphalt and oils, bitumen and cut backs | 3 | II | 89 | 5 | | • |
| | | | III | 89 | 5 | | |
| UN2000 | CELLULOID in block, rods, rolls, sheets, tubes, etc., except scrap | 4.1 | III | | 5 | | |
| UN2001 | COBALT NAPHTHENATES, POWDER | 4.1 | III | | 5 | | |
| UN2002 | CELLULOID, SCRAP | 4.2 | III | | 0 | | |
| UN2003 | METAL ALKYLS, WATER-REACTIVE, N.O.S.; or METAL ARYLS, WATER-REACTIVE, N.O.S. | 4.2 (4.3) | I | 16 | 0 | 1 000 | • |
| UN2004 | MAGNESIUM DIAMIDE | 4.2 | II | | 0 | | |
| UN2005 | MAGNESIUM DIPHENYL | 4.2 | I | | 0 | 1 000 | |
| UN2006 | PLASTICS, NITROCELLULOSE-BASED, SELF-HEATING, N.O.S. | 4.2 | III | 16, 38 | 0 | | • |
| UN2008 | ZIRCONIUM POWDER, DRY | 4.2 | I | 38 | 0 | 1 000 | |
| | | | II | | 0 | | |
| | | | III | | 0 | | |
| UN2009 | ZIRCONIUM, DRY, finished sheets, strip or coiled wire | 4.2 | III | | 0 | | |
| UN2010 | MAGNESIUM HYDRIDE | 4.3 | I | 38 | 0 | 1 000 | |
| UN2011 | MAGNESIUM PHOSPHIDE | 4.3 (6.1) | I | 38 | 0 | 1 000 | |
| UN2012 | POTASSIUM PHOSPHIDE | 4.3 (6.1) | I | 38 | 0 | 1 000 | |
| UN2013 | STRONTIUM PHOSPHIDE | 4.3 (6.1) | I | 38 | 0 | 1 000 | |
| UN2014 | HYDROGEN PEROXIDE, AQUEOUS SOLUTION with not less than 20 per cent but not more than 60 per cent hydrogen peroxide (stabilized as necessary) | 5.1 (8) | II | | 0.5 | | |
| UN2015 | HYDROGEN PEROXIDE, AQUEOUS SOLUTION, STABILIZED with more than 60 per cent hydrogen peroxide; or HYDROGEN PEROXIDE, STABILIZED | 5.1 (8) | I | | 0 | 1 000 | |
| UN2016 | AMMUNITION, TOXIC, NON-EXPLOSIVE without burster or expelling charge, non-fuzed | 6.1 | II | | 0 | | |
| UN2017 | AMMUNITION, TEAR-PRODUCING, NON-EXPLOSIVE without burster or expelling charge, non-fuzed | 6.1 (8) | II | | 0 | | |
| UN2018 | CHLOROANILINES, SOLID | 6.1 | II | | 0.5 | | |
| UN2019 | CHLOROANILINES, LIQUID | 6.1 | II | | 0.1 | | |
| UN2020 | CHLOROPHENOLS, SOLID | 6.1 | III | | 5 | | |
| UN2021 | CHLOROPHENOLS, LIQUID | 6.1 | III | | 5 | | |
| UN2022 | CRESYLIC ACID | 6.1 (8) | II | | 0.1 | | |
| UN2023 | EPICHLOROHYDRIN | 6.1 (3) | II | 43 | 0.1 | 1 000 | P |
| UN2024 | MERCURY COMPOUND, LIQUID, N.O.S., excluding mercurous chloride and cinnabar | 6.1 | I | 23 | 0 | 1 000 | |
| | | | II | | 0.1 | | PP |
| | | | III | | 5 | | |

| 1 | 2 | 3 | 4 | 5 | 6 | 7 | 10 |
|---|---|---|---|---|---|---|---|
| UN Number | Shipping Name and Description | Class | Packing Group/Category | Special Provisions | Explosive Limit & Limited Quantity Index | ERAP Index | Marine Pollut |
| UN2025 | MERCURY COMPOUND, SOLID, N.O.S., excluding mercurous chloride and cinnabar | 6.1 | I<br>II<br>III | | 0<br>0.5<br>5 | 1 000 | PP |
| UN2026 | PHENYLMERCURIC COMPOUND, N.O.S. | 6.1 | I<br>II<br>III | | 0<br>0.5<br>5 | 1 000 | PP |
| UN2027 | SODIUM ARSENITE, SOLID | 6.1 | II | | 0.5 | | |
| UN2028 | BOMBS, SMOKE, NON-EXPLOSIVE with corrosive liquid, without initiating device | 8 | II | | 1 | | |
| UN2029 | HYDRAZINE, ANHYDROUS | 8<br>(3)<br>(6.1) | I | | 0 | 1 000 | |
| UN2030 | HYDRAZINE, AQUEOUS SOLUTION with more than 37 per cent but not more than 64 per cent hydrazine, by mass; or HYDRAZINE HYDRATE with more than 37 per cent but not more than 64 per cent hydrazine, by mass | 8<br>(6.1) | II | | 0.5 | | |
| UN2031 | NITRIC ACID, other than red fuming, with more than 70 per cent nitric acid | 8<br>(5.1) | I | | 0 | 3 000 | |
| UN2031 | NITRIC ACID, other than red fuming, with not more than 70 per cent nitric acid | 8 | II | | 0.5 | | |
| UN2032 | NITRIC ACID, RED FUMING | 8<br>(5.1)<br>(6.1) | I | | 0 | 1 000 | |
| UN2033 | POTASSIUM MONOXIDE | 8 | II | | 1 | | |
| UN2034 | HYDROGEN AND METHANE MIXTURE, COMPRESSED | 2.1 | | | 0.125 | 3 000 | |
| UN2035 | REFRIGERANT GAS R 143a; or 1,1,1-TRIFLUOROETHANE | 2.1 | | | 0.125 | 3 000 | |
| UN2036 | XENON, COMPRESSED | 2.2 | | | 0.125 | | |
| UN2037 | GAS CARTRIDGES without a release device, non-refillable; or RECEPTACLES, SMALL, CONTAINING GAS without a release device, non-refillable | 2.1 | | | 0.125 | | |
| UN2037 | GAS CARTRIDGES without a release device, non-refillable; or RECEPTACLES, SMALL, CONTAINING GAS without a release device, non-refillable | 2.2 | | | 0.125 | | |
| UN2038 | DINITROTOLUENES, LIQUID | 6.1 | II | | 0.1 | | |
| UN2038 | DINITROTOLUENES, SOLID | 6.1 | II | | 0.5 | | |
| UN2044 | 2,2-DIMETHYLPROPANE | 2.1 | | | 0.125 | 3 000 | |
| UN2045 | ISOBUTYLALDEHYDE; or ISOBUTYRALDEHYDE | 3 | II | | 1 | | |
| UN2046 | CYMENES | 3 | III | | 5 | | PP |
| UN2047 | DICHLOROPROPENES | 3 | II<br>III | | 1<br>5 | | |
| UN2048 | DICYCLOPENTADIENE | 3 | III | | 5 | | |
| UN2049 | DIETHYLBENZENE | 3 | III | | 5 | | |
| UN2050 | DIISOBUTYLENE, ISOMERIC COMPOUNDS | 3 | II | | 1 | | |
| UN2051 | 2-DIMETHYLAMINOETHANOL | 8<br>(3) | II | | 0.5 | | |
| UN2052 | DIPENTENE | 3 | III | | 5 | | P |
| UN2053 | METHYL ISOBUTYL CARBINOL | 3 | III | | 5 | | |
| UN2054 | MORPHOLINE | 8<br>(3) | I | | 0 | 3 000 | |
| UN2055 | STYRENE MONOMER, STABILIZED | 3 | III | | 5 | | |
| UN2056 | TETRAHYDROFURAN | 3 | II | | 1 | | |
| UN2057 | TRIPROPYLENE | 3 | II<br>III | | 1<br>5 | | |
| UN2058 | VALERALDEHYDE | 3 | II | | 1 | | |

| 1 | 2 | 3 | 4 | 5 | 6 | 7 | 10 |
|---|---|---|---|---|---|---|---|
| UN Number | Shipping Name and Description | Class | Packing Group/Category | Special Provisions | Explosive Limit & Limited Quantity Index | ERAP Index | Marine Pollut. |
| UN2059 | NITROCELLULOSE SOLUTION, FLAMMABLE with not more than 12.6 per cent nitrogen, by dry mass, and not more than 55 per cent nitrocellulose | 3 | I<br>II<br>III | | 0<br>1<br>5 | | |
| UN2067 | AMMONIUM NITRATE FERTILIZERS: uniform non-segregating mixtures of ammonium nitrate with added matter which is inorganic and chemically inert towards ammonium nitrate, with not less than 90 per cent ammonium nitrate and not more than 0.2 per cent combustible material (including organic material calculated as carbon) or with more than 70 per cent but less than 90 per cent ammonium nitrate and not more than 0.4 per cent total combustible material | 5.1 | III | 37, 68 | 5 | | |
| UN2068 | AMMONIUM NITRATE FERTILIZERS: uniform non-segregating mixtures of ammonium nitrate with calcium carbonate and/or dolomite, with more than 80 per cent but less than 90 per cent ammonium nitrate and not more than 0.4 per cent total combustible material | 5.1 | III | 37, 68 | 5 | | |
| UN2069 | AMMONIUM NITRATE FERTILIZERS: uniform non-segregating mixtures of ammonium nitrate/ammonium sulphate, with more than 45 per cent but not more than 70 per cent ammonium nitrate and not more than 0.4 per cent total combustible material | 5.1 | III | 37, 68 | 5 | | |
| UN2070 | AMMONIUM NITRATE FERTILIZERS: uniform non-segregating mixtures of nitrogen/phosphate or nitrogen/potash types or complete fertilizers of nitrogen/phosphate/potash type, with more than 70 per cent but less than 90 per cent ammonium nitrate and not more than 0.4 per cent total combustible material | 5.1 | III | 37, 68 | 5 | | |
| UN2071 | AMMONIUM NITRATE FERTILIZERS: uniform non-segregating mixtures of nitrogen/phosphate or nitrogen/potash types or complete fertilizers of nitrogen/phosphate/potash type, with not more than 70 per cent ammonium nitrate and not more than 0.4 per cent total added combustible material or with not more than 45 per cent ammonium nitrate with unrestricted combustible material | 9 | III | 37 | 5 | | |
| UN2072 | AMMONIUM NITRATE FERTILIZER, N.O.S. | 5.1 | I<br>II<br>III | 37, 68 | 0<br>1<br>5 | 1 000 | |
| UN2073 | AMMONIA SOLUTION, relative density less than 0.880 at 15 °C in water, with more than 35 per cent but not more than 50 per cent ammonia | 2.2 | | | 0.125 | 3 000 | |
| UN2074 | ACRYLAMIDE | 6.1 | III | | 5 | | |
| UN2075 | CHLORAL, ANHYDROUS, STABILIZED | 6.1 | II | | 0.1 | | |
| UN2076 | CRESOLS, LIQUID | 6.1 (8) | II | | 0.1 | | |
| UN2076 | CRESOLS, SOLID | 6.1 (8) | II | | 0.5 | | |
| UN2077 | alpha-NAPHTHYLAMINE | 6.1 | III | | 5 | | |
| UN2078 | TOLUENE DIISOCYANATE | 6.1 | II | 43 | 0.1 | 1 000 | |
| UN2079 | DIETHYLENETRIAMINE | 8 | II | | 1 | | |
| UN2186 | HYDROGEN CHLORIDE, REFRIGERATED LIQUID | 2.3 (8) | | | 0 | 500 | |
| UN2187 | CARBON DIOXIDE, REFRIGERATED LIQUID | 2.2 | | | 0.125 | | |
| UN2188 | ARSINE | 2.3 (2.1) | | 38 | 0 | 0 | |
| UN2189 | DICHLOROSILANE | 2.3 (2.1) (8) | | 38 | 0 | 50 | |
| UN2190 | OXYGEN DIFLUORIDE, COMPRESSED | 2.3 (5.1) (8) | | 38 | 0 | 0 | |
| UN2191 | SULFURYL FLUORIDE; or SULPHURYL FLUORIDE | 2.3 | | | 0 | 500 | |
| UN2192 | GERMANE | 2.3 (2.1) | | 38 | 0 | 0 | |
| UN2193 | HEXAFLUOROETHANE, COMPRESSED; or REFRIGERANT GAS R 116, COMPRESSED | 2.2 | | | 0.125 | | |
| UN2194 | SELENIUM HEXAFLUORIDE | 2.3 (8) | | 38 | 0 | 25 | |

| 1 UN Number | 2 Shipping Name and Description | 3 Class | 4 Packing Group/Category | 5 Special Provisions | 6 Explosive Limit & Limited Quantity Index | 7 ERAP Index | 10 Marine Pollut. |
|---|---|---|---|---|---|---|---|
| UN2195 | TELLURIUM HEXAFLUORIDE | 2.3 (8) | | 38 | 0 | 25 | |
| UN2196 | TUNGSTEN HEXAFLUORIDE | 2.3 (8) | | 38 | 0 | 25 | |
| UN2197 | HYDROGEN IODIDE, ANHYDROUS | 2.3 (8) | | 38 | 0 | 500 | |
| UN2198 | PHOSPHORUS PENTAFLUORIDE, COMPRESSED | 2.3 (8) | | 38 | 0 | 25 | |
| UN2199 | PHOSPHINE | 2.3 (2.1) | | 38 | 0 | 0 | |
| UN2200 | PROPADIENE, STABILIZED | 2.1 | | | 0.125 | 3 000 | |
| UN2201 | NITROUS OXIDE, REFRIGERATED LIQUID | 2.2 (5.1) | | | 0 | 3 000 | |
| UN2202 | HYDROGEN SELENIDE, ANHYDROUS | 2.3 (2.1) | | 38 | 0 | 0 | |
| UN2203 | SILANE, COMPRESSED | 2.1 | | 38 | 0.125 | 25 | |
| UN2204 | CARBONYL SULFIDE; or CARBONYL SULPHIDE | 2.3 (2.1) | | 38 | 0 | 500 | |
| UN2205 | ADIPONITRILE | 6.1 | III | | 5 | | |
| UN2206 | ISOCYANATE SOLUTION, TOXIC, N.O.S.; or ISOCYANATES, TOXIC, N.O.S. | 6.1 | II III | 16, 23 16 | 0.1 5 | 3 000 | • |
| UN2208 | CALCIUM HYPOCHLORITE MIXTURE, DRY with more than 10 per cent but not more than 39 per cent available chlorine | 5.1 | III | | 5 | | |
| UN2209 | FORMALDEHYDE SOLUTION with not less than 25 per cent formaldehyde | 8 | III | | 5 | | |
| UN2210 | MANEB; or MANEB PREPARATION with not less than 60 per cent maneb | 4.2 (4.3) | III | 45 | 0 | | P |
| UN2211 | POLYMERIC BEADS, EXPANDABLE, evolving flammable vapour | 9 | III | | 5 | | |
| UN2212 | ASBESTOS BLUE (crocidolite) when not fixed in a natural or artificial binder material or included in a manufactured product; ASBESTOS BROWN (amosite, mysorite) when not fixed in a natural or artificial binder material or included in a manufactured product; BLUE ASBESTOS (crocidolite) when not fixed in a natural or artificial binder material or included in a manufactured product; or BROWN ASBESTOS (amosite, mysorite) when not fixed in a natural or artificial binder material or included in a manufactured product | 9 | II | | 1 | | |
| UN2213 | PARAFORMALDEHYDE | 4.1 | III | | 5 | | |
| UN2214 | PHTHALIC ANHYDRIDE with more than 0.05 per cent of maleic anhydride | 8 | III | | 5 | | |
| UN2215 | MALEIC ANHYDRIDE | 8 | III | | 5 | | |
| UN2215 | MALEIC ANHYDRIDE, MOLTEN | 8 | III | | 5 | | |
| UN2216 | FISH MEAL, STABILIZED, regulated by ship only; or FISH SCRAP, STABILIZED, regulated by ship only | 9 | III | 64 | 5 | | |
| UN2217 | SEED CAKE with not more than 1.5 per cent oil and not more than 11 per cent moisture | 4.2 | III | 36 | 0 | | |
| UN2218 | ACRYLIC ACID, STABILIZED | 8 (3) | II | | 0.5 | | |
| UN2219 | ALLYL GLYCIDYL ETHER | 3 | III | | 5 | | |
| UN2222 | ANISOLE | 3 | III | | 5 | | |
| UN2224 | BENZONITRILE | 6.1 | II | | 0.1 | | |
| UN2225 | BENZENESULFONYL CHLORIDE; or BENZENESULPHONYL CHLORIDE | 8 | III | | 5 | | |
| UN2226 | BENZOTRICHLORIDE | 8 | II | | 1 | 3 000 | |
| UN2227 | n-BUTYL METHACRYLATE, STABILIZED | 3 | III | | 5 | | |
| UN2232 | 2-CHLOROETHANAL | 6.1 | I | | 0 | 1 000 | |
| UN2233 | CHLOROANISIDINES | 6.1 | III | | 5 | | |
| UN2234 | CHLOROBENZOTRIFLUORIDES | 3 | III | | 5 | | |

| 1 | 2 | 3 | 4 | 5 | 6 | 7 | 10 |
|---|---|---|---|---|---|---|---|
| UN Number | Shipping Name and Description | Class | Packing Group/Category | Special Provisions | Explosive Limit & Limited Quantity Index | ERAP Index | Marine Pollut. |
| UN2235 | CHLOROBENZYL CHLORIDES | 6.1 | III | 53 | 5 | | P |
| UN2236 | 3-CHLORO-4-METHYLPHENYL ISOCYANATE | 6.1 | II | | 0.1 | | |
| UN2237 | CHLORONITROANILINES | 6.1 | III | | 5 | | P |
| UN2238 | CHLOROTOLUENES | 3 | III | | 5 | | P |
| UN2239 | CHLOROTOLUIDINES, liquid; or CHLOROTOLUIDINES, LIQUID (ICAO/IMO terminology) | 6.1 | III | | 5 | | |
| UN2239 | CHLOROTOLUIDINES, solid; or CHLOROTOLUIDINES, SOLID (ICAO/IMO terminology) | 6.1 | III | | 5 | | |
| UN2240 | CHROMOSULFURIC ACID; or CHROMOSULPHURIC ACID | 8 | I | | 0 | 3 000 | |
| UN2241 | CYCLOHEPTANE | 3 | II | | 1 | | |
| UN2242 | CYCLOHEPTENE | 3 | II | | 1 | | |
| UN2243 | CYCLOHEXYL ACETATE | 3 | III | | 5 | | |
| UN2244 | CYCLOPENTANOL | 3 | III | | 5 | | |
| UN2245 | CYCLOPENTANONE | 3 | III | | 5 | | |
| UN2246 | CYCLOPENTENE | 3 | II | | 1 | | |
| UN2247 | n-DECANE | 3 | III | | 5 | | |
| UN2248 | DI-n-BUTYLAMINE | 8 (3) | II | | 0.5 | 3 000 | |
| UN2249 | DICHLORODIMETHYL ETHER, SYMMETRICAL | F | | | | | |
| UN2250 | DICHLOROPHENYL ISOCYANATES | 6.1 | II | | 0.5 | | |
| UN2251 | BICYCLO[2.2.1]HEPTA-2,5-DIENE, STABILIZED; or 2,5-NORBORNADIENE, STABILIZED | 3 | II | | 1 | | |
| UN2252 | 1,2-DIMETHOXYETHANE | 3 | II | | 1 | | |
| UN2253 | N,N-DIMETHYLANILINE | 6.1 | II | | 0.1 | | |
| UN2254 | MATCHES, FUSEE | 4.1 | III | | 5 | | |
| UN2256 | CYCLOHEXENE | 3 | II | | 1 | | |
| UN2257 | POTASSIUM | 4.3 | I | | 0 | 1 000 | |
| UN2258 | 1,2-PROPYLENEDIAMINE | 8 (3) | II | | 0.5 | 3 000 | |
| UN2259 | TRIETHYLENETETRAMINE | 8 | II | | 1 | | |
| UN2260 | TRIPROPYLAMINE | 3 (8) | III | | 5 | | |
| UN2261 | XYLENOLS | 6.1 | II | | 0.5 | | P |
| UN2262 | DIMETHYLCARBAMOYL CHLORIDE | 8 | II | | 1 | | |
| UN2263 | DIMETHYLCYCLOHEXANES | 3 | II | | 1 | | |
| UN2264 | DIMETHYLCYCLOHEXYLAMINE | 8 (3) | II | | 0.5 | | |
| UN2265 | N,N-DIMETHYLFORMAMIDE | 3 | III | | 5 | | |
| UN2266 | DIMETHYL-N-PROPYLAMINE | 3 (8) | II | | 1 | | |
| UN2267 | DIMETHYL THIOPHOSPHORYL CHLORIDE | 6.1 (8) | II | | 0.1 | | |
| UN2269 | 3,3'-IMINODIPROPYLAMINE | 8 | III | | 5 | | |
| UN2270 | ETHYLAMINE, AQUEOUS SOLUTION with not less than 50 per cent but not more than 70 per cent ethylamine | 3 (8) | II | | 1 | | |
| UN2271 | ETHYL AMYL KETONE | 3 | III | | 5 | | |
| UN2272 | N-ETHYLANILINE | 6.1 | III | | 5 | | |
| UN2273 | 2-ETHYLANILINE | 6.1 | III | | 5 | | |
| UN2274 | N-ETHYL-N-BENZYLANILINE | 6.1 | III | | 5 | | |
| UN2275 | 2-ETHYLBUTANOL | 3 | III | | 5 | | |
| UN2276 | 2-ETHYLHEXYLAMINE | 3 (8) | III | | 5 | | |

| 1 UN Number | 2 Shipping Name and Description | 3 Class | 4 Packing Group/Category | 5 Special Provisions | 6 Explosive Limit & Limited Quantity Index | 7 ERAP Index | 10 Marine Pollut |
|---|---|---|---|---|---|---|---|
| UN2277 | ETHYL METHACRYLATE | 3 | II | | 1 | | |
| UN2278 | n-HEPTENE | 3 | II | | 1 | | |
| UN2279 | HEXACHLOROBUTADIENE | 6.1 | III | | 5 | | PP |
| UN2280 | HEXAMETHYLENEDIAMINE, SOLID | 8 | III | | 5 | | |
| UN2281 | HEXAMETHYLENE DIISOCYANATE | 6.1 | II | | 0.1 | | |
| UN2282 | HEXANOLS | 3 | III | | 5 | | |
| UN2283 | ISOBUTYL METHACRYLATE, STABILIZED | 3 | III | | 5 | | |
| UN2284 | ISOBUTYRONITRILE | 3 (6.1) | II | | 1 | | |
| UN2285 | ISOCYANATOBENZOTRIFLUORIDES | 6.1 (3) | II | | 0.1 | 1 000 | |
| UN2286 | PENTAMETHYLHEPTANE | 3 | III | | 5 | | |
| UN2287 | ISOHEPTENE | 3 | II | | 1 | | |
| UN2288 | ISOHEXENE | 3 | II | | 1 | | |
| UN2289 | ISOPHORONEDIAMINE | 8 | III | | 5 | | |
| UN2290 | ISOPHORONE DIISOCYANATE | 6.1 | III | | 5 | | |
| UN2291 | LEAD COMPOUND, SOLUBLE, N.O.S. | 6.1 | III | 24 | 5 | | P |
| UN2293 | 4-METHOXY-4-METHYLPENTAN-2-ONE | 3 | III | | 5 | | |
| UN2294 | N-METHYLANILINE | 6.1 | III | | 5 | | |
| UN2295 | METHYL CHLOROACETATE | 6.1 (3) | I | | 0 | 1 000 | |
| UN2296 | METHYLCYCLOHEXANE | 3 | II | | 1 | | |
| UN2297 | METHYLCYCLOHEXANONE | 3 | III | | 5 | | |
| UN2298 | METHYLCYCLOPENTANE | 3 | II | | 1 | | |
| UN2299 | METHYL DICHLOROACETATE | 6.1 | III | | 5 | | |
| UN2300 | 2-METHYL-5-ETHYLPYRIDINE | 6.1 | III | | 5 | | |
| UN2301 | 2-METHYLFURAN | 3 | II | | 1 | | |
| UN2302 | 5-METHYLHEXAN-2-ONE | 3 | III | | 5 | | |
| UN2303 | ISOPROPENYLBENZENE | 3 | III | | 5 | | |
| UN2304 | NAPHTHALENE, MOLTEN | 4.1 | III | | 0 | | |
| UN2305 | NITROBENZENESULFONIC ACID; or NITROBENZENESULPHONIC ACID | 8 | II | | 1 | | |
| UN2306 | NITROBENZOTRIFLUORIDES | 6.1 | II | | 0.1 | | P |
| UN2307 | 3-NITRO-4-CHLOROBENZOTRIFLUORIDE | 6.1 | II | | 0.1 | | P |
| UN2308 | NITROSYLSULFURIC ACID, LIQUID; or NITROSYLSULPHURIC ACID, LIQUID | 8 | II | | 1 | | |
| UN2308 | NITROSYLSULFURIC ACID, SOLID; or NITROSYLSULPHURIC ACID, SOLID | 8 | II | | 1 | | |
| UN2309 | OCTADIENE | 3 | II | | 1 | | |
| UN2310 | PENTANE-2,4-DIONE | 3 (6.1) | III | | 5 | | |
| UN2311 | PHENETIDINES | 6.1 | III | 43 | 5 | | |
| UN2312 | PHENOL, MOLTEN | 6.1 | II | | 0 | 3 000 | |
| UN2313 | PICOLINES | 3 | III | | 5 | | |
| UN2315 | ARTICLES CONTAINING POLYCHLORINATED BIPHENYLS (PCB) regulated only when the concentration is more than 50 ppm by mass; or POLYCHLORINATED BIPHENYLS (PCB) regulated only when the concentration is more than 50 ppm by mass | 9 | II | | 1 | | PP |
| UN2316 | SODIUM CUPROCYANIDE, SOLID | 6.1 | I | | 0 | 1 000 | PP |
| UN2317 | SODIUM CUPROCYANIDE SOLUTION | 6.1 | I | | 0 | 1 000 | PP |

| UN Number | Shipping Name and Description | Class | Packing Group/Category | Special Provisions | Explosive Limit & Limited Quantity Index | ERAP Index | Marine Pollut. |
|---|---|---|---|---|---|---|---|
| UN2318 | SODIUM HYDROSULFIDE with less than 25 per cent water of crystallization; or SODIUM HYDROSULPHIDE with less than 25 per cent water of crystallization | 4.2 | II | | 0 | | |
| UN2319 | TERPENE HYDROCARBONS, N.O.S. | 3 | III | | 5 | | • |
| UN2320 | TETRAETHYLENEPENTAMINE | 8 | III | | 5 | | |
| UN2321 | TRICHLOROBENZENES, LIQUID | 6.1 | III | | 5 | | P |
| UN2322 | TRICHLOROBUTENE | 6.1 | II | | 0.1 | | P |
| UN2323 | TRIETHYL PHOSPHITE | 3 | III | | 5 | | |
| UN2324 | TRIISOBUTYLENE | 3 | III | | 5 | | |
| UN2325 | 1,3,5-TRIMETHYLBENZENE | 3 | III | | 5 | | |
| UN2326 | TRIMETHYLCYCLOHEXYLAMINE | 8 | III | | 5 | | |
| UN2327 | TRIMETHYLHEXAMETHYLENEDIAMINES | 8 | III | | 5 | | |
| UN2328 | TRIMETHYLHEXAMETHYLENE DIISOCYANATE | 6.1 | III | | 5 | | |
| UN2329 | TRIMETHYL PHOSPHITE | 3 | III | | 5 | | |
| UN2330 | UNDECANE | 3 | III | | 5 | | |
| UN2331 | ZINC CHLORIDE, ANHYDROUS | 8 | III | | 5 | | |
| UN2332 | ACETALDEHYDE OXIME | 3 | III | | 5 | | |
| UN2333 | ALLYL ACETATE | 3 (6.1) | II | | 1 | 1 000 | |
| UN2334 | ALLYLAMINE | 6.1 (3) | I | | 0 | 1 000 | |
| UN2335 | ALLYL ETHYL ETHER | 3 (6.1) | II | | 1 | 1 000 | |
| UN2336 | ALLYL FORMATE | 3 (6.1) | I | | 0 | 1 000 | |
| UN2337 | PHENYL MERCAPTAN | 6.1 (3) | I | | 0 | 1 000 | |
| UN2338 | BENZOTRIFLUORIDE | 3 | II | | 1 | | |
| UN2339 | 2-BROMOBUTANE | 3 | II | | 1 | | |
| UN2340 | 2-BROMOETHYL ETHYL ETHER | 3 | II | | 1 | | |
| UN2341 | 1-BROMO-3-METHYLBUTANE | 3 | III | | 5 | | |
| UN2342 | BROMOMETHYLPROPANES | 3 | II | | 1 | | |
| UN2343 | 2-BROMOPENTANE | 3 | II | | 1 | | |
| UN2344 | BROMOPROPANES | 3 | II III | | 1 5 | | |
| UN2345 | 3-BROMOPROPYNE | 3 | II | | 1 | | |
| UN2346 | BUTANEDIONE | 3 | II | | 1 | | P |
| UN2347 | BUTYL MERCAPTAN | 3 | II | | 1 | | P |
| UN2348 | BUTYL ACRYLATES, STABILIZED | 3 | III | | 5 | | |
| UN2350 | BUTYL METHYL ETHER | 3 | II | | 1 | | |
| UN2351 | BUTYL NITRITES | 3 | II III | | 1 5 | | |
| UN2352 | BUTYL VINYL ETHER, STABILIZED | 3 | II | | 1 | | |
| UN2353 | BUTYRYL CHLORIDE | 3 (8) | II | | 1 | | |
| UN2354 | CHLOROMETHYL ETHYL ETHER | 3 (6.1) | II | | 1 | 3 000 | |
| UN2356 | 2-CHLOROPROPANE | 3 | I | | 0 | | |
| UN2357 | CYCLOHEXYLAMINE | 8 (3) | II | | 0.5 | | |
| UN2358 | CYCLOOCTATETRAENE | 3 | II | | 1 | | |
| UN2359 | DIALLYLAMINE | 3 (6.1) (8) | II | | 1 | 1 000 | |
| UN2360 | DIALLYL ETHER | 3 (6.1) | II | | 1 | 1 000 | |

| 1 | 2 | 3 | 4 | 5 | 6 | 7 | 10 |
|---|---|---|---|---|---|---|---|
| UN Number | Shipping Name and Description | Class | Packing Group/Category | Special Provisions | Explosive Limit & Limited Quantity Index | ERAP Index | Marine Pollut. |
| UN2361 | DIISOBUTYLAMINE | 3 (8) | III | | 5 | | |
| UN2362 | 1,1-DICHLOROETHANE | 3 | II | | 1 | | |
| UN2363 | ETHYL MERCAPTAN | 3 | I | | 0 | | P |
| UN2364 | n-PROPYLBENZENE | 3 | III | | 5 | | |
| UN2366 | DIETHYL CARBONATE | 3 | III | | 5 | | |
| UN2367 | alpha-METHYLVALERALDEHYDE | 3 | II | | 1 | | |
| UN2368 | alpha-PINENE | 3 | III | | 5 | | |
| UN2370 | 1-HEXENE | 3 | II | | 1 | | |
| UN2371 | ISOPENTENES | 3 | I | | 0 | | |
| UN2372 | 1,2-DI-(DIMETHYLAMINO) ETHANE | 3 | II | | 1 | | |
| UN2373 | DIETHOXYMETHANE | 3 | II | | 1 | | |
| UN2374 | 3,3-DIETHOXYPROPENE | 3 | II | | 1 | | |
| UN2375 | DIETHYL SULFIDE; or DIETHYL SULPHIDE | 3 | II | | 1 | | |
| UN2376 | 2,3-DIHYDROPYRAN | 3 | II | | 1 | | |
| UN2377 | 1,1-DIMETHOXYETHANE | 3 | II | | 1 | | |
| UN2378 | 2-DIMETHYLAMINOACETONITRILE | 3 (6.1) | II | | 1 | 1 000 | |
| UN2379 | 1,3-DIMETHYLBUTYLAMINE | 3 (8) | II | | 1 | | |
| UN2380 | DIMETHYLDIETHOXYSILANE | 3 | II | | 1 | | |
| UN2381 | DIMETHYL DISULFIDE; or DIMETHYL DISULPHIDE | 3 | II | | 1 | 1 000 | |
| UN2382 | DIMETHYLHYDRAZINE, SYMMETRICAL | 6.1 (3) | I | | 0 | 1 000 | P |
| UN2383 | DIPROPYLAMINE | 3 (8) | II | | 1 | 3 000 | |
| UN2384 | DI-n-PROPYL ETHER | 3 | II | | 1 | | |
| UN2385 | ETHYL ISOBUTYRATE | 3 | II | | 1 | | |
| UN2386 | 1-ETHYLPIPERIDINE | 3 (8) | II | | 1 | 3 000 | |
| UN2387 | FLUOROBENZENE | 3 | II | | 1 | | |
| UN2388 | FLUOROTOLUENES | 3 | II | | 1 | | |
| UN2389 | FURAN | 3 | I | | 0 | | |
| UN2390 | 2-IODOBUTANE | 3 | II | | 1 | | |
| UN2391 | IODOMETHYLPROPANES | 3 | II | | 1 | | |
| UN2392 | IODOPROPANES | 3 | III | | 5 | | |
| UN2393 | ISOBUTYL FORMATE | 3 | II | | 1 | | |
| UN2394 | ISOBUTYL PROPIONATE | 3 | III | | 5 | | |
| UN2395 | ISOBUTYRYL CHLORIDE | 3 (8) | II | | 1 | 3 000 | |
| UN2396 | METHACRYLALDEHYDE, STABILIZED | 3 (6.1) | II | | 1 | 1 000 | |
| UN2397 | 3-METHYLBUTAN-2-ONE | 3 | II | | 1 | | |
| UN2398 | METHYL tert-BUTYL ETHER | 3 | II | | 1 | | |
| UN2399 | 1-METHYLPIPERIDINE | 3 (8) | II | | 1 | | |
| UN2400 | METHYL ISOVALERATE | 3 | II | | 1 | | |
| UN2401 | PIPERIDINE | 8 (3) | I | | 0 | 3 000 | |
| UN2402 | PROPANETHIOLS | 3 | II | | 1 | | |
| UN2403 | ISOPROPENYL ACETATE | 3 | II | | 1 | | |
| UN2404 | PROPIONITRILE | 3 (6.1) | II | | 1 | 1 000 | |
| UN2405 | ISOPROPYL BUTYRATE | 3 | III | | 5 | | |

| 1 UN Number | 2 Shipping Name and Description | 3 Class | 4 Packing Group/Category | 5 Special Provisions | 6 Explosive Limit & Limited Quantity Index | 7 ERAP Index | 10 Marine Pollut. |
|---|---|---|---|---|---|---|---|
| UN2406 | ISOPROPYL ISOBUTYRATE | 3 | II | | 1 | | |
| UN2407 | ISOPROPYL CHLOROFORMATE | 6.1 (3) (8) | I | | 0 | 1 000 | |
| UN2409 | ISOPROPYL PROPIONATE | 3 | II | | 1 | | |
| UN2410 | 1,2,3,6-TETRAHYDROPYRIDINE | 3 | II | | 1 | | |
| UN2411 | BUTYRONITRILE | 3 (6.1) | II | | 1 | 3 000 | |
| UN2412 | TETRAHYDROTHIOPHENE | 3 | II | | 1 | | |
| UN2413 | TETRAPROPYL ORTHOTITANATE | 3 | III | | 5 | | |
| UN2414 | THIOPHENE | 3 | II | | 1 | | |
| UN2416 | TRIMETHYL BORATE | 3 | II | | 1 | | |
| UN2417 | CARBONYL FLUORIDE, COMPRESSED | 2.3 (8) | | 38 | 0 | 50 | |
| UN2418 | SULFUR TETRAFLUORIDE; or SULPHUR TETRAFLUORIDE | 2.3 (8) | | 38 | 0 | 25 | |
| UN2419 | BROMOTRIFLUOROETHYLENE | 2.1 | | | 0.125 | 3 000 | |
| UN2420 | HEXAFLUOROACETONE | 2.3 (8) | | 38 | 0 | 25 | |
| UN2421 | NITROGEN TRIOXIDE | 2.3 (5.1) (8) | | 38 | 0 | 25 | |
| UN2422 | OCTAFLUOROBUT-2-ENE; or REFRIGERANT GAS R 1318 | 2.2 | | | 0.125 | | |
| UN2424 | OCTAFLUOROPROPANE; or REFRIGERANT GAS R 218 | 2.2 | | | 0.125 | | |
| UN2426 | AMMONIUM NITRATE, LIQUID (hot concentrated solution) with not more than 0.2 per cent combustible material, in a concentration exceeding 80 per cent | 5.1 | | | 0 | 1 000 | |
| UN2427 | POTASSIUM CHLORATE, AQUEOUS SOLUTION | 5.1 | II III | | 1 5 | | |
| UN2428 | SODIUM CHLORATE, AQUEOUS SOLUTION | 5.1 | II III | | 1 5 | | |
| UN2429 | CALCIUM CHLORATE, AQUEOUS SOLUTION | 5.1 | II III | | 1 5 | | |
| UN2430 | ALKYLPHENOLS, SOLID, N.O.S. including C2-C12 homologues | 8 | I II III | 50 50 50 | 0 1 5 | 3 000 | • |
| UN2431 | ANISIDINES, liquid; or ANISIDINES, LIQUID (ICAO/IMO terminology) | 6.1 | III | | 5 | | |
| UN2431 | ANISIDINES, solid; or ANISIDINES, SOLID (ICAO/IMO terminology) | 6.1 | III | | 5 | | |
| UN2432 | N,N-DIETHYLANILINE | 6.1 | III | 43 | 5 | | |
| UN2433 | CHLORONITROTOLUENES, LIQUID | 6.1 | III | | 5 | | P |
| UN2433 | CHLORONITROTOLUENES, SOLID | 6.1 | III | | 5 | | P |
| UN2434 | DIBENZYLDICHLOROSILANE | 8 | II | | 1 | | |
| UN2435 | ETHYLPHENYLDICHLOROSILANE | 8 | II | | 1 | | |
| UN2436 | THIOACETIC ACID | 3 | II | | 1 | | |
| UN2437 | METHYLPHENYLDICHLOROSILANE | 8 | II | | 1 | | |
| UN2438 | TRIMETHYLACETYL CHLORIDE | 6.1 (3) (8) | I | | 0 | 1 000 | |
| UN2439 | SODIUM HYDROGENDIFLUORIDE, solution; or SODIUM HYDROGENDIFLUORIDE, SOLUTION (ICAO terminology) | 8 | II | | 1 | | |

| 1 UN Number | 2 Shipping Name and Description | 3 Class | 4 Packing Group/Category | 5 Special Provisions | 6 Explosive Limit & Limited Quantity Index | 7 ERAP Index | 10 Marine Pollut. |
|---|---|---|---|---|---|---|---|
| UN2439 | SODIUM HYDROGENDIFLUORIDE, solid; or SODIUM HYDROGENDIFLUORIDE, SOLID (ICAO terminology) | 8 | II | | 1 | | |
| UN2440 | STANNIC CHLORIDE PENTAHYDRATE | 8 | III | | 5 | | |
| UN2441 | TITANIUM TRICHLORIDE MIXTURE, PYROPHORIC; or TITANIUM TRICHLORIDE, PYROPHORIC | 4.2 (8) | I | | 0 | 1 000 | |
| UN2442 | TRICHLOROACETYL CHLORIDE | 8 | II | | 1 | | |
| UN2443 | VANADIUM OXYTRICHLORIDE | 8 | II | | 1 | | |
| UN2444 | VANADIUM TETRACHLORIDE | 8 | I | | 0 | 3 000 | |
| UN2445 | LITHIUM ALKYLS | 4.2 (4.3) | I | | 0 | 1 000 | |
| UN2446 | NITROCRESOLS | 6.1 | III | | 5 | | |
| UN2447 | PHOSPHORUS, WHITE, MOLTEN | 4.2 (6.1) | I | | 0 | 1 000 | PP |
| UN2448 | MOLTEN SULFUR; MOLTEN SULPHUR; SULFUR, MOLTEN; or SULPHUR, MOLTEN | 4.1 | III | 32 | 0 | | |
| UN2451 | NITROGEN TRIFLUORIDE, COMPRESSED | 2.2 (5.1) | | 38 | 0 | 25 | |
| UN2452 | ETHYLACETYLENE, STABILIZED | 2.1 | | | 0.125 | 3 000 | |
| UN2453 | ETHYL FLUORIDE; or REFRIGERANT GAS R 161 | 2.1 | | | 0.125 | 3 000 | |
| UN2454 | METHYL FLUORIDE; or REFRIGERANT GAS R 41 | 2.1 | | | 0.125 | 3 000 | |
| UN2455 | METHYL NITRITE | F | | | | | |
| UN2456 | 2-CHLOROPROPENE | 3 | I | | 0 | | |
| UN2457 | 2,3-DIMETHYLBUTANE | 3 | II | | 1 | | |
| UN2458 | HEXADIENE | 3 | II | | 1 | | |
| UN2459 | 2-METHYL-1-BUTENE | 3 | I | | 0 | | |
| UN2460 | 2-METHYL-2-BUTENE | 3 | II | | 1 | | |
| UN2461 | METHYLPENTADIENE | 3 | II | | 1 | | |
| UN2463 | ALUMINUM HYDRIDE | 4.3 | I | 38 | 0 | 1 000 | |
| UN2464 | BERYLLIUM NITRATE | 5.1 (6.1) | II | | 0.5 | 1 000 | |
| UN2465 | DICHLOROISOCYANURIC ACID, DRY; or DICHLOROISOCYANURIC ACID SALTS excluding the dihydrated sodium salts | 5.1 | II | | 1 | | |
| UN2466 | POTASSIUM SUPEROXIDE | 5.1 | I | 38 | 0 | 1 000 | |
| UN2468 | TRICHLOROISOCYANURIC ACID, DRY | 5.1 | II | | 1 | | |
| UN2469 | ZINC BROMATE | 5.1 | III | | 5 | | |
| UN2470 | PHENYLACETONITRILE, LIQUID | 6.1 | III | | 5 | | |
| UN2471 | OSMIUM TETROXIDE | 6.1 | I | 38 | 0 | 1 000 | PP |
| UN2473 | SODIUM ARSANILATE | 6.1 | III | | 5 | | |
| UN2474 | THIOPHOSGENE | 6.1 | II | 43 | 0.1 | 1 000 | |
| UN2475 | VANADIUM TRICHLORIDE | 8 | III | | 5 | | |
| UN2477 | METHYL ISOTHIOCYANATE | 6.1 (3) | I | | 0 | 1 000 | |
| UN2478 | ISOCYANATES, FLAMMABLE, TOXIC, N.O.S.; or ISOCYANATE SOLUTION, FLAMMABLE, TOXIC, N.O.S. | 3 (6.1) | II III | 16 16 | 1 5 | 1 000 | • |
| UN2480 | METHYL ISOCYANATE | 6.1 (3) | I | 38 | 0 | 1 000 | |
| UN2481 | ETHYL ISOCYANATE | 3 (6.1) | I | | 0 | 1 000 | |
| UN2482 | n-PROPYL ISOCYANATE | 6.1 (3) | I | | 0 | 1 000 | |

| 1 UN Number | 2 Shipping Name and Description | 3 Class | 4 Packing Group/Category | 5 Special Provisions | 6 Explosive Limit & Limited Quantity Index | 7 ERAP Index | 10 Marine Pollut. |
|---|---|---|---|---|---|---|---|
| UN2483 | ISOPROPYL ISOCYANATE | 3 (6.1) | I | | 0 | 1 000 | |
| UN2484 | tert-BUTYL ISOCYANATE | 6.1 (3) | I | | 0 | 1 000 | |
| UN2485 | n-BUTYL ISOCYANATE | 6.1 (3) | I | | 0 | 1 000 | |
| UN2486 | ISOBUTYL ISOCYANATE | 3 (6.1) | II | | 1 | 1 000 | |
| UN2487 | PHENYL ISOCYANATE | 6.1 (3) | I | | 0 | 1 000 | |
| UN2488 | CYCLOHEXYL ISOCYANATE | 6.1 (3) | I | | 0 | 1 000 | |
| UN2490 | DICHLOROISOPROPYL ETHER | 6.1 | II | | 0.1 | | |
| UN2491 | ETHANOLAMINE; or ETHANOLAMINE SOLUTION | 8 | III | | 5 | | |
| UN2493 | HEXAMETHYLENEIMINE | 3 (8) | II | | 1 | | |
| UN2495 | IODINE PENTAFLUORIDE | 5.1 (6.1) (8) | I | | 0 | 1 000 | |
| UN2496 | PROPIONIC ANHYDRIDE | 8 | III | | 5 | | |
| UN2498 | 1,2,3,6-TETRAHYDROBENZALDEHYDE | 3 | III | | 5 | | |
| UN2501 | TRIS-(1-AZIRIDINYL) PHOSPHINE OXIDE SOLUTION | 6.1 | II III | | 0.1 5 | | |
| UN2502 | VALERYL CHLORIDE | 8 (3) | II | | 0.5 | | |
| UN2503 | ZIRCONIUM TETRACHLORIDE | 8 | III | | 5 | | |
| UN2504 | TETRABROMOETHANE | 6.1 | III | | 5 | | |
| UN2505 | AMMONIUM FLUORIDE | 6.1 | III | | 5 | | |
| UN2506 | AMMONIUM HYDROGEN SULFATE; or AMMONIUM HYDROGEN SULPHATE | 8 | II | | 1 | | |
| UN2507 | CHLOROPLATINIC ACID, SOLID | 8 | III | | 5 | | |
| UN2508 | MOLYBDENUM PENTACHLORIDE | 8 | III | | 5 | | |
| UN2509 | POTASSIUM HYDROGEN SULFATE; or POTASSIUM HYDROGEN SULPHATE | 8 | II | | 1 | | |
| UN2511 | 2-CHLOROPROPIONIC ACID, SOLUTION | 8 | III | | 5 | | |
| UN2511 | 2-CHLOROPROPIONIC ACID, SOLID | 8 | III | | 5 | | |
| UN2512 | AMINOPHENOLS (o-,m-,p-) | 6.1 | III | 43 | 5 | | |
| UN2513 | BROMOACETYL BROMIDE | 8 | II | | 1 | | |
| UN2514 | BROMOBENZENE | 3 | III | | 5 | | P |
| UN2515 | BROMOFORM | 6.1 | III | | 5 | | P |
| UN2516 | CARBON TETRABROMIDE | 6.1 | III | | 5 | | P |
| UN2517 | 1-CHLORO-1,1-DIFLUOROETHANE; or REFRIGERANT GAS R 142b | 2.1 | | | 0.125 | 3 000 | |
| UN2518 | 1,5,9-CYCLODODECATRIENE | 6.1 | III | | 5 | | PP |
| UN2520 | CYCLOOCTADIENES | 3 | III | | 5 | | |
| UN2521 | DIKETENE, STABILIZED | 6.1 (3) | I | | 0 | 1 000 | |
| UN2522 | 2-DIMETHYLAMINOETHYL METHACRYLATE | 6.1 | II | | 0.1 | | |
| UN2524 | ETHYL ORTHOFORMATE | 3 | III | | 5 | | |
| UN2525 | ETHYL OXALATE | 6.1 | III | | 5 | | |
| UN2526 | FURFURYLAMINE | 3 (8) | III | | 5 | | |
| UN2527 | ISOBUTYL ACRYLATE, STABILIZED | 3 | III | | 5 | | |
| UN2528 | ISOBUTYL ISOBUTYRATE | 3 | III | | 5 | | |
| UN2529 | ISOBUTYRIC ACID | 3 (8) | III | | 5 | | |
| UN2531 | METHACRYLIC ACID, STABILIZED | 8 | II | | 1 | | |

| 1<br>UN Number | 2<br>Shipping Name and Description | 3<br>Class | 4<br>Packing Group/Category | 5<br>Special Provisions | 6<br>Explosive Limit & Limited Quantity Index | 7<br>ERAP Index | 10<br>Marine Pollut. |
|---|---|---|---|---|---|---|---|
| UN2533 | METHYL TRICHLOROACETATE | 6.1 | III | | 5 | | |
| UN2534 | METHYLCHLOROSILANE | 2.3 (2.1) (8) | | | 0 | 25 | |
| UN2535 | 4-METHYLMORPHOLINE; or N-METHYLMORPHOLINE | 3 (8) | II | | 1 | 3 000 | |
| UN2536 | METHYLTETRAHYDROFURAN | 3 | II | | 1 | | |
| UN2538 | NITRONAPHTHALENE | 4.1 | III | | 5 | | |
| UN2541 | TERPINOLENE | 3 | III | | 5 | | |
| UN2542 | TRIBUTYLAMINE | 6.1 | II | | 0.1 | | |
| UN2545 | HAFNIUM POWDER, DRY | 4.2 | I<br>II<br>III | 38 | 0<br>0<br>0 | 1 000 | |
| UN2546 | TITANIUM POWDER, DRY | 4.2 | I<br>II<br>III | 38 | 0<br>0<br>0 | 1 000 | |
| UN2547 | SODIUM SUPEROXIDE | 5.1 | I | 38 | 0 | 1 000 | |
| UN2548 | CHLORINE PENTAFLUORIDE | 2.3 (5.1) (8) | | 38 | 0 | 25 | |
| UN2552 | HEXAFLUOROACETONE HYDRATE | 6.1 | II | | 0.1 | | |
| UN2554 | METHYLALLYL CHLORIDE | 3 | II | | 1 | | |
| UN2555 | NITROCELLULOSE WITH WATER, not less than 25 per cent water, by mass | 4.1 | II | 38 | 0 | | |
| UN2556 | NITROCELLULOSE WITH ALCOHOL, not less than 25 per cent alcohol, by mass, and not more than 12.6 per cent nitrogen, by dry mass | 4.1 | II | 38 | 0 | | |
| UN2557 | NITROCELLULOSE, MIXTURE, WITHOUT PIGMENT with not more than 12.6 per cent nitrogen, by dry mass; NITROCELLULOSE, MIXTURE, WITHOUT PLASTICIZER with not more than 12.6 per cent nitrogen, by dry mass; NITROCELLULOSE, MIXTURE, WITH PIGMENT with not more than 12.6 per cent nitrogen, by dry mass; or NITROCELLULOSE, MIXTURE, WITH PLASTICIZER with not more than 12.6 per cent nitrogen, by dry mass | 4.1 | II | 38, 70 | 0 | | • |
| UN2558 | EPIBROMOHYDRIN | 6.1 (3) | I | | 0 | 1 000 | P |
| UN2560 | 2-METHYLPENTAN-2-OL | 3 | III | | 5 | | |
| UN2561 | 3-METHYL-1-BUTENE | 3 | I | | 0 | | |
| UN2564 | TRICHLOROACETIC ACID SOLUTION | 8 | II<br>III | | 1<br>5 | | |
| UN2565 | DICYCLOHEXYLAMINE | 8 | III | | 5 | | |
| UN2567 | SODIUM PENTACHLOROPHENATE | 6.1 | II | | 0.5 | | PP |
| UN2570 | CADMIUM COMPOUND | 6.1 | I<br>II<br>III | 23, 51 | 0<br>0.5<br>5 | 1 000 | PP |
| UN2571 | ALKYLSULFURIC ACIDS; or ALKYLSULPHURIC ACIDS | 8 | II | 16 | 1 | | |
| UN2572 | PHENYLHYDRAZINE | 6.1 | II | | 0.1 | | |
| UN2573 | THALLIUM CHLORATE | 5.1 (6.1) | II | | 0.5 | 1 000 | P |
| UN2574 | TRICRESYL PHOSPHATE with more than 3 per cent ortho isomer | 6.1 | II | | 0.1 | | PP |
| UN2576 | PHOSPHORUS OXYBROMIDE, MOLTEN | 8 | II | | 1 | | |
| UN2577 | PHENYLACETYL CHLORIDE | 8 | II | | 1 | | |
| UN2578 | PHOSPHORUS TRIOXIDE | 8 | III | | 5 | | |
| UN2579 | PIPERAZINE | 8 | III | | 5 | | |
| UN2580 | ALUMINUM BROMIDE SOLUTION | 8 | III | | 5 | | |

| 1<br>UN Number | 2<br>Shipping Name and Description | 3<br>Class | 4<br>Packing Group/Category | 5<br>Special Provisions | 6<br>Explosive Limit & Limited Quantity Index | 7<br>ERAP Index | 10<br>Marine Pollut. |
|---|---|---|---|---|---|---|---|
| UN2581 | ALUMINUM CHLORIDE SOLUTION | 8 | III | | 5 | | |
| UN2582 | FERRIC CHLORIDE SOLUTION | 8 | III | | 5 | | |
| UN2583 | ALKYLSULFONIC ACIDS, SOLID with more than 5 per cent free sulfuric acid;<br>ALKYLSULPHONIC ACIDS, SOLID with more than 5 per cent free sulphuric acid;<br>ARYLSULFONIC ACIDS, SOLID with more than 5 per cent free sulfuric acid; or<br>ARYLSULPHONIC ACIDS, SOLID with more than 5 per cent free sulphuric acid | 8 | II | | 1 | | |
| UN2584 | ALKYLSULFONIC ACIDS, LIQUID with more than 5 per cent free sulfuric acid;<br>ALKYLSULPHONIC ACIDS, LIQUID with more than 5 per cent free sulphuric acid;<br>ARYLSULFONIC ACIDS, LIQUID with more than 5 per cent free sulfuric acid; or<br>ARYLSULPHONIC ACIDS, LIQUID with more than 5 per cent free sulphuric acid | 8 | II | | 1 | | |
| UN2585 | ALKYLSULFONIC ACIDS, SOLID with not more than 5 per cent free sulfuric acid;<br>ALKYLSULPHONIC ACIDS, SOLID with not more than 5 per cent free sulphuric acid;<br>ARYLSULFONIC ACIDS, SOLID with not more than 5 per cent free sulfuric acid; or<br>ARYLSULPHONIC ACIDS, SOLID with not more than 5 per cent free sulphuric acid | 8 | III | | 5 | | |
| UN2586 | ALKYLSULFONIC ACIDS, LIQUID with not more than 5 per cent free sulfuric acid;<br>ALKYLSULPHONIC ACIDS, LIQUID with not more than 5 per cent free sulphuric acid;<br>ARYLSULFONIC ACIDS, LIQUID with not more than 5 per cent free sulfuric acid; or<br>ARYLSULPHONIC ACIDS, LIQUID with not more than 5 per cent free sulphuric acid | 8 | III | | 5 | | |
| UN2587 | BENZOQUINONE | 6.1 | II | | 0.5 | | |
| UN2588 | PESTICIDE, SOLID, TOXIC, N.O.S. | 6.1 | I<br>II<br>III | 16<br>16<br>16 | 0<br>0.5<br>5 | 1 000 | • |
| UN2589 | VINYL CHLOROACETATE | 6.1<br>(3) | II | | 0.1 | 1 000 | |
| UN2590 | ASBESTOS, WHITE (chrysotile, actinolite, anthophyllite, tremolite) when not fixed in a natural or artificial binder material or included in a manufactured product | 9 | III | | 5 | | |
| UN2591 | XENON, REFRIGERATED LIQUID | 2.2 | | 38 | 0.125 | | |
| UN2599 | CHLOROTRIFLUOROMETHANE AND TRIFLUOROMETHANE AZEOTROPIC MIXTURE with approximately 60 per cent chlorotrifluoromethane; or<br>REFRIGERANT GAS R 503 | 2.2 | | | 0.125 | | |
| UN2600 | CARBON MONOXIDE AND HYDROGEN MIXTURE, COMPRESSED | 2.3<br>(2.1) | | | 0 | 500 | |
| UN2601 | CYCLOBUTANE | 2.1 | | | 0.125 | 3 000 | |
| UN2602 | DICHLORODIFLUOROMETHANE AND DIFLUOROETHANE AZEOTROPIC MIXTURE with approximately 74 per cent dichlorodifluoromethane; or<br>REFRIGERANT GAS R 500 | 2.2 | | | 0.125 | | |
| UN2603 | CYCLOHEPTATRIENE | 3<br>(6.1) | II | | 1 | | |
| UN2604 | BORON TRIFLUORIDE DIETHYL ETHERATE | 8<br>(3) | I | | 0 | 3 000 | |
| UN2605 | METHOXYMETHYL ISOCYANATE | 3<br>(6.1) | I | | 0 | 1 000 | |
| UN2606 | METHYL ORTHOSILICATE | 6.1<br>(3) | I | | 0 | 1 000 | |
| UN2607 | ACROLEIN DIMER, STABILIZED | 3 | III | | 5 | | |
| UN2608 | NITROPROPANES | 3 | III | | 5 | | |

| 1 UN Number | 2 Shipping Name and Description | 3 Class | 4 Packing Group/Category | 5 Special Provisions | 6 Explosive Limit & Limited Quantity Index | 7 ERAP Index | 10 Marine Pollut. |
|---|---|---|---|---|---|---|---|
| UN2609 | TRIALLYL BORATE | 6.1 | III | | 5 | | |
| UN2610 | TRIALLYLAMINE | 3 (8) | III | | 5 | | |
| UN2611 | PROPYLENE CHLOROHYDRIN | 6.1 (3) | II | | 0.1 | 1 000 | |
| UN2612 | METHYL PROPYL ETHER | 3 | II | | 1 | | |
| UN2614 | METHALLYL ALCOHOL | 3 | III | | 5 | | |
| UN2615 | ETHYL PROPYL ETHER | 3 | II | | 1 | | |
| UN2616 | TRIISOPROPYL BORATE | 3 | II III | | 1 5 | | |
| UN2617 | METHYLCYCLOHEXANOLS, flammable | 3 | III | | 5 | | |
| UN2618 | VINYLTOLUENES, STABILIZED | 3 | III | | 5 | | |
| UN2619 | BENZYLDIMETHYLAMINE | 8 (3) | II | | 0.5 | | |
| UN2620 | AMYL BUTYRATES | 3 | III | | 5 | | |
| UN2621 | ACETYL METHYL CARBINOL | 3 | III | | 5 | | |
| UN2622 | GLYCIDALDEHYDE | 3 (6.1) | II | | 1 | 1 000 | |
| UN2623 | FIRELIGHTERS, SOLID with flammable liquid | 4.1 | III | | 5 | | • |
| UN2624 | MAGNESIUM SILICIDE | 4.3 | II | | 0.5 | | |
| UN2626 | CHLORIC ACID, AQUEOUS SOLUTION with not more than 10 per cent chloric acid | 5.1 | II | 38, 68 | 1 | | |
| UN2627 | NITRITES, INORGANIC, N.O.S. | 5.1 | II | 38, 68, 71 | 1 | | • |
| UN2628 | POTASSIUM FLUOROACETATE | 6.1 | I | | 0 | 1 000 | |
| UN2629 | SODIUM FLUOROACETATE | 6.1 | I | | 0 | 1 000 | |
| UN2630 | SELENATES; or SELENITES | 6.1 | I | | 0 | 1 000 | • |
| UN2642 | FLUOROACETIC ACID | 6.1 | I | | 0 | 1 000 | |
| UN2643 | METHYL BROMOACETATE | 6.1 | II | | 0.1 | | |
| UN2644 | METHYL IODIDE | 6.1 | I | | 0 | 1 000 | |
| UN2645 | PHENACYL BROMIDE | 6.1 | II | | 0.5 | | |
| UN2646 | HEXACHLOROCYCLOPENTADIENE | 6.1 | I | | 0 | 1 000 | |
| UN2647 | MALONONITRILE | 6.1 | II | | 0.5 | | |
| UN2648 | 1,2-DIBROMOBUTAN-3-ONE | 6.1 | II | | 0.1 | | |
| UN2649 | 1,3-DICHLOROACETONE | 6.1 | II | | 0.5 | | |
| UN2650 | 1,1-DICHLORO-1-NITROETHANE | 6.1 | II | | 0.1 | | |
| UN2651 | 4,4'-DIAMINODIPHENYLMETHANE | 6.1 | III | | 5 | | P |
| UN2653 | BENZYL IODIDE | 6.1 | II | | 0.1 | | |
| UN2655 | POTASSIUM FLUOROSILICATE | 6.1 | III | | 5 | | |
| UN2656 | QUINOLINE | 6.1 | III | | 5 | | |
| UN2657 | SELENIUM DISULFIDE; or SELENIUM DISULPHIDE | 6.1 | II | | 0.5 | | |
| UN2659 | SODIUM CHLOROACETATE | 6.1 | III | | 5 | | |
| UN2660 | MONONITROTOLUIDINES; or NITROTOLUIDINES | 6.1 | III | | 5 | | |
| UN2661 | HEXACHLOROACETONE | 6.1 | III | | 5 | | |
| UN2662 | HYDROQUINONE | 6.1 | III | | 5 | | |
| UN2664 | DIBROMOMETHANE | 6.1 | III | | 5 | | |
| UN2667 | BUTYLTOLUENES | 6.1 | III | | 5 | | • |
| UN2668 | CHLOROACETONITRILE | 6.1 (3) | II | | 0.1 | 1 000 | |

| 1 | 2 | 3 | 4 | 5 | 6 | 7 | 10 |
|---|---|---|---|---|---|---|---|
| UN Number | Shipping Name and Description | Class | Packing Group/Category | Special Provisions | Explosive Limit & Limited Quantity Index | ERAP Index | Marine Pollut. |
| UN2669 | CHLOROCRESOLS, liquid; CHLOROCRESOLS, LIQUID (ICAO terminology); or CHLOROCRESOLS, SOLUTION (IMO terminology) | 6.1 | II | | 0.1 | | |
| UN2669 | CHLOROCRESOLS, solid; or CHLOROCRESOLS, SOLID (ICAO terminology) | 6.1 | II | | 0.5 | | |
| UN2670 | CYANURIC CHLORIDE | 8 | II | | 1 | | |
| UN2671 | AMINOPYRIDINES (o-,m-,p-) | 6.1 | II | | 0.5 | | |
| UN2672 | AMMONIA SOLUTION, relative density between 0.880 and 0.957 at 15 °C in water, with more than 10 per cent but not more than 35 per cent ammonia | 8 | III | | 5 | | |
| UN2673 | 2-AMINO-4-CHLOROPHENOL | 6.1 | II | | 0.5 | | |
| UN2674 | SODIUM FLUOROSILICATE | 6.1 | III | | 5 | | |
| UN2676 | STIBINE | 2.3 (2.1) | | 38 | 0 | 0 | |
| UN2677 | RUBIDIUM HYDROXIDE SOLUTION | 8 | II III | | 1 5 | | |
| UN2678 | RUBIDIUM HYDROXIDE | 8 | II | | 1 | | |
| UN2679 | LITHIUM HYDROXIDE SOLUTION | 8 | II III | | 1 5 | | |
| UN2680 | LITHIUM HYDROXIDE MONOHYDRATE | 8 | II | | 1 | | |
| UN2681 | CAESIUM HYDROXIDE SOLUTION | 8 | II III | | 1 5 | | |
| UN2682 | CAESIUM HYDROXIDE | 8 | II | | 1 | | |
| UN2683 | AMMONIUM SULFIDE SOLUTION; or AMMONIUM SULPHIDE SOLUTION | 8 (3) (6.1) | II | | 0.5 | 1 000 | |
| UN2684 | DIETHYLAMINOPROPYLAMINE | 3 (8) | III | | 5 | | |
| UN2685 | N,N-DIETHYLETHYLENEDIAMINE | 8 (3) | II | | 0.5 | | |
| UN2686 | 2-DIETHYLAMINOETHANOL | 8 (3) | II | | 0.5 | | |
| UN2687 | DICYCLOHEXYLAMMONIUM NITRITE | 4.1 | III | | 5 | | |
| UN2688 | 1-BROMO-3-CHLOROPROPANE | 6.1 | III | | 5 | | P |
| UN2689 | GLYCEROL alpha-MONOCHLOROHYDRIN | 6.1 | III | | 5 | | |
| UN2690 | N,n-BUTYLIMIDAZOLE | 6.1 | II | | 0.1 | | |
| UN2691 | PHOSPHORUS PENTABROMIDE | 8 | II | | 1 | | |
| UN2692 | BORON TRIBROMIDE | 8 | I | | 0 | 1 000 | |
| UN2693 | BISULFITES, AQUEOUS SOLUTION, N.O.S.; or BISULPHITES, AQUEOUS SOLUTION, N.O.S. | 8 | III | 16 | 5 | | • |
| UN2698 | TETRAHYDROPHTHALIC ANHYDRIDES with more than 0.05 per cent of maleic anhydride | 8 | III | | 5 | | |
| UN2699 | TRIFLUOROACETIC ACID | 8 | I | | 0 | 3 000 | |
| UN2705 | 1-PENTOL | 8 | II | | 1 | | |
| UN2707 | DIMETHYLDIOXANES | 3 | II III | | 1 5 | | |
| UN2709 | BUTYLBENZENES | 3 | III | | 5 | | |
| UN2710 | DIPROPYL KETONE | 3 | III | | 5 | | |
| UN2713 | ACRIDINE | 6.1 | III | | 5 | | |
| UN2714 | ZINC RESINATE | 4.1 | III | | 5 | | |
| UN2715 | ALUMINUM RESINATE | 4.1 | III | | 5 | | |
| UN2716 | 1,4-BUTYNEDIOL | 6.1 | III | | 5 | | |
| UN2717 | CAMPHOR, synthetic | 4.1 | III | | 5 | | |
| UN2719 | BARIUM BROMATE | 5.1 (6.1) | II | | 0.5 | 1 000 | |

| 1 UN Number | 2 Shipping Name and Description | 3 Class | 4 Packing Group/Category | 5 Special Provisions | 6 Explosive Limit & Limited Quantity Index | 7 ERAP Index | 10 Marine Pollut. |
|---|---|---|---|---|---|---|---|
| UN2720 | CHROMIUM NITRATE | 5.1 | III | | 5 | | |
| UN2721 | COPPER CHLORATE | 5.1 | II | | 1 | | |
| UN2722 | LITHIUM NITRATE | 5.1 | III | | 5 | | |
| UN2723 | MAGNESIUM CHLORATE | 5.1 | II | | 1 | | |
| UN2724 | MANGANESE NITRATE | 5.1 | III | | 5 | | |
| UN2725 | NICKEL NITRATE | 5.1 | III | | 5 | | |
| UN2726 | NICKEL NITRITE | 5.1 | III | | 5 | | |
| UN2727 | THALLIUM NITRATE | 6.1 (5.1) | II | | 0.5 | | P |
| UN2728 | ZIRCONIUM NITRATE | 5.1 | III | | 5 | | |
| UN2729 | HEXACHLOROBENZENE | 6.1 | III | | 5 | | |
| UN2730 | NITROANISOLES, LIQUID | 6.1 | III | | 5 | | |
| UN2730 | NITROANISOLES, SOLID | 6.1 | III | 43 | 5 | | |
| UN2732 | NITROBROMOBENZENES, LIQUID | 6.1 | III | | 5 | | |
| UN2732 | NITROBROMOBENZENES, SOLID | 6.1 | III | | 5 | | |
| UN2733 | AMINES, FLAMMABLE, CORROSIVE, N.O.S.; or POLYAMINES, FLAMMABLE, CORROSIVE, N.O.S. | 3 (8) | I<br>II<br>III | 16<br>16<br>16 | 0<br>1<br>5 | 1 000 | • |
| UN2734 | AMINES, LIQUID, CORROSIVE, FLAMMABLE, N.O.S.; or POLYAMINES, LIQUID, CORROSIVE, FLAMMABLE, N.O.S. | 8 (3) | I<br>II | 16<br>16 | 0<br>0.5 | 1 000 | • |
| UN2735 | AMINES, LIQUID, CORROSIVE, N.O.S.; or POLYAMINES, LIQUID, CORROSIVE, N.O.S. | 8 | I<br>II<br>III | 16<br>16<br>16 | 0<br>1<br>5 | 1 000 | • |
| UN2738 | N-BUTYLANILINE | 6.1 | II | | 0.1 | | |
| UN2739 | BUTYRIC ANHYDRIDE | 8 | III | | 5 | | |
| UN2740 | n-PROPYL CHLOROFORMATE | 6.1 (3) (8) | I | | 0 | 1 000 | |
| UN2741 | BARIUM HYPOCHLORITE with more than 22 per cent available chlorine | 5.1 (6.1) | II | 38 | 0.5 | 1 000 | |
| UN2742 | CHLOROFORMATES, TOXIC, CORROSIVE, FLAMMABLE, N.O.S. | 6.1 (3) (8) | II | | 0.1 | 1 000 | • |
| UN2743 | n-BUTYL CHLOROFORMATE | 6.1 (3) (8) | II | | 0.1 | 1 000 | |
| UN2744 | CYCLOBUTYL CHLOROFORMATE | 6.1 (3) (8) | II | | 0.1 | 1 000 | |
| UN2745 | CHLOROMETHYL CHLOROFORMATE | 6.1 (8) | II | | 0.1 | 1 000 | |
| UN2746 | PHENYL CHLOROFORMATE | 6.1 (8) | II | | 0.1 | 1 000 | |
| UN2747 | tert-BUTYLCYCLOHEXYL CHLOROFORMATE | 6.1 | III | | 5 | | |
| UN2748 | 2-ETHYLHEXYL CHLOROFORMATE | 6.1 (8) | II | | 0.1 | 3 000 | |
| UN2749 | TETRAMETHYLSILANE | 3 | I | | 0 | | |
| UN2750 | 1,3-DICHLOROPROPANOL-2 | 6.1 | II | | 0.1 | | |
| UN2751 | DIETHYLTHIOPHOSPHORYL CHLORIDE | 8 | II | | 1 | | |
| UN2752 | 1,2-EPOXY-3-ETHOXYPROPANE | 3 | III | | 5 | | |
| UN2753 | N-ETHYLBENZYLTOLUIDINES, LIQUID | 6.1 | III | | 5 | | |
| UN2753 | N-ETHYLBENZYLTOLUIDINES, SOLID | 6.1 | III | | 5 | | |
| UN2754 | N-ETHYLTOLUIDINES | 6.1 | II | | 0.1 | | |
| UN2757 | CARBAMATE PESTICIDE, SOLID, TOXIC | 6.1 | I<br>II<br>III | 16<br>16<br>16 | 0<br>0.5<br>5 | 1 000 | • |

| 1 UN Number | 2 Shipping Name and Description | 3 Class | 4 Packing Group/Category | 5 Special Provisions | 6 Explosive Limit & Limited Quantity Index | 7 ERAP Index | 10 Marine Pollut. |
|---|---|---|---|---|---|---|---|
| UN2758 | CARBAMATE PESTICIDE, LIQUID, FLAMMABLE, TOXIC, flash point less than 23 °C | 3 (6.1) | I | 16 | 0 | 1 000 | |
| | | | II | 16 | 1 | | • |
| UN2759 | ARSENICAL PESTICIDE, SOLID, TOXIC | 6.1 | I | 16 | 0 | 1 000 | |
| | | | II | 16 | 0.5 | | |
| | | | III | 16 | 5 | | • |
| UN2760 | ARSENICAL PESTICIDE, LIQUID, FLAMMABLE, TOXIC, flash point less than 23 °C | 3 (6.1) | I | 16 | 0 | 1 000 | |
| | | | II | 16 | 1 | | • |
| UN2761 | ORGANOCHLORINE PESTICIDE, SOLID, TOXIC | 6.1 | I | 16 | 0 | 1 000 | |
| | | | II | 16 | 0.5 | | |
| | | | III | 16 | 5 | | • |
| UN2762 | ORGANOCHLORINE PESTICIDE, LIQUID, FLAMMABLE, TOXIC, flash point less than 23 °C | 3 (6.1) | I | 16 | 0 | 1 000 | |
| | | | II | 16 | 1 | | • |
| UN2763 | TRIAZINE PESTICIDE, SOLID, TOXIC | 6.1 | I | 16 | 0 | 1 000 | |
| | | | II | 16 | 0.5 | | |
| | | | III | 16 | 5 | | • |
| UN2764 | TRIAZINE PESTICIDE, LIQUID, FLAMMABLE, TOXIC, flash point less than 23 °C | 3 (6.1) | I | 16 | 0 | 1 000 | |
| | | | II | 16 | 1 | | • |
| UN2771 | THIOCARBAMATE PESTICIDE, SOLID, TOXIC | 6.1 | I | 16 | 0 | 1 000 | |
| | | | II | 16 | 0.5 | | |
| | | | III | 16 | 5 | | |
| UN2772 | THIOCARBAMATE PESTICIDE, LIQUID, FLAMMABLE, TOXIC, flash point less than 23 °C | 3 (6.1) | I | 16 | 0 | 1 000 | |
| | | | II | 16 | 1 | | • |
| UN2775 | COPPER BASED PESTICIDE, SOLID, TOXIC | 6.1 | I | 16 | 0 | 1 000 | |
| | | | II | 16 | 0.5 | | |
| | | | III | 16 | 5 | | • |
| UN2776 | COPPER BASED PESTICIDE, LIQUID, FLAMMABLE, TOXIC, flash point less than 23 °C | 3 (6.1) | I | 16 | 0 | 1 000 | |
| | | | II | 16 | 1 | | • |
| UN2777 | MERCURY BASED PESTICIDE, SOLID, TOXIC | 6.1 | I | 16 | 0 | 1 000 | |
| | | | II | 16 | 0.5 | | PP |
| | | | III | 16 | 5 | | |
| UN2778 | MERCURY BASED PESTICIDE, LIQUID, FLAMMABLE, TOXIC, flash point less than 23 °C | 3 (6.1) | I | 16 | 0 | 1 000 | |
| | | | II | 16 | 1 | | PP |
| UN2779 | SUBSTITUTED NITROPHENOL PESTICIDE, SOLID, TOXIC | 6.1 | I | 16 | 0 | 1 000 | |
| | | | II | 16 | 0.5 | | |
| | | | III | 16 | 5 | | • |
| UN2780 | SUBSTITUTED NITROPHENOL PESTICIDE, LIQUID, FLAMMABLE, TOXIC, flash point less than 23 °C | 3 (6.1) | I | 16 | 0 | 1 000 | |
| | | | II | 16 | 1 | | • |
| UN2781 | BIPYRIDILIUM PESTICIDE, SOLID, TOXIC | 6.1 | I | 16, 23 | 0 | 1 000 | |
| | | | II | 16 | 0.5 | | |
| | | | III | 16 | 5 | | • |
| UN2782 | BIPYRIDILIUM PESTICIDE, LIQUID, FLAMMABLE, TOXIC, flash point less than 23 °C | 3 (6.1) | I | 16 | 0 | 1 000 | |
| | | | II | 16 | 1 | | • |
| UN2783 | ORGANOPHOSPHORUS PESTICIDE, SOLID, TOXIC | 6.1 | I | 16 | 0 | 1 000 | |
| | | | II | 16 | 0.5 | | |
| | | | III | 16 | 5 | | • |
| UN2784 | ORGANOPHOSPHORUS PESTICIDE, LIQUID, FLAMMABLE, TOXIC, flash point less than 23 °C | 3 (6.1) | I | 16, 23 | 0 | 1 000 | |
| | | | II | 16 | 1 | | • |
| UN2785 | 4-THIAPENTANAL | 6.1 | III | | 5 | | |
| UN2786 | ORGANOTIN PESTICIDE, SOLID, TOXIC | 6.1 | I | 16 | 0 | 1 000 | |
| | | | II | 16 | 0.5 | | |
| | | | III | 16 | 5 | | PP |
| UN2787 | ORGANOTIN PESTICIDE, LIQUID, FLAMMABLE, TOXIC, flash point less than 23 °C | 3 (6.1) | I | 16 | 0 | 1 000 | |
| | | | II | 16 | 1 | | PP |
| UN2788 | ORGANOTIN COMPOUND, LIQUID, N.O.S. | 6.1 | I | 16, 23 | 0 | 1 000 | |
| | | | II | 16 | 0.1 | | |
| | | | III | 16 | 5 | | PP |

Schedule 1

| 1<br>UN Number | 2<br>Shipping Name and Description | 3<br>Class | 4<br>Packing Group/Category | 5<br>Special Provisions | 6<br>Explosive Limit & Limited Quantity Index | 7<br>ERAP Index | 10<br>Marine Pollut. |
|---|---|---|---|---|---|---|---|
| UN2789 | ACETIC ACID, GLACIAL; or<br>ACETIC ACID SOLUTION, more than 80 per cent acid, by mass | 8<br>(3) | II | | 0.5 | 3 000 | |
| UN2790 | ACETIC ACID SOLUTION, not less than 50 per cent but not more than 80 per cent acid, by mass | 8 | III | | 1 | | |
| UN2790 | ACETIC ACID SOLUTION, more than 10 per cent and less than 50 per cent acid, by mass | 8 | II | | 5 | | |
| UN2793 | FERROUS METAL BORINGS, SHAVINGS, TURNINGS or CUTTINGS in a form liable to self-heating | 4.2 | III | | 0 | | |
| UN2794 | BATTERIES, WET, FILLED WITH ACID, electric storage | 8 | III | | 5 | | |
| UN2795 | BATTERIES, WET, FILLED WITH ALKALI, electric storage | 8 | III | | 5 | | |
| UN2796 | BATTERY FLUID, ACID;<br>SULFURIC ACID with not more than 51 per cent acid; or SULPHURIC ACID with not more than 51 per cent acid | 8 | II | | 1 | | |
| UN2797 | BATTERY FLUID, ALKALI | 8 | II | | 1 | | |
| UN2798 | PHENYLPHOSPHORUS DICHLORIDE | 8 | II | | 1 | | |
| UN2799 | PHENYLPHOSPHORUS THIODICHLORIDE | 8 | II | | 1 | | |
| UN2800 | BATTERIES, WET, NON-SPILLABLE, electric storage | 8 | III | 39 | 5 | | |
| UN2801 | DYE INTERMEDIATE, LIQUID, CORROSIVE, N.O.S.; or DYE, LIQUID, CORROSIVE, N.O.S. | 8 | I<br>II<br>III | 16<br>16<br>16 | 0<br>1<br>5 | 3 000 | • |
| UN2802 | COPPER CHLORIDE | 8 | III | | 5 | | PP |
| UN2803 | GALLIUM | 8 | III | | 5 | | |
| UN2805 | LITHIUM HYDRIDE, FUSED SOLID | 4.3 | II | | 0.5 | | |
| UN2806 | LITHIUM NITRIDE | 4.3 | I | 38 | 0 | 1 000 | |
| UN2807 | MAGNETIZED MATERIAL, regulated by aircraft only | 9 | III | 63,81 | 5 | | |
| UN2809 | MERCURY | 8 | III | | 5 | | |
| UN2810 | TOXIC LIQUID, ORGANIC, N.O.S. | 6.1 | I<br>II<br>III | 16, 23<br>16<br>16 | 0<br>0.1<br>5 | 1 000 | • |
| UN2811 | TOXIC SOLID, ORGANIC, N.O.S. | 6.1 | I<br>II<br>III | 16<br>16<br>16 | 0<br>0.5<br>5 | 1 000 | • |
| UN2812 | SODIUM ALUMINATE, SOLID, regulated by aircraft only | 8 | III | 63 | 5 | | |
| UN2813 | WATER-REACTIVE SOLID, N.O.S. | 4.3 | I<br>II<br>III | 16, 38<br>16<br>16 | 0<br>0.5<br>1 | 1 000 | • |
| UN2814 | INFECTIOUS SUBSTANCE, AFFECTING HUMANS | 6.2 | Category A | 84 | 0 | SP84 | |
| UN2815 | N-AMINOETHYLPIPERAZINE | 8 | III | | 5 | | |
| UN2817 | AMMONIUM HYDROGENDIFLUORIDE SOLUTION | 8<br>(6.1) | II<br>III | | 0.5<br>1 | 3 000 | |
| UN2818 | AMMONIUM POLYSULFIDE SOLUTION; or AMMONIUM POLYSULPHIDE SOLUTION | 8<br>(6.1) | II<br>III | | 0.5<br>1 | 3 000 | |
| UN2819 | AMYL ACID PHOSPHATE | 8 | III | | 5 | | |
| UN2820 | BUTYRIC ACID | 8 | III | | 5 | | |
| UN2821 | PHENOL SOLUTION | 6.1 | II<br>III | | 0.1<br>5 | | |
| UN2822 | 2-CHLOROPYRIDINE | 6.1 | II | | 0.1 | | |
| UN2823 | CROTONIC ACID, liquid; or CROTONIC ACID, LIQUID (ICAO terminology) | 8 | III | | 5 | | |
| UN2823 | CROTONIC ACID, solid; or CROTONIC ACID, SOLID (ICAO terminology) | 8 | III | | 5 | | |
| UN2826 | ETHYL CHLOROTHIOFORMATE | 8<br>(3) | II | | 0 | 1 000 | P |

| UN Number | Shipping Name and Description | Class | Packing Group/Category | Special Provisions | Explosive Limit & Limited Quantity Index | ERAP Index | Marine Pollut. |
|---|---|---|---|---|---|---|---|
| | 1 | 3 | 4 | 5 | 6 | 7 | 10 |
| | 2 | | | | | | |
| UN2829 | CAPROIC ACID | 8 | III | | 5 | | |
| UN2830 | LITHIUM FERROSILICON | 4.3 | II | | 0.5 | 3 000 | |
| UN2831 | 1,1,1-TRICHLOROETHANE | 6.1 | III | | 5 | | |
| UN2834 | PHOSPHOROUS ACID | 8 | III | | 5 | | |
| UN2835 | SODIUM ALUMINIUM HYDRIDE | 4.3 | II | | 0.5 | | |
| UN2837 | BISULFATES, AQUEOUS SOLUTION; or BISULPHATES, AQUEOUS SOLUTION | 8 | II III | | 1 5 | | • |
| UN2838 | VINYL BUTYRATE, STABILIZED | 3 | II | | 1 | | |
| UN2839 | ALDOL | 6.1 | II | | 0.1 | | |
| UN2840 | BUTYRALDOXIME | 3 | III | | 5 | | |
| UN2841 | DI-n-AMYLAMINE | 3 (6.1) | III | | 5 | | |
| UN2842 | NITROETHANE | 3 | III | | 5 | | |
| UN2844 | CALCIUM MANGANESE SILICON | 4.3 | III | | 1 | | |
| UN2845 | PYROPHORIC LIQUID, ORGANIC, N.O.S. | 4.2 | I | 16 | 0 | 1 000 | • |
| UN2846 | PYROPHORIC SOLID, ORGANIC, N.O.S. | 4.2 | I | 16, 38 | 0 | 1 000 | • |
| UN2849 | 3-CHLOROPROPANOL-1 | 6.1 | III | | 5 | | |
| UN2850 | PROPYLENE TETRAMER | 3 | III | | 5 | | |
| UN2851 | BORON TRIFLUORIDE DIHYDRATE | 8 | II | | 1 | | |
| UN2852 | DIPICRYL SULFIDE, WETTED with not less than 10 per cent water, by mass; or DIPICRYL SULPHIDE, WETTED with not less than 10 per cent water, by mass | 4.1 | I | 38 | 0 | 75 | |
| UN2853 | MAGNESIUM FLUOROSILICATE | 6.1 | III | | 5 | | |
| UN2854 | AMMONIUM FLUOROSILICATE | 6.1 | III | | 5 | | |
| UN2855 | ZINC FLUOROSILICATE | 6.1 | III | | 5 | | |
| UN2856 | FLUOROSILICATES, N.O.S. | 6.1 | III | | 5 | | • |
| UN2857 | REFRIGERATING MACHINES containing non-flammable, non-toxic, liquefied gas or ammonia solutions (UN2672) | 2.2 | | | 0.125 | | |
| UN2858 | ZIRCONIUM, DRY, coiled wire, finished metal sheets, strip (thinner than 254 microns but not thinner than 18 microns) | 4.1 | III | | 5 | | |
| UN2859 | AMMONIUM METAVANADATE | 6.1 | II | | 0.5 | | |
| UN2861 | AMMONIUM POLYVANADATE | 6.1 | II | | 0.5 | | |
| UN2862 | VANADIUM PENTOXIDE, non-fused form | 6.1 | III | | 5 | | |
| UN2863 | SODIUM AMMONIUM VANADATE | 6.1 | II | | 0.5 | | |
| UN2864 | POTASSIUM METAVANADATE | 6.1 | II | | 0.5 | | |
| UN2865 | HYDROXYLAMINE SULFATE; or HYDROXYLAMINE SULPHATE | 8 | III | | 5 | | |
| UN2869 | TITANIUM TRICHLORIDE MIXTURE | 8 | II III | | 1 5 | | |
| UN2870 | ALUMINUM BOROHYDRIDE; or ALUMINUM BOROHYDRIDE IN DEVICES | 4.2 (4.3) | I | 38 | 0 | 1 000 | |
| UN2871 | ANTIMONY POWDER | 6.1 | III | | 5 | | |
| UN2872 | DIBROMOCHLOROPROPANES | 6.1 | II III | | 0.1 5 | 1 000 | |
| UN2873 | DIBUTYLAMINOETHANOL | 6.1 | III | | 5 | | |
| UN2874 | FURFURYL ALCOHOL | 6.1 | III | | 5 | | |
| UN2875 | HEXACHLOROPHENE | 6.1 | III | | 5 | | |
| UN2876 | RESORCINOL | 6.1 | III | | 5 | | |
| UN2878 | TITANIUM SPONGE GRANULES; or TITANIUM SPONGE POWDERS | 4.1 | III | | 5 | | |
| UN2879 | SELENIUM OXYCHLORIDE | 8 (6.1) | I | | 0 | 1 000 | |

| 1 | 2 | 3 | 4 | 5 | 6 | 7 | 10 |
|---|---|---|---|---|---|---|---|
| UN Number | Shipping Name and Description | Class | Packing Group/Category | Special Provisions | Explosive Limit & Limited Quantity Index | ERAP Index | Marine Pollut. |
| UN2880 | CALCIUM HYPOCHLORITE, HYDRATED MIXTURE with not less than 5.5 per cent but not more than 10 per cent water; or CALCIUM HYPOCHLORITE, HYDRATED with not less than 5.5 per cent but not more than 10 per cent water | 5.1 | II | | 1 | | |
| UN2881 | METAL CATALYST, DRY | 4.2 | I | 38 | 0 | 1 000 | |
| | | | II | | 0 | | |
| | | | III | | 0 | | |
| UN2900 | INFECTIOUS SUBSTANCE, AFFECTING ANIMALS only | 6.2 | Category A | 84 | 0 | SP84 | |
| UN2901 | BROMINE CHLORIDE | 2.3 (5.1) (8) | | 38 | 0 | 25 | |
| UN2902 | PESTICIDE, LIQUID, TOXIC, N.O.S. | 6.1 | I | 16, 23 | 0 | 1 000 | |
| | | | II | 16 | 0.1 | | • |
| | | | III | 16 | 5 | | • |
| UN2903 | PESTICIDE, LIQUID, TOXIC, FLAMMABLE, N.O.S., flash point not less than 23 °C | 6.1 (3) | I | 16, 23 | 0 | 1 000 | |
| | | | II | 16 | 0.1 | | • |
| | | | III | 16 | 1 | | • |
| UN2904 | CHLOROPHENOLATES, LIQUID; or PHENOLATES, LIQUID | 8 | III | | 5 | | • |
| UN2905 | CHLOROPHENOLATES, SOLID; or PHENOLATES, SOLID | 8 | III | | 5 | | • |
| UN2907 | ISOSORBIDE DINITRATE MIXTURE with not less than 60 per cent lactose, mannose, starch or calcium hydrogen phosphate | 4.1 | II | 38 | 0 | 75 | |
| UN2908 | RADIOACTIVE MATERIAL, EXCEPTED PACKAGE - EMPTY PACKAGING | 7 | | 72 | 0 | | |
| UN2909 | RADIOACTIVE MATERIAL, EXCEPTED PACKAGE - ARTICLES MANUFACTURED FROM DEPLETED URANIUM; RADIOACTIVE MATERIAL, EXCEPTED PACKAGE - ARTICLES MANUFACTURED FROM NATURAL THORIUM; or RADIOACTIVE MATERIAL, EXCEPTED PACKAGE - ARTICLES MANUFACTURED FROM NATURAL URANIUM | 7 | | 72 | 0 | | |
| UN2910 | RADIOACTIVE MATERIAL, EXCEPTED PACKAGE - LIMITED QUANTITY OF MATERIAL | 7 | | 72 | 0 | | |
| UN2911 | RADIOACTIVE MATERIAL, EXCEPTED PACKAGE - ARTICLES; or RADIOACTIVE MATERIAL, EXCEPTED PACKAGE - INSTRUMENTS | 7 | | 72 | 0 | | |
| UN2912 | RADIOACTIVE MATERIAL, LOW SPECIFIC ACTIVITY (LSA-I) non-fissile or fissile excepted | 7 | | 74 | 0 | 100 | |
| UN2913 | RADIOACTIVE MATERIAL, SURFACE CONTAMINATED OBJECTS (SCO-I), non-fissile or fissile excepted; or RADIOACTIVE MATERIAL, SURFACE CONTAMINATED OBJECTS (SCO-II), non-fissile or fissile excepted | 7 | | 74 | 0 | | |
| UN2915 | RADIOACTIVE MATERIAL, TYPE A PACKAGE, non-special form, non-fissile or fissile excepted | 7 | | 74 | 0 | | |
| UN2916 | RADIOACTIVE MATERIAL, TYPE B(U) PACKAGE, non-fissile or fissile excepted | 7 | | 74 | 0 | | |
| UN2917 | RADIOACTIVE MATERIAL, TYPE B(M) PACKAGE, non-fissile or fissile excepted | 7 | | 74 | 0 | | |
| UN2919 | RADIOACTIVE MATERIAL, TRANSPORTED UNDER SPECIAL ARRANGEMENT, non-fissile or fissile excepted | 7 | | 74 | 0 | | |
| UN2920 | CORROSIVE LIQUID, FLAMMABLE, N.O.S. | 8 (3) | I | 16 | 0 | 3 000 | |
| | | | II | 16 | 0.5 | | • |
| UN2921 | CORROSIVE SOLID, FLAMMABLE, N.O.S. | 8 (4.1) | I | 16 | 0 | 3 000 | |
| | | | II | 16 | 1 | | • |
| UN2922 | CORROSIVE LIQUID, TOXIC, N.O.S. | 8 (6.1) | I | 16 | 0 | 3 000 | |
| | | | II | 16 | 0.5 | | |
| | | | III | 16 | 1 | | • |
| UN2923 | CORROSIVE SOLID, TOXIC, N.O.S. | 8 (6.1) | I | 16 | 0 | 3 000 | |
| | | | II | 16 | 1 | | |
| | | | III | 16 | 2 | | • |

| 1 UN Number | 2 Shipping Name and Description | 3 Class | 4 Packing Group/Category | 5 Special Provisions | 6 Explosive Limit & Limited Quantity Index | 7 ERAP Index | 10 Marine Pollut. |
|---|---|---|---|---|---|---|---|
| UN2924 | FLAMMABLE LIQUID, CORROSIVE, N.O.S. | 3 (8) | I / II / III | 16 / 16 / 16 | 0 / 1 / 5 | 1 000 | · |
| UN2925 | FLAMMABLE SOLID, CORROSIVE, ORGANIC, N.O.S. | 4.1 (8) | II / III | 16 / 16 | 0.5 / 3 | 1 000 | · |
| UN2926 | FLAMMABLE SOLID, TOXIC, ORGANIC, N.O.S. | 4.1 (6.1) | II / III | 16 / 16 | 0.5 / 3 | 1 000 | · |
| UN2927 | TOXIC LIQUID, CORROSIVE, ORGANIC, N.O.S. | 6.1 (8) | I / II | 16, 23 / 16 | 0 / 0.1 | 1 000 | · |
| UN2928 | TOXIC SOLID, CORROSIVE, ORGANIC, N.O.S. | 6.1 (8) | I / II | 16 / 16 | 0 / 0.5 | 1 000 | · |
| UN2929 | TOXIC LIQUID, FLAMMABLE, ORGANIC, N.O.S. | 6.1 (3) | I / II | 16, 23 / 16 | 0 / 0.1 | 1 000 | · |
| UN2930 | TOXIC SOLID, FLAMMABLE, ORGANIC, N.O.S. | 6.1 (4.1) | I / II | 16 / 16 | 0 / 0.5 | 1 000 | · |
| UN2931 | VANADYL SULFATE; or VANADYL SULPHATE | 6.1 | II | | 0.5 | | |
| UN2933 | METHYL 2-CHLOROPROPIONATE | 3 | III | | 5 | | |
| UN2934 | ISOPROPYL 2-CHLOROPROPIONATE | 3 | III | | 5 | | |
| UN2935 | ETHYL 2-CHLOROPROPIONATE | 3 | III | | 5 | | |
| UN2936 | THIOLACTIC ACID | 6.1 | II | | 0.5 | | |
| UN2937 | alpha-METHYLBENZYL ALCOHOL | 6.1 | III | | 5 | | |
| UN2940 | CYCLOOCTADIENE PHOSPHINES; or 9-PHOSPHABICYCLONONANES | 4.2 | II | | 0 | | |
| UN2941 | FLUOROANILINES | 6.1 | III | | 5 | | |
| UN2942 | 2-TRIFLUOROMETHYLANILINE | 6.1 | III | | 5 | | |
| UN2943 | TETRAHYDROFURFURYLAMINE | 3 | III | | 5 | | |
| UN2945 | N-METHYLBUTYLAMINE | 3 (8) | II | | 1 | | |
| UN2946 | 2-AMINO-5-DIETHYLAMINOPENTANE | 6.1 | III | | 5 | | |
| UN2947 | ISOPROPYL CHLOROACETATE | 3 | III | | 5 | | |
| UN2948 | 3-TRIFLUOROMETHYLANILINE | 6.1 | II | | 0.1 | | |
| UN2949 | SODIUM HYDROSULFIDE with not less than 25 per cent water of crystallization; or SODIUM HYDROSULPHIDE with not less than 25 per cent water of crystallization | 8 | II | | 1 | | |
| UN2950 | MAGNESIUM GRANULES, COATED, particle size not less than 149 microns | 4.3 | III | | 1 | | |
| UN2956 | 5-tert-BUTYL-2,4,6-TRINITRO-m-XYLENE; or MUSK XYLENE | 4.1 | III | 38 | 3 | 75 | P |
| UN2965 | BORON TRIFLUORIDE DIMETHYL ETHERATE | 4.3 (3) (8) | I | | 0 | 1 000 | |
| UN2966 | THIOGLYCOL | 6.1 | II | | 0.1 | | |
| UN2967 | SULFAMIC ACID; or SULPHAMIC ACID | 8 | III | | 5 | | |
| UN2968 | MANEB PREPARATION, STABILIZED against self-heating; or MANEB, STABILIZED against self-heating | 4.3 | III | | 1 | | P |
| UN2969 | CASTOR BEANS; CASTOR FLAKE; CASTOR MEAL; or CASTOR POMACE | 9 | II | 81 | 5 | | |
| UN2977 | RADIOACTIVE MATERIAL, URANIUM HEXAFLUORIDE, FISSILE | 7 (8) | | | 0 | 25 | |
| UN2978 | RADIOACTIVE MATERIAL, URANIUM HEXAFLUORIDE, non-fissile or fissile excepted | 7 (8) | | | 0 | 25 | |

| 1 | 2 | 3 | 4 | 5 | 6 | 7 | 10 |
|---|---|---|---|---|---|---|---|
| UN Number | Shipping Name and Description | Class | Packing Group/Category | Special Provisions | Explosive Limit & Limited Quantity Index | ERAP Index | Marine Pollut. |
| UN2983 | ETHYLENE OXIDE AND PROPYLENE OXIDE MIXTURE, not more than 30 per cent ethylene oxide | 3 (6.1) | I | | 0 | 1 000 | |
| UN2984 | HYDROGEN PEROXIDE, AQUEOUS SOLUTION with not less than 8 per cent but less than 20 per cent hydrogen peroxide (stabilized as necessary) | 5.1 | III | | 5 | | |
| UN2985 | CHLOROSILANES, FLAMMABLE, CORROSIVE, N.O.S. | 3 (8) | II | | 0 | | • |
| UN2986 | CHLOROSILANES, CORROSIVE, FLAMMABLE, N.O.S. | 8 (3) | II | | 0 | | • |
| UN2987 | CHLOROSILANES, CORROSIVE, N.O.S. | 8 | II | | 1 | | • |
| UN2988 | CHLOROSILANES, WATER-REACTIVE, FLAMMABLE, CORROSIVE, N.O.S. | 4.3 (3) (8) | I | 38 | 0 | 1 000 | • |
| UN2989 | LEAD PHOSPHITE, DIBASIC | 4.1 | II III | | 1 5 | | |
| UN2990 | LIFE-SAVING APPLIANCES, SELF-INFLATING | 9 | | 21,81 | 0 | | |
| UN2991 | CARBAMATE PESTICIDE, LIQUID, TOXIC, FLAMMABLE, flash point not less than 23 °C | 6.1 (3) | I II III | 16, 23 16 16 | 0 0.1 1 | 1 000 | • |
| UN2992 | CARBAMATE PESTICIDE, LIQUID, TOXIC | 6.1 | I II III | 16, 23 16 16 | 0 0.1 5 | 1 000 | • |
| UN2993 | ARSENICAL PESTICIDE, LIQUID, TOXIC, FLAMMABLE, flash point not less than 23 °C | 6.1 (3) | I II III | 16, 23 16 16 | 0 0.1 1 | 1 000 | • |
| UN2994 | ARSENICAL PESTICIDE, LIQUID, TOXIC | 6.1 | I II III | 16, 23 16 16 | 0 0.1 5 | 1 000 | • |
| UN2995 | ORGANOCHLORINE PESTICIDE, LIQUID, TOXIC, FLAMMABLE, flash point not less than 23 °C | 6.1 (3) | I II III | 16, 23 16 16 | 0 0.1 1 | 1 000 | • |
| UN2996 | ORGANOCHLORINE PESTICIDE, LIQUID, TOXIC | 6.1 | I II III | 16, 23 16 16 | 0 0.1 5 | 1 000 | • |
| UN2997 | TRIAZINE PESTICIDE, LIQUID, TOXIC, FLAMMABLE, flash point not less than 23 °C | 6.1 (3) | I II III | 16, 23 16 16 | 0 0.1 1 | 1 000 | • |
| UN2998 | TRIAZINE PESTICIDE, LIQUID, TOXIC | 6.1 | I II III | 16, 23 16 16 | 0 0.1 5 | 1 000 | • |
| UN3005 | THIOCARBAMATE PESTICIDE, LIQUID, TOXIC, FLAMMABLE, flash point not less than 23 °C | 6.1 (3) | I II III | 16, 23 16 16 | 0 0.1 1 | 1 000 | • |
| UN3006 | THIOCARBAMATE PESTICIDE, LIQUID, TOXIC | 6.1 | I II III | 16, 23 16 16 | 0 0.1 5 | 1 000 | • |
| UN3009 | COPPER BASED PESTICIDE, LIQUID, TOXIC, FLAMMABLE, flash point not less than 23 °C | 6.1 (3) | I II III | 16, 23 16 16 | 0 0.1 1 | 1 000 | • |
| UN3010 | COPPER BASED PESTICIDE, LIQUID, TOXIC | 6.1 | I II III | 16, 23 16 16 | 0 0.1 5 | 1 000 | |
| UN3011 | MERCURY BASED PESTICIDE, LIQUID, TOXIC, FLAMMABLE, flash point not less than 23 °C | 6.1 (3) | I II III | 16, 23 16 16 | 0 0.1 1 | 1 000 | PP |
| UN3012 | MERCURY BASED PESTICIDE, LIQUID, TOXIC | 6.1 | I II III | 16, 23 16 16 | 0 0.1 5 | 1 000 | PP |

| 1 | 2 | 3 | 4 | 5 | 6 | 7 | 10 |
|---|---|---|---|---|---|---|---|
| UN Number | Shipping Name and Description | Class | Packing Group/Category | Special Provisions | Explosive Limit & Limited Quantity Index | ERAP Index | Marine Pollut. |
| UN3013 | SUBSTITUTED NITROPHENOL PESTICIDE, LIQUID, TOXIC, FLAMMABLE, flash point not less than 23 °C | 6.1 (3) | I | 16, 23 | 0 | 1 000 | • |
| | | | II | 16 | 0.1 | | |
| | | | III | 16 | 1 | | |
| UN3014 | SUBSTITUTED NITROPHENOL PESTICIDE, LIQUID, TOXIC | 6.1 | I | 16, 23 | 0 | 1 000 | • |
| | | | II | 16 | 0.1 | | |
| | | | III | 16 | 5 | | |
| UN3015 | BIPYRIDILIUM PESTICIDE, LIQUID, TOXIC, FLAMMABLE, flash point not less than 23 °C | 6.1 (3) | I | 16, 23 | 0 | 1 000 | • |
| | | | II | 16 | 0.1 | | |
| | | | III | 16 | 1 | | |
| UN3016 | BIPYRIDILIUM PESTICIDE, LIQUID, TOXIC | 6.1 | I | 16, 23 | 0 | 1 000 | • |
| | | | II | 16 | 0.1 | | |
| | | | III | 16 | 5 | | |
| UN3017 | ORGANOPHOSPHORUS PESTICIDE, LIQUID, TOXIC, FLAMMABLE, flash point not less than 23 °C | 6.1 (3) | I | 16, 23 | 0 | 1 000 | • |
| | | | II | 16 | 0.1 | | |
| | | | III | 16 | 1 | | |
| UN3018 | ORGANOPHOSPHORUS PESTICIDE, LIQUID, TOXIC | 6.1 | I | 16, 23 | 0 | 1 000 | • |
| | | | II | 16 | 0.1 | | |
| | | | III | 16 | 5 | | |
| UN3019 | ORGANOTIN PESTICIDE, LIQUID, TOXIC, FLAMMABLE, flash point not less than 23 °C | 6.1 (3) | I | 16, 23 | 0 | 1 000 | PP |
| | | | II | 16 | 0.1 | | |
| | | | III | 16 | 1 | | |
| UN3020 | ORGANOTIN PESTICIDE, LIQUID, TOXIC | 6.1 | I | 16, 23 | 0 | 1 000 | PP |
| | | | II | 16 | 0.1 | | |
| | | | III | 16 | 5 | | |
| UN3021 | PESTICIDE, LIQUID, FLAMMABLE, TOXIC, N.O.S., flash point less than 23 °C | 3 (6.1) | I | 16 | 0 | 1 000 | • |
| | | | II | 16 | 1 | | |
| UN3022 | 1,2-BUTYLENE OXIDE, STABILIZED | 3 | II | | 1 | | |
| UN3023 | 2-METHYL-2-HEPTANETHIOL | 6.1 (3) | I | | 0 | 1 000 | |
| UN3024 | COUMARIN DERIVATIVE PESTICIDE, LIQUID, FLAMMABLE, TOXIC, flash point less than 23 °C | 3 (6.1) | I | 16 | 0 | 1 000 | • |
| | | | II | 16 | 1 | | |
| UN3025 | COUMARIN DERIVATIVE PESTICIDE, LIQUID, TOXIC, FLAMMABLE, flash point not less than 23 °C | 6.1 (3) | I | 16, 23 | 0 | 1 000 | • |
| | | | II | 16 | 0.1 | | |
| | | | III | 16 | 1 | | |
| UN3026 | COUMARIN DERIVATIVE PESTICIDE, LIQUID, TOXIC | 6.1 | I | 16, 23 | 0 | 1 000 | • |
| | | | II | 16 | 0.1 | | |
| | | | III | 16 | 5 | | |
| UN3027 | COUMARIN DERIVATIVE PESTICIDE, SOLID, TOXIC | 6.1 | I | 16 | 0 | 1 000 | • |
| | | | II | 16 | 0.5 | | |
| | | | III | 16 | 5 | | |
| UN3028 | BATTERIES, DRY, CONTAINING POTASSIUM HYDROXIDE SOLID, electric storage | 8 | III | | 5 | | |
| UN3048 | ALUMINUM PHOSPHIDE PESTICIDE | 6.1 | I | 38 | 0 | 1 000 | |
| UN3049 | METAL ALKYL HALIDES, WATER-REACTIVE, N.O.S.; or METAL ARYL HALIDES, WATER-REACTIVE, N.O.S. | 4.2 (4.3) | I | 16 | 0 | 1 000 | • |
| UN3050 | METAL ALKYL HYDRIDES, WATER-REACTIVE, N.O.S.; or METAL ARYL HYDRIDES, WATER-REACTIVE, N.O.S. | 4.2 (4.3) | I | 16 | 0 | 1 000 | • |
| UN3051 | ALUMINUM ALKYLS | 4.2 (4.3) | I | | 0 | 1 000 | |
| UN3052 | ALUMINUM ALKYL HALIDES, LIQUID | 4.2 (4.3) | I | | 0 | 1 000 | |
| UN3052 | ALUMINUM ALKYL HALIDES, SOLID | 4.2 (4.3) | I | | 0 | 1 000 | |
| UN3053 | MAGNESIUM ALKYLS | 4.2 (4.3) | I | | 0 | 1 000 | |
| UN3054 | CYCLOHEXYL MERCAPTAN | 3 | III | | 5 | | |
| UN3055 | 2-(2-AMINOETHOXY)ETHANOL | 8 | III | | 5 | | |
| UN3056 | n-HEPTALDEHYDE | 3 | III | | 5 | | |

Schedule 1

| UN Number | Shipping Name and Description | Class | Packing Group/Category | Special Provisions | Explosive Limit & Limited Quantity Index | ERAP Index | Marine Pollut. |
|---|---|---|---|---|---|---|---|
| UN3057 | TRIFLUOROACETYL CHLORIDE | 2.3 (8) | | | 0 | 25 | |
| UN3064 | NITROGLYCERIN, SOLUTION IN ALCOHOL with more than 1 per cent but not more than 5 per cent nitroglycerin | 3 | II | 38 | 0 | | |
| UN3065 | ALCOHOLIC BEVERAGES, more than 70 per cent alcohol, by volume | 3 | II | | 5 | | |
| UN3065 | ALCOHOLIC BEVERAGES, more than 24 per cent but not more than 70 per cent alcohol, by volume | 3 | III | | 5 | | |
| UN3066 | PAINT (including paint, lacquer, enamel, stain, shellac, varnish, polish, liquid filler and liquid lacquer base) with not more than 20 per cent nitrocellulose by mass if the nitrogen content of the nitrocellulose is not more than 12.6 per cent by mass; or PAINT RELATED MATERIAL (including paint thinning or reducing compound) with not more than 20 per cent nitrocellulose by mass if the nitrogen content of the nitrocellulose is not more than 12.6 per cent by mass | 8 | II<br>III | 59<br>59 | 1<br>5 | | • |
| UN3070 | ETHYLENE OXIDE AND DICHLORODIFLUOROMETHANE MIXTURE with not more than 12.5 per cent ethylene oxide | 2.2 | | | 0.125 | | |
| UN3071 | MERCAPTAN MIXTURE, LIQUID, TOXIC, FLAMMABLE, N.O.S.; or MERCAPTANS, LIQUID, TOXIC, FLAMMABLE, N.O.S. | 6.1 (3) | II | 16 | 0.1 | 1 000 | • |
| UN3072 | LIFE-SAVING APPLIANCES NOT SELF-INFLATING, containing dangerous goods as equipment | 9 | | 21,81 | 0 | | |
| UN3073 | VINYLPYRIDINES, STABILIZED | 6.1 (3) (8) | II | | 0.1 | 1 000 | |
| UN3076 | ALUMINUM ALKYL HYDRIDES | 4.2 (4.3) | I | | 0 | 1 000 | |
| UN3077 | ENVIRONMENTALLY HAZARDOUS SUBSTANCE, SOLID, N.O.S. | 9 | III | 16 | 5 | | • |
| UN3078 | CERIUM, turnings or gritty powder | 4.3 | II | | 0.5 | | |
| UN3079 | METHACRYLONITRILE, STABILIZED | 3 (6.1) | I | | 0 | 1 000 | |
| UN3080 | ISOCYANATE SOLUTION, TOXIC, FLAMMABLE, N.O.S.; or ISOCYANATES, TOXIC, FLAMMABLE, N.O.S. | 6.1 (3) | II | 16, 23 | 0.1 | 1 000 | • |
| UN3082 | ENVIRONMENTALLY HAZARDOUS SUBSTANCE, LIQUID, N.O.S. | 9 | III | 16 | 5 | | • |
| UN3083 | PERCHLORYL FLUORIDE | 2.3 (5.1) | | 38 | 0 | 25 | |
| UN3084 | CORROSIVE SOLID, OXIDIZING, N.O.S. | 8 (5.1) | I<br>II | 16<br>16 | 0<br>1 | | • |
| UN3085 | OXIDIZING SOLID, CORROSIVE, N.O.S. | 5.1 (8) | I<br>II<br>III | 16<br>16<br>16 | 0<br>0.5<br>1 | 1 000 | |
| UN3086 | TOXIC SOLID, OXIDIZING, N.O.S. | 6.1 (5.1) | I<br>II | 16<br>16 | 0<br>0.5 | 1 000 | |
| UN3087 | OXIDIZING SOLID, TOXIC, N.O.S. | 5.1 (6.1) | I<br>II<br>III | 16<br>16<br>16 | 0<br>0.5<br>1 | 1 000 | |
| UN3088 | SELF-HEATING SOLID, ORGANIC, N.O.S. | 4.2 | II<br>III | 16<br>16 | 0<br>0 | | • |
| UN3089 | METAL POWDER, FLAMMABLE, N.O.S. | 4.1 | II<br>III | | 1<br>5 | | • |
| UN3090 | LITHIUM BATTERIES | 9 | II | 34 | 0 | | |
| UN3091 | LITHIUM BATTERIES CONTAINED IN EQUIPMENT; or LITHIUM BATTERIES PACKED WITH EQUIPMENT | 9 | II | 34 | 0 | | |
| UN3092 | 1-METHOXY-2-PROPANOL | 3 | III | | 5 | | |
| UN3093 | CORROSIVE LIQUID, OXIDIZING, N.O.S. | 8 (5.1) | I<br>II | 16<br>16 | 0<br>0.5 | 3 000 | |
| UN3094 | CORROSIVE LIQUID, WATER-REACTIVE, N.O.S. | 8 (4.3) | I<br>II | 16, 38<br>16 | 0<br>0.5 | 3 000 | |
| UN3095 | CORROSIVE SOLID, SELF-HEATING, N.O.S. | 8 (4.2) | I<br>II | 16, 38<br>16 | 0<br>1 | | • |

Schedule 1

| 1 | 2 | 3 | 4 | 5 | 6 | 7 | 10 |
|---|---|---|---|---|---|---|---|
| UN Number | Shipping Name and Description | Class | Packing Group/Category | Special Provisions | Explosive Limit & Limited Quantity Index | ERAP Index | Marine Pollut. |
| UN3096 | CORROSIVE SOLID, WATER-REACTIVE, N.O.S. | 8 (4.3) | I | 16, 38 | 0 | | • |
| | | | II | 16 | 1 | | |
| UN3097 | FLAMMABLE SOLID, OXIDIZING, N.O.S. | F | | | | | |
| UN3098 | OXIDIZING LIQUID, CORROSIVE, N.O.S. | 5.1 (8) | I | 16 | 0 | 1 000 | |
| | | | II | 16 | 0.5 | | • |
| | | | III | 16 | 1 | | |
| UN3099 | OXIDIZING LIQUID, TOXIC, N.O.S. | 5.1 (6.1) | I | 16 | 0 | 1 000 | |
| | | | II | 16 | 0.5 | | • |
| | | | III | 16 | 1 | | |
| UN3100 | OXIDIZING SOLID, SELF-HEATING, N.O.S. | F | | | | | |
| UN3101 | ORGANIC PEROXIDE TYPE B, LIQUID | 5.2 (1) | II | 16, 38 | 0.025 | 75 | |
| UN3102 | ORGANIC PEROXIDE TYPE B, SOLID | 5.2 (1) | II | 16, 38 | 0.1 | 75 | |
| UN3103 | ORGANIC PEROXIDE TYPE C, LIQUID | 5.2 | II | 16, 38 | 0.025 | | |
| UN3104 | ORGANIC PEROXIDE TYPE C, SOLID | 5.2 | II | 16, 38 | 0.1 | | |
| UN3105 | ORGANIC PEROXIDE TYPE D, LIQUID | 5.2 | II | 16, 38 | 0.125 | | |
| UN3106 | ORGANIC PEROXIDE TYPE D, SOLID | 5.2 | II | 16, 38 | 0.5 | | |
| UN3107 | ORGANIC PEROXIDE TYPE E, LIQUID | 5.2 | II | 16, 38 | 0.125 | | |
| UN3108 | ORGANIC PEROXIDE TYPE E, SOLID | 5.2 | II | 16, 38 | 0.5 | | |
| UN3109 | ORGANIC PEROXIDE TYPE F, LIQUID | 5.2 | II | 16 | 0.125 | | |
| UN3110 | ORGANIC PEROXIDE TYPE F, SOLID | 5.2 | II | 16 | 0.5 | | |
| UN3111 | ORGANIC PEROXIDE TYPE B, LIQUID, TEMPERATURE CONTROLLED | 5.2 (1) | II | 16, 28 | 0 | 75 | |
| UN3112 | ORGANIC PEROXIDE TYPE B, SOLID, TEMPERATURE CONTROLLED | 5.2 (1) | II | 16, 28 | 0 | 75 | • |
| UN3113 | ORGANIC PEROXIDE TYPE C, LIQUID, TEMPERATURE CONTROLLED | 5.2 | II | 16, 28 | 0 | 75 | |
| UN3114 | ORGANIC PEROXIDE TYPE C, SOLID, TEMPERATURE CONTROLLED | 5.2 | II | 16, 28 | 0 | 75 | |
| UN3115 | ORGANIC PEROXIDE TYPE D, LIQUID, TEMPERATURE CONTROLLED | 5.2 | II | 16, 28 | 0 | | |
| UN3116 | ORGANIC PEROXIDE TYPE D, SOLID, TEMPERATURE CONTROLLED | 5.2 | II | 16, 28 | 0 | | |
| UN3117 | ORGANIC PEROXIDE TYPE E, LIQUID, TEMPERATURE CONTROLLED | 5.2 | II | 16, 28 | 0 | | |
| UN3118 | ORGANIC PEROXIDE TYPE E, SOLID, TEMPERATURE CONTROLLED | 5.2 | II | 16, 28 | 0 | | |
| UN3119 | ORGANIC PEROXIDE TYPE F, LIQUID, TEMPERATURE CONTROLLED | 5.2 | II | 16 | 0 | | |
| UN3120 | ORGANIC PEROXIDE TYPE F, SOLID, TEMPERATURE CONTROLLED | 5.2 | II | 16 | 0 | | |
| UN3121 | OXIDIZING SOLID, WATER-REACTIVE, N.O.S. | F | | | | | |
| UN3122 | TOXIC LIQUID, OXIDIZING, N.O.S. | 6.1 (5.1) | I | 16, 23 | 0 | 3 000 | • |
| | | | II | 16 | 0.1 | | |
| UN3123 | TOXIC LIQUID, WATER-REACTIVE, N.O.S. | 6.1 (4.3) | I | 16, 23 | 0 | 1 000 | • |
| | | | II | 16 | 0.1 | 3 000 | |
| UN3124 | TOXIC SOLID, SELF-HEATING, N.O.S. | 6.1 (4.2) | I | 16, 38 | 0 | 1 000 | |
| | | | II | 16 | 0 | | |
| UN3125 | TOXIC SOLID, WATER-REACTIVE, N.O.S. | 6.1 (4.3) | I | 16, 38 | 0 | 1 000 | • |
| | | | II | 16 | 0.5 | | |
| UN3126 | SELF-HEATING SOLID, CORROSIVE, ORGANIC, N.O.S. | 4.2 (8) | II | 16 | 0 | | • |
| | | | III | 16 | 0 | | |
| UN3127 | SELF-HEATING SOLID, OXIDIZING, N.O.S. | F | | | | | |
| UN3128 | SELF-HEATING SOLID, TOXIC, ORGANIC, N.O.S. | 4.2 (6.1) | II | 16 | 0 | | • |
| | | | III | 16 | 0 | | |
| UN3129 | WATER-REACTIVE LIQUID, CORROSIVE, N.O.S. | 4.3 (8) | I | 16, 38 | 0 | 1 000 | • |
| | | | II | 16 | 0.5 | | |
| | | | III | 16 | 1 | | |

| 1 | 2 | 3 | 4 | 5 | 6 | 7 | 10 |
|---|---|---|---|---|---|---|---|
| UN Number | Shipping Name and Description | Class | Packing Group/Category | Special Provisions | Explosive Limit & Limited Quantity Index | ERAP Index | Marine Pollut. |
| UN3130 | WATER-REACTIVE LIQUID, TOXIC, N.O.S. | 4.3 (6.1) | I II III | 16, 38 16 16 | 0 0.5 1 | 1 000 | • |
| UN3131 | WATER-REACTIVE SOLID, CORROSIVE, N.O.S. | 4.3 (8) | I II III | 16, 38 16 16 | 0 0.5 1 | 1 000 | • |
| UN3132 | WATER-REACTIVE SOLID, FLAMMABLE, N.O.S. | 4.3 (4.1) | I II III | 16, 38 16 16 | 0 0.5 1 | 1 000 | |
| UN3133 | WATER-REACTIVE SOLID, OXIDIZING, N.O.S. | F | | | | | |
| UN3134 | WATER-REACTIVE SOLID, TOXIC, N.O.S. | 4.3 (6.1) | I II III | 16, 38 16 16 | 0 0.5 1 | 1 000 | • |
| UN3135 | WATER-REACTIVE SOLID, SELF-HEATING, N.O.S. | 4.3 (4.2) | I II III | 16, 38 16 16 | 0 0 0 | 1 000 | • |
| UN3136 | TRIFLUOROMETHANE, REFRIGERATED LIQUID | 2.2 | | | 0.125 | | |
| UN3137 | OXIDIZING SOLID, FLAMMABLE, N.O.S. | F | | | | | |
| UN3138 | ETHYLENE, ACETYLENE AND PROPYLENE MIXTURE, REFRIGERATED LIQUID containing at least 71.5 percent ethylene with not more than 22.5 percent acetylene and not more than 6 percent propylene | 2.1 | | | 0.125 | | |
| UN3139 | OXIDIZING LIQUID, N.O.S. | 5.1 | I II III | 16 16 16 | 0 1 5 | 1 000 | • |
| UN3140 | ALKALOID SALTS, LIQUID, N.O.S; or ALKALOIDS, LIQUID, N.O.S. | 6.1 | I II III | 16, 23 16 16 | 0 0.5 1 | 1 000 | • |
| UN3141 | ANTIMONY COMPOUND, INORGANIC, LIQUID, N.O.S. except antimony oxides and sulphides containing less than 0.5 per cent arsenic, by mass | 6.1 | III | | 5 | | |
| UN3142 | DISINFECTANT, LIQUID, TOXIC, N.O.S. | 6.1 | I II III | 16, 23 16 16 | 0 0.1 5 | 1 000 | |
| UN3143 | DYE INTERMEDIATE, SOLID, TOXIC, N.O.S.; or DYE, SOLID, TOXIC, N.O.S. | 6.1 | I II III | 16 16 16 | 0 0.5 5 | 1 000 | • |
| UN3144 | NICOTINE COMPOUND, LIQUID, N.O.S.; or NICOTINE PREPARATION, LIQUID, N.O.S. | 6.1 | I II III | 23 | 0 0.1 5 | 1 000 | |
| UN3145 | ALKYLPHENOLS, LIQUID, N.O.S. including C2-C12 homologues | 8 | I II III | 50 50 50 | 0 1 5 | 3 000 | • |
| UN3146 | ORGANOTIN COMPOUND, SOLID, N.O.S. | 6.1 | I II III | 16 16 16 | 0 0.5 5 | 1 000 | PP |
| UN3147 | DYE INTERMEDIATE, SOLID, CORROSIVE, N.O.S.; or DYE, SOLID, CORROSIVE, N.O.S. | 8 | I II III | 16 16 16 | 0 1 5 | 3 000 | • |
| UN3148 | WATER-REACTIVE LIQUID, N.O.S. | 4.3 | I II III | 16, 38 16 16 | 0 0.5 1 | 1 000 | • |
| UN3149 | HYDROGEN PEROXIDE AND PEROXYACETIC ACID MIXTURE STABILIZED with acid(s), water and not more than 5 per cent peroxyacetic acid | 5.1 (8) | II | | 0.5 | | |
| UN3150 | DEVICES, SMALL, HYDROCARBON GAS POWERED with release device; or HYDROCARBON GAS REFILLS FOR SMALL DEVICES with release device | 2.1 | | | 0.125 | 3 000 | |

| 1 | 2 | 3 | 4 | 5 | 6 | 7 | 10 |
|---|---|---|---|---|---|---|---|
| UN Number | Shipping Name and Description | Class | Packing Group/Category | Special Provisions | Explosive Limit & Limited Quantity Index | ERAP Index | Marine Pollut. |
| UN3151 | POLYHALOGENATED BIPHENYLS, LIQUID regulated only when the concentration is more than 50 ppm by mass; or POLYHALOGENATED TERPHENYLS, LIQUID regulated only when the concentration is more than 50 ppm by mass | 9 | II | | 1 | | PP |
| UN3152 | POLYHALOGENATED BIPHENYLS, SOLID regulated only when the concentration is more than 50 ppm by mass; or POLYHALOGENATED TERPHENYLS, SOLID regulated only when the concentration is more than 50 ppm by mass | 9 | II | | 1 | | PP |
| UN3153 | PERFLUORO(METHYLVINYL ETHER) | 2.1 | | | 0.125 | 3 000 | |
| UN3154 | PERFLUORO(ETHYLVINYL ETHER) | 2.1 | | | 0.125 | 3 000 | |
| UN3155 | PENTACHLOROPHENOL | 6.1 | II | | 0.5 | | PP |
| UN3156 | COMPRESSED GAS, OXIDIZING, N.O.S. | 2.2 (5.1) | | 16 | 0 | 3 000 | • |
| UN3157 | LIQUEFIED GAS, OXIDIZING, N.O.S. | 2.2 (5.1) | | 16 | 0 | 3 000 | • |
| UN3158 | GAS, REFRIGERATED LIQUID, N.O.S. | 2.2 | | 16 | 0.125 | | • |
| UN3159 | REFRIGERANT GAS R 134a; or 1,1,1,2-TETRAFLUOROETHANE | 2.2 | | | 0.125 | | |
| UN3160 | LIQUEFIED GAS, TOXIC, FLAMMABLE, N.O.S. | 2.3 (2.1) | | 16, 38 | 0 | 0 | • |
| UN3161 | LIQUEFIED GAS, FLAMMABLE, N.O.S. | 2.1 | | 16 | 0.125 | 3 000 | • |
| UN3162 | LIQUEFIED GAS, TOXIC, N.O.S. | 2.3 | | 16, 38 | 0 | 0 | • |
| UN3163 | LIQUEFIED GAS, N.O.S. | 2.2 | | 16 | 0.125 | | • |
| UN3164 | ARTICLES, PRESSURIZED, HYDRAULIC (containing non-flammable gas); or ARTICLES, PRESSURIZED, PNEUMATIC (containing non-flammable gas) | 2.2 | | 40 | 0.125 | | |
| UN3165 | AIRCRAFT HYDRAULIC POWER UNIT FUEL TANK containing a mixture of anhydrous hydrazine and methylhydrazine (M86 fuel) | 3 (6.1) (8) | I | | 0 | 1 000 | |
| UN3166 | ENGINES, INTERNAL COMBUSTION (FLAMMABLE GAS POWERED) including when fitted in machinery or vehicles, regulated by aircraft only (ICAO terminology) | 9 | | 63,81 | 0 | | |
| UN3166 | ENGINES, INTERNAL COMBUSTION (FLAMMABLE LIQUID POWERED) including when fitted in machinery or vehicles, regulated by aircraft only (ICAO terminology) | 9 | | 63,81 | 0 | | |
| UN3167 | GAS SAMPLE, NON-PRESSURIZED, FLAMMABLE, N.O.S., not refrigerated liquid | 2.1 | | | 0.125 | | • |
| UN3168 | GAS SAMPLE, NON-PRESSURIZED, TOXIC, FLAMMABLE, N.O.S., not refrigerated liquid | 2.3 (2.1) | | | 0 | | • |
| UN3169 | GAS SAMPLE, NON-PRESSURIZED, TOXIC, N.O.S., not refrigerated liquid | 2.3 | | | 0 | | • |
| UN3170 | ALUMINUM REMELTING BY-PRODUCTS including, but not limited to, aluminum dross, aluminum skimmings, spent cathodes, spent potliner and aluminum salt slags; or ALUMINUM SMELTING BY-PRODUCTS including, but not limited to, aluminum dross, aluminum skimmings, spent cathodes, spent potliner and aluminum salt slags | 4.3 | II III | | 0.5 1 | | |
| UN3171 | BATTERY-POWERED EQUIPMENT, regulated by aircraft only; or BATTERY-POWERED VEHICLE, regulated by aircraft only | 9 | | 63, 67,81 | 0 | | |
| UN3172 | TOXINS, EXTRACTED FROM LIVING SOURCES, LIQUID, N.O.S., not containing infectious substances | 6.1 | I II III | 16 16 16 | 0 0.1 5 | 1 000 | • |
| UN3172 | TOXINS, EXTRACTED FROM LIVING SOURCES, SOLID, N.O.S., not containing infectious substances | 6.1 | I II III | 16 16 16 | 0 0.5 5 | 1 000 | |
| UN3174 | TITANIUM DISULFIDE; or TITANIUM DISULPHIDE | 4.2 | III | | 0 | | |
| UN3175 | SOLIDS CONTAINING FLAMMABLE LIQUID, N.O.S. | 4.1 | II | 16, 56 | 1 | | • |
| UN3176 | FLAMMABLE SOLID, ORGANIC, MOLTEN, N.O.S. | 4.1 | II III | 16 16 | 0 0 | | • |
| UN3178 | FLAMMABLE SOLID, INORGANIC, N.O.S. | 4.1 | II III | 16 16 | 1 5 | | • |

| 1 | 2 | 3 | 4 | 5 | 6 | 7 | 10 |
|---|---|---|---|---|---|---|---|
| UN Number | Shipping Name and Description | Class | Packing Group/Category | Special Provisions | Explosive Limit & Limited Quantity Index | ERAP Index | Marine Pollut. |
| UN3179 | FLAMMABLE SOLID, TOXIC, INORGANIC, N.O.S. | 4.1 (6.1) | II<br>III | 16<br>16 | 0.5<br>3 | | • |
| UN3180 | FLAMMABLE SOLID, CORROSIVE, INORGANIC, N.O.S. | 4.1 (8) | II<br>III | 16<br>16 | 0.5<br>3 | | • |
| UN3181 | METAL SALTS OF ORGANIC COMPOUNDS, FLAMMABLE, N.O.S. | 4.1 | II<br>III | 16<br>16 | 1<br>5 | | • |
| UN3182 | METAL HYDRIDES, FLAMMABLE, N.O.S. | 4.1 | II<br>III | 16<br>16 | 1<br>5 | | • |
| UN3183 | SELF-HEATING LIQUID, ORGANIC, N.O.S. | 4.2 | II<br>III | 16<br>16 | 0<br>0 | | • |
| UN3184 | SELF-HEATING LIQUID, TOXIC, ORGANIC, N.O.S. | 4.2 (6.1) | II<br>III | 16<br>16 | 0<br>0 | 1 000 | • |
| UN3185 | SELF-HEATING LIQUID, CORROSIVE, ORGANIC, N.O.S. | 4.2 (8) | II<br>III | 16<br>16 | 0<br>0 | 1 000 | • |
| UN3186 | SELF-HEATING LIQUID, INORGANIC, N.O.S. | 4.2 | II<br>III | 16<br>16 | 0<br>0 | 1 000 | • |
| UN3187 | SELF-HEATING LIQUID, TOXIC, INORGANIC, N.O.S. | 4.2 (6.1) | II<br>III | 16<br>16 | 0<br>0 | 1 000 | • |
| UN3188 | SELF-HEATING LIQUID, CORROSIVE, INORGANIC, N.O.S. | 4.2 (8) | II<br>III | 16<br>16 | 0<br>0 | | • |
| UN3189 | METAL POWDER, SELF-HEATING, N.O.S. | 4.2 | II<br>III | 16<br>16 | 0<br>0 | | • |
| UN3190 | SELF-HEATING SOLID, INORGANIC, N.O.S. | 4.2 | II<br>III | 16<br>16 | 0<br>0 | | • |
| UN3191 | SELF-HEATING SOLID, TOXIC, INORGANIC, N.O.S. | 4.2 (6.1) | II<br>III | 16<br>16 | 0<br>0 | 1 000 | • |
| UN3192 | SELF-HEATING SOLID, CORROSIVE, INORGANIC, N.O.S. | 4.2 (8) | II<br>III | 16<br>16 | 0<br>0 | 1 000 | • |
| UN3194 | PYROPHORIC LIQUID, INORGANIC, N.O.S. | 4.2 | I | 16 | 0 | 1 000 | • |
| UN3200 | PYROPHORIC SOLID, INORGANIC, N.O.S. | 4.2 | I | 16 | 0 | 1 000 | • |
| UN3203 | PYROPHORIC ORGANOMETALLIC COMPOUND, WATER-REACTIVE, N.O.S., liquid | 4.2 (4.3) | I | 16 | 0 | 1 000 | • |
| UN3203 | PYROPHORIC ORGANOMETALLIC COMPOUND, WATER-REACTIVE, N.O.S., solid | 4.2 (4.3) | I | 16 | 0 | 1 000 | • |
| UN3205 | ALKALINE EARTH METAL ALCOHOLATES, N.O.S. | 4.2 | II<br>III | 16<br>16 | 0<br>0 | | • |
| UN3206 | ALKALI METAL ALCOHOLATES, SELF-HEATING, CORROSIVE, N.O.S. | 4.2 (8) | II<br>III | 16<br>16 | 0<br>0 | | • |
| UN3207 | ORGANOMETALLIC COMPOUND DISPERSION, WATER-REACTIVE, FLAMMABLE, N.O.S.;<br>ORGANOMETALLIC COMPOUND SOLUTION, WATER-REACTIVE, FLAMMABLE, N.O.S.; or<br>ORGANOMETALLIC COMPOUND, WATER-REACTIVE, FLAMMABLE, N.O.S. | 4.3 (3) | I<br>II<br>III | 16<br>16<br>16 | 0<br>0.5<br>1 | 1 000 | • |
| UN3208 | METALLIC SUBSTANCE, WATER-REACTIVE, N.O.S. | 4.3 | I<br>II<br>III | 16<br>16<br>16 | 0<br>0.5<br>1 | 1 000 | • |
| UN3209 | METALLIC SUBSTANCE, WATER-REACTIVE, SELF-HEATING, N.O.S. | 4.3 (4.2) | I<br>II<br>III | 16<br>16<br>16 | 0<br>0<br>0 | 1 000 | • |
| UN3210 | CHLORATES, INORGANIC, AQUEOUS SOLUTION, N.O.S. | 5.1 | II<br>III | 68 | 1<br>5 | | • |
| UN3211 | PERCHLORATES, INORGANIC, AQUEOUS SOLUTION, N.O.S. | 5.1 | II<br>III | | 1<br>5 | | • |
| UN3212 | HYPOCHLORITES, INORGANIC, N.O.S. | 5.1 | II | 68 | 1 | | • |
| UN3213 | BROMATES, INORGANIC, AQUEOUS SOLUTION, N.O.S. | 5.1 | II<br>III | 68 | 1<br>5 | | • |

| 1 UN Number | 2 Shipping Name and Description | 3 Class | 4 Packing Group/Category | 5 Special Provisions | 6 Explosive Limit & Limited Quantity Index | 7 ERAP Index | 10 Marine Pollut. |
|---|---|---|---|---|---|---|---|
| UN3214 | PERMANGANATES, INORGANIC, AQUEOUS SOLUTION, N.O.S. | 5.1 | II | 68 | 1 | | • |
| UN3215 | PERSULFATES, INORGANIC, N.O.S.; or<br><br>PERSULPHATES, INORGANIC, N.O.S. | 5.1 | III | | 5 | | • |
| UN3216 | PERSULFATES, INORGANIC, AQUEOUS SOLUTION, N.O.S.; or<br>PERSULPHATES, INORGANIC, AQUEOUS SOLUTION, N.O.S. | 5.1 | III | | 5 | | • |
| UN3218 | NITRATES, INORGANIC, AQUEOUS SOLUTION, N.O.S. | 5.1 | II<br>III | 55<br>55 | 1<br>5 | | • |
| UN3219 | NITRITES, INORGANIC, AQUEOUS SOLUTION, N.O.S. | 5.1 | II<br>III | 68 | 1<br>5 | | • |
| UN3220 | PENTAFLUOROETHANE; or<br>REFRIGERANT GAS R 125 | 2.2 | | | 0.125 | | |
| UN3221 | SELF-REACTIVE LIQUID TYPE B | 4.1 (1) | II | 16, 38 | 0 | 75 | |
| UN3222 | SELF-REACTIVE SOLID TYPE B | 4.1 (1) | II | 16, 38 | 0 | 75 | |
| UN3223 | SELF-REACTIVE LIQUID TYPE C | 4.1 | II | 16, 38 | 1 | | |
| UN3224 | SELF-REACTIVE SOLID TYPE C | 4.1 | II | 16, 38 | 1 | 3 000 | |
| UN3225 | SELF-REACTIVE LIQUID TYPE D | 4.1 | II | 16, 38 | 1 | 3 000 | |
| UN3226 | SELF-REACTIVE SOLID TYPE D | 4.1 | II | 16, 38 | 1 | | |
| UN3227 | SELF-REACTIVE LIQUID TYPE E | 4.1 | II | 16, 38 | 1 | | |
| UN3228 | SELF-REACTIVE SOLID TYPE E | 4.1 | II | 16, 38 | 1 | | |
| UN3229 | SELF-REACTIVE LIQUID TYPE F | 4.1 | II | 16, 38 | 1 | | |
| UN3230 | SELF-REACTIVE SOLID TYPE F | 4.1 | II | 16, 38 | 1 | | |
| UN3231 | SELF-REACTIVE LIQUID TYPE B, TEMPERATURE CONTROLLED | 4.1 (1) | II | 16, 28 | 0 | 75 | |
| UN3232 | SELF-REACTIVE SOLID TYPE B, TEMPERATURE CONTROLLED | 4.1 (1) | II | 16, 28 | 0 | 75 | |
| UN3233 | SELF-REACTIVE LIQUID TYPE C, TEMPERATURE CONTROLLED | 4.1 | II | 16, 28 | 1 | 75 | |
| UN3234 | SELF-REACTIVE SOLID TYPE C, TEMPERATURE CONTROLLED | 4.1 | II | 16, 28 | 1 | 75 | |
| UN3235 | SELF-REACTIVE LIQUID TYPE D, TEMPERATURE CONTROLLED | 4.1 | II | 16, 28 | 1 | 75 | |
| UN3236 | SELF-REACTIVE SOLID TYPE D, TEMPERATURE CONTROLLED | 4.1 | II | 16, 28 | 1 | | |
| UN3237 | SELF-REACTIVE LIQUID TYPE E, TEMPERATURE CONTROLLED | 4.1 | II | 16, 28 | 1 | | |
| UN3238 | SELF-REACTIVE SOLID TYPE E, TEMPERATURE CONTROLLED | 4.1 | II | 16, 28 | 1 | | |
| UN3239 | SELF-REACTIVE LIQUID TYPE F, TEMPERATURE CONTROLLED | 4.1 | II | 16, 28 | 1 | | |
| UN3240 | SELF-REACTIVE SOLID TYPE F, TEMPERATURE CONTROLLED | 4.1 | II | 16, 28 | 1 | | |
| UN3241 | 2-BROMO-2-NITROPROPANE-1,3-DIOL | 4.1 | III | 73 | 5 | | |
| UN3242 | AZODICARBONAMIDE, technically pure or preparations having an SADT higher than 75 °C | 4.1 | II | | 1 | | P |
| UN3243 | SOLIDS CONTAINING TOXIC LIQUID, N.O.S. | 6.1 | II | 16, 57 | 0.5 | | • |
| UN3244 | SOLIDS CONTAINING CORROSIVE LIQUID, N.O.S. | 8 | II | 16, 26, 58 | 1 | | • |
| UN3245 | GENETICALLY MODIFIED MICRO-ORGANISMS not containing infectious substances | 9 | | 81 | 0 | | |
| UN3246 | METHANESULFONYL CHLORIDE; or<br>METHANESULPHONYL CHLORIDE | 6.1 (8) | I | | 0 | 1 000 | |
| UN3247 | SODIUM PEROXOBORATE, ANHYDROUS | 5.1 | II | | 1 | | |
| UN3248 | MEDICINE, LIQUID, FLAMMABLE, TOXIC, N.O.S. | 3 (6.1) | II<br>III | 16, 38<br>16 | 1<br>5 | 1 000 | • |

| 1 UN Number | 2 Shipping Name and Description | 3 Class | 4 Packing Group/Category | 5 Special Provisions | 6 Explosive Limit & Limited Quantity Index | 7 ERAP Index | 10 Marine Pollut. |
|---|---|---|---|---|---|---|---|
| UN3249 | MEDICINE, SOLID, TOXIC, N.O.S. | 6.1 | II | 16, 38 | 0.5 | | • |
| | | | III | 16 | 5 | | |
| UN3250 | CHLOROACETIC ACID, MOLTEN | 6.1 (8) | II | | 0 | 1 000 | |
| UN3251 | ISOSORBIDE-5-MONONITRATE with less than 30 per cent non-volatile, non-flammable phlegmatizer | 4.1 | III | | 5 | | |
| UN3252 | DIFLUOROMETHANE; or REFRIGERANT GAS R 32 | 2.1 | | | 0.125 | 3 000 | |
| UN3253 | DISODIUM TRIOXOSILICATE | 8 | III | | 5 | | |
| UN3254 | TRIBUTYLPHOSPHANE | 4.2 | I | | 0 | 1 000 | |
| UN3255 | tert-BUTYL HYPOCHLORITE | F | | | | | |
| UN3256 | ELEVATED TEMPERATURE LIQUID, FLAMMABLE, N.O.S., with flash point above 60.5 °C, at or above its flash point | 3 | III | | 0 | | • |
| UN3257 | ELEVATED TEMPERATURE LIQUID, N.O.S., at or above 100 °C and below its flash point including molten metals, molten salts, etc. | 9 | III | | 5 | | • |
| UN3258 | ELEVATED TEMPERATURE SOLID, N.O.S., at or above 240 °C | 9 | III | | 5 | | • |
| UN3259 | AMINES, SOLID, CORROSIVE, N.O.S.; or POLYAMINES, SOLID, CORROSIVE, N.O.S. | 8 | I | 16 | 0 | 3 000 | |
| | | | II | 16 | 1 | | • |
| | | | III | 16 | 5 | | |
| UN3260 | CORROSIVE SOLID, ACIDIC, INORGANIC, N.O.S. | 8 | I | 16 | 0 | | |
| | | | II | 16 | 1 | | • |
| | | | III | 16 | 5 | | |
| UN3261 | CORROSIVE SOLID, ACIDIC, ORGANIC, N.O.S. | 8 | I | 16 | 0 | | |
| | | | II | 16 | 1 | | |
| | | | III | 16 | 5 | | |
| UN3262 | CORROSIVE SOLID, BASIC, INORGANIC, N.O.S. | 8 | I | 16 | 0 | | |
| | | | II | 16 | 1 | | • |
| | | | III | 16 | 5 | | |
| UN3263 | CORROSIVE SOLID, BASIC, ORGANIC, N.O.S. | 8 | I | 16 | 0 | | |
| | | | II | 16 | 1 | | |
| | | | III | 16 | 5 | | |
| UN3264 | CORROSIVE LIQUID, ACIDIC, INORGANIC, N.O.S. | 8 | I | 16 | 0 | 3 000 | |
| | | | II | 16 | 1 | | • |
| | | | III | 16 | 5 | | |
| UN3265 | CORROSIVE LIQUID, ACIDIC, ORGANIC, N.O.S. | 8 | I | 16 | 0 | 3 000 | |
| | | | II | 16 | 1 | | • |
| | | | III | 16 | 5 | | |
| UN3266 | CORROSIVE LIQUID, BASIC, INORGANIC, N.O.S. | 8 | I | 16 | 0 | 3 000 | |
| | | | II | 16 | 1 | | • |
| | | | III | 16 | 5 | | |
| UN3267 | CORROSIVE LIQUID, BASIC, ORGANIC, N.O.S. | 8 | I | 16 | 0 | 3 000 | |
| | | | II | 16 | 1 | | • |
| | | | III | 16 | 5 | | |
| UN3268 | AIR BAG INFLATORS, pyrotechnic; AIR BAG MODULES, pyrotechnic; or SEAT-BELT PRETENSIONERS, pyrotechnic | 9 | III | 25 | 5 | | |
| UN3269 | POLYESTER RESIN KIT | 3 | II | | 5 | | |
| | | | III | | 0 | | |
| UN3270 | NITROCELLULOSE MEMBRANE FILTERS, with not more than 12.6 percent nitrogen, by dry mass | 4.1 | II | | 0 | | |
| UN3271 | ETHERS, N.O.S. | 3 | II | 16 | 1 | | |
| | | | III | 16 | 5 | | |
| UN3272 | ESTERS, N.O.S. | 3 | II | 16 | 1 | | |
| | | | III | 16 | 5 | | • |
| UN3273 | NITRILES, FLAMMABLE, TOXIC, N.O.S. | 3 (6.1) | I | 16 | 0 | 1 000 | • |
| | | | II | 16 | 1 | | |

| 1 UN Number | 2 Shipping Name and Description | 3 Class | 4 Packing Group/Category | 5 Special Provisions | 6 Explosive Limit & Limited Quantity Index | 7 ERAP Index | 10 Marine Pollut. |
|---|---|---|---|---|---|---|---|
| UN3274 | ALCOHOLATES SOLUTION, N.O.S., in alcohol | 3 (8) | II | 16 | 1 | | • |
| UN3275 | NITRILES, TOXIC, FLAMMABLE, N.O.S. | 6.1 (3) | I | 16, 23 | 0 | 1 000 | • |
| | | | II | 16 | 0.1 | | |
| UN3276 | NITRILES, TOXIC, liquid, N.O.S.; or NITRILES, TOXIC, LIQUID, N.O.S. (ICAO terminology) | 6.1 | I | 16 | 0 | 1 000 | • |
| | | | II | 16 | 0.1 | | |
| | | | III | 16 | 5 | | |
| UN3276 | NITRILES, TOXIC, solid, N.O.S.; or NITRILES, TOXIC, SOLID, N.O.S. (ICAO terminology) | 6.1 | I | 16, 23 | 0 | 1 000 | • |
| | | | II | 16 | 0.5 | | |
| | | | III | 16 | 5 | | |
| UN3277 | CHLOROFORMATES, TOXIC, CORROSIVE, N.O.S. | 6.1 (8) | II | 16 | 0.1 | 1 000 | • |
| UN3278 | ORGANOPHOSPHORUS COMPOUND, TOXIC, N.O.S., liquid | 6.1 | I | 16 | 0 | 1 000 | • |
| | | | II | 16 | 0.1 | | |
| | | | III | 16 | 5 | | |
| UN3278 | ORGANOPHOSPHORUS COMPOUND, TOXIC, N.O.S., solid | 6.1 | I | 16, 23 | 0 | 1 000 | |
| | | | II | 16 | 0.5 | | |
| | | | III | 16 | 5 | | |
| UN3279 | ORGANOPHOSPHORUS COMPOUND, TOXIC, FLAMMABLE, N.O.S. | 6.1 (3) | I | 16, 23 | 0 | 1 000 | • |
| | | | II | 16 | 0.1 | | |
| UN3280 | ORGANOARSENIC COMPOUND, N.O.S., liquid | 6.1 | I | 16 | 0 | 1 000 | • |
| | | | II | 16 | 0.1 | | |
| | | | III | 16 | 5 | | |
| UN3280 | ORGANOARSENIC COMPOUND, N.O.S., solid | 6.1 | I | 16, 23 | 0 | 1 000 | • |
| | | | II | 16 | 0.5 | | |
| | | | III | 16 | 5 | | |
| UN3281 | METAL CARBONYLS, N.O.S., liquid | 6.1 | I | 16 | 0 | 1 000 | • |
| | | | II | 16 | 0.1 | | |
| | | | III | 16 | 5 | | |
| UN3281 | METAL CARBONYLS, N.O.S., solid | 6.1 | I | 16, 23 | 0 | 1 000 | • |
| | | | II | 16 | 0.5 | | |
| | | | III | 16 | 5 | | |
| UN3282 | ORGANOMETALLIC COMPOUND, TOXIC, N.O.S., liquid | 6.1 | I | 16 | 0 | 1 000 | • |
| | | | II | 16 | 0.1 | | |
| | | | III | 16 | 5 | | |
| UN3282 | ORGANOMETALLIC COMPOUND, TOXIC, N.O.S., solid | 6.1 | I | 16, 23 | 0 | 1 000 | • |
| | | | II | 16 | 0.5 | | |
| | | | III | 16 | 5 | | |
| UN3283 | SELENIUM COMPOUND, N.O.S. | 6.1 | I | | 0 | 1 000 | |
| | | | II | | 0.5 | | |
| | | | III | | 5 | | |
| UN3284 | TELLURIUM COMPOUND, N.O.S. | 6.1 | I | | 0 | 1 000 | • |
| | | | II | | 0.5 | | |
| | | | III | | 5 | | |
| UN3285 | VANADIUM COMPOUND, N.O.S. | 6.1 | I | | 0 | 1 000 | • |
| | | | II | | 0.5 | | |
| | | | III | | 5 | | |
| UN3286 | FLAMMABLE LIQUID, TOXIC, CORROSIVE, N.O.S. | 3 (6.1) (8) | I | 16 | 0 | 1 000 | • |
| | | | II | 16 | 1 | | |
| UN3287 | TOXIC LIQUID, INORGANIC, N.O.S. | 6.1 | I | 16 | 0 | 1 000 | • |
| | | | II | 16 | 0.1 | | |
| | | | III | 16 | 5 | | |
| UN3288 | TOXIC SOLID, INORGANIC, N.O.S. | 6.1 | I | 16 | 0 | 1 000 | • |
| | | | II | 16 | 0.5 | | |
| | | | III | 16 | 5 | | |
| UN3289 | TOXIC LIQUID, CORROSIVE, INORGANIC, N.O.S. | 6.1 (8) | I | 16 | 0 | 1 000 | • |
| | | | II | 16 | 0.1 | | |

| 1 | 2 | 3 | 4 | 5 | 6 | 7 | 10 |
|---|---|---|---|---|---|---|---|
| UN Number | Shipping Name and Description | Class | Packing Group/Category | Special Provisions | Explosive Limit & Limited Quantity Index | ERAP Index | Marine Pollut. |
| UN3290 | TOXIC SOLID, CORROSIVE, INORGANIC, N.O.S. | 6.1 (8) | I II | 16 16 | 0 0.5 | 1 000 | • |
| UN3292 | BATTERIES, CONTAINING SODIUM; or CELLS, CONTAINING SODIUM | 4.3 | II | | 0 | | |
| UN3293 | HYDRAZINE, AQUEOUS SOLUTION with not more than 37 per cent hydrazine, by mass | 6.1 | III | | 5 | | |
| UN3294 | HYDROGEN CYANIDE, SOLUTION IN ALCOHOL with not more than 45 per cent hydrogen cyanide | 6.1 (3) | I | 68 | 0 | 1 000 | P |
| UN3295 | HYDROCARBONS, LIQUID, N.O.S. | 3 | I II III | | 0.5 1 5 | | • |
| UN3296 | HEPTAFLUOROPROPANE; or REFRIGERANT GAS R 227 | 2.2 | | | 0.125 | | |
| UN3297 | ETHYLENE OXIDE AND CHLOROTETRAFLUOROETHANE MIXTURE with not more than 8.8 per cent ethylene oxide | 2.2 | | | 0.125 | | |
| UN3298 | ETHYLENE OXIDE AND PENTAFLUOROETHANE MIXTURE with not more than 7.9 per cent ethylene oxide | 2.2 | | | 0.125 | | |
| UN3299 | ETHYLENE OXIDE AND TETRAFLUOROETHANE MIXTURE with not more than 5.6 per cent ethylene oxide | 2.2 | | | 0.125 | | |
| UN3300 | ETHYLENE OXIDE AND CARBON DIOXIDE MIXTURE with more than 87 per cent ethylene oxide | 2.3 (2.1) | | | 0 | 500 | |
| UN3301 | CORROSIVE LIQUID, SELF-HEATING, N.O.S. | 8 (4.2) | I II | 16 16 | 0 0 | 3 000 | • |
| UN3302 | 2-DIMETHYLAMINOETHYL ACRYLATE | 6.1 | II | | 0.1 | | |
| UN3303 | COMPRESSED GAS, TOXIC, OXIDIZING, N.O.S. | 2.3 (5.1) | | 16, 38 | 0 | 0 | • |
| UN3304 | COMPRESSED GAS, TOXIC, CORROSIVE, N.O.S. | 2.3 (8) | | 16, 38 | 0 | 0 | • |
| UN3305 | COMPRESSED GAS, TOXIC, FLAMMABLE, CORROSIVE, N.O.S. | 2.3 (2.1) (8) | | 16, 38 | 0 | 0 | • |
| UN3306 | COMPRESSED GAS, TOXIC, OXIDIZING, CORROSIVE, N.O.S. | 2.3 (5.1) (8) | | 16, 38 | 0 | 0 | • |
| UN3307 | LIQUEFIED GAS, TOXIC, OXIDIZING, N.O.S. | 2.3 (5.1) | | 16, 38 | 0 | 0 | • |
| UN3308 | LIQUEFIED GAS, TOXIC, CORROSIVE, N.O.S. | 2.3 (8) | | 16, 38 | 0 | 0 | • |
| UN3309 | LIQUEFIED GAS, TOXIC, FLAMMABLE, CORROSIVE, N.O.S. | 2.3 (2.1) (8) | | 16, 38 | 0 | 0 | • |
| UN3310 | LIQUEFIED GAS, TOXIC, OXIDIZING, CORROSIVE, N.O.S. | 2.3 (5.1) (8) | | 16, 38 | 0 | 0 | • |
| UN3311 | GAS, REFRIGERATED LIQUID, OXIDIZING, N.O.S. | 2.2 (5.1) | | 16 | 0.125 | 3 000 | • |
| UN3312 | GAS, REFRIGERATED LIQUID, FLAMMABLE, N.O.S. | 2.1 | | 16 | 0.125 | 3 000 | • |
| UN3313 | ORGANIC PIGMENTS, SELF-HEATING | 4.2 | II III | | 0 0 | | |
| UN3314 | PLASTICS MOULDING COMPOUND in dough, sheet or extruded rope form evolving flammable vapour | 9 | III | | 5 | | |
| UN3315 | CHEMICAL SAMPLE, TOXIC, liquid or solid | F | | | | | |
| UN3316 | CHEMICAL KIT; or FIRST AID KIT | 9 | | 65 | 0 | | |
| UN3317 | 2-AMINO-4,6-DINITROPHENOL, WETTED with not less than 20 per cent water, by mass | 4.1 | I | 38, 62 | 0 | 75 | |
| UN3318 | AMMONIA SOLUTION, relative density less than 0.880 at 15 °C in water, with more than 50 per cent ammonia | 2.3 (8) | | | 0 | 3 000 | |
| UN3319 | NITROGLYCERIN MIXTURE, DESENSITIZED, SOLID, N.O.S. with more than 2 per cent but not more than 10 per cent nitroglycerin, by mass | F | | | | | |
| UN3320 | SODIUM BOROHYDRIDE AND SODIUM HYDROXIDE SOLUTION, with not more than 12 per cent sodium borohydride and not more than 40 per cent sodium hydroxide, by mass | 8 | II III | | 1 5 | | |

| 1 UN Number | 2 Shipping Name and Description | 3 Class | 4 Packing Group/Category | 5 Special Provisions | 6 Explosive Limit & Limited Quantity Index | 7 ERAP Index | 10 Marine Pollut. |
|---|---|---|---|---|---|---|---|
| UN3321 | RADIOACTIVE MATERIAL, LOW SPECIFIC ACTIVITY (LSA-II), non-fissile or fissile excepted | 7 | | 74 | 0 | 100 | |
| UN3322 | RADIOACTIVE MATERIAL, LOW SPECIFIC ACTIVITY (LSA-III), non-fissile or fissile excepted | 7 | | 74 | 0 | 100 | |
| UN3323 | RADIOACTIVE MATERIAL, TYPE C PACKAGE, non-fissile or fissile excepted | 7 | | 74 | 0 | | |
| UN3324 | RADIOACTIVE MATERIAL, LOW SPECIFIC ACTIVITY (LSA-II), FISSILE | 7 | | 74 | 0 | 25 | |
| UN3325 | RADIOACTIVE MATERIAL, LOW SPECIFIC ACTIVITY, (LSA-III), FISSILE | 7 | | 74 | 0 | 25 | |
| UN3326 | RADIOACTIVE MATERIAL, SURFACE CONTAMINATED OBJECTS (SCO-I), FISSILE; or RADIOACTIVE MATERIAL, SURFACE CONTAMINATED OBJECTS (SCO-II), FISSILE | 7 | | 74 | 0 | 0 | |
| UN3327 | RADIOACTIVE MATERIAL, TYPE A PACKAGE, FISSILE, non-special form | 7 | | 74 | 0 | 0 | |
| UN3328 | RADIOACTIVE MATERIAL, TYPE B(U) PACKAGE, FISSILE | 7 | | 74 | 0 | 0 | |
| UN3329 | RADIOACTIVE MATERIAL, TYPE B(M) PACKAGE, FISSILE | 7 | | 74 | 0 | 0 | |
| UN3330 | RADIOACTIVE MATERIAL, TYPE C PACKAGE, FISSILE | 7 | | 74 | 0 | 0 | |
| UN3331 | RADIOACTIVE MATERIAL, TRANSPORTED UNDER SPECIAL ARRANGEMENT, FISSILE | 7 | | 74 | 0 | 0 | |
| UN3332 | RADIOACTIVE MATERIAL, TYPE A PACKAGE, SPECIAL FORM, non-fissile or fissile excepted | 7 | | 74 | 0 | | |
| UN3333 | RADIOACTIVE MATERIAL, TYPE A PACKAGE, SPECIAL FORM, FISSILE | 7 | | 74 | 0 | 0 | |
| UN3336 | MERCAPTAN MIXTURE, LIQUID, FLAMMABLE, N.O.S.; or MERCAPTANS, LIQUID, FLAMMABLE, N.O.S. | 3 | I | 16 | 0 | | • |
| | | | II | 16 | 1 | | |
| | | | III | 16 | 5 | | |
| UN3337 | REFRIGERANT GAS R 404A | 2.2 | | | 0.125 | | |
| UN3338 | REFRIGERANT GAS R 407A | 2.2 | | | 0.125 | | |
| UN3339 | REFRIGERANT GAS R 407B | 2.2 | | | 0.125 | | |
| UN3340 | REFRIGERANT GAS R 407C | 2.2 | | | 0.125 | | |
| UN3341 | THIOUREA DIOXIDE | 4.2 | II | | 0 | | |
| | | | III | | 0 | | |
| UN3342 | XANTHATES | 4.2 | II | | 0 | | |
| | | | III | | 0 | | |
| UN3343 | NITROGLYCERIN MIXTURE, DESENSITIZED, LIQUID, FLAMMABLE, N.O.S. with not more than 30 per cent nitroglycerin, by mass | F | | | | | |
| UN3344 | PENTAERYTHRITE TETRANITRATE MIXTURE, DESENSITIZED, SOLID, N.O.S. with more than 10 per cent but not more than 20 per cent pentaerythrite tetranitrate (PETN), by mass | F | | | | | |
| UN3345 | PHENOXYACETIC ACID DERIVATIVE PESTICIDE, SOLID, TOXIC | 6.1 | I | 16 | 0 | 1 000 | |
| | | | II | 16 | 0.5 | | |
| | | | III | 16 | 5 | | |
| UN3346 | PHENOXYACETIC ACID DERIVATIVE PESTICIDE, LIQUID, FLAMMABLE, TOXIC, flash point less than 23 °C | 3 (6.1) | I | 16 | 0 | 1 000 | |
| | | | II | 16 | 1 | | |
| UN3347 | PHENOXYACETIC ACID DERIVATIVE PESTICIDE, LIQUID, TOXIC, FLAMMABLE, flash point not less than 23 °C | 6.1 (3) | I | 16 | 0 | 1 000 | P |
| | | | II | 16 | 0.1 | | |
| | | | III | 16 | 1 | | |
| UN3348 | PHENOXYACETIC ACID DERIVATIVE PESTICIDE, LIQUID, TOXIC | 6.1 | I | 16 | 0 | 1 000 | |
| | | | II | 16 | 0.1 | | |
| | | | III | 16 | 5 | | |
| UN3349 | PYRETHROID PESTICIDE, SOLID, TOXIC | 6.1 | I | 16 | 0 | 1 000 | |
| | | | II | 16 | 0.5 | | |
| | | | III | 16 | 5 | | |
| UN3350 | PYRETHROID PESTICIDE, LIQUID, FLAMMABLE, TOXIC, flash point less than 23 °C | 3 (6.1) | I | 16 | 0 | 1 000 | |
| | | | II | 16 | 1 | | |

| 1 | 2 | 3 | 4 | 5 | 6 | 7 | 10 |
|---|---|---|---|---|---|---|---|
| UN Number | Shipping Name and Description | Class | Packing Group/Category | Special Provisions | Explosive Limit & Limited Quantity Index | ERAP Index | Marine |
| UN3351 | PYRETHROID PESTICIDE, LIQUID, TOXIC, FLAMMABLE, flash point not less than 23 °C | 6.1 (3) | I | 16 | 0 | 1 000 | |
| | | | II | 16 | 0.1 | | |
| | | | III | 16 | 1 | | |
| UN3352 | PYRETHROID PESTICIDE, LIQUID, TOXIC | 6.1 | I | 16 | 0 | 1 000 | |
| | | | II | 16 | 0.1 | | |
| | | | III | 16 | 5 | | |
| UN3354 | INSECTICIDE GAS, FLAMMABLE, N.O.S. | 2.1 | | 16 | 0.125 | 3 000 | • |
| UN3355 | INSECTICIDE GAS, TOXIC, FLAMMABLE, N.O.S. | 2.3 (2.1) | | 16, 38 | 0 | 0 | • |
| UN3356 | OXYGEN GENERATOR, CHEMICAL | 5.1 | II | 41 | 1 | | |
| UN3357 | NITROGLYCERIN MIXTURE, DESENSITIZED, LIQUID, N.O.S. with not more than 30 per cent nitroglycerin, by mass | F | | | | | |
| UN3358 | REFRIGERATING MACHINES containing flammable, non-toxic, liquefied gas | 2.1 | | | 0 | | |
| UN3373 | BIOLOGICAL SUBSTANCE, CATEGORY B | 6.2 | Category B | | 0 | | |
| UN3475 | ETHANOL AND GASOLINE MIXTURE, with more than 10%ethanol ETHANOL AND MOTOR SPIRIT MIXTURE, with more than 10%ethanol ETHANOL AND PETROL MIXTURE, with more than 10%ethanol | 3 | II | | 30 | | |

The 14th Edition of the UN recommendation regarding the classification of dangerous goods includes substances and/or articles that are not currently listed in Schedule 1. Use of these numbers is permitted by the regulations.

Dangerous goods shown in the 14th Edition of the UN Recommendations that require an ERAP are as follows:

> UN3361; UN3362; UN3664; UN3365; UN3666; UN3667; UN3368; UN3369; UN3370; UN3375; UN3376; UN3380; UN3381; UN3382; UN3383; UN3384; UN3385; UN3386; UN3387; UN3388; UN3389; UN3390; UN3391; UN3392; UN3393; UN3394; UN3395; UN3396; UN3397; UN3398; UN3399; UN3401; UN3402; UN3403; UN3404; UN3413; UN3414; UN3421; UN3433; UN3439; UN3440; UN3448; UN3449; UN3450; UN3461; UN3462; UN3464; UN3465; UN3466; UN3467; UN3468; UN3471.

The corresponding ERAP information can be found at www.tc.gc.ca/tdg/clear/newerapnumbers.htm

Dangerous goods that do not require an ERAP are as follows:

> UN3359; UN3360; UN3371; UN3372; UN3373; UN3377; UN3378; UN3379; UN3400; UN3405; UN3406; UN3407; UN3408; UN3408; UN3409; UN3410; UN3411; UN3412; UN3415; UN3416; UN3417; UN3418; UN3419; UN3420; UN3422; UN3423; UN3424; UN3425; UN3426; UN3427; UN3428; UN3429; UN3430; UN3431; UN3432; UN3434; UN3435; UN3436; UN3437; UN3438; UN3441; UN3442; UN3443; UN3444; UN3445; UN3446; UN3447; UN3451; UN3452; UN3453; UN3454; UN3455; UN3456; UN3457; UN3458; UN3459; UN3460; UN3463; UN3469; UN3470; UN3472; UN3473.

The full Shipping Name, Classification and Packing Group of these dangerous can be found at

www.unece.org/trans/danger/publi/unrec/rev14/English/05E_Index.pdf

# SCHEDULE 2

## Special Provisions

*This Schedule gives the text of the special provisions that apply to dangerous goods. The numbers of the special provisions in this Schedule correspond to the numbers in column 5 of Schedule 1. Each UN Number that has the special provision against it is included in italics at the end of each special provision.*

1    If these explosives contain chlorates, they must not be packed in the same means of containment with explosives containing ammonium nitrate or any other ammonium salt. In addition, if these explosives are to be transported in the same means of transport with explosives containing ammonium nitrate or any other ammonium salt, they must be separated from those explosives so that there will be no reaction in the event of an accident.

     *UN0083*

| 2 | **DELETED** |

3    A person must not load UN0337, FIREWORKS, on a means of transport with dangerous goods that are included in Class 1.1 or Class 1.2.

     *UN0337*

4    The net explosives quantity for these dangerous goods is calculated as 50% of the gross mass expressed in kilograms when the true net explosives quantity cannot reasonably be determined.

     *UN0333, UN0334, UN0335, UN0428, UN0429, UN0430*

5    The net explosives quantity for these dangerous goods is calculated as 25% of the gross mass expressed in kilograms when the true net explosives quantity cannot reasonably be determined.

     *UN0336, UN0337, UN0431, UN0432 UN0336, UN0337, UN0431, UN0432*

| 6 | **DELETED** |
| 7 | **DELETED** |
| 8 | **DELETED** |
| 9 | **DELETED** |

10    These dangerous goods may be included in Class 4.1 if

     (a) they are in a quantity less than or equal to 500 g per means of containment;

     (b) they contain not less than 10 per cent water by mass; and

     (c) a negative test result is obtained when they are tested in accordance with the Series 6 type (c) test referred to in Section 16 of Part I of the Manual of Tests and Criteria.

     *UN0154, UN0155, UN0209, UN0214, UN0215, UN0234, UN0401, UN1344, UN1354, UN1355, UN1356*

11    These dangerous goods must be in a means of containment that is in compliance with Packing Instruction EP14(b) of CGSB-43.151.

     *UN0501*

12 These dangerous goods must be in a means of containment that is in compliance with Packing Instruction EP30 of CGSB-43.151.

*UN0502*

13 These dangerous goods must be in a means of containment that is in compliance with Packing Instruction EP35 of CGSB-43.151.

*UN0503*

14 These dangerous goods must be in a means of containment that is in compliance with Packing Instruction EP12(c) of CGSB-43.151.

*UN0504*

16 (1) The technical name of the most dangerous substance related to the primary class must be shown, in parentheses, on the shipping document following the shipping name in accordance with clause 3.5(1)(c)(i)(A) of Part 3, Documentation. The technical name must also be shown, in parentheses, on a small means of containment or on a tag following the shipping name in accordance with subsections 4.11(2) and (3) of Part 4, Dangerous Goods Safety Marks.

(2) Despite subsection (1), the technical name for the following dangerous goods is not required to be shown on a shipping document when Canadian law for domestic transport or an international convention for international transport prohibits the disclosure of the technical name:

(a) UN1544, ALKALOID SALTS, SOLID, N.O.S. or ALKALOIDS, SOLID, N.O.S.;

(b) UN1851, MEDICINE, LIQUID, TOXIC, N.O.S.;

(c) UN3140, ALKALOID SALTS, LIQUID, N.O.S. or ALKALOIDS, LIQUID, N.O.S.;

(d) UN3248, MEDICINE, LIQUID, FLAMMABLE, TOXIC, N.O.S.; or

(e) UN3249, MEDICINE, SOLID, TOXIC, N.O.S.

*An example in Canada is the "Food and Drugs Act".*

*UN0020, UN0021, UN0190, UN0248, UN0249, UN0349 to UN0359, UN0382, UN0383, UN0384, UN0461 to UN0482, UN0485, UN1078, UN1224, UN1228, UN1325, UN1383, UN1409, UN1479, UN1544, UN1588, UN1601, UN1602, UN1693, UN1719, UN1759, UN1760, UN1851, UN1903, UN1953, UN1954, UN1955, UN1964, UN1965, UN1967, UN1968, UN1986, UN1987, UN1988, UN1989, UN1992, UN1993, UN2003, UN2006, UN2206, UN2478, UN2571, UN2588, UN2693, UN2733, UN2734, UN2735, UN2757, UN2758 to UN2764, UN2771, UN2772, UN2775 to UN2784, UN2786, UN2787, UN2788, UN2801, UN2810, UN2811, UN2813, UN2845, UN2846, UN2902, UN2903, UN2920 to UN2930, UN2991 to UN2998, UN3005, UN3006, UN3009 to UN3021, UN3024, UN3025, UN3026, UN3027, UN3049, UN3050, UN3071, UN3077, UN3080, UN3082, UN3084 to UN3088, UN3093, UN3094, UN3095, UN3096, UN3098, UN3099, UN3101 to UN3120, UN3122 toUN3126, UN3128 to UN3132, UN3134, UN3135,UN3139, UN3140, UN3142, UN3143, UN3146, UN3147, UN3148, UN3156, UN3157, UN3158, UN3160, UN3161, UN3162, UN3163, UN3172, UN3175, UN3176, UN3178 to UN3192, UN3194, UN3200, UN3203, UN3205 to UN3209, UN3221 to UN3240, UN3243, UN3244, UN3248, UN3249,UN3259, UN3260 to UN3267, UN3271 to UN3282, UN3286 to UN3290, UN3301, UN3303 to UN3312, UN3336, UN3345 to UN3352, UN3354, UN3355*

17 These dangerous goods may be handled, offered for transport or transported under the UN number and shipping name UN1268, PETROLEUM DISTILLATES, N.O.S., PETROLEUM PRODUCTS N.O.S., DISTILLATS DE PÉTROLE, N.S.A. or PRODUITS PÉTROLIERS, N.S.A.

*UN1203, UN1863*

18   These Regulations do not apply to UN1845, CARBON DIOXIDE, SOLID, or DRY ICE that is transported by a road vehicle, a railway vehicle or a ship on a domestic voyage and that is used as a refrigerant in a small means of containment if

    (a) the consignor includes, on a document that accompanies the small means of containment, the words "Dry ice as refrigerant" or "Neige carbonique comme réfrigérant"; and

    (b) the small means of containment in which the dry ice is used as a refrigerant is designed and constructed to permit the release of carbon dioxide to prevent the build-up of pressure that could rupture the small means of containment.

    *UN1845*

---

19   A person must not handle, offer for transport or transport chemically unstable mixtures of these dangerous goods.

    *UN1826, UN1832*

---

21   This shipping name has the UN number

 (1)  (a) UN2990 if it is a life saving appliance that is self-inflating and that presents a hazard when the self-inflating device is activated accidentally;

    (b) UN2990 if it is a life saving appliance that is self-inflating and includes as equipment one or more of the dangerous goods set out in subsection (2); and

    (c) UN3072 if it is a life saving appliance that is not self-inflating and includes as equipment one or more of the dangerous goods set out in subsection (2).

 (2)  The dangerous goods are

    (a) signal devices included in Class 1;

    (b) non-flammable, non-toxic gases included in Class 2.2;

    (c) dangerous goods included in Class 3, Class 4.1 or Class 5.2;

    (d) electric storage batteries included in Class 8; and

    (e) corrosive solids included in Class 8.

    *UN2990, UN3072*

Schedule 2

---

23 (1)  A consignor of these dangerous goods must include on a shipping document, after the classification of the dangerous goods, the words "toxic by inhalation" or "toxic - inhalation hazard" or "toxique par inhalation" or "toxicité par inhalation" if the dangerous goods meet the criteria for inclusion in Class 6.1, Packing Group I, due to inhalation toxicity.

    *For example:*
    *CYANIDE SOLUTION, N.O.S., Class 6.1, UN1935, PG I, toxic by inhalation*

 (2)  A person must not handle, offer for transport or transport these dangerous goods by passenger carrying road vehicle, passenger carrying railway vehicle or passenger carrying ship if they meet the criteria for inclusion in Class 6.1, Packing Group I, due to inhalation toxicity.

 (3)  This special provision does not apply to a person who transports these dangerous goods in accordance with the exemption in section 1.15 of Part 1, Coming Into Force, Repeal, Interpretation, General Provisions and Special Cases.

    *UN1556, UN1602, UN1935, UN2024, UN2206, UN2570, UN2781, UN2784, UN2788, UN2810, UN2902, UN2903, UN2927, UN2929, UN2991 to UN2998, UN3005, UN3006, UN3009 to UN3020, UN3025, UN3026, UN3080, UN3122, UN3123, UN3140, UN3142, UN3144, UN3275, UN3276, UN3278 to UN3282*

24    Lead compounds are considered to be insoluble if they exhibit a solubility of 5 per cent or less when they are mixed in a ratio of 1:1000 with 0.07 molar hydrochloric acid and stirred for one hour at a temperature of $23^{o}C \pm 2^{o}C$.

*UN2291*

---

25 (1) These dangerous goods may be handled, offered for transport or transported under this shipping name as component parts of vehicle air bags or seat belt pretensioners if they are tested in accordance with the Series 6 type (c) test in Section 16 of Part I of the Manual of Tests and Criteria and show no explosion of the device, no fragmentation of device casings and no projection hazard or thermal effect that could hinder fire fighting or other emergency response efforts. If the air bag inflator unit passes the Series 6 type (c) test, the test does not have to be repeated on the air bag module itself.

   (2) These Regulations do not apply to air bags or seat belts installed in vehicles or in completed vehicle components such as steering columns, door panels and seats.

*UN3268*

---

26    When these dangerous goods are nickel sulphate that contains more than 15 per cent free sulphuric acid or more than 30 per cent water and water of crystallization and are contained in a drum, the drum must be in compliance with specification 1H2 for drums described in CGSB-43.150.

*UN3244*

---

28    A person must not handle, offer for transport or transport these dangerous goods unless they are stabilized and their temperature is maintained below the control temperature while they are being transported.

*UN1026, UN3111 to UN3118, UN3231 to UN3240*

---

29    ***DELETED***

---

31    These Regulations do not apply to dangerous goods transported under this shipping name if the dangerous goods contain more than 70 per cent double salt (calcium nitrate and ammonium nitrate), at least 12 per cent water and no more than 10 per cent ammonium nitrate.

*UN1454*

---

32    These Regulations, except for Part 3, Documentation, do not apply to these dangerous goods if they are transported by road vehicle or railway vehicle in a large means of containment and

   (a) the large means of containment is in standard with CSA B621 for transport by road vehicle or with CGSB-43.147 for transport by railway vehicle; and

   **(b) DELETED**

---

33    These Regulations do not apply to these dangerous goods if the dangerous goods

   (a) are in a quantity less than or equal to 400 kg per means of containment; or

   (b) have been formed to a specific shape such as prills, granules, pellets, pastilles or flakes.

*UN1350*

---

34 (1) Lithium cells and batteries may be transported under this shipping name, if

   (a) each cell or battery is included in Class 9 in accordance with section 38.3 of Part III of the Manual of Tests and Criteria;

Schedule 2

(b) each cell contains not more than 12 g of lithium or lithium alloy;

(c) each battery contains not more than 500 g of lithium or lithium alloy;

(d) each cell or battery has a safety venting device or is designed to prevent a violent rupture under normal conditions of transport;

(e) each cell or battery is equipped with an effective means of preventing external short circuits;

(f) each battery containing cells or a series of cells connected in parallel is equipped with diodes to prevent reverse current flow; and

(g) the cells and batteries are packed in a means of containment to prevent short circuits and movement that could lead to short circuits.

(2) These Regulations do not apply to lithium cells and batteries if

(a) each cell with a liquid cathode contains not more than 0.5 g of lithium or lithium alloy;

(b) each battery with a liquid cathode contains a total quantity of not more than 1 g of lithium or lithium alloy;

(c) each cell or battery with a liquid cathode is hermetically sealed;

(d) each cell with a solid cathode contains not more than 1 g of lithium or lithium alloy;

(e) each battery with a solid cathode contains a total quantity of not more than 2 g of lithium or lithium alloy;

(f) each lithium-ion cell contains a total quantity of not more than 1.5 g of equivalent lithium content, where the equivalent lithium content in grams is 0.3 times the rated capacity of the cell in ampere-hours;

(g) each lithium-ion battery contains a total quantity of not more than 8 g of equivalent lithium content, where the equivalent lithium content in grams is 0.3 times the rated capacity of the battery in ampere-hours;

(h) for a liquid cathode battery that contains more than 0.5 g of lithium or lithium alloy or a solid cathode battery that contains more than 1 g of lithium or lithium alloy, the battery does not contain a liquid or gas that is dangerous goods unless the liquid or gas, if free, would be completely absorbed or neutralized by other materials in the battery;

(i) the cells are separated to prevent short circuits; and

(j) the batteries are separated to prevent short circuits and, except when they are installed in electronic devices, are packed in strong means of containment.

(3) These Regulations do not apply to lithium cells or batteries if

(a) the cells or batteries are not included in Class 9 in accordance with section 38.3 of Part III of the Manual of Tests and Criteria;

(b) each cell contains not more than 5 g of lithium or lithium alloy;

(c) each battery contains not more than 25 g of lithium or lithium alloy; and

(d) the cells and batteries are packed or are designed to prevent short circuits under normal conditions of transport.

*UN3090, UN3091*

36    These Regulations do not apply to the handling, offering for transport or transporting of these dangerous goods by road vehicle or railway vehicle if they are in the form of pellets or dry bulk mash meeting the requirements in CGSB-32.301.

*UN1386, UN2217*

37  Part 3, Documentation, Part 4, Dangerous Goods Safety Marks, and Part 6, Training, do not apply to these dangerous goods or mixtures or solutions of them if they are transported by road vehicle and are

(a) purchased by retail sale and are being transported between any of the following places:

   (i)  the place of purchase,

   (ii)  the place of use or consumption, and

   (iii) the purchaser's place of residence;

(b) in a quantity less than or equal to 13.6 tonnes; and

(c) accompanied by a record sheet that includes the shipping name, the UN number and the quantity of the dangerous goods or mixtures or solutions of them.
   *UN1942, UN2067 to UN2072*

38  A person must not handle, offer for transport or transport these dangerous goods in a large means of containment if they are in direct contact with the large means of containment.
   *UN1001, UN1045, UN1058, UN1081, UN1194, UN1204, UN1222, UN1259, UN1261, UN1308, UN1310, UN1320, UN1321, UN1322, UN1324, UN1336, UN1337, UN1344, UN1347, UN1348, UN1349, UN1354, UN1355, UN1356, UN1357, UN1360, UN1378, UN1380, UN1383, UN1389, UN1391, UN1392, UN1396, UN1404, UN1407, UN1409, UN1410, UN1411, UN1413, UN1414, UN1415, UN1418, UN1419, UN1421, UN1426, UN1427, UN1432, UN1433, UN1436, UN1491, UN1504, UN1510, UN1517, UN1556, UN1557, UN1569, UN1571, UN1575, UN1582, UN1589, UN1612, UN1614, UN1660, UN1693, UN1697 to UN1701, UN1714, UN1748, UN1749, UN1854, UN1855, UN1859, UN1865, UN1868, UN1870, UN1889, UN1911, UN1913, UN1953, UN1955, UN1957, UN1959, UN1967, UN1975, UN1982, UN1994, UN2006, UN2008, UN2010, UN2011, UN2012, UN2013, UN2188, UN2189, UN2190, UN2192, UN2194 to UN2199, UN2202, UN2203, UN2204, UN2417, UN2418, UN2420, UN2421, UN2451, UN2463, UN2466, UN2471, UN2480, UN2545, UN2546, UN2547, UN2548, UN2555, UN2556, UN2557, UN2626, UN2627, UN2676, UN2741, UN2806, UN2813, UN2814, UN2846, UN2852, UN2870, UN2881, UN2900, UN2901, UN2907, UN2956, UN2988, UN3048, UN3064, UN3083, UN3094, UN3095, UN3096, UN3101 to UN3108, UN3124, UN3125, UN3129, UN3130, UN3131, UN3132, UN3134, UN3135, UN3148, UN3160, UN3162, UN3221 to UN3230, UN3248, UN3249, UN3303 to UN3310, UN3317, UN3355*

39 (1) These dangerous goods may be handled, offered for transport or transported under this shipping name if the dangerous goods are

(a) protected from short circuits; and

(b) capable of withstanding, without leakage of battery fluid, the following tests:

   (i)  a vibration test, in which

      (A)  the battery is rigidly clamped to the platform of a vibration machine and a simple harmonic motion having an amplitude of 0.8 mm (1.6 mm maximum total excursion) is applied,

      (B)  the frequency is varied in steps of 1 Hz each minute between the limits of 10 Hz and 55 Hz,

      (C)  the entire range of frequencies and return is traversed in 95 ± 5 minutes with 2 minutes spent at each frequency for each mounting position (direction of vibration) of the battery, and

(D) the battery is tested in three mutually perpendicular positions (to include testing with fill openings and vents, if any, in an inverted position) for equal time periods, and

    (ii) after the vibration test, a pressure differential test, in which

        (A) the battery is stored for 6 hours at 24°C ± 4°C while subjected to a pressure differential greater than or equal to 88 kPa, and

        (B) the battery is tested in three mutually perpendicular positions (to include testing with fill openings and vents, if any, in an inverted position) for at least 6 hours in each position.

(2) These Regulations do not apply to UN2800, BATTERIES, WET, NON-SPILLABLE, electric storage, that are not intended for disposal if,

(a) at a temperature of 55°C, electrolyte will not flow from a ruptured or cracked battery case and there is no free liquid to flow; and

(b) when the battery is prepared for transport, the battery's terminals are protected from short circuits.

*UN2800*

---

40   These Regulations do not apply to these articles if each article

(a) has a gas space capacity less than or equal to 1.6 L and a charge pressure less than or equal to 28 000 kPa and, when the capacity (litres) is multiplied by the charge pressure (kilopascals) and then divided by 100, the result is less than or equal to 80;

(b) has a minimum burst pressure that is 4 times the charge pressure at 20°C for an article that has a gas space capacity less than or equal to 0.5 L and 5 times the charge pressure at 20°C for an article that has a gas space capacity greater than 0.5 L;

(c) is manufactured from material that will not fragment if ruptured; and

(d) is protected from rupture by means of a fire degradable seal or a pressure relief device to relieve internal pressure.

*UN3164*

---

41 (1) A person must not handle, offer for transport or transport UN3356, OXYGEN GENERATOR, CHEMICAL, that contains dangerous goods included in Class 5.1, Oxidizing Substances, unless:

(a) the oxygen generator is capable of withstanding a 1.8 m drop test onto a rigid, non-resilient, flat and horizontal surface, in the position that is most likely to cause damage, without loss of its contents and without its activation;

(b) if the oxygen generator is equipped with an activating device, it has at least two positive means to prevent an unintentional activation; and

(c) the oxygen generator is transported in a means of containment that is inside another means of containment so that, if the oxygen generator is activated,

    (i) it will not activate other oxygen generators being transported in the same means of transport,

    (ii) the means of containment will not ignite, and

    (iii) the outside surface temperature of the outer means of containment will not exceed 100°C.

(2) A person must not handle, offer for transport or transport an oxygen generator under this shipping name if it is equipped with an activating device that meets the criteria for inclusion in Class 1, Explosives.

*UN3356*

---

42   ***DELETED***

---

43   Despite section 2.1 of Part 2, Classification, these dangerous goods are assigned to this classification based on human experience.

*UN1230, UN1547, UN1577, UN1578, UN1590, UN1591, UN1661, UN1662, UN1663, UN1671, UN1673, UN1708, UN2023, UN2078, UN2311, UN2432, UN2474, UN2512, UN2730*

---

45   Maneb and maneb preparations that have been stabilized against self-heating do not have to be classified with a primary class of Class 4.2 or be assigned the UN number UN2210 if it can be demonstrated by testing that I m3 of the substance does not self-ignite and that the temperature at the centre of a I m3 sample does not exceed 200°C when the sample is kept in a storage area maintained at a temperature of not less than $75^O C \pm 2^O C$ for a period of 24 hours. In this case, the dangerous goods have the classification assigned to the UN number UN2968.

*UN2210*

---

50   Dodecylphenol is a severe marine pollutant.

*UN2430, UN3145*

---

51 (1) Cadmium sulphide, UN2570, CADMIUM COMPOUND, is a marine pollutant but not a severe marine pollutant.

(2) Cadmium selenite, UN2570, CADMIUM COMPOUND, is not a marine pollutant or a severe marine pollutant.

*UN2570*

---

52   Tetraethyllead, UN1649, MOTOR FUEL ANTI-KNOCK MIXTURE, is a severe marine pollutant.

*UN1649*

---

53   Para-chlorobenzyl chloride, UN2235, CHLOROBENZYL CHLORIDE, liquid or solid, is a marine pollutant.

*UN2235*

---

55   Aqueous solutions of inorganic nitrate substances do not meet the criteria for inclusion in Class 5.1 if the concentration of the inorganic nitrate substances in the aqueous solution at the minimum temperature that may be encountered in transport is not more than 80 per cent of the saturation limit of the inorganic nitrate substance in solution.

*UN3218*

---

56   When solids that are not dangerous goods and liquids included in Class 3, Flammable Liquids, are in a mixture, the mixture may be handled, offered for transport or transported under this shipping name without the tests and criteria for including substances in Class 4.1, Flammable Solids, first being applied, if

(a) there is no free liquid visible at the time the mixture is loaded into a means of containment or at the time the means of containment is closed; and

(b) each means of containment is leakproof.

57 When solids that are not dangerous goods and liquids included in Class 6.1, Toxic Substances, are in a mixture, the mixture may be handled, offered for transport or transported under this shipping name without the tests and criteria for including substances in Class 6.1, Toxic Substances, first being applied, if

(a) the mixture is included in Packing Group II or III;

(b) there is no free liquid visible at the time the mixture is loaded into a means of containment or at the time the means of containment is closed; and

(c) each means of containment is leakproof.
    UN3243

58 When solids that are not dangerous goods and liquids included in Class 8, Corrosives, are in a mixture, the mixture may be handled, offered for transport or transported under this shipping name without the tests and criteria for including substances in Class 8, Corrosives, first being applied, if

(a) there is no free liquid visible at the time the mixture is loaded into a means of containment or at the time the means of containment is closed; and

(b) each means of containment is leakproof.
    UN3244

59 Substances that are listed by name in Schedule 1 must not be transported under this shipping name. Substances transported under this shipping name may contain not more than 20 per cent nitrocellulose if the nitrocellulose contains not more than 12.6 per cent nitrogen (by dry mass).
    UN1210, UN1263, UN3066

60 These dangerous goods may be included in Class 4.1 if

(a) they are in a quantity less than or equal to 11.5 kg per means of containment;

(b) they contain more than 10 per cent water by mass; and

(c) a negative test result is obtained when they are tested in accordance with the Series 6 type (c) test referred to in Section 16 of Part I of the Manual of Tests and Criteria.
    UN0220, UN1357

61 This substance may be handled, offered for transport or transported under a class other than Class 1 if it is packed so that the percentage of water that it contains will not, at any time during transport, fall below the percentage stated in the descriptive text associated with the shipping name. When phlegmatized with water and inorganic inert material the content of urea nitrate must not exceed 75 per cent by mass and the mixture must not be capable of being detonated by the Test Series 1 type (a) test referred to in section 11 of Part I in the Manual of Tests and Criteria.
    UN1357

62 These dangerous goods may be handled, offered for transport or transported under Class 4.1 if they are packed in a means of containment so that the percentage of diluent in them will not, at any time during transport, fall below the percentage stated for the diluent in the descriptive text associated with the shipping name.
    UN1310, UN1320, UN1321, UN1322, UN1336, UN1337, UN1344, UN1348, UN1349, UN1354, UN1355, UN1356, UN1517, UN3317

63   These Regulations do not apply to these dangerous goods unless they are to be transported by aircraft.

*UN1910, UN2807, UN2812, UN3166, UN3171*

64 (1) These Regulations do not apply to these dangerous goods unless they are to be transported by ship.

(2) These dangerous goods must not be transported by ship when they are wet, damp or contaminated with oil.

*UN1327, UN2216*

65   A CHEMICAL KIT or FIRST AID KIT must be included in the packing group that is the most stringent packing group assigned to any one of the dangerous goods in the kit and must not contain

(a) dangerous goods that are not allowed to be transported as limited quantities or that are forbidden for transport in Schedule 1 or Schedule 3;

(b) dangerous goods that react dangerously with each other; or

(c) a total quantity of dangerous goods that is greater than 1 L for liquids or 1 kg for solids.

*UN3316*

66   These dangerous goods are forbidden for transport by ship.

*UN1347, UN1512*

67   This shipping name applies to vehicles and equipment powered by wet batteries, sodium batteries or lithium batteries if they are handled, offered for transport or transported with these batteries installed.

*Examples of these vehicles and equipment include electrically powered cars, lawnmowers, wheelchairs and other mobility aids.*

*UN3171*

68   These dangerous goods are forbidden for transport by ship if they contain one or more of the following substances:

(a) ammonium chlorite;

(b) ammonium compound, mixture;

(c) ammonium compounds, solution;

(d) AMMONIUM NITRATE, liable to self-heating sufficient to initiate a decomposition;

(e) CHLORIC ACID, AQUEOUS SOLUTION, with a concentration greater than 10 per cent by mass;

(f) HYDROCYANIC ACID, AQUEOUS SOLUTION, with greater than 20 per cent acid, by mass;

(g) HYDROGEN CYANIDE, SOLUTION IN ALCOHOL, with greater than 45 per cent hydrogen cyanide by mass; or

(h) SILVER PICRATE, WETTED, with less than 30 per cent water by mass.

*UN1194, UN1347, UN1450, UN1461, UN1462, UN1482, UN1512, UN1613, UN1642, UN1802, UN1873, UN2067, UN2068, UN2069, UN2070, UN2072, UN2626, UN2627, UN3210, UN3212, UN3213, UN3214, UN3219, UN3294*

69   The following definitions apply to matches:

(a) fusee matches are matches the heads of which are prepared with a friction-sensitive igniter composition and a pyrotechnic composition that burns with little or no flame but with intense heat;

(b) safety matches are matches that are combined with or attached to the box, book or card and that can be ignited by friction only on a prepared surface;

(c) strike-anywhere matches are matches that can be ignited by friction on a solid surface; and

(d) Wax Vesta matches are matches that can be ignited by friction either on a prepared surface or on a solid surface.

*UN1331*

---

70 (1) These dangerous goods must be formulated so that during transport they remain homogeneous and do not separate.

(2) These Regulations do not apply to formulations of these dangerous goods when they have a low nitrocellulose content and

(a) are not capable of detonating or deflagrating when tested using the Test Series 1 type (a) test referred to in section 11 of Part I of the Manual of Tests and Criteria;

(b) do not explode when heated under confinement when tested using the Test Series 1 type (b) test and Test Series 1 type (c) test referred to in section 11 of Part I of the Manual of Tests and Criteria; and

(c) are not flammable solids when tested using Test N.1 referred to in section 33.2.1.4 of Part III of the Manual of Tests and Criteria; to perform this test, the particle size of the nitrocellulose must be less than 1.25 mm or the nitrocellulose must be crushed and sieved to this size.

*UN2557*

---

71 Ammonium nitrites and mixtures of an inorganic nitrite with an ammonium salt are forbidden for transport.

*UN2627*

---

72 Despite paragraph 2.5(d) of Part 2, Classification, if these dangerous goods meet the definitions and criteria for inclusion in other classes in accordance with Part 2, Classification, the subsidiary class or classes must be shown on a shipping document along with the primary class for the dangerous goods.

*UN2908 to UN2911*

---

73 During transport, these dangerous goods must be protected from direct sunlight and stored away from all sources of heat in a cool and well-ventilated place.

*UN3241*

---

74 (1) If these dangerous goods have a subsidiary class or classes, they must be assigned to Packing Group I, II or III, as appropriate, in accordance with the criteria in Part 2, Classification, for the subsidiary class that takes precedence.

(2) The description of the subsidiary class or classes of the dangerous goods and the labels and placards must be displayed on a means of containment in accordance with the requirements in Part 4, Dangerous Goods Safety Marks.

(3) The description of the subsidiary class or classes on a shipping document must be in accordance with Part 3, Documentation.

*UN2912, UN2913, UN2915, UN2916, UN2917, UN2919, UN3321 to UN3333*

Schedule 2

| 75 | **DELETED** |
|---|---|

| 76 | Despite section 5.7 of Part 5, Means of Containment, any combination of these dangerous goods included in Class 1, Explosives, may be handled, offered for transport or transported in a road vehicle if |
|---|---|

(a) the total quantity of all the dangerous goods included in Class 1, expressed in net explosives quantity, is less than or equal to 5 kg;

(b) the total number of articles of dangerous goods subject to special provision 86 is less than or equal to 100 articles; and

(c) the operator of the road vehicle has a valid Pyrotechnic Card that has been issued to the operator by the Explosives Regulatory Division of Natural Resources Canada.

*UN0027, UN0066, UN0094, UN0101, UN0105, UN0161, UN0197, UN0255, UN0305, UN0325, UN0335, UN0336, UN0337, UN0349, UN0430, UN0431, UN0432, UN0454, UN0499 UN0027, UN0066, UN0094, UN0101, UN0105, UN0161, UN0197, UN0255, UN0305, UN0325, UN0335, UN0336, UN0337, UN0349, UN0430, UN0431, UN0432, UN0454, UN0499*

| 77 | **DELETED** |
|---|---|

78 These dangerous goods do not include ammonium permanganate which is forbidden for transport. (See Schedule 3)

*UN1482*

79 These dangerous goods are forbidden for transport if they contain less alcohol, water or phlegmatizer than specified in the descriptive text associated with the shipping name.

*UN0072, UN0074, UN0075, UN0113, UN0114, UN0129, UN0130, UN0133, UN0135, UN0143, UN0150, UN0159, UN0226, UN0391, UN0433*

80 Despite section 1.17, a person must not offer for transport or transport these dangerous goods unless they are in a means of containment that is in compliance with Part 5, Means of Containment.

*UN1950*

81 Section 5.12 of Part 5, Means of Containment, does not apply to these dangerous goods if they are handled, offered for transport or transported in a means of containment designed, constructed, filled, closed, secured and maintained so that under normal conditions of transport, including handling, there will be no accidental release of the dangerous goods that could endanger public safety.

*UN1841, UN1845, UN1931, UN2807, UN2969, UN2990, UN3072, UN3166, UN3171, UN3245 UN1841, UN1845, UN1931, UN2807, UN2969, UN2990, UN3072, UN3166, UN3171, UN3245*

82 These dangerous goods require an emergency response assistance plan in accordance with subsection 7.1(5) of Part 7, Emergency Response Assistance Plan.

*UN1202, UN1203, UN1863*

83 Section 5.12 of Part 5, Means of Containment, does not apply to these dangerous goods if

(a) the dangerous goods are included in Packing Group II or III;

(b) the dangerous goods are in quantities less than or equal to 5 L and are in a metal or plastic means of containment;

(c) the metal or plastic means of containment is inside an outer means of containment and the gross mass of the outer means of containment is less than or equal to 40 kg;

(d) the means of containment are designed, constructed, filled, closed, secured and maintained

so that under normal conditions of transport, including handling, there will be no accidental release of the dangerous goods that could endanger public safety;

(e) the dangerous goods are transported in palletized loads, a pallet box or unit load device so that individual means of containment are placed or stacked and secured to the pallet by strapping, shrink- or stretch-wrapping or other suitable means; and

(f) when the dangerous goods are on a road vehicle or a railway vehicle that is to be transported by ship, the pallets, pallet boxes or unit load devices are secured inside the vehicle and the vehicle is closed.
*UN1133, UN1210, UN1263, UN1866 UN1133, UN1210, UN1263, UN1866*

---

84 The infectious substances identified in subsection 7.1(6) of Part 7, Emergency Response Assistance Plan, require an emergency response assistance plan.
*UN2814, UN2900*

---

85 Despite the index number in column 6 of Schedule 1, these dangerous goods may be handled, offered for transport or transported in accordance with section 1.31 of Part 1, Coming into Force, Repeal, Interpretation, General Provisions and Special Cases, when they are in a quantity that is less than or equal to 15 000 articles.
*UN0044*

---

86 Despite the index number in column 6 of Schedule 1, these dangerous goods may be handled, offered for transport or transported in accordance with section 1.31 of Part 1, Coming into Force, Repeal, Interpretation, General Provisions and Special Cases, when they are in a quantity that is less than or equal to 100 articles.
*UN0029, UN0030, UN0121, UN0131, UN0255, UN0267, UN0315, UN0325, UN0349, UN0360, UN0361, UN0367, UN0368, UN0454, UN0455, UN0456, UN0500*

---

87 Despite the word "Forbidden" in column 9 of Schedule 1, these dangerous goods may be transported on a passenger carrying road vehicle or a passenger carrying railway vehicle in accordance with section 1.15 of Part 1, Coming into Force, Repeal, Interpretation, General Provisions and Special Cases, when they are used for medical purposes during transport and are in a means of containment with a capacity less than or equal to 1 L.
*UN1073*

---

88 Despite the quantity limits in column 9 of Schedule 1 for these dangerous goods, a road vehicle is not a passenger carrying road vehicle unless the passengers in it are transported for hire or reward
*UN1202, UN1203, UN1978*

---

89 Despite subsection 5.12(1) of Part 5, Means of Containment, until January 1, 2010, these dangerous goods may be transported on a road vehicle or a ship on a domestic voyage in a small means of containment if the small means of containment

(a) is a welded metal tank;

(b) is used for the application of liquid tar to pavement, concrete or metallic structures and is fitted with the appropriate application equipment; and

(c) is designed, constructed, filled, closed, secured and maintained so that under normal conditions of transport, including handling, there will be no accidental release of the dangerous goods that could endanger public safety.
*UN1999*

# SCHEDULE 3

## Index of Emergency Response Guides (ERG)

### (Alphabetical Listing of Dangerous Goods with ERG Numbers)

#### PURPOSE OF THIS SCHEDULE

This Schedule when used in conjunction with Schedule 4 satisfies the requirements of 49CFR 172.602 with respect to the information that must accompany a shipment of dangerous goods. The information is obtained from the 2008 Emergency Response Guidebook developed by Transport Canada and the US Department of Transportation.

The potential hazards posed by each substance and suitable response and protective actions are identified in sixty-one different Emergency Response Guides. This Schedule provides the Shipping Names of dangerous goods in alphabetical order followed by the UN Number and Emergency Response Guide number. Upon identifying a Emergency Response Guide number, refer to Schedule 4, where the safety recommendations for each hazard are provided. (Some substances that are forbidden for transport, whether or not the substances have a UN Number, are also included in this Schedule.)

Emergency Response Guide numbers may also be obtained from the cross-reference of UN Numbers with Emergency Response Guide numbers in Schedule 5 (page 226).

*Refer to Schedule 4 (page 162) for instructions on the use and application of the Emergency Response Guide numbers.*

*Guide notations:*

The letter "**T**" following the ERG number indicates substances that are toxic-by-inhalation (TIH). (When TIH substances are spilled, isolation and protective action distances may be involved. These are shown in Schedule 6 along with an explanation of their application on page 233.)

**In an emergency involving Dangerous Goods shown with a "T" and also involving a fire, refer to the information under the PUBLIC SAFETY heading in the appropriate ERG. In an emergency involving Dangerous Goods shown with a "T" but no fire is involved, refer to the Initial Isolation and Protective Action Distances shown in Schedule 6.**

The letter "**P**" following the ERG number indicates substances that may polymerize explosively when heated or involved in a fire.

The Emergency Response Guide includes dangerous goods with UN numbers which are not yet included in the Transportation of Dangerous Goods Regulations. These dangerous goods are shown with an "**\***" beside the UN Number.

| Description | UN # | ERG # |
|---|---|---|
| ACETAL | UN1088 | 127 |
| ACETALDEHYDE | UN1089 | 129 |
| ACETALDEHYDE AMMONIA | UN1841 | 171 |
| ACETALDEHYDE OXIME | UN2332 | 129 |
| ACETIC ACID, GLACIAL | UN2789 | 132 |
| ACETIC ACID SOLUTION, more than 10 per cent and less than 50 per cent acid, by mass | UN2790 | 153 |
| ACETIC ACID SOLUTION, more than 80 per cent acid, by mass | UN2789 | 132 |
| ACETIC ACID SOLUTION, not less than 50 per cent but not more than 80 per cent acid, by mass | UN2790 | 153 |
| ACETIC ANHYDRIDE | UN1715 | 137 |
| ACETONE | UN1090 | 127 |
| ACETONE CYANOHYDRIN, STABILIZED | UN1541 | 155T |
| ACETONE OILS | UN1091 | 127 |
| ACETONITRILE | UN1648 | 131 |
| ACETYL ACETONE PEROXIDE with more than 9 percent by mass active oxygen | Forbidden | |
| ACETYL BENZOYL PEROXIDE, SOLID | Forbidden | |
| ACETYL BROMIDE | UN1716 | 156T |
| ACETYL CHLORIDE | UN1717 | 132T |
| ACETYL CYCLOHEXANESULFONYL PEROXIDE, with more than 82 percent wetted with less than 12 percent water | Forbidden | |
| ACETYL CYCLOHEXANESULPHONYL PEROXIDE, with more than 82 percent wetted with less than 12 percent water | Forbidden | |
| ACETYLENE, DISSOLVED | UN1001 | 116 |
| ACETYLENE, LIQUEFIED | Forbidden | |
| ACETYLENE SILVER NITRATE | Forbidden | |
| ACETYL IODIDE | UN1898 | 156T |
| ACETYL METHYL CARBINOL | UN2621 | 127 |
| ACETYL PEROXIDE, SOLID, or with more than 25 percent in solution | Forbidden | |
| ACRIDINE | UN2713 | 153 |
| ACROLEIN DIMER, STABILIZED | UN2607 | 129P |
| ACROLEIN, STABILIZED | UN1092 | 131PT |
| ACRYLAMIDE | UN2074 | 153P |
| ACRYLIC ACID, STABILIZED | UN2218 | 132P |
| ACRYLONITRILE, STABILIZED | UN1093 | 131P |
| ADHESIVES containing flammable liquid | UN1133 | 128 |
| ADIPONITRILE | UN2205 | 153 |
| AEROSOLS, containing a toxic gas in class 2.3 | Forbidden | |
| AEROSOLS, containing compressed oxygen | UN1950 | 126 |
| AEROSOLS, containing substances in class 6.1, packing group I | Forbidden | |
| AEROSOLS, containing substances in class 8, packing group I | Forbidden | |
| AEROSOLS, flammable | UN1950 | 126 |
| AEROSOLS, flammable, containing substances in Class 6.1, packing group II | UN1950 | 126 |
| AEROSOLS, flammable, containing substances in Class 6.1, packing group III | UN1950 | 126 |
| AEROSOLS, flammable, containing substances in Class 6.1, packing group III and in Class 8, packing group II | UN1950 | 126 |
| AEROSOLS, flammable, containing substances in Class 6.1, packing group III and in Class 8, packing group III | UN1950 | 126 |
| AEROSOLS, flammable, containing substances in Class 8, packing group II | UN1950 | 126 |
| AEROSOLS, flammable, containing substances in Class 8, packing group III | UN1950 | 126 |
| AEROSOLS, non-flammable | UN1950 | 126 |
| AEROSOLS, non-flammable, containing substances in Class 6.1, packing group II | UN1950 | 126 |
| AEROSOLS, non-flammable, containing substances in Class 6.1, packing group III | UN1950 | 126 |
| AEROSOLS, non-flammable, containing substances in Class 6.1, packing group III and in Class 8, packing group II | UN1950 | 126 |

| Description | UN # | ERG # |
|---|---|---|
| AEROSOLS, non-flammable, containing substances in Class 6.1, packing group III and in Class 8, packing group III | UN1950 | 126 |
| AEROSOLS, non-flammable, containing substances in Class 8, packing group II | UN1950 | 126 |
| AEROSOLS, non-flammable, containing substances in Class 8, packing group III | UN1950 | 126 |
| AIR BAG INFLATORS, pyrotechnic | UN0503 | 114 |
| AIR BAG INFLATORS, pyrotechnic | UN3268 | 171 |
| AIR BAG MODULES, pyrotechnic | UN0503 | 114 |
| AIR BAG MODULES, pyrotechnic | UN3268 | 171 |
| AIR, COMPRESSED, with not more than 23.5 per cent oxygen, by volume | UN1002 | 122 |
| AIRCRAFT HYDRAULIC POWER UNIT FUEL TANK containing a mixture of anhydrous hydrazine and methylhydrazine (M86 fuel) | UN3165 | 131 |
| AIR, REFRIGERATED LIQUID | UN1003 | 122 |
| ALCOHOLATES SOLUTION, N.O.S., in alcohol | UN3274 | 127 |
| ALCOHOLIC BEVERAGES, more than 24 per cent but not more than 70 per cent alcohol, by volume | UN3065 | 127 |
| ALCOHOLIC BEVERAGES, more than 70 per cent alcohol, by volume | UN3065 | 127 |
| ALCOHOLS, FLAMMABLE, TOXIC, N.O.S. | UN1986 | 131 |
| ALCOHOLS, N.O.S. | UN1987 | 127 |
| ALDEHYDES, FLAMMABLE, TOXIC, N.O.S. | UN1988 | 131 |
| ALDEHYDES, N.O.S. | UN1989 | 129 |
| ALDOL | UN2839 | 153 |
| ALKALI METAL ALCOHOLATES, SELF-HEATING, CORROSIVE, N.O.S. | UN3206 | 136 |
| ALKALI METAL ALLOY, LIQUID, N.O.S. | UN1421 | 138 |
| ALKALI METAL AMALGAM, liquid | UN1389 | 138 |
| ALKALI METAL AMALGAM, LIQUID (ICAO/IMO terminology) | UN1389 | 138 |
| ALKALI METAL AMALGAM, solid | UN1389 | 138 |
| ALKALI METAL AMALGAM, SOLID (ICAO/IMO terminology) | UN1389 | 138 |
| ALKALI METAL AMIDES | UN1390 | 139 |
| ALKALI METAL DISPERSION | UN1391 | 138 |
| ALKALI METAL DISPERSION in a liquid with a flash point that is equal to or less than 60.5 °C | UN1391 | 138 |
| ALKALINE EARTH METAL ALCOHOLATES, N.O.S. | UN3205 | 135 |
| ALKALINE EARTH METAL ALLOY, N.O.S. | UN1393 | 138 |
| ALKALINE EARTH METAL AMALGAM | UN1392 | 138 |
| ALKALINE EARTH METAL DISPERSION | UN1391 | 138 |
| ALKALINE EARTH METAL DISPERSION in a liquid with a flash point that is equal to or less than 60.5 °C | UN1391 | 138 |
| ALKALOID SALTS, LIQUID, N.O.S. | UN3140 | 151 |
| ALKALOID SALTS, SOLID, N.O.S. | UN1544 | 151 |
| ALKALOIDS, LIQUID, N.O.S. | UN3140 | 151 |
| ALKALOIDS, SOLID, N.O.S. | UN1544 | 151 |
| ALKYLPHENOLS, LIQUID, N.O.S. including C2-C12 homologues | UN3145 | 153 |
| ALKYLPHENOLS, SOLID, N.O.S. including C2-C12 homologues | UN2430 | 153 |
| ALKYLSULFONIC ACIDS, LIQUID with more than 5 per cent free sulfuric acid | UN2584 | 153 |
| ALKYLSULFONIC ACIDS, LIQUID with not more than 5 per cent free sulfuric acid | UN2586 | 153 |
| ALKYLSULFONIC ACIDS, SOLID with more than 5 per cent free sulfuric acid | UN2583 | 153 |
| ALKYLSULFONIC ACIDS, SOLID with not more than 5 per cent free sulfuric acid | UN2585 | 153 |
| ALKYLSULFURIC ACIDS | UN2571 | 156 |
| ALKYLSULPHONIC ACIDS, LIQUID with more than 5 per cent free sulphuric acid | UN2584 | 153 |
| ALKYLSULPHONIC ACIDS, LIQUID with not more than 5 per cent free sulphuric acid | UN2586 | 153 |

| Description | UN # | ERG # |
|---|---|---|
| ALKYLSULPHONIC ACIDS, SOLID with more than 5 per cent free sulphuric acid | UN2583 | 153 |
| ALKYLSULPHONIC ACIDS, SOLID with not more than 5 per cent free sulphuric acid | UN2585 | 153 |
| ALKYLSULPHURIC ACIDS | UN2571 | 156 |
| ALLYL ACETATE | UN2333 | 131 |
| ALLYL ALCOHOL | UN1098 | 131T |
| ALLYLAMINE | UN2334 | 131T |
| ALLYL BROMIDE | UN1099 | 131 |
| ALLYL CHLORIDE | UN1100 | 131 |
| ALLYL CHLOROFORMATE | UN1722 | 155T |
| ALLYL ETHYL ETHER | UN2335 | 131 |
| ALLYL FORMATE | UN2336 | 131 |
| ALLYL GLYCIDYL ETHER | UN2219 | 129 |
| ALLYL IODIDE | UN1723 | 132 |
| ALLYL ISOTHIOCYANATE, STABILIZED | UN1545 | 155 |
| ALLYLTRICHLOROSILANE, STABILIZED | UN1724 | 155T |
| ALUMINUM ALKYL HALIDES, LIQUID | UN3052 | 135T |
| ALUMINUM ALKYL HALIDES, SOLID | UN3052 | 135T |
| ALUMINUM ALKYL HYDRIDES | UN3076 | 138 |
| ALUMINUM ALKYLS | UN3051 | 135 |
| ALUMINUM BOROHYDRIDE | UN2870 | 135 |
| ALUMINUM BOROHYDRIDE IN DEVICES | UN2870 | 135 |
| ALUMINUM BROMIDE, ANHYDROUS | UN1725 | 137T |
| ALUMINUM BROMIDE SOLUTION | UN2580 | 154 |
| ALUMINUM CARBIDE | UN1394 | 138 |
| ALUMINUM CHLORIDE, ANHYDROUS | UN1726 | 137 |
| ALUMINUM CHLORIDE SOLUTION | UN2581 | 154 |
| ALUMINUM DROSS, HOT | Forbidden | |
| ALUMINUM FERROSILICON POWDER | UN1395 | 139 |
| ALUMINUM HYDRIDE | UN2463 | 138 |
| ALUMINUM NITRATE | UN1438 | 140 |
| ALUMINUM PHOSPHIDE | UN1397 | 139T |
| ALUMINUM PHOSPHIDE PESTICIDE | UN3048 | 157T |
| ALUMINUM POWDER, COATED | UN1309 | 170 |
| ALUMINUM POWDER, UNCOATED | UN1396 | 138 |
| ALUMINUM REMELTING BY-PRODUCTS including, but not limited to, aluminum dross, aluminum skimmings, spent cathodes, spent potliner and aluminum salt slags | UN3170 | 138 |
| ALUMINUM RESINATE | UN2715 | 133 |
| ALUMINUM SILICON POWDER, UNCOATED | UN1398 | 138 |
| ALUMINUM SMELTING BY-PRODUCTS including, but not limited to, aluminum dross, aluminum skimmings, spent cathodes, spent potliner and aluminum salt slags | UN3170 | 138 |
| AMINES, FLAMMABLE, CORROSIVE, N.O.S. | UN2733 | 132 |
| AMINES, LIQUID, CORROSIVE, FLAMMABLE, N.O.S. | UN2734 | 132 |
| AMINES, LIQUID, CORROSIVE, N.O.S. | UN2735 | 153 |
| AMINES, SOLID, CORROSIVE, N.O.S. | UN3259 | 154 |
| 2-AMINO-4-CHLOROPHENOL | UN2673 | 151 |
| 2-AMINO-5-DIETHYLAMINOPENTANE | UN2946 | 153 |
| 2-AMINO-4,6-DINITROPHENOL, WETTED with not less than 20 per cent water, by mass | UN3317 | 113 |
| 2-(2-AMINOETHOXY)ETHANOL | UN3055 | 154 |
| N-AMINOETHYLPIPERAZINE | UN2815 | 153 |
| AMINOPHENOLS (o-,m-,p-) | UN2512 | 152 |
| AMINOPYRIDINES (o-,m-,p-) | UN2671 | 153 |
| AMMONIA, ANHYDROUS | UN1005 | 125T |
| AMMONIA SOLUTION, relative density between 0.880 and 0.957 at 15 °C in water, with more than 10 per cent but not more than 35 per cent ammonia | UN2672 | 154 |
| AMMONIA SOLUTION, relative density less than 0.880 at 15 °C in water, with more than 35 per cent but not more than 50 per cent ammonia | UN2073 | 125 |

| Description | UN # | ERG # |
|---|---|---|
| AMMONIA SOLUTION, relative density less than 0.880 at 15 °C in water, with more than 50 per cent ammonia | UN3318 | 125T |
| AMMONIUM ARSENATE | UN1546 | 151 |
| AMMONIUM AZIDE | Forbidden | |
| AMMONIUM BROMATE | Forbidden | |
| AMMONIUM CHLORATE | Forbidden | |
| AMMONIUM DICHROMATE | UN1439 | 141 |
| AMMONIUM DINITRO-o-CRESOLATE | UN1843 | 141 |
| AMMONIUM FLUORIDE | UN2505 | 154 |
| AMMONIUM FLUOROSILICATE | UN2854 | 151 |
| AMMONIUM FULMINATE | Forbidden | |
| AMMONIUM HYDROGENDIFLUORIDE, SOLID | UN1727 | 154 |
| AMMONIUM HYDROGENDIFLUORIDE SOLUTION | UN2817 | 154 |
| AMMONIUM HYDROGEN SULFATE | UN2506 | 154 |
| AMMONIUM HYDROGEN SULPHATE | UN2506 | 154 |
| AMMONIUM METAVANADATE | UN2859 | 154 |
| AMMONIUM NITRATE FERTILIZER, N.O.S. | UN2072 | 140 |
| AMMONIUM NITRATE FERTILIZERS: uniform non-segregating mixtures of ammonium nitrate/ammonium sulphate, with more than 45 per cent but not more than 70 per cent ammonium nitrate and not more than 0.4 per cent total combustible material | UN2069 | 140 |
| AMMONIUM NITRATE FERTILIZERS: uniform non-segregating mixtures of ammonium nitrate with added matter which is inorganic and chemically inert towards ammonium nitrate, with not less than 90 per cent ammonium nitrate and not more than 0.2 per cent combustible material (including organic material calculated as carbon) or with more than 70 per cent but less than 90 per cent ammonium nitrate and not more than 0.4 per cent total combustible material | UN2067 | 140 |
| AMMONIUM NITRATE FERTILIZERS: uniform non-segregating mixtures of ammonium nitrate with calcium carbonate and/or dolomite, with more than 80 per cent but less than 90 per cent ammonium nitrate and not more than 0.4 per cent total combustible material | UN2068 | 140 |
| AMMONIUM NITRATE FERTILIZERS: uniform non-segregating mixtures of nitrogen/phosphate or nitrogen/potash types or complete fertilizers of nitrogen/phosphate/potash type, with more than 70 per cent but less than 90 per cent ammonium nitrate and not more than 0.4 per cent total combustible material | UN2070 | 143 |
| AMMONIUM NITRATE FERTILIZERS: uniform non-segregating mixtures of nitrogen/phosphate or nitrogen/potash types or complete fertilizers of nitrogen/phosphate/potash type, with not more than 70 per cent ammonium nitrate and not more than 0.4 per cent total added combustible material or with not more than 45 per cent ammonium nitrate with unrestricted combustible material | UN2071 | 140 |
| AMMONIUM NITRATE FERTILIZER which is more liable to explode than ammonium nitrate with 0.2 per cent combustible substances, including any organic substance calculated as carbon, to the exclusion of any other added substance | UN0223 | 112 |
| AMMONIUM NITRATE, LIQUID (hot concentrated solution) with not more than 0.2 per cent combustible material, in a concentration exceeding 80 per cent | UN2426 | 140 |
| AMMONIUM NITRATE with more than 0.2 per cent combustible substances, including any organic substance calculated as carbon, to the exclusion of any other added substance | UN0222 | 112 |
| AMMONIUM NITRATE with not more than 0.2 per cent combustible substances, including any organic substance calculated as carbon, to the exclusion of any other added substance | UN1942 | 140 |
| AMMONIUM NITRITE | Forbidden | |
| AMMONIUM NITRITES and mixtures of an inorganic nitrite with an ammonium salt | Forbidden | |
| AMMONIUM PERCHLORATE | UN0402 | 112 |

| Description | UN # | ERG # |
|---|---|---|
| AMMONIUM PERCHLORATE for substances that are not ammonium perchlorate, Class 1.1D, UN0402 | UN1442 | 143 |
| AMMONIUM PERMANGANATE | Forbidden | |
| AMMONIUM PERSULFATE | UN1444 | 140 |
| AMMONIUM PERSULPHATE | UN1444 | 140 |
| AMMONIUM PICRATE dry or wetted with less than 10 per cent water, by mass | UN0004 | 112 |
| AMMONIUM PICRATE, WETTED with not less than 10 per cent water, by mass | UN1310 | 113 |
| AMMONIUM POLYSULFIDE SOLUTION | UN2818 | 154 |
| AMMONIUM POLYSULPHIDE SOLUTION | UN2818 | 154 |
| AMMONIUM POLYVANADATE | UN2861 | 151 |
| AMMONIUM SULFIDE SOLUTION | UN2683 | 132 |
| AMMONIUM SULPHIDE SOLUTION | UN2683 | 132 |
| AMMUNITION, ILLUMINATING with or without burster, expelling charge or propelling charge | UN0171 | 112 |
| AMMUNITION, ILLUMINATING with or without burster, expelling charge or propelling charge | UN0254 | 112 |
| AMMUNITION, ILLUMINATING with or without burster, expelling charge or propelling charge | UN0297 | 114 |
| AMMUNITION, INCENDIARY, liquid or gel, with burster, expelling charge or propelling charge | UN0247 | 112 |
| AMMUNITION, INCENDIARY, WHITE PHOSPHORUS with burster, expelling charge or propelling charge | UN0243 | 112 |
| AMMUNITION, INCENDIARY, WHITE PHOSPHORUS with burster, expelling charge or propelling charge | UN0244 | 112 |
| AMMUNITION, INCENDIARY with or without burster, expelling charge or propelling charge | UN0009 | 112 |
| AMMUNITION, INCENDIARY with or without burster, expelling charge or propelling charge | UN0010 | 112 |
| AMMUNITION, INCENDIARY with or without burster, expelling charge or propelling charge | UN0300 | 114 |
| AMMUNITION, PRACTICE | UN0362 | 114 |
| AMMUNITION, PRACTICE | UN0488 | 112 |
| AMMUNITION, PROOF | UN0363 | 114 |
| AMMUNITION, SMOKE, WHITE PHOSPHORUS with burster, expelling charge or propelling charge | UN0245 | 112 |
| AMMUNITION, SMOKE, WHITE PHOSPHORUS with burster, expelling charge or propelling charge | UN0246 | 112 |
| AMMUNITION, SMOKE with or without burster, expelling charge or propelling charge | UN0015 | 112 |
| AMMUNITION, SMOKE with or without burster, expelling charge or propelling charge | UN0016 | 112 |
| AMMUNITION, SMOKE with or without burster, expelling charge or propelling charge | UN0303 | 114 |
| AMMUNITION, TEAR-PRODUCING, NON-EXPLOSIVE without burster or expelling charge, non-fuzed | UN2017 | 159 |
| AMMUNITION, TEAR-PRODUCING with burster, expelling charge or propelling charge | UN0018 | 112 |
| AMMUNITION, TEAR-PRODUCING with burster, expelling charge or propelling charge | UN0019 | 112 |
| AMMUNITION, TEAR-PRODUCING with burster, expelling charge or propelling charge | UN0301 | 114 |
| AMMUNITION, TOXIC, NON-EXPLOSIVE without burster or expelling charge, non-fuzed | UN2016 | 151 |
| AMMUNITION, TOXIC with burster, expelling charge or propelling charge | UN0020 | 112 |
| AMMUNITION, TOXIC with burster, expelling charge or propelling charge | UN0021 | 112 |
| AMYL ACETATES | UN1104 | 129 |
| AMYL ACID PHOSPHATE | UN2819 | 153 |
| AMYLAMINE | UN1106 | 132 |
| AMYL BUTYRATES | UN2620 | 130 |
| AMYL CHLORIDE | UN1107 | 129 |
| n-AMYLENE | UN1108 | 127 |
| AMYL FORMATES | UN1109 | 129 |

| Description | UN # | ERG # |
|---|---|---|
| AMYL MERCAPTAN | UN1111 | 130 |
| n-AMYL METHYL KETONE | UN1110 | 127 |
| AMYL NITRATE | UN1112 | 140 |
| AMYL NITRITE | UN1113 | 129 |
| AMYLTRICHLOROSILANE | UN1728 | 155T |
| ANHYDROUS AMMONIA | UN1005 | 125T |
| ANILINE | UN1547 | 153 |
| ANILINE HYDROCHLORIDE | UN1548 | 153 |
| ANISIDINES, liquid | UN2431 | 153 |
| ANISIDINES, LIQUID (ICAO/IMO terminology) | UN2431 | 153 |
| ANISIDINES, solid | UN2431 | 153 |
| ANISIDINES, SOLID (ICAO/IMO terminology) | UN2431 | 153 |
| ANISOLE | UN2222 | 127 |
| ANISOYL CHLORIDE | UN1729 | 156 |
| ANTIMONY COMPOUND, INORGANIC, LIQUID, N.O.S. except antimony oxides and sulphides containing less than 0.5 per cent arsenic, by mass | UN3141 | 157 |
| ANTIMONY COMPOUND, INORGANIC, SOLID, N.O.S. except antimony oxides and sulphides containing less than 0.5 per cent arsenic, by mass | UN1549 | 157 |
| ANTIMONY LACTATE | UN1550 | 151 |
| ANTIMONY PENTACHLORIDE, LIQUID | UN1730 | 157 |
| ANTIMONY PENTACHLORIDE SOLUTION | UN1731 | 157 |
| ANTIMONY PENTAFLUORIDE | UN1732 | 157T |
| ANTIMONY POTASSIUM TARTRATE | UN1551 | 151 |
| ANTIMONY POWDER | UN2871 | 170 |
| ANTIMONY SULFIDE AND A CHLORATE, MIXTURES OF | Forbidden | |
| ANTIMONY SULPHIDE AND A CHLORATE, MIXTURES OF | Forbidden | |
| ANTIMONY TRICHLORIDE, liquid | UN1733 | 157 |
| ANTIMONY TRICHLORIDE, LIQUID (ICAO terminology) | UN1733 | 157 |
| ANTIMONY TRICHLORIDE, solid | UN1733 | 157 |
| ANTIMONY TRICHLORIDE, SOLID (ICAO terminology) | UN1733 | 157 |
| ARGON, COMPRESSED | UN1006 | 121 |
| ARGON, REFRIGERATED LIQUID | UN1951 | 120 |
| ARSENIC | UN1558 | 152 |
| ARSENIC ACID, LIQUID | UN1553 | 154 |
| ARSENIC ACID, SOLID | UN1554 | 154 |
| ARSENICAL DUST | UN1562 | 152 |
| ARSENICAL PESTICIDE, LIQUID, FLAMMABLE, TOXIC, flash point less than 23 °C | UN2760 | 131 |
| ARSENICAL PESTICIDE, LIQUID, TOXIC | UN2994 | 151 |
| ARSENICAL PESTICIDE, LIQUID, TOXIC, FLAMMABLE, flash point not less than 23 °C | UN2993 | 131 |
| ARSENICAL PESTICIDE, SOLID, TOXIC | UN2759 | 151 |
| ARSENIC BROMIDE | UN1555 | 151 |
| ARSENIC COMPOUND, LIQUID, N.O.S., inorganic, including: Arsenates, n.o.s.; Arsenites, n.o.s.; and Arsenic sulphides, n.o.s. | UN1556 | 152T |
| ARSENIC COMPOUND, SOLID, N.O.S., inorganic, including: Arsenates, n.o.s.; Arsenites, n.o.s.; and Arsenic sulphides, n.o.s. | UN1557 | 152 |
| ARSENIC PENTOXIDE | UN1559 | 151 |
| ARSENIC SULFIDE AND A CHLORATE, MIXTURES OF | Forbidden | |
| ARSENIC SULPHIDE AND A CHLORATE, MIXTURES OF | Forbidden | |
| ARSENIC TRICHLORIDE | UN1560 | 157T |
| ARSENIC TRIOXIDE | UN1561 | 151 |
| ARSINE | UN2188 | 119T |
| ARTICLES CONTAINING POLYCHLORINATED BIPHENYLS (PCB) regulated only when the concentration is more than 50 ppm by mass | UN2315 | 171 |
| ARTICLES, EEI | UN0486 | 112 |

| Description | UN # | ERG # |
|---|---|---|
| ARTICLES, EXPLOSIVE, EXTREMELY INSENSITIVE | UN0486 | 112 |
| ARTICLES, EXPLOSIVE, N.O.S. | UN0349 | 114 |
| ARTICLES, EXPLOSIVE, N.O.S. | UN0350 | 114 |
| ARTICLES, EXPLOSIVE, N.O.S. | UN0351 | 114 |
| ARTICLES, EXPLOSIVE, N.O.S. | UN0352 | 114 |
| ARTICLES, EXPLOSIVE, N.O.S. | UN0353 | 114 |
| ARTICLES, EXPLOSIVE, N.O.S. | UN0354 | 112 |
| ARTICLES, EXPLOSIVE, N.O.S. | UN0355 | 112 |
| ARTICLES, EXPLOSIVE, N.O.S. | UN0356 | 112 |
| ARTICLES, EXPLOSIVE, N.O.S. | UN0462 | 112 |
| ARTICLES, EXPLOSIVE, N.O.S. | UN0463 | 112 |
| ARTICLES, EXPLOSIVE, N.O.S. | UN0464 | 112 |
| ARTICLES, EXPLOSIVE, N.O.S. | UN0465 | 112 |
| ARTICLES, EXPLOSIVE, N.O.S. | UN0466 | 112 |
| ARTICLES, EXPLOSIVE, N.O.S. | UN0467 | 112 |
| ARTICLES, EXPLOSIVE, N.O.S. | UN0468 | 112 |
| ARTICLES, EXPLOSIVE, N.O.S. | UN0469 | 112 |
| ARTICLES, EXPLOSIVE, N.O.S. | UN0470 | 112 |
| ARTICLES, EXPLOSIVE, N.O.S. | UN0471 | 114 |
| ARTICLES, EXPLOSIVE, N.O.S. | UN0472 | 114 |
| ARTICLES, PRESSURIZED, HYDRAULIC (containing non-flammable gas) | UN3164 | 126 |
| ARTICLES, PRESSURIZED, PNEUMATIC (containing non-flammable gas) | UN3164 | 126 |
| ARTICLES, PYROPHORIC | UN0380 | 112 |
| ARTICLES, PYROTECHNIC for technical purposes | UN0428 | 112 |
| ARTICLES, PYROTECHNIC for technical purposes | UN0429 | 112 |
| ARTICLES, PYROTECHNIC for technical purposes | UN0430 | 112 |
| ARTICLES, PYROTECHNIC for technical purposes | UN0431 | 114 |
| ARTICLES, PYROTECHNIC for technical purposes | UN0432 | 114 |
| ARYLSULFONIC ACIDS, LIQUID with more than 5 per cent free sulfuric acid | UN2584 | 153 |
| ARYLSULFONIC ACIDS, LIQUID with not more than 5 per cent free sulfuric acid | UN2586 | 153 |
| ARYLSULFONIC ACIDS, SOLID with more than 5 per cent free sulfuric acid | UN2583 | 153 |
| ARYLSULFONIC ACIDS, SOLID with not more than 5 per cent free sulfuric acid | UN2585 | 153 |
| ARYLSULPHONIC ACIDS, LIQUID with more than 5 per cent free sulphuric acid | UN2584 | 153 |
| ARYLSULPHONIC ACIDS, LIQUID with not more than 5 per cent free sulphuric acid | UN2586 | 153 |
| ARYLSULPHONIC ACIDS, SOLID with more than 5 per cent free sulphuric acid | UN2583 | 153 |
| ARYLSULPHONIC ACIDS, SOLID with not more than 5 per cent free sulphuric acid | UN2585 | 153 |
| ASBESTOS BLUE (crocidolite) when not fixed in a natural or artificial binder material or included in a manufactured product | UN2212 | 171 |
| ASBESTOS BROWN (amosite, mysorite) when not fixed in a natural or artificial binder material or included in a manufactured product | UN2212 | 171 |
| ASBESTOS, WHITE (chrysotile, actinolite, anthophyllite, tremolite) when not fixed in a natural or artificial binder material or included in a manufactured product | UN2590 | 171 |
| ASCARIDOLE (ORGANIC PEROXIDE) | Forbidden | |
| AZAUROLIC ACID (SALT OF), (DRY) | Forbidden | |
| AZIDODITHIOCARBONIC ACID | Forbidden | |
| AZIDOETHYL NITRATE | Forbidden | |
| AZIDO GUANIDINE PICRATE (DRY) | Forbidden | |
| 5-AZIDO-1-HYDROXY TETRAZOLE | Forbidden | |
| AZIDO HYDROXY TETRAZOLE (MERCURY AND SILVER SALTS) | Forbidden | |
| 3-AZIDO-1,2-PROPYLENE GLYCOL DINITRATE | Forbidden | |

| Description | UN # | ERG # |
|---|---|---|
| AZODICARBONAMIDE, technically pure or preparation having an SADT higher than 75 °C | UN3242 | 171 |
| AZOTETRAZOLE (DRY) | Forbidden | |
| BARIUM | UN1400 | 138 |
| BARIUM ALLOYS, PYROPHORIC | UN1854 | 135 |
| BARIUM AZIDE, dry or wetted with less than 50 per cent water, by mass | UN0224 | 112 |
| BARIUM AZIDE, WETTED with not less than 50 per cent water, by mass | UN1571 | 113 |
| BARIUM BROMATE | UN2719 | 141 |
| BARIUM CHLORATE | UN1445 | 141 |
| BARIUM COMPOUND, N.O.S. other than barium sulphate | UN1564 | 154 |
| BARIUM CYANIDE | UN1565 | 157 |
| BARIUM HYPOCHLORITE with more than 22 per cent available chlorine | UN2741 | 141 |
| BARIUM NITRATE | UN1446 | 141 |
| BARIUM OXIDE | UN1884 | 157 |
| BARIUM PERCHLORATE | UN1447 | 141 |
| BARIUM PERMANGANATE | UN1448 | 141 |
| BARIUM PEROXIDE | UN1449 | 141 |
| BATTERIES, CONTAINING SODIUM | UN3292 | 138 |
| BATTERIES, DRY, CONTAINING POTASSIUM HYDROXIDE SOLID, electric storage | UN3028 | 154 |
| BATTERIES, WET, FILLED WITH ACID, electric storage | UN2794 | 154 |
| BATTERIES, WET, FILLED WITH ALKALI, electric storage | UN2795 | 154 |
| BATTERIES, WET, NON-SPILLABLE, electric storage | UN2800 | 154 |
| BATTERY FLUID, ACID | UN2796 | 157 |
| BATTERY FLUID, ALKALI | UN2797 | 154 |
| BATTERY-POWERED EQUIPMENT, regulated by aircraft only | UN3171 | 154 |
| BATTERY-POWERED VEHICLE, regulated by aircraft only | UN3171 | 154 |
| BENZALDEHYDE | UN1990 | 129 |
| BENZENE | UN1114 | 130 |
| BENZENE DIAZONIUM CHLORIDE, DRY | Forbidden | |
| BENZENE DIAZONIUM NITRATE, DRY | Forbidden | |
| BENZENESULFONYL CHLORIDE | UN2225 | 156 |
| BENZENESULPHONYL CHLORIDE | UN2225 | 156 |
| BENZENE TRIOZONIDE | Forbidden | |
| BENZIDINE | UN1885 | 153 |
| BENZONITRILE | UN2224 | 152 |
| BENZOQUINONE | UN2587 | 153 |
| BENZOTRICHLORIDE | UN2226 | 156 |
| BENZOTRIFLUORIDE | UN2338 | 131 |
| BENZOXIDIAZOLES (DRY) | Forbidden | |
| BENZOYL AZIDE | Forbidden | |
| BENZOYL CHLORIDE | UN1736 | 137 |
| BENZYL BROMIDE | UN1737 | 156 |
| BENZYL CHLORIDE | UN1738 | 156 |
| BENZYL CHLOROFORMATE | UN1739 | 137 |
| BENZYLDIMETHYLAMINE | UN2619 | 132 |
| BENZYLIDENE CHLORIDE | UN1886 | 156 |
| BENZYL IODIDE | UN2653 | 156 |
| BERYLLIUM COMPOUND, N.O.S. | UN1566 | 154 |
| BERYLLIUM NITRATE | UN2464 | 141 |
| BERYLLIUM POWDER | UN1567 | 134 |
| BHUSA, regulated by ship only | UN1327 | 133 |
| BHUSA, wet, damp or contaminated with oil, by ship only | Forbidden | |
| BICYCLO[2.2.1]HEPTA-2,5-DIENE, STABILIZED | UN2251 | 127P |
| BIOLOGICAL SUBSTANCES, CATEGORY B | UN3373 | 158 |
| BIPHENYL TRIOZONIDE | Forbidden | |

Schedule 3

| Description | UN # | ERG # |
|---|---|---|
| BIPYRIDILIUM PESTICIDE, LIQUID, FLAMMABLE, TOXIC, flash point less than 23 °C | UN2782 | 131 |
| BIPYRIDILIUM PESTICIDE, LIQUID, TOXIC | UN3016 | 151 |
| BIPYRIDILIUM PESTICIDE, LIQUID, TOXIC, FLAMMABLE, flash point not less than 23 °C | UN3015 | 131 |
| BIPYRIDILIUM PESTICIDE, SOLID, TOXIC | UN2781 | 151 |
| BISULFATES, AQUEOUS SOLUTION | UN2837 | 154 |
| BISULFITES, AQUEOUS SOLUTION, N.O.S. | UN2693 | 154 |
| BISULPHATES, AQUEOUS SOLUTION | UN2837 | 154 |
| BISULPHITES, AQUEOUS SOLUTION, N.O.S. | UN2693 | 154 |
| BLACK POWDER, COMPRESSED | UN0028 | 112 |
| BLACK POWDER granular or as a meal | UN0027 | 112 |
| BLACK POWDER, IN PELLETS | UN0028 | 112 |
| BLUE ASBESTOS (crocidolite) when not fixed in a natural or artificial binder material or included in a manufactured product | UN2212 | 171 |
| BOMBS, PHOTO-FLASH | UN0037 | 112 |
| BOMBS, PHOTO-FLASH | UN0038 | 112 |
| BOMBS, PHOTO-FLASH | UN0039 | 112 |
| BOMBS, PHOTO-FLASH | UN0299 | 112 |
| BOMBS, SMOKE, NON-EXPLOSIVE with corrosive liquid, without initiating device | UN2028 | 153 |
| BOMBS with bursting charge | UN0033 | 112 |
| BOMBS with bursting charge | UN0034 | 112 |
| BOMBS with bursting charge | UN0035 | 112 |
| BOMBS with bursting charge | UN0291 | 112 |
| BOMBS WITH FLAMMABLE LIQUID with bursting charge | UN0399 | 112 |
| BOMBS WITH FLAMMABLE LIQUID with bursting charge | UN0400 | 112 |
| BOOSTERS WITH DETONATOR | UN0225 | 112 |
| BOOSTERS WITH DETONATOR | UN0268 | 112 |
| BOOSTERS without detonator | UN0042 | 112 |
| BOOSTERS without detonator | UN0283 | 112 |
| BORNEOL | UN1312 | 133 |
| BORON TRIBROMIDE | UN2692 | 157T |
| BORON TRICHLORIDE | UN1741 | 125T |
| BORON TRIFLUORIDE ACETIC ACID COMPLEX | UN1742 | 157 |
| BORON TRIFLUORIDE, COMPRESSED | UN1008 | 125T |
| BORON TRIFLUORIDE DIETHYL ETHERATE | UN2604 | 132 |
| BORON TRIFLUORIDE DIHYDRATE | UN2851 | 157 |
| BORON TRIFLUORIDE DIMETHYL ETHERATE | UN2965 | 139 |
| BORON TRIFLUORIDE PROPIONIC ACID COMPLEX | UN1743 | 157 |
| BROMATES, INORGANIC, AQUEOUS SOLUTION, N.O.S. | UN3213 | 140 |
| BROMATES, INORGANIC, N.O.S. | UN1450 | 141 |
| BROMINE | UN1744 | 154T |
| BROMINE AZIDE | Forbidden | |
| BROMINE CHLORIDE | UN2901 | 124T |
| BROMINE PENTAFLUORIDE | UN1745 | 124T |
| BROMINE SOLUTION | UN1744 | 154T |
| BROMINE TRIFLUORIDE | UN1746 | 144T |
| BROMOACETIC ACID | UN1938 | 156 |
| BROMOACETONE | UN1569 | 131T |
| BROMOACETYL BROMIDE | UN2513 | 156 |
| BROMOBENZENE | UN2514 | 129 |
| BROMOBENZYL CYANIDES, LIQUID | UN1694 | 159T |
| BROMOBENZYL CYANIDES, SOLID | UN1694 | 159T |
| 1-BROMOBUTANE | UN1126 | 129 |
| 2-BROMOBUTANE | UN2339 | 130 |
| BROMOCHLOROMETHANE | UN1887 | 160 |
| 1-BROMO-3-CHLOROPROPANE | UN2688 | 159 |

| Description | UN # | ERG # |
|---|---|---|
| 4-BROMO-1,2-DINITROBENZENE (UNSTABLE AT 59 °C) | Forbidden | |
| 2-BROMOETHYL ETHYL ETHER | UN2340 | 130 |
| BROMOFORM | UN2515 | 159 |
| 1-BROMO-3-METHYLBUTANE | UN2341 | 130 |
| BROMOMETHYLPROPANES | UN2342 | 130 |
| 1-BROMO-3-NITROBENZENE (UNSTABLE AT 56 °C) | Forbidden | |
| 2-BROMO-2-NITROPROPANE-1,3-DIOL | UN3241 | 133 |
| 2-BROMOPENTANE | UN2343 | 130 |
| BROMOPROPANES | UN2344 | 130 |
| 3-BROMOPROPYNE | UN2345 | 129 |
| BROMOSILANE | Forbidden | |
| BROMOTRIFLUOROETHYLENE | UN2419 | 116 |
| BROMOTRIFLUOROMETHANE | UN1009 | 126 |
| BROWN ASBESTOS (amosite, mysorite) when not fixed in a natural or artificial binder material or included in a manufactured product | UN2212 | 171 |
| BRUCINE | UN1570 | 152 |
| BURSTERS, explosive | UN0043 | 112 |
| BUTADIENES, STABILIZED | UN1010 | 116P |
| BUTANE | UN1011 | 115 |
| BUTANEDIONE | UN2346 | 127 |
| 1,2,4-BUTANETRIOL TRINITRATE | Forbidden | |
| BUTANOLS | UN1120 | 129 |
| tert-BUTOXYCARBONYL AZIDE | Forbidden | |
| BUTYL ACETATES | UN1123 | 129 |
| BUTYL ACID PHOSPHATE | UN1718 | 153 |
| BUTYL ACRYLATES, STABILIZED | UN2348 | 129P |
| n-BUTYLAMINE | UN1125 | 132 |
| N-BUTYLANILINE | UN2738 | 153 |
| BUTYLBENZENES | UN2709 | 128 |
| n-BUTYL CHLOROFORMATE | UN2743 | 155T |
| tert-BUTYLCYCLOHEXYL CHLOROFORMATE | UN2747 | 156 |
| BUTYLENE | UN1012 | 115 |
| 1,2-BUTYLENE OXIDE, STABILIZED | UN3022 | 127P |
| n-BUTYL FORMATE | UN1128 | 129 |
| tert-BUTYL HYDROPEROXIDE, with more than 90 percent with water | Forbidden | |
| tert-BUTYL HYPOCHLORITE | UN3255 | 135 |
| N,n-BUTYLIMIDAZOLE | UN2690 | 152 |
| n-BUTYL ISOCYANATE | UN2485 | 155T |
| tert-BUTYL ISOCYANATE | UN2484 | 155T |
| BUTYL MERCAPTAN | UN2347 | 130 |
| n-BUTYL METHACRYLATE, STABILIZED | UN2227 | 129P |
| BUTYL METHYL ETHER | UN2350 | 127 |
| BUTYL NITRITES | UN2351 | 129 |
| tert-BUTYL PEROXYACETATE, with more than 76 percent in solution | Forbidden | |
| n-BUTYL PEROXYDICARBONATE, with more than 52 percent in solution | Forbidden | |
| tert-BUTYL PEROXYISOBUTYRATE, with more than 77 percent in solution | Forbidden | |
| BUTYL PROPIONATES | UN1914 | 130 |
| BUTYLTOLUENES | UN2667 | 131 |
| BUTYLTRICHLOROSILANE | UN1747 | 155T |
| 5-tert-BUTYL-2,4,6-TRINITRO-m-XYLENE | UN2956 | 149 |
| BUTYL VINYL ETHER, STABILIZED | UN2352 | 127P |
| 1,4-BUTYNEDIOL | UN2716 | 153 |
| BUTYRALDEHYDE | UN1129 | 129 |
| BUTYRALDOXIME | UN2840 | 129 |
| BUTYRIC ACID | UN2820 | 153 |
| BUTYRIC ANHYDRIDE | UN2739 | 156 |
| BUTYRONITRILE | UN2411 | 131 |
| BUTYRYL CHLORIDE | UN2353 | 132 |
| CABAZIDE | Forbidden | |

| Description | UN # | ERG # |
|---|---|---|
| CACODYLIC ACID | UN1572 | 151 |
| CADMIUM COMPOUND | UN2570 | 154 |
| CAESIUM | UN1407 | 138 |
| CAESIUM HYDROXIDE | UN2682 | 157 |
| CAESIUM HYDROXIDE SOLUTION | UN2681 | 154 |
| CAESIUM NITRATE | UN1451 | 140 |
| CALCIUM | UN1401 | 138 |
| CALCIUM ALLOYS, PYROPHORIC | UN1855 | 135 |
| CALCIUM ARSENATE | UN1573 | 151 |
| CALCIUM ARSENATE AND CALCIUM ARSENITE MIXTURE, SOLID | UN1574 | 151 |
| CALCIUM CARBIDE | UN1402 | 138 |
| CALCIUM CHLORATE | UN1452 | 140 |
| CALCIUM CHLORATE, AQUEOUS SOLUTION | UN2429 | 140 |
| CALCIUM CHLORITE | UN1453 | 140 |
| CALCIUM CYANAMIDE with more than 0.1 per cent calcium carbide | UN1403 | 138 |
| CALCIUM CYANIDE | UN1575 | 157 |
| CALCIUM DITHIONITE | UN1923 | 135T |
| CALCIUM HYDRIDE | UN1404 | 138 |
| CALCIUM HYDROSULFITE | UN1923 | 135T |
| CALCIUM HYDROSULPHITE | UN1923 | 135T |
| CALCIUM HYPOCHLORITE, DRY with more than 39 per cent available chlorine (8.8 per cent available oxygen) | UN1748 | 140 |
| CALCIUM HYPOCHLORITE, HYDRATED MIXTURE with not less than 5.5 per cent but not more than 10 per cent water | UN2880 | 140 |
| CALCIUM HYPOCHLORITE, HYDRATED with not less than 5.5 per cent but not more than 10 per cent water | UN2880 | 140 |
| CALCIUM HYPOCHLORITE MIXTURE, DRY with more than 10 per cent but not more than 39 per cent available chlorine | UN2208 | 140 |
| CALCIUM HYPOCHLORITE MIXTURE, DRY with more than 39 per cent available chlorine (8.8 per cent available oxygen) | UN1748 | 140 |
| CALCIUM MANGANESE SILICON | UN2844 | 138 |
| CALCIUM NITRATE | UN1454 | 140 |
| CALCIUM OXIDE, regulated by aircraft only | UN1910 | 157 |
| CALCIUM PERCHLORATE | UN1455 | 140 |
| CALCIUM PERMANGANATE | UN1456 | 140 |
| CALCIUM PEROXIDE | UN1457 | 140 |
| CALCIUM PHOSPHIDE | UN1360 | 139T |
| CALCIUM, PYROPHORIC | UN1855 | 135 |
| CALCIUM RESINATE | UN1313 | 133 |
| CALCIUM RESINATE, FUSED | UN1314 | 133 |
| CALCIUM SILICIDE | UN1405 | 138 |
| CAMPHOR OIL | UN1130 | 128 |
| CAMPHOR, synthetic | UN2717 | 133 |
| CAPROIC ACID | UN2829 | 153 |
| CARBAMATE PESTICIDE, LIQUID, FLAMMABLE, TOXIC, flash point less than 23 °C | UN2758 | 131 |
| CARBAMATE PESTICIDE, LIQUID, TOXIC | UN2992 | 151 |
| CARBAMATE PESTICIDE, LIQUID, TOXIC, FLAMMABLE, flash point not less than 23 °C | UN2991 | 131 |
| CARBAMATE PESTICIDE, SOLID, TOXIC | UN2757 | 151 |
| CARBON, ACTIVATED | UN1362 | 133 |
| CARBON, animal or vegetable origin | UN1361 | 133 |
| CARBON DIOXIDE | UN1013 | 120 |
| CARBON DIOXIDE AND NITROUS OXIDE MIXTURE | UN1015 | 126 |
| CARBON DIOXIDE AND OXYGEN MIXTURE, COMPRESSED | UN1014 | 122 |
| CARBON DIOXIDE, REFRIGERATED LIQUID | UN2187 | 120 |
| CARBON DIOXIDE, SOLID | UN1845 | 120 |
| CARBON DISULFIDE | UN1131 | 131 |
| CARBON DISULPHIDE | UN1131 | 131 |

| Description | UN # | ERG # |
|---|---|---|
| CARBON MONOXIDE AND HYDROGEN MIXTURE, COMPRESSED | UN2600 | 119T |
| CARBON MONOXIDE, COMPRESSED | UN1016 | 119T |
| CARBON MONOXIDE, REFRIGERATED LIQUID | Forbidden | |
| CARBON TETRABROMIDE | UN2516 | 151 |
| CARBON TETRACHLORIDE | UN1846 | 151 |
| CARBONYL FLUORIDE, COMPRESSED | UN2417 | 125T |
| CARBONYL SULFIDE | UN2204 | 119T |
| CARBONYL SULPHIDE | UN2204 | 119T |
| CARTRIDGES, FLASH | UN0049 | 112 |
| CARTRIDGES, FLASH | UN0050 | 112 |
| CARTRIDGES FOR WEAPONS, BLANK | UN0014 | 114 |
| CARTRIDGES FOR WEAPONS, BLANK | UN0326 | 112 |
| CARTRIDGES FOR WEAPONS, BLANK | UN0327 | 112 |
| CARTRIDGES FOR WEAPONS, BLANK | UN0338 | 114 |
| CARTRIDGES FOR WEAPONS, BLANK | UN0413 | 112 |
| CARTRIDGES FOR WEAPONS, INERT PROJECTILE | UN0012 | 114 |
| CARTRIDGES FOR WEAPONS, INERT PROJECTILE | UN0328 | 112 |
| CARTRIDGES FOR WEAPONS, INERT PROJECTILE | UN0339 | 114 |
| CARTRIDGES FOR WEAPONS, INERT PROJECTILE | UN0417 | 112 |
| CARTRIDGES FOR WEAPONS with bursting charge | UN0005 | 112 |
| CARTRIDGES FOR WEAPONS with bursting charge | UN0006 | 112 |
| CARTRIDGES FOR WEAPONS with bursting charge | UN0007 | 112 |
| CARTRIDGES FOR WEAPONS with bursting charge | UN0321 | 112 |
| CARTRIDGES FOR WEAPONS with bursting charge | UN0348 | 114 |
| CARTRIDGES FOR WEAPONS with bursting charge | UN0412 | 114 |
| CARTRIDGES, OIL WELL | UN0277 | 112 |
| CARTRIDGES, OIL WELL | UN0278 | 114 |
| CARTRIDGES, POWER DEVICE | UN0275 | 112 |
| CARTRIDGES, POWER DEVICE | UN0276 | 114 |
| CARTRIDGES, POWER DEVICE | UN0323 | 114 |
| CARTRIDGES, POWER DEVICE | UN0381 | 112 |
| CARTRIDGES, SIGNAL | UN0054 | 112 |
| CARTRIDGES, SIGNAL | UN0312 | 114 |
| CARTRIDGES, SIGNAL | UN0405 | 114 |
| CARTRIDGES, SMALL ARMS | UN0012 | 114 |
| CARTRIDGES, SMALL ARMS | UN0339 | 114 |
| CARTRIDGES, SMALL ARMS | UN0417 | 112 |
| CARTRIDGES, SMALL ARMS, BLANK | UN0014 | 114 |
| CARTRIDGES, SMALL ARMS, BLANK | UN0327 | 112 |
| CARTRIDGES, SMALL ARMS, BLANK | UN0338 | 114 |
| CASES, CARTRIDGE, EMPTY, WITH PRIMER | UN0055 | 114 |
| CASES, CARTRIDGE, EMPTY, WITH PRIMER | UN0379 | 114 |
| CASES, COMBUSTIBLE, EMPTY, WITHOUT PRIMER | UN0446 | 114 |
| CASES, COMBUSTIBLE, EMPTY, WITHOUT PRIMER | UN0447 | 112 |
| CASTOR BEANS | UN2969 | 171 |
| CASTOR FLAKE | UN2969 | 171 |
| CASTOR MEAL | UN2969 | 171 |
| CASTOR POMACE | UN2969 | 171 |
| CAUSTIC ALKALI LIQUID, N.O.S. | UN1719 | 154 |
| CELLS, CONTAINING SODIUM | UN3292 | 138 |
| CELLULOID in block, rods, rolls, sheets, tubes, etc., except scrap | UN2000 | 133 |
| CELLULOID, SCRAP | UN2002 | 135 |
| CERIUM, slabs, ingots or rods | UN1333 | 170 |

Schedule 3

| Description | UN # | ERG # |
|---|---|---|
| CERIUM, turnings or gritty powder | UN3078 | 138 |
| CHARGES, BURSTING, PLASTICS BONDED | UN0457 | 112 |
| CHARGES, BURSTING, PLASTICS BONDED | UN0458 | 112 |
| CHARGES, BURSTING, PLASTICS BONDED | UN0459 | 114 |
| CHARGES, BURSTING, PLASTICS BONDED | UN0460 | 114 |
| CHARGES, DEMOLITION | UN0048 | 112 |
| CHARGES, DEPTH | UN0056 | 112 |
| CHARGES, EXPLOSIVE, COMMERCIAL without detonator | UN0442 | 112 |
| CHARGES, EXPLOSIVE, COMMERCIAL without detonator | UN0443 | 112 |
| CHARGES, EXPLOSIVE, COMMERCIAL without detonator | UN0444 | 114 |
| CHARGES, EXPLOSIVE, COMMERCIAL without detonator | UN0445 | 114 |
| CHARGES, PROPELLING | UN0271 | 112 |
| CHARGES, PROPELLING | UN0272 | 112 |
| CHARGES, PROPELLING | UN0415 | 112 |
| CHARGES, PROPELLING | UN0491 | 114 |
| CHARGES, PROPELLING, FOR CANNON | UN0242 | 112 |
| CHARGES, PROPELLING, FOR CANNON | UN0279 | 112 |
| CHARGES, PROPELLING, FOR CANNON | UN0414 | 112 |
| CHARGES, SHAPED, FLEXIBLE, LINEAR | UN0237 | 114 |
| CHARGES, SHAPED, FLEXIBLE, LINEAR | UN0288 | 112 |
| CHARGES, SHAPED, without detonator | UN0059 | 112 |
| CHARGES, SHAPED, without detonator | UN0439 | 112 |
| CHARGES, SHAPED, without detonator | UN0440 | 114 |
| CHARGES, SHAPED, without detonator | UN0441 | 114 |
| CHARGES, SUPPLEMENTARY, EXPLOSIVE | UN0060 | 112 |
| CHEMICAL KIT | UN3316 | 171 |
| CHEMICAL SAMPLE, TOXIC, liquid or solid | UN3315 | 151 |
| CHLORAL, ANHYDROUS, STABILIZED | UN2075 | 153 |
| CHLORATE AND BORATE MIXTURE | UN1458 | 140 |
| CHLORATE AND MAGNESIUM CHLORIDE MIXTURE | UN1459 | 140 |
| CHLORATES, INORGANIC, AQUEOUS SOLUTION, N.O.S. | UN3210 | 140 |
| CHLORATES, INORGANIC, N.O.S. | UN1461 | 140 |
| CHLORIC ACID, AQUEOUS SOLUTION with not more than 10 per cent chloric acid | UN2626 | 140 |
| CHLORINE | UN1017 | 124T |
| CHLORINE AZIDE | Forbidden | |
| CHLORINE DIOXIDE HYDRATE, FROZEN | Forbidden | |
| CHLORINE DIOXIDE (NOT HYDRATED) | Forbidden | |
| CHLORINE PENTAFLUORIDE | UN2548 | 124T |
| CHLORINE TRIFLUORIDE | UN1749 | 124T |
| CHLORITES, INORGANIC, N.O.S. | UN1462 | 143 |
| CHLORITE SOLUTION | UN1908 | 154 |
| CHLOROACETIC ACID, MOLTEN | UN3250 | 153 |
| CHLOROACETIC ACID, SOLID | UN1751 | 153 |
| CHLOROACETIC ACID SOLUTION | UN1750 | 153 |
| CHLOROACETONE, STABILIZED | UN1695 | 153T |
| CHLOROACETONE (UNSTABILIZED) | Forbidden | |
| CHLOROACETONITRILE | UN2668 | 131T |
| CHLOROACETOPHENONE, liquid | UN1697 | 153T |
| CHLOROACETOPHENONE, LIQUID (ICAO terminology) | UN1697 | 153T |
| CHLOROACETOPHENONE, solid | UN1697 | 153T |
| CHLOROACETOPHENONE, SOLID (ICAO terminology) | UN1697 | 153T |
| CHLOROACETYL CHLORIDE | UN1752 | 156T |
| CHLOROANILINES, LIQUID | UN2019 | 152 |
| CHLOROANILINES, SOLID | UN2018 | 152 |
| CHLOROANISIDINES | UN2233 | 152 |
| CHLOROBENZENE | UN1134 | 130 |
| CHLOROBENZOTRIFLUORIDES | UN2234 | 130 |
| CHLOROBENZYL CHLORIDES | UN2235 | 153 |

| Description | UN # | ERG # |
|---|---|---|
| CHLOROBUTANES | UN1127 | 130 |
| CHLOROCRESOLS, liquid | UN2669 | 152 |
| CHLOROCRESOLS, LIQUID (ICAO terminology) | UN2669 | 152 |
| CHLOROCRESOLS, solid | UN2669 | 152 |
| CHLOROCRESOLS, SOLID (ICAO terminology) | UN2669 | 152 |
| CHLOROCRESOLS, SOLUTION (IMO terminology) | UN2669 | 152 |
| CHLORODIFLUOROBROMOMETHANE | UN1974 | 126 |
| 1-CHLORO-1,1-DIFLUOROETHANE | UN2517 | 115 |
| CHLORODIFLUOROMETHANE | UN1018 | 126 |
| CHLORODIFLUOROMETHANE AND CHLOROPENTAFLUOROETHANE MIXTURE with fixed boiling point, with approximately 49 per cent chlorodifluoromethane | UN1973 | 126 |
| CHLORODINITROBENZENES, LIQUID | UN1577 | 153 |
| CHLORODINITROBENZENES, SOLID | UN1577 | 153 |
| 2-CHLOROETHANAL | UN2232 | 153T |
| CHLOROFORM | UN1888 | 151 |
| CHLOROFORMATES, TOXIC, CORROSIVE, FLAMMABLE, N.O.S. | UN2742 | 155T |
| CHLOROFORMATES, TOXIC, CORROSIVE, N.O.S. | UN3277 | 154 |
| CHLOROMETHYL CHLOROFORMATE | UN2745 | 157 |
| CHLOROMETHYL ETHYL ETHER | UN2354 | 131 |
| 3-CHLORO-4-METHYLPHENYL ISOCYANATE | UN2236 | 156 |
| CHLORONITROANILINES | UN2237 | 153 |
| CHLORONITROBENZENES | UN1578 | 152 |
| CHLORONITROTOLUENES, LIQUID | UN2433 | 152 |
| CHLORONITROTOLUENES, SOLID | UN2433 | 152 |
| CHLOROPENTAFLUOROETHANE | UN1020 | 126 |
| CHLOROPHENOLATES, LIQUID | UN2904 | 154 |
| CHLOROPHENOLATES, SOLID | UN2905 | 154 |
| CHLOROPHENOLS, LIQUID | UN2021 | 153 |
| CHLOROPHENOLS, SOLID | UN2020 | 153 |
| CHLOROPHENYLTRICHLOROSILANE | UN1753 | 156 |
| CHLOROPICRIN | UN1580 | 154T |
| CHLOROPICRIN AND METHYL BROMIDE MIXTURE | UN1581 | 123T |
| CHLOROPICRIN AND METHYL CHLORIDE MIXTURE | UN1582 | 119T |
| CHLOROPICRIN MIXTURE, N.O.S. | UN1583 | 154T |
| CHLOROPLATINIC ACID, SOLID | UN2507 | 154 |
| CHLOROPRENE, STABILIZED | UN1991 | 131P |
| CHLOROPRENE, UNINHIBITED | Forbidden | |
| 2-CHLOROPROPANE | UN2356 | 129 |
| 3-CHLOROPROPANOL-1 | UN2849 | 153 |
| 2-CHLOROPROPENE | UN2456 | 130P |
| 2-CHLOROPROPIONIC ACID, SOLID | UN2511 | 153 |
| 2-CHLOROPROPIONIC ACID, SOLUTION | UN2511 | 153 |
| 2-CHLOROPYRIDINE | UN2822 | 153 |
| CHLOROSILANES, CORROSIVE, FLAMMABLE, N.O.S. | UN2986 | 155T |
| CHLOROSILANES, CORROSIVE, N.O.S. | UN2987 | 156T |
| CHLOROSILANES, FLAMMABLE, CORROSIVE, N.O.S. | UN2985 | 155T |
| CHLOROSILANES, WATER-REACTIVE, FLAMMABLE, CORROSIVE, N.O.S. | UN2988 | 139T |
| CHLOROSULFONIC ACID with or without sulfur trioxide | UN1754 | 137T |
| CHLOROSULPHONIC ACID with or without sulphur trioxide | UN1754 | 137T |
| 1-CHLORO-1,2,2,2-TETRAFLUOROETHANE | UN1021 | 126 |
| CHLOROTOLUENES | UN2238 | 130 |
| 4-CHLORO-o-TOLUIDINE HYDROCHLORIDE | UN1579 | 153 |
| CHLOROTOLUIDINES, liquid | UN2239 | 153 |

Schedule 3

| Description | UN # | ERG # |
|---|---|---|
| CHLOROTOLUIDINES, LIQUID (ICAO/IMO terminology) | UN2239 | 153 |
| CHLOROTOLUIDINES, solid | UN2239 | 153 |
| CHLOROTOLUIDINES, SOLID (ICAO/IMO terminology) | UN2239 | 153 |
| 1-CHLORO-2,2,2-TRIFLUOROETHANE | UN1983 | 126 |
| CHLOROTRIFLUOROMETHANE | UN1022 | 126 |
| CHLOROTRIFLUOROMETHANE AND TRIFLUOROMETHANE AZEOTROPIC MIXTURE with approximately 60 per cent chlorotrifluoromethane | UN2599 | 126 |
| CHROMIC ACID SOLUTION | UN1755 | 154 |
| CHROMIC FLUORIDE, SOLID | UN1756 | 154 |
| CHROMIC FLUORIDE SOLUTION | UN1757 | 154 |
| CHROMIUM NITRATE | UN2720 | 141 |
| CHROMIUM OXYCHLORIDE | UN1758 | 137T |
| CHROMIUM TRIOXIDE, ANHYDROUS | UN1463 | 141 |
| CHROMOSULFURIC ACID | UN2240 | 154 |
| CHROMOSULPHURIC ACID | UN2240 | 154 |
| CHRYSAMMINIC ACID | Forbidden | |
| COAL BRIQUETTES, HOT | Forbidden | |
| COAL GAS, COMPRESSED | UN1023 | 119T |
| COAL TAR DISTILLATES, FLAMMABLE | UN1136 | 128 |
| COATING SOLUTION (includes surface treatments or coatings used for industrial or other purposes such as vehicle undercoating, drum or barrel lining) | UN1139 | 127 |
| COBALT NAPHTHENATES, POWDER | UN2001 | 133 |
| COBALT RESINATE, PRECIPITATED | UN1318 | 133 |
| COKE, HOT, other than petroleum coke | Forbidden | |
| COMPONENTS, EXPLOSIVE TRAIN, N.O.S. | UN0382 | 112 |
| COMPONENTS, EXPLOSIVE TRAIN, N.O.S. | UN0383 | 114 |
| COMPONENTS, EXPLOSIVE TRAIN, N.O.S. | UN0384 | 114 |
| COMPONENTS, EXPLOSIVE TRAIN, N.O.S. | UN0461 | 112 |
| COMPRESSED GAS, FLAMMABLE, N.O.S. | UN1954 | 115 |
| COMPRESSED GAS, N.O.S. | UN1956 | 126 |
| COMPRESSED GAS, OXIDIZING, N.O.S. | UN3156 | 122 |
| COMPRESSED GAS, TOXIC, CORROSIVE, N.O.S. | UN3304 | 123T |
| COMPRESSED GAS, TOXIC, FLAMMABLE, CORROSIVE, N.O.S. | UN3305 | 119T |
| COMPRESSED GAS, TOXIC, FLAMMABLE, N.O.S. | UN1953 | 119T |
| COMPRESSED GAS, TOXIC, N.O.S. | UN1955 | 123T |
| COMPRESSED GAS, TOXIC, OXIDIZING, CORROSIVE, N.O.S. | UN3306 | 124T |
| COMPRESSED GAS, TOXIC, OXIDIZING, N.O.S. | UN3303 | 124T |
| CONTRIVANCES, WATER-ACTIVATED with burster, expelling charge or propelling charge | UN0248 | 112 |
| CONTRIVANCES, WATER-ACTIVATED with burster, expelling charge or propelling charge | UN0249 | 112 |
| COPPER ACETOARSENITE | UN1585 | 151 |
| COPPER ACETYLIDE | Forbidden | |
| COPPER AMINE AZIDE | Forbidden | |
| COPPER ARSENITE | UN1586 | 151 |
| COPPER BASED PESTICIDE, LIQUID, FLAMMABLE, TOXIC, flash point less than 23 °C | UN2776 | 131 |
| COPPER BASED PESTICIDE, LIQUID, TOXIC | UN3010 | 151 |
| COPPER BASED PESTICIDE, LIQUID, TOXIC, FLAMMABLE, flash point not less than 23 °C | UN3009 | 131 |
| COPPER BASED PESTICIDE, SOLID, TOXIC | UN2775 | 151 |
| COPPER CHLORATE | UN2721 | 141 |
| COPPER CHLORIDE | UN2802 | 154 |
| COPPER CYANIDE | UN1587 | 151 |
| COPPER TETRAMINE NITRATE | Forbidden | |
| COPRA | UN1363 | 135 |
| CORD, DETONATING, flexible | UN0065 | 112 |
| CORD, DETONATING, flexible | UN0289 | 114 |
| CORD, DETONATING, metal clad | UN0102 | 112 |
| CORD, DETONATING, metal clad | UN0290 | 112 |
| CORD, DETONATING, MILD EFFECT, metal clad | UN0104 | 114 |
| CORD, IGNITER | UN0066 | 114 |
| CORROSIVE LIQUID, ACIDIC, INORGANIC, N.O.S. | UN3264 | 154 |
| CORROSIVE LIQUID, ACIDIC, ORGANIC, N.O.S. | UN3265 | 153 |
| CORROSIVE LIQUID, BASIC, INORGANIC, N.O.S. | UN3266 | 154 |
| CORROSIVE LIQUID, BASIC, ORGANIC, N.O.S. | UN3267 | 153 |
| CORROSIVE LIQUID, FLAMMABLE, N.O.S. | UN2920 | 132 |
| CORROSIVE LIQUID, N.O.S. | UN1760 | 154 |
| CORROSIVE LIQUID, OXIDIZING, N.O.S. | UN3093 | 140 |
| CORROSIVE LIQUID, SELF-HEATING, N.O.S. | UN3301 | 136 |
| CORROSIVE LIQUID, TOXIC, N.O.S. | UN2922 | 154 |
| CORROSIVE LIQUID, WATER-REACTIVE, N.O.S. | UN3094 | 138 |
| CORROSIVE SOLID, ACIDIC, INORGANIC, N.O.S. | UN3260 | 154 |
| CORROSIVE SOLID, ACIDIC, ORGANIC, N.O.S. | UN3261 | 154 |
| CORROSIVE SOLID, BASIC, INORGANIC, N.O.S. | UN3262 | 154 |
| CORROSIVE SOLID, BASIC, ORGANIC, N.O.S. | UN3263 | 154 |
| CORROSIVE SOLID, FLAMMABLE, N.O.S. | UN2921 | 134 |
| CORROSIVE SOLID, N.O.S. | UN1759 | 154 |
| CORROSIVE SOLID, OXIDIZING, N.O.S. | UN3084 | 140 |
| CORROSIVE SOLID, SELF-HEATING, N.O.S. | UN3095 | 136 |
| CORROSIVE SOLID, TOXIC, N.O.S. | UN2923 | 154 |
| CORROSIVE SOLID, WATER-REACTIVE, N.O.S. | UN3096 | 138 |
| COTTON WASTE, OILY | UN1364 | 133 |
| COTTON, WET | UN1365 | 133 |
| COUMARIN DERIVATIVE PESTICIDE, LIQUID, FLAMMABLE, TOXIC, flash point less than 23 °C | UN3024 | 131 |
| COUMARIN DERIVATIVE PESTICIDE, LIQUID, TOXIC | UN3026 | 151 |
| COUMARIN DERIVATIVE PESTICIDE, LIQUID, TOXIC, FLAMMABLE, flash point not less than 23 °C | UN3025 | 131 |
| COUMARIN DERIVATIVE PESTICIDE, SOLID, TOXIC | UN3027 | 151 |
| CRESOLS, LIQUID | UN2076 | 153 |
| CRESOLS, SOLID | UN2076 | 153 |
| CRESYLIC ACID | UN2022 | 153 |
| CROTONALDEHYDE, STABILIZED | UN1143 | 131PT |
| CROTONIC ACID, liquid | UN2823 | 153 |
| CROTONIC ACID, solid | UN2823 | 153 |
| CROTONIC ACID, liquid | UN3472 | 153 |
| CROTONYLENE | UN1144 | 128 |
| CUPRIETHYLENEDIAMINE SOLUTION | UN1761 | 154 |
| CUTTERS, CABLE, EXPLOSIVE | UN0070 | 114 |
| CYANIDES, INORGANIC, SOLID, N.O.S., excluding ferricyanides and ferrocyanides | UN1588 | 157 |
| CYANIDE SOLUTION, N.O.S. | UN1935 | 157 |
| CYANOGEN | UN1026 | 119T |
| CYANOGEN BROMIDE | UN1889 | 157 |
| CYANOGEN CHLORIDE, STABILIZED | UN1589 | 125T |
| CYANURIC CHLORIDE | UN2670 | 157 |
| CYANURIC TRIAZIDE | Forbidden | |
| CYCLOBUTANE | UN2601 | 115 |
| CYCLOBUTYL CHLOROFORMATE | UN2744 | 155 |
| 1,5,9-CYCLODODECATRIENE | UN2518 | 153 |

| Description | UN # | ERG # |
|---|---|---|
| CYCLOHEPTANE | UN2241 | 128 |
| CYCLOHEPTATRIENE | UN2603 | 131 |
| CYCLOHEPTENE | UN2242 | 128 |
| CYCLOHEXANE | UN1145 | 128 |
| CYCLOHEXANONE | UN1915 | 127 |
| CYCLOHEXENE | UN2256 | 130 |
| CYCLOHEXENYLTRICHLOROSILANE | UN1762 | 156 |
| CYCLOHEXYL ACETATE | UN2243 | 130 |
| CYCLOHEXYLAMINE | UN2357 | 132 |
| CYCLOHEXYL ISOCYANATE | UN2488 | 155T |
| CYCLOHEXYL MERCAPTAN | UN3054 | 131 |
| CYCLOHEXYLTRICHLOROSILANE | UN1763 | 156T |
| CYCLONITE and CYCLOTETRAMETHYLENETETRANITRAMINE MIXTURE, DESENSITIZED with not less than 10 per cent phelgmatizer, by mass | UN0391 | 112 |
| CYCLONITE and CYCLOTETRAMETHYLENETETRANITRAMINE MIXTURE, WETTED with not less than 15 per cent water, by mass | UN0391 | 112 |
| CYCLONITE and HMX MIXTURE, DESENSITIZED with not less than 10 per cent phelgmatizer, by mass; | UN0391 | 112 |
| CYCLONITE and HMX MIXTURE, WETTED with not less than 15 per cent water, by mass; | UN0391 | 112 |
| CYCLONITE and OCTOGEN MIXTURE, DESENSITIZED with not less than 10 per cent phelgmatizer, by mass; | UN0391 | 112 |
| CYCLONITE and OCTOGEN MIXTURE, WETTED with not less than 15 per cent water, by mass; | UN0391 | 112 |
| CYCLONITE, DESENSITIZED | UN0483 | 112 |
| CYCLONITE WETTED with not less than 15 per cent water, by mass | UN0072 | 112 |
| CYCLOOCTADIENE PHOSPHINES | UN2940 | 135 |
| CYCLOOCTADIENES | UN2520 | 130P |
| CYCLOOCTATETRAENE | UN2358 | 128P |
| CYCLOPENTANE | UN1146 | 128 |
| CYCLOPENTANOL | UN2244 | 129 |
| CYCLOPENTANONE | UN2245 | 127 |
| CYCLOPENTENE | UN2246 | 128 |
| CYCLOPROPANE | UN1027 | 115 |
| CYCLOTETRAMETHYLENETETRANITRAMINE, DESENSITIZED | UN0484 | 112 |
| CYCLOTETRAMETHYLENETETRANITRAMINE (DRY) or unphlegmatized | Forbidden | |
| CYCLOTETRAMETHYLENETETRANITRAMINE WETTED with not less than 15 per cent water, by mass | UN0226 | 112 |
| CYCLOTRIMETHYLENETRINITRAMINE AND CYCLOTETRAMETHYLENETETRANITRAMINE MIXTURE, DESENSITIZED with not less than 10 per cent phlegmatizer, by mass | UN0391 | 112 |
| CYCLOTRIMETHYLENETRINITRAMINE AND CYCLOTETRAMETHYLENETETRANITRAMINE MIXTURE, WETTED with not less than 15 per cent water, by mass | UN0391 | 112 |
| CYCLOTRIMETHYLENETRINITRAMINE AND HMX MIXTURE, DESENSITIZED with not less than 10 per cent phlegmatizer, by mass | UN0391 | 112 |
| CYCLOTRIMETHYLENETRINITRAMINE AND HMX MIXTURE, WETTED with not less than 15 per cent water, by mass | UN0391 | 112 |
| CYCLOTRIMETHYLENETRINITRAMINE AND OCTOGEN MIXTURE, DESENSITIZED with not less than 10 per cent phlegmatizer, by mass | UN0391 | 112 |
| CYCLOTRIMETHYLENETRINITRAMINE AND OCTOGEN MIXTURE, WETTED with not less than 15 per cent water, by mass | UN0391 | 112 |
| CYCLOTRIMETHYLENETRINITRAMINE, DESENSITIZED | UN0483 | 112 |
| CYCLOTRIMETHYLENETRINITRAMINE WETTED with not less than 15 per cent water, by mass | UN0072 | 112 |

| Description | UN # | ERG # |
|---|---|---|
| CYMENES | UN2046 | 130 |
| DECABORANE | UN1868 | 134 |
| DECAHYDRONAPHTHALENE | UN1147 | 130 |
| n-DECANE | UN2247 | 128 |
| DEFLAGRATING METAL SALTS OF AROMATIC NITRO DERIVATIVES, N.O.S. | UN0132 | 112 |
| DETONATOR ASSEMBLIES, NON-ELECTRIC for blasting | UN0360 | 112 |
| DETONATOR ASSEMBLIES, NON-ELECTRIC for blasting | UN0361 | 114 |
| DETONATOR ASSEMBLIES, NON-ELECTRIC, for blasting | UN0500 | 114 |
| DETONATORS, ELECTRIC for blasting | UN0030 | 112 |
| DETONATORS, ELECTRIC for blasting | UN0255 | 114 |
| DETONATORS, ELECTRIC for blasting | UN0456 | 114 |
| DETONATORS FOR AMMUNITION | UN0073 | 112 |
| DETONATORS FOR AMMUNITION | UN0364 | 112 |
| DETONATORS FOR AMMUNITION | UN0365 | 114 |
| DETONATORS FOR AMMUNITION | UN0366 | 114 |
| DETONATORS, NON-ELECTRIC for blasting | UN0029 | 112 |
| DETONATORS, NON-ELECTRIC for blasting | UN0267 | 114 |
| DETONATORS, NON-ELECTRIC for blasting | UN0455 | 114 |
| DEUTERIUM, COMPRESSED | UN1957 | 115 |
| DEVICES, SMALL, HYDROCARBON GAS POWERED with release device | UN3150 | 115 |
| DIACETONE ALCOHOL | UN1148 | 129 |
| DIACETONE ALCOHOL PEROXIDES, with more than 57 percent in solution with more than 9 percent hydrogen peroxide, less than 26 percent diacetone alcohol and less than 9 percent water; total active oxygen content more than 9 percent by mass | Forbidden | |
| DIACETYL PEROXIDE, SOLID, or with more than 25 percent in solution | Forbidden | |
| DIALLYLAMINE | UN2359 | 132 |
| DIALLYL ETHER | UN2360 | 131P |
| 4,4'-DIAMINODIPHENYLMETHANE | UN2651 | 153 |
| DI-n-AMYLAMINE | UN2841 | 131 |
| p-DIAZIDOBENZENE | Forbidden | |
| 1,2-DIAZIDOETHANE | Forbidden | |
| 1,1-DIAZOAMINONAPTHALENE | Forbidden | |
| DIAZOAMINOTETRAZOLE (DRY) | Forbidden | |
| DIAZODINITROPHENOL (DRY) | Forbidden | |
| DIAZODINITROPHENOL, WETTED with not less than 40 per cent water, or mixture of alcohol and water, by mass | UN0074 | 112 |
| DIAZODIPHENYLMETHANE | Forbidden | |
| DIAZONIUM NITRATES (DRY) | Forbidden | |
| DIAZONIUM PERCHLORATES (DRY) | Forbidden | |
| 1,3-DIAZOPROPANE | Forbidden | |
| DIBENZYLDICHLOROSILANE | UN2434 | 156 |
| DIBENZYL PEROXYDICARBONATE, with more than 87 percent with water | Forbidden | |
| DIBORANE, COMPRESSED | UN1911 | 119T |
| DIBROMOACETYLENE | Forbidden | |
| 1,2-DIBROMOBUTAN-3-ONE | UN2648 | 154 |
| DIBROMOCHLOROPROPANES | UN2872 | 159 |
| DIBROMODIFLUOROMETHANE | UN1941 | 171 |
| DIBROMOMETHANE | UN2664 | 160 |
| DI-n-BUTYLAMINE | UN2248 | 132 |
| DIBUTYLAMINOETHANOL | UN2873 | 153 |
| DIBUTYL ETHERS | UN1149 | 127 |
| 2,2-DI-(tert-BUTYLPEROXY) BUTANE, with more than 55 percent in solution | Forbidden | |
| DI-n-BUTYL PEROXYDICARBONATE, with more than 52 percent in solution | Forbidden | |
| DI-(tert-BUTYLPEROXY) PHTHALATE, with more than 55 percent in solution | Forbidden | |
| N,N'-DICHLORAZODICARBONAMIDINE (SALTS OF), (DRY) | Forbidden | |

Schedule 3

| Description | UN # | ERG # |
|---|---|---|
| DICHLOROACETIC ACID | UN1764 | 153 |
| 1,3-DICHLOROACETONE | UN2649 | 153 |
| DICHLOROACETYL CHLORIDE | UN1765 | 156 |
| DICHLOROACETYLENE | Forbidden | |
| DICHLOROANILINES, LIQUID | UN1590 | 153 |
| DICHLOROANILINES, SOLID | UN1590 | 153 |
| o-DICHLOROBENZENE | UN1591 | 152 |
| 2,2'-DICHLORODIETHYL ETHER | UN1916 | 152 |
| DICHLORODIFLUOROMETHANE | UN1028 | 126 |
| DICHLORODIFLUOROMETHANE AND DIFLUOROETHANE AZEOTROPIC MIXTURE with approximately 74 per cent dichlorodifluoromethane | UN2602 | 126 |
| DICHLORODIMETHYL ETHER, SYMMETRICAL | UN2249 | 153 |
| 1,1-DICHLOROETHANE | UN2362 | 130 |
| 1,2-DICHLOROETHYLENE | UN1150 | 130P |
| DICHLOROETHYL SULFIDE | Forbidden | |
| DICHLOROETHYL SULPHIDE | Forbidden | |
| DICHLOROFLUOROMETHANE | UN1029 | 126 |
| DICHLOROISOCYANURIC ACID, DRY | UN2465 | 140 |
| DICHLOROISOCYANURIC ACID SALTS excluding the dihydrated sodium salts | UN2465 | 140 |
| DICHLOROISOPROPYL ETHER | UN2490 | 153 |
| DICHLOROMETHANE | UN1593 | 160 |
| 1,1-DICHLORO-1-NITROETHANE | UN2650 | 153 |
| DICHLOROPENTANES | UN1152 | 130 |
| DICHLOROPHENYL ISOCYANATES | UN2250 | 156 |
| DICHLOROPHENYLTRICHLOROSILANE | UN1766 | 156T |
| 1,2-DICHLOROPROPANE | UN1279 | 130 |
| 1,3-DICHLOROPROPANOL-2 | UN2750 | 153 |
| DICHLOROPROPENES | UN2047 | 132 |
| DICHLOROSILANE | UN2189 | 119T |
| 1,2-DICHLORO-1,1,2,2-TETRAFLUOROETHANE | UN1958 | 126 |
| DICHLOROVINYLCHLORARSINE | Forbidden | |
| DICYCLOHEXYLAMINE | UN2565 | 153 |
| DICYCLOHEXYLAMMONIUM NITRITE | UN2687 | 133 |
| DICYCLOPENTADIENE | UN2048 | 129 |
| 2,2-DI-(4,4-DI-tert-BUTYLPEROXYCYCLOHEXYL) PROPANE, with more than 42 percent with inert solid | Forbidden | |
| DI-2,4-DICHLOROBENZOYL PEROXIDE, with more than 75 percent with water | Forbidden | |
| 1,2-DI-(DIMETHYLAMINO) ETHANE | UN2372 | 129 |
| DIDYMIUM NITRATE | UN1465 | 140 |
| DIESEL FUEL | UN1202 | 128 |
| DIETHANOL NITROSAMINE DINITRATE (DRY) | Forbidden | |
| DIETHOXYMETHANE | UN2373 | 127 |
| 3,3-DIETHOXYPROPENE | UN2374 | 127 |
| DIETHYLAMINE | UN1154 | 132 |
| 2-DIETHYLAMINOETHANOL | UN2686 | 132 |
| DIETHYLAMINOPROPYLAMINE | UN2684 | 132 |
| N,N-DIETHYLANILINE | UN2432 | 153 |
| DIETHYLBENZENE | UN2049 | 130 |
| DIETHYL CARBONATE | UN2366 | 127 |
| DIETHYLDICHLOROSILANE | UN1767 | 155T |
| DIETHYLENEGLYCOL DINITRATE, DESENSITIZED with not less than 25 per cent non-volatile, water-insoluble phlegmatizer, by mass | UN0075 | 112 |
| DIETHYLENEGLYCOL DINITRATE (DRY) | Forbidden | |
| DIETHYLENETRIAMINE | UN2079 | 154 |
| DIETHYL ETHER | UN1155 | 127 |
| N,N-DIETHYLETHYLENEDIAMINE | UN2685 | 132 |
| DIETHYLGOLD BROMIDE | Forbidden | |
| DIETHYL KETONE | UN1156 | 127 |

| Description | UN # | ERG # |
|---|---|---|
| DIETHYL PEROXYDICARBONATE, with more than 27 percent in solution | Forbidden | |
| DIETHYL SULFATE | UN1594 | 152 |
| DIETHYL SULFIDE | UN2375 | 129 |
| DIETHYL SULPHATE | UN1594 | 152 |
| DIETHYL SULPHIDE | UN2375 | 129 |
| DIETHYLTHIOPHOSPHORYL CHLORIDE | UN2751 | 155 |
| DIETHYLZINC | UN1366 | 135 |
| 1,1-DIFLUOROETHANE | UN1030 | 115 |
| 1,1-DIFLUOROETHYLENE | UN1959 | 116P |
| DIFLUOROMETHANE | UN3252 | 115 |
| DIFLUOROPHOSPHORIC ACID, ANHYDROUS | UN1768 | 154 |
| 2,3-DIHYDROPYRAN | UN2376 | 127 |
| 1,8-DIHYDROXY-2,4,5,7-TETRANITROANTHRAQUINONE | Forbidden | |
| DI-(1-HYDROXYTETRAZOLE) (DRY) | Forbidden | |
| DIIODOACETYLENE | Forbidden | |
| DIISOBUTYLAMINE | UN2361 | 132 |
| DIISOBUTYLENE, ISOMERIC COMPOUNDS | UN2050 | 127 |
| DIISOBUTYL KETONE | UN1157 | 127 |
| DIISOOCTYL ACID PHOSPHATE | UN1902 | 153 |
| DIISOPROPYLAMINE | UN1158 | 132 |
| DIISOPROPYLBENZENE HYDROPEROXIDE, with more than 72 percent in solution | Forbidden | |
| DIISOPROPYL ETHER | UN1159 | 127 |
| DIKETENE, STABILIZED | UN2521 | 131PT |
| 1,1-DIMETHOXYETHANE | UN2377 | 127 |
| 1,2-DIMETHOXYETHANE | UN2252 | 127 |
| DIMETHYLAMINE, ANHYDROUS | UN1032 | 118 |
| DIMETHYLAMINE, AQUEOUS SOLUTION | UN1160 | 129 |
| 2-DIMETHYLAMINOACETONITRILE | UN2378 | 131 |
| 2-DIMETHYLAMINOETHANOL | UN2051 | 132 |
| 2-DIMETHYLAMINOETHYL ACRYLATE | UN3302 | 132 |
| 2-DIMETHYLAMINOETHYL METHACRYLATE | UN2522 | 153P |
| N,N-DIMETHYLANILINE | UN2253 | 153 |
| 2,3-DIMETHYLBUTANE | UN2457 | 128 |
| 1,3-DIMETHYLBUTYLAMINE | UN2379 | 132 |
| DIMETHYLCARBAMOYL CHLORIDE | UN2262 | 156 |
| DIMETHYL CARBONATE | UN1161 | 129 |
| DIMETHYLCYCLOHEXANES | UN2263 | 128 |
| DIMETHYLCYCLOHEXYLAMINE | UN2264 | 132 |
| DIMETHYLDICHLOROSILANE | UN1162 | 155T |
| DIMETHYLDIETHOXYSILANE | UN2380 | 127 |
| 2,5-DIMETHYL-2,5-DIHYDROPEROXY HEXANE, with more than 82 percent with water | Forbidden | |
| DIMETHYLDIOXANES | UN2707 | 128 |
| DIMETHYL DISULFIDE | UN2381 | 130 |
| DIMETHYL DISULPHIDE | UN2381 | 130 |
| DIMETHYL ETHER | UN1033 | 115 |
| N,N-DIMETHYLFORMAMIDE | UN2265 | 129 |
| DIMETHYLHEXANE DIHYDROPEROXIDE (DRY) | Forbidden | |
| DIMETHYLHYDRAZINE, SYMMETRICAL | UN2382 | 131T |
| DIMETHYLHYDRAZINE, UNSYMMETRICAL | UN1163 | 131T |
| 2,2-DIMETHYLPROPANE | UN2044 | 115 |
| DIMETHYL-N-PROPYLAMINE | UN2266 | 132 |
| DIMETHYL SULFATE | UN1595 | 156T |
| DIMETHYL SULFIDE | UN1164 | 130 |
| DIMETHYL SULPHATE | UN1595 | 156T |
| DIMETHYL SULPHIDE | UN1164 | 130 |
| DIMETHYL THIOPHOSPHORYL CHLORIDE | UN2267 | 156 |
| DIMETHYLZINC | UN1370 | 135 |
| DI-(1-NAPHTHOYL) PEROXIDE | Forbidden | |

| Description | UN # | ERG # |
|---|---|---|
| DINGU | UN0489 | 112 |
| DINITROANILINES | UN1596 | 153 |
| DINITROBENZENES, LIQUID | UN1597 | 152 |
| DINITROBENZENES, SOLID | UN1597 | 152 |
| DINITRO-o-CRESOL, solid | UN1598 | 153 |
| DINITRO-o-CRESOL, SOLID (ICAO terminology) | UN1598 | 153 |
| DINITRO-o-CRESOL, solution | UN1598 | 153 |
| DINITRO-o-CRESOL, SOLUTION (ICAO terminology) | UN1598 | 153 |
| DINITRO-7,8-DIMETHYLGLYCOLURIL (DRY) | Forbidden | |
| 1,3-DINITRO-5,5-DIMETHYL HYDANTOIN | Forbidden | |
| 1,3-DINITRO-4,5-DINITROSOBENZENE | Forbidden | |
| 1,1-DINITROETHANE (DRY) | Forbidden | |
| 1,2-DINITROETHANE | Forbidden | |
| DINITROGEN TETROXIDE | UN1067 | 124T |
| DINITROGLYCOLURIL | UN0489 | 112 |
| DINITROMETHANE | Forbidden | |
| DINITROPHENOLATES, alkali metals, dry or wetted with less than 15 per cent water, by mass | UN0077 | 112 |
| DINITROPHENOLATES, WETTED with not less than 15 per cent water, by mass | UN1321 | 113 |
| DINITROPHENOL, dry or wetted with less than 15 per cent water, by mass | UN0076 | 112 |
| DINITROPHENOL SOLUTION | UN1599 | 153 |
| DINITROPHENOL, WETTED with not less than 15 per cent water, by mass | UN1320 | 113 |
| 2,4-DINITROPHENYLHYDRAZINE (DRY) | Forbidden | |
| 2,4-DINITROPHENYLHYDRAZINE, WETTED with not less than 30 per cent water | Forbidden | |
| DINITROPROPYLENE GLYCOL | Forbidden | |
| DINITRORESORCINOL, dry or wetted with less than 15 per cent water, by mass | UN0078 | 112 |
| 2,4-DINITRORESORCINOL (HEAVY METAL SALTS OF) (DRY) | Forbidden | |
| 4,6-DINITRORESORCINOL (HEAVY METAL SALTS OF) (DRY) | Forbidden | |
| DINITRORESORCINOL, WETTED with not less than 15 per cent water, by mass | UN1322 | 113 |
| 3,5-DINITROSALICYLIC ACID (LEAD SALT) (DRY) | Forbidden | |
| DINITROSOBENZENE | UN0406 | 112 |
| DINITROSOBENZYLAMIDINE AND SALTS OF (DRY) | Forbidden | |
| 2,2'-DINITROSTILBENE | Forbidden | |
| 1,4-DINITRO-1,1,4,4-TETRAMETHYLOLBUTANETETRANITRATE (DRY) | Forbidden | |
| DINITROTOLUENES, LIQUID | UN2038 | 152 |
| DINITROTOLUENES, MOLTEN | UN1600 | 152 |
| DINITROTOLUENES, SOLID | UN2038 | 152 |
| 2,4-DINITRO-1,3,5-TRIMETHYLBENZENE | Forbidden | |
| DI-(beta-NITROXYETHYL) AMMONIUM NITRATE | Forbidden | |
| a,a'-DI-(NITROXY) METHYLETHER | Forbidden | |
| 1,9-DINITROXY PENTAMETHYLENE-2,4,6,8-TETRAMINE (DRY) | Forbidden | |
| DIOXANE | UN1165 | 127 |
| DIOXOLANE | UN1166 | 127 |
| DIPENTENE | UN2052 | 128 |
| DIPHENYLAMINE CHLOROARSINE | UN1698 | 154T |
| DIPHENYLCHLOROARSINE, LIQUID | UN1699 | 151 |
| DIPHENYLCHLOROARSINE, SOLID | UN1699 | 151 |
| DIPHENYLDICHLOROSILANE | UN1769 | 156T |
| DIPHENYLMETHYL BROMIDE | UN1770 | 153 |
| DIPICRYLAMINE | UN0079 | 112 |
| DIPICRYL SULFIDE, dry or wetted with less than 10 per cent water, by mass | UN0401 | 112 |
| DIPICRYL SULFIDE, WETTED with not less than 10 per cent water, by mass | UN2852 | 113 |

| Description | UN # | ERG # |
|---|---|---|
| DIPICRYL SULPHIDE, dry or wetted with less than 10 per cent water, by mass | UN0401 | 112 |
| DIPICRYL SULPHIDE, WETTED with not less than 10 per cent water, by mass | UN2852 | 113 |
| DIPROPIONYL PEROXIDE, with more than 28 percent in solution | Forbidden | |
| DIPROPYLAMINE | UN2383 | 132 |
| DI-n-PROPYL ETHER | UN2384 | 127 |
| DIPROPYL KETONE | UN2710 | 127 |
| DISINFECTANT, LIQUID, CORROSIVE, N.O.S. | UN1903 | 153 |
| DISINFECTANT, LIQUID, TOXIC, N.O.S. | UN3142 | 151 |
| DISINFECTANT, SOLID, TOXIC, N.O.S. | UN1601 | 151 |
| DISODIUM TRIOXOSILICATE | UN3253 | 154 |
| DIVINYL ETHER, STABILIZED | UN1167 | 131P |
| DODECYLTRICHLOROSILANE | UN1771 | 156T |
| DRY ICE | UN1845 | 120 |
| DYE INTERMEDIATE, LIQUID, CORROSIVE, N.O.S. | UN2801 | 154 |
| DYE INTERMEDIATE, LIQUID, TOXIC, N.O.S. | UN1602 | 151 |
| DYE INTERMEDIATE, SOLID, CORROSIVE, N.O.S. | UN3147 | 154 |
| DYE INTERMEDIATE, SOLID, TOXIC, N.O.S. | UN3143 | 151 |
| DYE, LIQUID, CORROSIVE, N.O.S. | UN2801 | 154 |
| DYE, LIQUID, TOXIC, N.O.S. | UN1602 | 151 |
| DYE, SOLID, CORROSIVE, N.O.S. | UN3147 | 154 |
| DYE, SOLID, TOXIC, N.O.S. | UN3143 | 151 |
| ELEVATED TEMPERATURE LIQUID, FLAMMABLE, N.O.S., with flash point above 60.5 °C, at or above its flash point | UN3256 | 128 |
| ELEVATED TEMPERATURE LIQUID, N.O.S., at or above 100 °C and below its flash point including molten metals, molten salts, etc. | UN3257 | 128 |
| ELEVATED TEMPERATURE SOLID, N.O.S., at or above 240 °C | UN3258 | 171 |
| ENGINES, INTERNAL COMBUSTION, (FLAMMABLE GAS POWERED) including when fitted in machinery or vehicles, regulated by aircraft only (ICAO terminology) | UN3166 | 128 |
| ENGINES, INTERNAL COMBUSTION, (FLAMMABLE LIQUID POWERED) including when fitted in machinery or vehicles, regulated by aircraft only (ICAO terminology) | UN3166 | 128 |
| ENVIRONMENTALLY HAZARDOUS SUBSTANCE, LIQUID, N.O.S. | UN3082 | 171 |
| ENVIRONMENTALLY HAZARDOUS SUBSTANCE, SOLID, N.O.S. | UN3077 | 171 |
| EPIBROMOHYDRIN | UN2558 | 131 |
| EPICHLOROHYDRIN | UN2023 | 131P |
| 1,2-EPOXY-3-ETHOXYPROPANE | UN2752 | 127 |
| ESTERS, N.O.S. | UN3272 | 127 |
| ETHANE | UN1035 | 115 |
| ETHANE, REFRIGERATED LIQUID | UN1961 | 115 |
| ETHANOLAMINE | UN2491 | 153 |
| ETHANOL AMINE DINITRATE | Forbidden | |
| ETHANOLAMINE SOLUTION | UN2491 | 153 |
| ETHANOL more than 24 per cent ethanol, by volume | UN1170 | 127 |
| ETHANOL SOLUTION more than 24 per cent ethanol, by volume | UN1170 | 127 |
| * ETHANOL AND GASOLINE MIXTURE, with more than 10%ethanol | UN3475 | 127 |
| ETHERS, N.O.S. | UN3271 | 127 |
| ETHYL ACETATE | UN1173 | 129 |
| ETHYLACETYLENE, STABILIZED | UN2452 | 116P |
| ETHYL ACRYLATE, STABILIZED | UN1917 | 129P |
| ETHYL ALCOHOL more than 24 per cent ethanol, by volume | UN1170 | 127 |
| ETHYL ALCOHOL SOLUTION more than 24 per cent ethanol, by volume | UN1170 | 127 |
| ETHYLAMINE | UN1036 | 118 |

Schedule 3

| Description | UN # | ERG # |
|---|---|---|
| ETHYLAMINE, AQUEOUS SOLUTION with not less than 50 per cent but not more than 70 per cent ethylamine | UN2270 | 132 |
| ETHYL AMYL KETONE | UN2271 | 127 |
| 2-ETHYLANILINE | UN2273 | 153 |
| N-ETHYLANILINE | UN2272 | 153 |
| ETHYLBENZENE | UN1175 | 129 |
| N-ETHYL-N-BENZYLANILINE | UN2274 | 153 |
| N-ETHYLBENZYLTOLUIDINES, LIQUID | UN2753 | 153 |
| N-ETHYLBENZYLTOLUIDINES, SOLID | UN2753 | 153 |
| ETHYL BORATE | UN1176 | 129 |
| ETHYL BROMIDE | UN1891 | 131 |
| ETHYL BROMOACETATE | UN1603 | 155 |
| 2-ETHYLBUTANOL | UN2275 | 129 |
| ETHYLBUTYL ACETATE | UN1177 | 129 |
| ETHYL BUTYL ETHER | UN1179 | 127 |
| 2-ETHYLBUTYRALDEHYDE | UN1178 | 129 |
| ETHYL BUTYRATE | UN1180 | 129 |
| ETHYL CHLORIDE | UN1037 | 115 |
| ETHYL CHLOROACETATE | UN1181 | 155 |
| ETHYL CHLOROFORMATE | UN1182 | 155T |
| ETHYL 2-CHLOROPROPIONATE | UN2935 | 132 |
| ETHYL CHLOROTHIOFORMATE | UN2826 | 155T |
| ETHYL CROTONATE | UN1862 | 129 |
| ETHYLDICHLOROARSINE | UN1892 | 151T |
| ETHYLDICHLOROSILANE | UN1183 | 139 |
| ETHYLENE, ACETYLENE AND PROPYLENE MIXTURE, REFRIGERATED LIQUID containing at least 71.5 percent ethylene with not more than 22.5 percent acetylene and not more than 6 percent propylene | UN3138 | 116 |
| ETHYLENE CHLOROHYDRIN | UN1135 | 131T |
| ETHYLENE, COMPRESSED | UN1962 | 116P |
| ETHYLENEDIAMINE | UN1604 | 132 |
| ETHYLENE DIAMINE DIPERCHLORATE | Forbidden | |
| ETHYLENE DIBROMIDE | UN1605 | 154T |
| ETHYLENE DICHLORIDE | UN1184 | 129 |
| ETHYLENE GLYCOL DIETHYL ETHER | UN1153 | 127 |
| ETHYLENE GLYCOL DINITRATE | Forbidden | |
| ETHYLENE GLYCOL MONOETHYL ETHER | UN1171 | 127 |
| ETHYLENE GLYCOL MONOETHYL ETHER ACETATE | UN1172 | 129 |
| ETHYLENE GLYCOL MONOMETHYL ETHER | UN1188 | 127 |
| ETHYLENE GLYCOL MONOMETHYL ETHER ACETATE | UN1189 | 129 |
| ETHYLENEIMINE, STABILIZED | UN1185 | 131PT |
| ETHYLENE OXIDE | UN1040 | 119PT |
| ETHYLENE OXIDE AND CARBON DIOXIDE MIXTURE with more than 9 per cent but not more than 87 per cent ethylene oxide | UN1041 | 115 |
| ETHYLENE OXIDE AND CARBON DIOXIDE MIXTURE with more than 87 per cent ethylene oxide | UN3300 | 119PT |
| ETHYLENE OXIDE AND CARBON DIOXIDE MIXTURE with not more than 9 per cent ethylene oxide | UN1952 | 126 |
| ETHYLENE OXIDE AND CHLOROTETRAFLUOROETHANE MIXTURE with not more than 8.8 per cent ethylene oxide | UN3297 | 126 |
| ETHYLENE OXIDE AND DICHLORODIFLUOROMETHANE MIXTURE with not more than 12.5 per cent ethylene oxide | UN3070 | 126 |
| ETHYLENE OXIDE AND PENTAFLUOROETHANE MIXTURE with not more than 7.9 per cent ethylene oxide | UN3298 | 126 |
| ETHYLENE OXIDE AND PROPYLENE OXIDE MIXTURE, not more than 30 per cent ethylene oxide | UN2983 | 129P |
| ETHYLENE OXIDE AND TETRAFLUOROETHANE MIXTURE with not more than 5.6 per cent ethylene oxide | UN3299 | 126 |

| Description | UN # | ERG # |
|---|---|---|
| ETHYLENE OXIDE WITH NITROGEN up to a total pressure of 1 MPa (10 bar) at 50 °C | UN1040 | 119PT |
| ETHYLENE, REFRIGERATED LIQUID | UN1038 | 115 |
| ETHYL ETHER | UN1155 | 127 |
| ETHYL FLUORIDE | UN2453 | 115 |
| ETHYL FORMATE | UN1190 | 129 |
| 2-ETHYLHEXYLAMINE | UN2276 | 132 |
| 2-ETHYLHEXYL CHLOROFORMATE | UN2748 | 156 |
| ETHYL HYDROPEROXIDE | Forbidden | |
| ETHYL ISOBUTYRATE | UN2385 | 129 |
| ETHYL ISOCYANATE | UN2481 | 155T |
| ETHYL LACTATE | UN1192 | 129 |
| ETHYL MERCAPTAN | UN2363 | 130 |
| ETHYL METHACRYLATE | UN2277 | 129P |
| ETHYL METHYL ETHER | UN1039 | 115 |
| ETHYL METHYL KETONE | UN1193 | 127 |
| ETHYL NITRATE | Forbidden | |
| ETHYL NITRITE | Forbidden | |
| ETHYL NITRITE SOLUTION | UN1194 | 131 |
| ETHYL ORTHOFORMATE | UN2524 | 129 |
| ETHYL OXALATE | UN2525 | 156 |
| ETHYL PERCHLORATE | Forbidden | |
| ETHYLPHENYLDICHLOROSILANE | UN2435 | 156 |
| 1-ETHYLPIPERIDINE | UN2386 | 132 |
| ETHYL PROPIONATE | UN1195 | 129 |
| ETHYL PROPYL ETHER | UN2615 | 127 |
| N-ETHYLTOLUIDINES | UN2754 | 153 |
| ETHYLTRICHLOROSILANE | UN1196 | 155T |
| EXPLOSIVE, BLASTING, TYPE A | UN0081 | 112 |
| EXPLOSIVE, BLASTING, TYPE B | UN0082 | 112 |
| EXPLOSIVE, BLASTING, TYPE B | UN0331 | 112 |
| EXPLOSIVE, BLASTING, TYPE C | UN0083 | 112 |
| EXPLOSIVE, BLASTING, TYPE D | UN0084 | 112 |
| EXPLOSIVE, BLASTING, TYPE E | UN0241 | 112 |
| EXPLOSIVE, BLASTING, TYPE E | UN0332 | 112 |
| EXTRACTS, AROMATIC, LIQUID | UN1169 | 127 |
| EXTRACTS, FLAVOURING, LIQUID | UN1197 | 127 |
| FABRICS, ANIMAL or VEGETABLE or SYNTHETIC, N.O.S. with oil | UN1373 | 133 |
| FABRICS IMPREGNATED WITH WEAKLY NITRATED NITROCELLULOSE, N.O.S. | UN1353 | 133 |
| FERRIC ARSENATE | UN1606 | 151 |
| FERRIC ARSENITE | UN1607 | 151 |
| FERRIC CHLORIDE, ANHYDROUS | UN1773 | 157 |
| FERRIC CHLORIDE SOLUTION | UN2582 | 154 |
| FERRIC NITRATE | UN1466 | 140 |
| FERROCERIUM, unstabilized against corrosion or with less than 10 per cent iron content | UN1323 | 170 |
| FERROSILICON with 30 per cent or more but less than 90 per cent silicon | UN1408 | 139 |
| FERROUS ARSENATE | UN1608 | 151 |
| FERROUS METAL BORINGS, SHAVINGS, TURNINGS or CUTTINGS in a form liable to self-heating | UN2793 | 170 |
| FERTILIZER AMMONIATING SOLUTION with free ammonia | UN1043 | 125 |
| FIBRES, ANIMAL or VEGETABLE or SYNTHETIC, N.O.S. with oil | UN1373 | 133 |
| FIBRES IMPREGNATED WITH WEAKLY NITRATED NITROCELLULOSE, N.O.S. | UN1353 | 133 |
| FILMS, NITROCELLULOSE BASE, gelatin coated, except scrap | UN1324 | 133 |
| FIRE EXTINGUISHER CHARGES, corrosive liquid | UN1774 | 154 |
| FIRE EXTINGUISHERS with compressed or liquefied gas | UN1044 | 126 |
| FIRELIGHTERS, SOLID with flammable liquid | UN2623 | 133 |
| FIREWORKS | UN0333 | 112 |

| Description | UN # | ERG # |
|---|---|---|
| FIREWORKS | UN0334 | 112 |
| FIREWORKS | UN0335 | 112 |
| FIREWORKS | UN0336 | 114 |
| FIREWORKS | UN0337 | 114 |
| FIRST AID KIT | UN3316 | 171 |
| FISH MEAL, STABILIZED, regulated by ship only | UN2216 | 171 |
| FISH MEAL, UNSTABILIZED | UN1374 | 133 |
| FISH SCRAP, STABILIZED, regulated by ship only | UN2216 | 171 |
| FISH SCRAP, UNSTABILIZED | UN1374 | 133 |
| FLAMMABLE LIQUID, CORROSIVE, N.O.S. | UN2924 | 132 |
| FLAMMABLE LIQUID, N.O.S. | UN1993 | 128 |
| FLAMMABLE LIQUID, TOXIC, CORROSIVE, N.O.S. | UN3286 | 131 |
| FLAMMABLE LIQUID, TOXIC, N.O.S. | UN1992 | 131 |
| FLAMMABLE SOLID, CORROSIVE, INORGANIC, N.O.S. | UN3180 | 134 |
| FLAMMABLE SOLID, CORROSIVE, ORGANIC, N.O.S. | UN2925 | 134 |
| FLAMMABLE SOLID, INORGANIC, N.O.S. | UN3178 | 133 |
| FLAMMABLE SOLID, ORGANIC, MOLTEN, N.O.S. | UN3176 | 133 |
| FLAMMABLE SOLID, ORGANIC, N.O.S. | UN1325 | 133 |
| FLAMMABLE SOLID, OXIDIZING, N.O.S. | UN3097 | 140 |
| FLAMMABLE SOLID, TOXIC, INORGANIC, N.O.S. | UN3179 | 134 |
| FLAMMABLE SOLID, TOXIC, ORGANIC, N.O.S. | UN2926 | 134 |
| FLARES, AERIAL | UN0093 | 112 |
| FLARES, AERIAL | UN0403 | 114 |
| FLARES, AERIAL | UN0404 | 114 |
| FLARES, AERIAL | UN0420 | 112 |
| FLARES, AERIAL | UN0421 | 112 |
| FLARES, SURFACE | UN0092 | 112 |
| FLARES, SURFACE | UN0418 | 112 |
| FLARES, SURFACE | UN0419 | 112 |
| FLASH POWDER | UN0094 | 112 |
| FLASH POWDER | UN0305 | 112 |
| FLUORINE, COMPRESSED | UN1045 | 124T |
| FLUOROACETIC ACID | UN2642 | 154 |
| FLUOROANILINES | UN2941 | 153 |
| FLUOROBENZENE | UN2387 | 130 |
| FLUOROBORIC ACID | UN1775 | 154 |
| FLUOROPHOSPHORIC ACID, ANHYDROUS | UN1776 | 154 |
| FLUOROSILICATES, N.O.S. | UN2856 | 151 |
| FLUOROSILICIC ACID | UN1778 | 154 |
| FLUOROSULFONIC ACID | UN1777 | 137T |
| FLUOROSULPHONIC ACID | UN1777 | 137T |
| FLUOROTOLUENES | UN2388 | 130 |
| FORMALDEHYDE SOLUTION, FLAMMABLE | UN1198 | 132 |
| FORMALDEHYDE SOLUTION with not less than 25 per cent formaldehyde | UN2209 | 132 |
| FORMIC ACID | UN1779 | 153 |
| FORMIC ACID with not more than 85% acid | UN3412 | 153 |
| FRACTURING DEVICES, EXPLOSIVE without detonator, for oil wells | UN0099 | 112 |
| FUEL, AVIATION, TURBINE ENGINE | UN1863 | 128 |
| * FUEL CELL CARTRIDGES, containing water-reactive substances | UN3476 | 138 |
| * FUEL CELL CARTRIDGES, containing flammable liquids | UN3473 | 153 |
| * FUEL CELL CARTRIDGES, containing corrosive substances | UN3477 | 153 |
| * FUEL CELL CARTRIDGES, containing liquefied flammable gas | UN3478 | 115 |
| * FUEL CELL CARTRIDGES, containing hydrogen in metal hydride | UN3479 | 115 |
| FUEL OIL | UN1202 | 128 |

| Description | UN # | ERG # |
|---|---|---|
| FULMINATE OF MERCURY (DRY) | Forbidden | |
| FULMINATING GOLD | Forbidden | |
| FULMINATING MERCURY | Forbidden | |
| FULMINATING PLATINUM | Forbidden | |
| FULMINATING SILVER | Forbidden | |
| FULMINIC ACID | Forbidden | |
| FUMARYL CHLORIDE | UN1780 | 156 |
| FURALDEHYDES | UN1199 | 132P |
| FURAN | UN2389 | 127 |
| FURFURYL ALCOHOL | UN2874 | 153 |
| FURFURYLAMINE | UN2526 | 132 |
| FUSE, DETONATING, metal clad | UN0102 | 112 |
| FUSE, DETONATING, metal clad | UN0290 | 112 |
| FUSE, DETONATING, MILD EFFECT, metal clad | UN0104 | 114 |
| FUSE, IGNITER, tubular, metal clad | UN0103 | 114 |
| FUSEL OIL | UN1201 | 127 |
| FUSE, NON-DETONATING | UN0101 | 112 |
| FUSE, SAFETY | UN0105 | 114 |
| FUZES, DETONATING | UN0106 | 112 |
| FUZES, DETONATING | UN0107 | 112 |
| FUZES, DETONATING | UN0257 | 114 |
| FUZES, DETONATING | UN0367 | 114 |
| FUZES, DETONATING with protective features | UN0408 | 112 |
| FUZES, DETONATING with protective features | UN0409 | 112 |
| FUZES, DETONATING with protective features | UN0410 | 114 |
| FUZES, IGNITING | UN0316 | 112 |
| FUZES, IGNITING | UN0317 | 114 |
| FUZES, IGNITING | UN0368 | 114 |
| GALACTAN TRINITRATE | Forbidden | |
| GALLIUM | UN2803 | 172 |
| GAS CARTRIDGES without a release device, non-refillable | UN2037 | 115 |
| GAS CARTRIDGES without a release device, non-refillable | UN2037 | 115 |
| GAS OIL | UN1202 | 128 |
| GASOLINE | UN1203 | 128 |
| GAS, REFRIGERATED LIQUID, FLAMMABLE, N.O.S. | UN3312 | 115 |
| GAS, REFRIGERATED LIQUID, N.O.S. | UN3158 | 120 |
| GAS, REFRIGERATED LIQUID, OXIDIZING, N.O.S. | UN3311 | 122 |
| GAS SAMPLE, NON-PRESSURIZED, FLAMMABLE, N.O.S., not refrigerated liquid | UN3167 | 115 |
| GAS SAMPLE, NON-PRESSURIZED, TOXIC, FLAMMABLE, N.O.S., not refrigerated liquid | UN3168 | 119 |
| GAS SAMPLE, NON-PRESSURIZED, TOXIC, N.O.S., not refrigerated liquid | UN3169 | 123 |
| GENETICALLY MODIFIED MICRO-ORGANISMS not containing infectious substances | UN3245 | 171 |
| GERMANE | UN2192 | 119T |
| GLYCEROL-1,3-DINITRATE | Forbidden | |
| GLYCEROL GLUCONATE TRINITRATE | Forbidden | |
| GLYCEROL LACTATE TRINITRATE | Forbidden | |
| GLYCEROL alpha-MONOCHLOROHYDRIN | UN2689 | 153 |
| GLYCIDALDEHYDE | UN2622 | 131P |
| GRENADES, hand or rifle, with bursting charge | UN0284 | 112 |
| GRENADES, hand or rifle, with bursting charge | UN0285 | 112 |
| GRENADES, hand or rifle, with bursting charge | UN0292 | 112 |
| GRENADES, hand or rifle, with bursting charge | UN0293 | 112 |
| GRENADES, PRACTICE, hand or rifle | UN0110 | 114 |
| GRENADES, PRACTICE, hand or rifle | UN0318 | 112 |

Schedule 3

| Description | UN # | ERG # |
|---|---|---|
| GRENADES, PRACTICE, hand or rifle | UN0372 | 112 |
| GRENADES, PRACTICE, hand or rifle | UN0452 | 114 |
| GUANIDINE NITRATE | UN1467 | 143 |
| GUANYL NITROSAMINOGUANYLIDENE HYDRAZINE (DRY) | Forbidden | |
| GUANYL NITROSAMINOGUANYLIDENE HYDRAZINE, WETTED with not less than 30 per cent water, by mass | UN0113 | 112 |
| GUANYL NITROSAMINOGUANYLTETRAZENE WETTED with not less than 30 per cent water, or mixture of alcohol and water, by mass | UN0114 | 112 |
| GUNPOWDER, COMPRESSED | UN0028 | 112 |
| GUNPOWDER granular or as a meal | UN0027 | 112 |
| GUNPOWDER, IN PELLETS | UN0028 | 112 |
| HAFNIUM POWDER, DRY | UN2545 | 135 |
| HAFNIUM POWDER, WETTED with not less than 25 per cent water (a visible excess of water must be present) (a) mechanically produced, particle size less than 53 microns; (b) chemically produced, particle size less than 840 microns | UN1326 | 170 |
| HAY, regulated by ship only | UN1327 | 133 |
| HAY, wet, damp or contaminated with oil, regulated by ship only | Forbidden | |
| HEATING OIL LIGHT | UN1202 | 128 |
| HELIUM, COMPRESSED | UN1046 | 121 |
| HELIUM, REFRIGERATED LIQUID | UN1963 | 120 |
| HEPTAFLUOROPROPANE | UN3296 | 126 |
| n-HEPTALDEHYDE | UN3056 | 129 |
| HEPTANES | UN1206 | 128 |
| n-HEPTENE | UN2278 | 128 |
| HEXACHLOROACETONE | UN2661 | 153 |
| HEXACHLOROBENZENE | UN2729 | 152 |
| HEXACHLOROBUTADIENE | UN2279 | 151 |
| HEXACHLOROCYCLOPENTADIENE | UN2646 | 151T |
| HEXACHLOROPHENE | UN2875 | 151 |
| HEXADECYLTRICHLOROSILANE | UN1781 | 156 |
| HEXADIENE | UN2458 | 130 |
| HEXAETHYL TETRAPHOSPHATE | UN1611 | 151 |
| HEXAETHYL TETRAPHOSPHATE AND COMPRESSED GAS MIXTURE | UN1612 | 123T |
| HEXAFLUOROACETONE | UN2420 | 125T |
| HEXAFLUOROACETONE HYDRATE | UN2552 | 151 |
| HEXAFLUOROETHANE, COMPRESSED | UN2193 | 126 |
| HEXAFLUOROPHOSPHORIC ACID | UN1782 | 154 |
| HEXAFLUOROPROPYLENE | UN1858 | 126 |
| HEXALDEHYDE | UN1207 | 129 |
| HEXAMETHYLENEDIAMINE, SOLID | UN2280 | 153 |
| HEXAMETHYLENEDIAMINE SOLUTION | UN1783 | 153 |
| HEXAMETHYLENE DIISOCYANATE | UN2281 | 156 |
| HEXAMETHYLENEIMINE | UN2493 | 132 |
| HEXAMETHYLENETETRAMINE | UN1328 | 133 |
| HEXAMETHYLENE TRIPEROXIDE DIAMINE (DRY) | Forbidden | |
| HEXAMETHYLOL BENZENE HEXANITRATE | Forbidden | |
| HEXANES | UN1208 | 128 |
| HEXANITROAZOXY BENZENE | Forbidden | |
| 2,2',4,4',6,6'-HEXANITRO-3,3'-DIHYDROXYAZOBENZENE (DRY) | Forbidden | |
| 2,2',3',4,4',6-HEXANITRODIPHENYLAMINE | Forbidden | |
| HEXANITRODIPHENYLAMINE | UN0079 | 112 |
| 2,3',4,4',6,6'-HEXANITRODIPHENYLETHER | Forbidden | |
| N,N'-(HEXANITRODIPHENYL) ETHYLENE DINITRAMINE (DRY) | Forbidden | |
| HEXANITRODIPHENYL UREA | Forbidden | |
| HEXANITROETHANE | Forbidden | |
| HEXANITROOXANILIDE | Forbidden | |
| HEXANITROSTILBENE | UN0392 | 112 |

| Description | UN # | ERG # |
|---|---|---|
| HEXANOLS | UN2282 | 129 |
| 1-HEXENE | UN2370 | 128 |
| HEXOGEN AND CYCLOTETRAMETHYLENETETRANITRAMINE MIXTURE, DESENSITIZED with not less than 10 per cent phelgmatizer, by mass | UN0391 | 112 |
| HEXOGEN AND CYCLOTETRAMETHYLENETETRANITRAMINE MIXTURE, WETTED with not less than 15 per cent water, by mass | UN0391 | 112 |
| HEXOGEN AND HMX MIXTURE, DESENSITIZED with not less than 10 per cent phelgmatizer, by mass | UN0391 | 112 |
| HEXOGEN AND HMX MIXTURE, WETTED with not less than 15 per cent water, by mass | UN0391 | 112 |
| HEXOGEN AND OCTOGEN MIXTURE, DESENSITIZED with not less than 10 per cent phelgmatizer, by mass | UN0391 | 112 |
| HEXOGEN AND OCTOGEN MIXTURE, WETTED with not less than 15 per cent water, by mass | UN0391 | 112 |
| HEXOGEN, DESENSITIZED | UN0483 | 112 |
| HEXOGEN WETTED with not less than 15 per cent water, by mass | UN0072 | 112 |
| HEXOLITE, dry or wetted with less than 15 per cent water, by mass | UN0118 | 112 |
| HEXOTOL, dry or wetted with less than 15 per cent water, by mass | UN0118 | 112 |
| HEXOTONAL | UN0393 | 112 |
| HEXYL | UN0079 | 112 |
| HEXYLTRICHLOROSILANE | UN1784 | 156T |
| HMX, DESENSITIZED | UN0484 | 112 |
| HMX, DRY or unphlegmatized | Forbidden | |
| HMX, WETTED with not less than 15 per cent water, by mass | UN0226 | 112 |
| HYDRAZINE, ANHYDROUS | UN2029 | 132 |
| HYDRAZINE, AQUEOUS SOLUTION with more than 37 per cent but not more than 64 per cent hydrazine, by mass | UN2030 | 153 |
| HYDRAZINE, AQUEOUS SOLUTION with not more than 37 per cent hydrazine, by mass | UN3293 | 152 |
| HYDRAZINE AZIDE | Forbidden | |
| HYDRAZINE CHLORATE | Forbidden | |
| HYDRAZINE DICARBONIC ACID DIAZIDE | Forbidden | |
| HYDRAZINE HYDRATE with more than 37 per cent but not more than 64 per cent hydrazine, by mass | UN2030 | 153 |
| HYDRAZINE PERCHLORATE | Forbidden | |
| HYDRAZINE SELENATE | Forbidden | |
| HYDRIODIC ACID | UN1787 | 154 |
| HYDROBROMIC ACID | UN1788 | 154 |
| HYDROCARBON GAS MIXTURE, COMPRESSED, N.O.S. | UN1964 | 115 |
| HYDROCARBON GAS MIXTURE, LIQUEFIED, N.O.S. | UN1965 | 115 |
| HYDROCARBON GAS REFILLS FOR SMALL DEVICES with release device | UN3150 | 115 |
| HYDROCARBONS, LIQUID, N.O.S. | UN3295 | 128 |
| HYDROCHLORIC ACID | UN1789 | 157 |
| HYDROCYANIC ACID, AQUEOUS SOLUTION with more than 20 per cent hydrogen cyanide | Forbidden | |
| HYDROCYANIC ACID, AQUEOUS SOLUTION with not more than 20 per cent hydrogen cyanide | UN1613 | 154T |
| HYDROCYANIC ACID (PRUSSIC), UNSTABILIZED | Forbidden | |
| HYDROFLUORIC ACID AND SULFURIC ACID MIXTURE | UN1786 | 157 |
| HYDROFLUORIC ACID AND SULPHURIC ACID MIXTURE | UN1786 | 157 |
| HYDROFLUORIC ACID, solution, with more than 60 per cent hydrofluoric acid | UN1790 | 157 |
| HYDROFLUORIC ACID, solution, with not more than 60 per cent hydrofluoric acid | UN1790 | 157 |

| Description | UN # | ERG # |
|---|---|---|
| HYDROGEN AND METHANE MIXTURE, COMPRESSED | UN2034 | 115 |
| HYDROGEN BROMIDE, ANHYDROUS | UN1048 | 125T |
| HYDROGEN CHLORIDE, ANHYDROUS | UN1050 | 125T |
| HYDROGEN CHLORIDE, REFRIGERATED LIQUID | UN2186 | 125T |
| HYDROGEN in a metal hydride storage system | UN3468 | 115 |
| HYDROGEN, COMPRESSED | UN1049 | 115 |
| HYDROGEN CYANIDE, AQUEOUS SOLUTION with more than 20 per cent hydrogen cyanide | Forbidden | |
| HYDROGEN CYANIDE, AQUEOUS SOLUTION with not more than 20 per cent hydrogen cyanide | UN1613 | 154T |
| HYDROGEN CYANIDE, SOLUTION IN ALCOHOL with not more than 45 per cent hydrogen cyanide | UN3294 | 131T |
| HYDROGEN CYANIDE, STABILIZED, containing less than 3 per cent water | UN1051 | 117T |
| HYDROGEN CYANIDE, STABILIZED, containing less than 3 per cent water and absorbed in a porous inert material | UN1614 | 131T |
| HYDROGENDIFLUORIDES, N.O.S., solid | UN1740 | 154 |
| HYDROGENDIFLUORIDES, N.O.S., solution | UN1740 | 154 |
| HYDROGENDIFLUORIDES SOLUTION, N.O.S., SOLUTION | UN3471 | 154 |
| HYDROGEN FLUORIDE, ANHYDROUS | UN1052 | 125T |
| HYDROGEN IODIDE, ANHYDROUS | UN2197 | 125T |
| HYDROGEN PEROXIDE AND PEROXYACETIC ACID MIXTURE STABILIZED with acid(s), water and not more than 5 per cent peroxyacetic acid | UN3149 | 140 |
| HYDROGEN PEROXIDE, AQUEOUS SOLUTION, STABILIZED with more than 60 per cent hydrogen peroxide | UN2015 | 143 |
| HYDROGEN PEROXIDE, AQUEOUS SOLUTION with not less than 8 per cent but less than 20 per cent hydrogen peroxide (stabilized as necessary) | UN2984 | 140 |
| HYDROGEN PEROXIDE, AQUEOUS SOLUTION with not less than 20 per cent but not more than 60 per cent hydrogen peroxide (stabilized as necessary) | UN2014 | 140 |
| HYDROGEN PEROXIDE, STABILIZED | UN2015 | 143 |
| HYDROGEN, REFRIGERATED LIQUID | UN1966 | 115 |
| HYDROGEN SELENIDE, ANHYDROUS | UN2202 | 117T |
| HYDROGEN SULFIDE | UN1053 | 117T |
| HYDROGEN SULPHIDE | UN1053 | 117T |
| HYDROQUINONE | UN2662 | 153 |
| HYDROXYLAMINE IODIDE | Forbidden | |
| HYDROXYLAMINE SULFATE | UN2865 | 154 |
| HYDROXYLAMINE SULPHATE | UN2865 | 154 |
| HYPOCHLORITES, INORGANIC, N.O.S. | UN3212 | 140 |
| HYPOCHLORITE SOLUTION, more than 7 per cent available chlorine | UN1791 | 154 |
| HYPONITROUS ACID | Forbidden | |
| * 1-HYDROXYBENZOTRIAZOLE, anhydrous, wetted with not less than 20% water | UN3474 | 113 |
| IGNITERS | UN0121 | 112 |
| IGNITERS | UN0314 | 112 |
| IGNITERS | UN0315 | 112 |
| IGNITERS | UN0325 | 114 |
| IGNITERS | UN0454 | 114 |
| 3,3'-IMINODIPROPYLAMINE | UN2269 | 153 |
| INFECTIOUS SUBSTANCE, AFFECTING ANIMALS only (Risk group IV, III or II) | UN2900 | 158 |
| INFECTIOUS SUBSTANCE, AFFECTING HUMANS (Risk group IV, III or II) | UN2814 | 158 |
| INITIATING EXPLOSIVES (DRY) | Forbidden | |
| INOSITOL HEXANITRATE (DRY) | Forbidden | |
| INSECTICIDE GAS, FLAMMABLE, N.O.S. | UN3354 | 115 |
| INSECTICIDE GAS, N.O.S. | UN1968 | 126 |

| Description | UN # | ERG # |
|---|---|---|
| INSECTICIDE GAS, TOXIC, FLAMMABLE, N.O.S. | UN3355 | 119T |
| INSECTICIDE GAS, TOXIC, N.O.S. | UN1967 | 123T |
| INULIN TRINITRATE (DRY) | Forbidden | |
| IODINE AZIDE (DRY) | Forbidden | |
| IODINE MONOCHLORIDE | UN1792 | 157 |
| IODINE PENTAFLUORIDE | UN2495 | 144T |
| 2-IODOBUTANE | UN2390 | 129 |
| IODOMETHYLPROPANES | UN2391 | 129 |
| IODOPROPANES | UN2392 | 129 |
| IODOXY COMPOUNDS (DRY) | Forbidden | |
| IRIDIUM NITRATOPENTAMINE IRIDIUM NITRATE | Forbidden | |
| IRON OXIDE, SPENT obtained from hydrocarbon gas purification | UN1376 | 135 |
| IRON PENTACARBONYL | UN1994 | 131T |
| IRON SPONGE, SPENT obtained from hydrocarbon gas purification | UN1376 | 135 |
| ISOBUTANE | UN1969 | 115 |
| ISOBUTANOL | UN1212 | 129 |
| ISOBUTYL ACETATE | UN1213 | 129 |
| ISOBUTYL ACRYLATE, STABILIZED | UN2527 | 129P |
| ISOBUTYL ALCOHOL | UN1212 | 129 |
| ISOBUTYLALDEHYDE | UN2045 | 129 |
| ISOBUTYLAMINE | UN1214 | 132 |
| ISOBUTYLENE | UN1055 | 115 |
| ISOBUTYL FORMATE | UN2393 | 132 |
| ISOBUTYL ISOBUTYRATE | UN2528 | 129 |
| ISOBUTYL ISOCYANATE | UN2486 | 155T |
| ISOBUTYL METHACRYLATE, STABILIZED | UN2283 | 130P |
| ISOBUTYL PROPIONATE | UN2394 | 129 |
| ISOBUTYRALDEHYDE | UN2045 | 129 |
| ISOBUTYRIC ACID | UN2529 | 132 |
| ISOBUTYRONITRILE | UN2284 | 131 |
| ISOBUTYRYL CHLORIDE | UN2395 | 132 |
| ISOCYANATE SOLUTION, FLAMMABLE, TOXIC, N.O.S. | UN2478 | 155 |
| ISOCYANATE SOLUTION, TOXIC, FLAMMABLE, N.O.S. | UN3080 | 155 |
| ISOCYANATE SOLUTION, TOXIC, N.O.S. | UN2206 | 155 |
| ISOCYANATES, FLAMMABLE, TOXIC, N.O.S. | UN2478 | 155 |
| ISOCYANATES, TOXIC, FLAMMABLE, N.O.S. | UN3080 | 155 |
| ISOCYANATES, TOXIC, N.O.S. | UN2206 | 155 |
| ISOCYANATOBENZOTRIFLUORIDES | UN2285 | 156 |
| ISOHEPTENE | UN2287 | 128 |
| ISOHEXENE | UN2288 | 128 |
| ISOOCTENE | UN1216 | 128 |
| ISOPENTENES | UN2371 | 128 |
| ISOPHORONEDIAMINE | UN2289 | 153 |
| ISOPHORONE DIISOCYANATE | UN2290 | 156 |
| ISOPRENE, STABILIZED | UN1218 | 130P |
| ISOPROPANOL | UN1219 | 129 |
| ISOPROPENYL ACETATE | UN2403 | 129P |
| ISOPROPENYLBENZENE | UN2303 | 128 |
| ISOPROPYL ACETATE | UN1220 | 129 |
| ISOPROPYL ACID PHOSPHATE | UN1793 | 153 |
| ISOPROPYL ALCOHOL | UN1219 | 129 |
| ISOPROPYLAMINE | UN1221 | 132 |
| ISOPROPYLBENZENE | UN1918 | 130 |
| ISOPROPYL BUTYRATE | UN2405 | 129 |
| ISOPROPYL CHLOROACETATE | UN2947 | 155 |
| ISOPROPYL CHLOROFORMATE | UN2407 | 155T |
| ISOPROPYL 2-CHLOROPROPIONATE | UN2934 | 132 |
| ISOPROPYLCUMYL HYDROPEROXIDE, with more than 72 percent in solution | Forbidden | |

| Description | UN # | ERG # |
|---|---|---|
| ISOPROPYL ISOBUTYRATE | UN2406 | 131 |
| ISOPROPYL ISOCYANATE | UN2483 | 155T |
| ISOPROPYL NITRATE | UN1222 | 130 |
| ISOPROPYL PROPIONATE | UN2409 | 129 |
| ISOSORBIDE DINITRATE MIXTURE with not less than 60 per cent lactose, mannose, starch or calcium hydrogen phosphate | UN2907 | 133 |
| ISOSORBIDE-5-MONONITRATE with less than 30 per cent non-volatile, non-flammable phlegmatizer | UN3251 | 133 |
| ISOTHIOCYANIC ACID | Forbidden | |
| JET PERFORATING GUNS, CHARGED, oil well, without detonator | UN0124 | 112 |
| JET PERFORATING GUNS, CHARGED, oil well, without detonator | UN0494 | 114 |
| KEROSENE | UN1223 | 128 |
| KETONES, LIQUID, N.O.S. | UN1224 | 127 |
| KRYPTON, COMPRESSED | UN1056 | 121 |
| KRYPTON, REFRIGERATED LIQUID | UN1970 | 120 |
| LEAD ACETATE | UN1616 | 151 |
| LEAD ARSENATES | UN1617 | 151 |
| LEAD ARSENITES | UN1618 | 151 |
| LEAD AZIDE (DRY) | Forbidden | |
| LEAD AZIDE, WETTED with not less than 20 per cent water, or mixture of alcohol and water, by mass | UN0129 | 112 |
| LEAD COMPOUND, SOLUBLE, N.O.S. | UN2291 | 151 |
| LEAD CYANIDE | UN1620 | 151 |
| LEAD DIOXIDE | UN1872 | 141 |
| LEAD NITRATE | UN1469 | 141 |
| LEAD NITRORESORCINATE (DRY) | Forbidden | |
| LEAD PERCHLORATE | UN1470 | 141 |
| LEAD PHOSPHITE, DIBASIC | UN2989 | 133 |
| LEAD PICRATE (DRY) | Forbidden | |
| LEAD STYPHNATE (DRY) | Forbidden | |
| LEAD STYPHNATE, WETTED with not less than 20 per cent water, or mixture of alcohol and water, by mass | UN0130 | 112 |
| LEAD SULFATE with more than 3 per cent free acid | UN1794 | 154 |
| LEAD SULPHATE with more than 3 per cent free acid | UN1794 | 154 |
| LEAD TRINITRORESORCINATE, WETTED with not less than 20 per cent water, or mixture of alcohol and water, by mass | UN0130 | 112 |
| LIFE-SAVING APPLIANCES NOT SELF-INFLATING, containing dangerous goods as equipment | UN3072 | 171 |
| LIFE-SAVING APPLIANCES, SELF-INFLATING | UN2990 | 171 |
| LIGHTER REFILLS (cigarettes) containing flammable gas and capable of passing the tests specified in the Hazardous Products (Lighters) Regulations | UN1057 | 115 |
| LIGHTERS (cigarettes) containing flammable gas and capable of passing the tests specified in the Hazardous Products (Lighters) Regulations | UN1057 | 115 |
| LIGHTERS (cigarettes) WITH LIGHTER FLUID | Forbidden | |
| LIGHTERS, FUSE | UN0131 | 114 |
| DELETED | | |
| LIQUEFIED GAS, FLAMMABLE, N.O.S. | UN3161 | 115 |
| LIQUEFIED GAS, N.O.S. | UN3163 | 126 |
| LIQUEFIED GAS, OXIDIZING, N.O.S. | UN3157 | 122 |
| LIQUEFIED GAS, TOXIC, CORROSIVE, N.O.S. | UN3308 | 123T |
| LIQUEFIED GAS, TOXIC, FLAMMABLE, CORROSIVE, N.O.S. | UN3309 | 119T |
| LIQUEFIED GAS, TOXIC, FLAMMABLE, N.O.S. | UN3160 | 119T |
| LIQUEFIED GAS, TOXIC, N.O.S. | UN3162 | 123T |
| LIQUEFIED GAS, TOXIC, OXIDIZING, CORROSIVE, N.O.S. | UN3310 | 124T |

| Description | UN # | ERG # |
|---|---|---|
| LIQUEFIED GAS, TOXIC, OXIDIZING, N.O.S. | UN3307 | 124T |
| LIQUEFIED PETROLEUM GASES | UN1075 | 115 |
| LITHIUM | UN1415 | 138 |
| LITHIUM ALKYLS | UN2445 | 135 |
| LITHIUM ALUMINUM HYDRIDE | UN1410 | 138 |
| LITHIUM ALUMINUM HYDRIDE, ETHEREAL | UN1411 | 138 |
| LITHIUM BATTERIES | UN3090 | 138 |
| LITHIUM BATTERIES CONTAINED IN EQUIPMENT | UN3091 | 138 |
| LITHIUM BATTERIES PACKED WITH EQUIPMENT | UN3091 | 138 |
| LITHIUM BOROHYDRIDE | UN1413 | 138 |
| LITHIUM FERROSILICON | UN2830 | 139 |
| LITHIUM HYDRIDE | UN1414 | 138 |
| LITHIUM HYDRIDE, FUSED SOLID | UN2805 | 138 |
| LITHIUM HYDROXIDE MONOHYDRATE | UN2680 | 154 |
| LITHIUM HYDROXIDE SOLUTION | UN2679 | 154 |
| LITHIUM HYPOCHLORITE, DRY | UN1471 | 140 |
| LITHIUM HYPOCHLORITE MIXTURE | UN1471 | 140 |
| LITHIUM ION BATTERIES (including lithium ion polymer batteries) | UN3480 | 147 |
| LITHIUM ION BATTERIES CONTAINED IN EQUIPMENT(including lithium ion polymer batteries) | UN3481 | 147 |
| LITHIUM NITRATE | UN2722 | 140 |
| LITHIUM NITRIDE | UN2806 | 138T |
| LITHIUM PEROXIDE | UN1472 | 143 |
| LITHIUM SILICON | UN1417 | 138 |
| LONDON PURPLE | UN1621 | 151 |
| MAGNESIUM ALKYLS | UN3053 | 135 |
| MAGNESIUM ALLOYS, POWDER | UN1418 | 138 |
| MAGNESIUM ALLOYS with more than 50 per cent magnesium in pellets, turnings or ribbons | UN1869 | 138 |
| MAGNESIUM ALUMINUM PHOSPHIDE | UN1419 | 139T |
| MAGNESIUM ARSENATE | UN1622 | 151 |
| MAGNESIUM BROMATE | UN1473 | 140 |
| MAGNESIUM CHLORATE | UN2723 | 140 |
| MAGNESIUM DIAMIDE | UN2004 | 135T |
| MAGNESIUM DIPHENYL | UN2005 | 135 |
| MAGNESIUM DROSS, WET OR HOT | Forbidden | |
| MAGNESIUM FLUOROSILICATE | UN2853 | 151 |
| MAGNESIUM GRANULES, COATED, particle size not less than 149 microns | UN2950 | 138 |
| MAGNESIUM HYDRIDE | UN2010 | 138 |
| MAGNESIUM in pellets, turnings or ribbons | UN1869 | 138 |
| MAGNESIUM NITRATE | UN1474 | 140 |
| MAGNESIUM PERCHLORATE | UN1475 | 140 |
| MAGNESIUM PEROXIDE | UN1476 | 140 |
| MAGNESIUM PHOSPHIDE | UN2011 | 139T |
| MAGNESIUM POWDER | UN1418 | 138 |
| MAGNESIUM SILICIDE | UN2624 | 138 |
| MAGNETIZED MATERIAL, regulated by aircraft only | UN2807 | 171 |
| MALEIC ANHYDRIDE | UN2215 | 156 |
| MALEIC ANHYDRIDE, MOLTEN | UN2215 | 156 |
| MALONONITRILE | UN2647 | 153 |
| MANEB | UN2210 | 135 |
| MANEB PREPARATION, STABILIZED against self-heating | UN2968 | 135 |
| MANEB PREPARATION with not less than 60 per cent maneb | UN2210 | 135 |
| MANEB, STABILIZED against self-heating | UN2968 | 135 |
| MANGANESE NITRATE | UN2724 | 140 |
| MANGANESE RESINATE | UN1330 | 133 |
| MANNITAN TETRANITRATE | Forbidden | |
| MANNITOL HEXANITRATE (DRY) | Forbidden | |

| Description | UN # | ERG # |
|---|---|---|
| MANNITOL HEXANITRATE, WETTED with not less than 40 per cent water, or mixture of alcohol and water, by mass | UN0133 | 112 |
| MATCHES, "STRIKE ANYWHERE" | UN1331 | 133 |
| MATCHES, FUSEE | UN2254 | 133 |
| MATCHES, SAFETY (book, card or strike on box) | UN1944 | 133 |
| MATCHES, WAX "VESTA" | UN1945 | 133 |
| MEDICINE, LIQUID, FLAMMABLE, TOXIC, N.O.S. | UN3248 | 131 |
| MEDICINE, LIQUID, TOXIC, N.O.S. | UN1851 | 151 |
| MEDICINE, SOLID, TOXIC, N.O.S. | UN3249 | 151 |
| MERCAPTAN MIXTURE, LIQUID, FLAMMABLE, N.O.S. | UN3336 | 130 |
| MERCAPTAN MIXTURE, LIQUID, FLAMMABLE, TOXIC, N.O.S | UN1228 | 131 |
| MERCAPTAN MIXTURE, LIQUID, TOXIC, FLAMMABLE, N.O.S. | UN3071 | 131 |
| MERCAPTANS, LIQUID, FLAMMABLE, N.O.S. | UN3336 | 130 |
| MERCAPTANS, LIQUID, FLAMMABLE, TOXIC, N.O.S. | UN1228 | 131 |
| MERCAPTANS, LIQUID, TOXIC, FLAMMABLE, N.O.S. | UN3071 | 131 |
| 5-MERCAPTOTETRAZOL-1-ACETIC ACID | UN0448 | 114 |
| MERCURIC ARSENATE | UN1623 | 151 |
| MERCURIC CHLORIDE | UN1624 | 154 |
| MERCURIC NITRATE | UN1625 | 141 |
| MERCURIC POTASSIUM CYANIDE | UN1626 | 157 |
| MERCUROUS NITRATE | UN1627 | 141 |
| MERCURY | UN2809 | 172 |
| MERCURY ACETATE | UN1629 | 151 |
| MERCURY ACETYLIDES | Forbidden | |
| MERCURY AMMONIUM CHLORIDE | UN1630 | 151 |
| MERCURY AZIDES | Forbidden | |
| MERCURY BASED PESTICIDE, LIQUID, FLAMMABLE, TOXIC, flash point less than 23 °C | UN2778 | 131 |
| MERCURY BASED PESTICIDE, LIQUID, TOXIC | UN3012 | 151 |
| MERCURY BASED PESTICIDE, LIQUID, TOXIC, FLAMMABLE, flash point not less than 23 °C | UN3011 | 131 |
| MERCURY BASED PESTICIDE, SOLID, TOXIC | UN2777 | 151 |
| MERCURY BENZOATE | UN1631 | 154 |
| MERCURY BROMIDES | UN1634 | 154 |
| MERCURY COMPOUND, LIQUID, N.O.S., excluding mercurous chloride and cinnabar | UN2024 | 151 |
| MERCURY COMPOUND, SOLID, N.O.S., excluding mercurous chloride and cinnabar | UN2025 | 151 |
| MERCURY CYANIDE | UN1636 | 154 |
| MERCURY FULMINATE, WETTED with not less than 20 per cent water, or mixture of alcohol and water, by mass | UN0135 | 112 |
| MERCURY GLUCONATE | UN1637 | 151 |
| MERCURY IODIDE AQUABASIC AMMONOBASIC (IODIDE OF MILLON'S BASE) | Forbidden | |
| MERCURY IODIDE, solid | UN1638 | 151 |
| MERCURY IODIDE, SOLID (ICAO terminology) | UN1638 | 151 |
| MERCURY IODIDE, solution | UN1638 | 151 |
| MERCURY IODIDE, SOLUTION (ICAO terminology) | UN1638 | 151 |
| MERCURY NITRIDE | Forbidden | |
| MERCURY NUCLEATE | UN1639 | 151 |
| MERCURY OLEATE | UN1640 | 151 |
| MERCURY OXIDE | UN1641 | 151 |
| MERCURY OXYCYANIDE | Forbidden | |
| MERCURY OXYCYANIDE, DESENSITIZED | UN1642 | 151 |
| MERCURY POTASSIUM IODIDE | UN1643 | 151 |

| Description | UN # | ERG # |
|---|---|---|
| MERCURY SALICYLATE | UN1644 | 151 |
| MERCURY SULFATE | UN1645 | 151 |
| MERCURY SULPHATE | UN1645 | 151 |
| MERCURY THIOCYANATE | UN1646 | 151 |
| MESITYL OXIDE | UN1229 | 129 |
| METAL ALKYL HALIDES, WATER-REACTIVE, N.O.S. | UN3049 | 138T |
| METAL ALKYL HYDRIDES, WATER-REACTIVE, N.O.S. | UN3050 | 138 |
| METAL ALKYLS, WATER-REACTIVE, N.O.S. | UN2003 | 135 |
| METAL ARYL HALIDES, WATER-REACTIVE, N.O.S. | UN3049 | 138T |
| METAL ARYL HYDRIDES, WATER-REACTIVE, N.O.S. | UN3050 | 138 |
| METAL ARYLS, WATER-REACTIVE, N.O.S. | UN2003 | 135 |
| METAL CARBONYLS, N.O.S., liquid | UN3281 | 151T |
| METAL CARBONYLS, N.O.S., solid | UN3281 | 151T |
| METAL CATALYST, DRY | UN2881 | 135 |
| METAL CATALYST, WETTED, with a visible excess of liquid | UN1378 | 170 |
| METALDEHYDE | UN1332 | 133 |
| METAL HYDRIDES, FLAMMABLE, N.O.S. | UN3182 | 170 |
| METAL HYDRIDES, WATER-REACTIVE, N.O.S. | UN1409 | 138 |
| METALLIC SUBSTANCE, WATER-REACTIVE, N.O.S. | UN3208 | 138 |
| METALLIC SUBSTANCE, WATER-REACTIVE, SELF-HEATING, N.O.S. | UN3209 | 138 |
| METAL POWDER, FLAMMABLE, N.O.S. | UN3089 | 170 |
| METAL POWDER, SELF-HEATING, N.O.S. | UN3189 | 135 |
| METAL SALTS OF METHYL NITRAMINE (DRY) | Forbidden | |
| METAL SALTS OF ORGANIC COMPOUNDS, FLAMMABLE, N.O.S. | UN3181 | 133 |
| METHACRYLALDEHYDE, STABILIZED | UN2396 | 131P |
| METHACRYLIC ACID, STABILIZED | UN2531 | 153P |
| METHACRYLONITRILE, STABILIZED | UN3079 | 131PT |
| METHALLYL ALCOHOL | UN2614 | 129 |
| METHANE, COMPRESSED | UN1971 | 115 |
| METHANE, REFRIGERATED LIQUID | UN1972 | 115 |
| METHANESULFONYL CHLORIDE | UN3246 | 156T |
| METHANESULPHONYL CHLORIDE | UN3246 | 156T |
| METHANOL | UN1230 | 131 |
| METHAZOIC ACID | Forbidden | |
| METHOXYMETHYL ISOCYANATE | UN2605 | 155T |
| 4-METHOXY-4-METHYLPENTAN-2-ONE | UN2293 | 127 |
| 1-METHOXY-2-PROPANOL | UN3092 | 129 |
| METHYL ACETATE | UN1231 | 129 |
| METHYLACETYLENE AND PROPADIENE MIXTURE, STABILIZED | UN1060 | 116P |
| METHYL ACRYLATE, STABILIZED | UN1919 | 129P |
| METHYLAL | UN1234 | 127 |
| METHYLALLYL CHLORIDE | UN2554 | 129P |
| METHYLAMINE, ANHYDROUS | UN1061 | 118 |
| METHYLAMINE, AQUEOUS SOLUTION | UN1235 | 132 |
| METHYLAMINE DINITRAMINE AND DRY SALTS THEREOF | Forbidden | |
| METHYLAMINE NITROFORM | Forbidden | |
| METHYLAMINE PERCHLORATE (DRY) | Forbidden | |
| METHYLAMYL ACETATE | UN1233 | 129 |
| N-METHYLANILINE | UN2294 | 153 |
| alpha-METHYLBENZYL ALCOHOL | UN2937 | 153 |
| METHYL BROMIDE | UN1062 | 123T |
| METHYL BROMIDE AND ETHYLENE DIBROMIDE MIXTURE, LIQUID | UN1647 | 151T |
| METHYL BROMOACETATE | UN2643 | 155 |
| 3-METHYLBUTAN-2-ONE | UN2397 | 127 |
| 2-METHYL-1-BUTENE | UN2459 | 127 |

Schedule 3

| Description | UN # | ERG # |
|---|---|---|
| 2-METHYL-2-BUTENE | UN2460 | 127 |
| 3-METHYL-1-BUTENE | UN2561 | 127 |
| N-METHYLBUTYLAMINE | UN2945 | 132 |
| METHYL tert-BUTYL ETHER | UN2398 | 127 |
| METHYL BUTYRATE | UN1237 | 129 |
| METHYL CHLORIDE | UN1063 | 115 |
| METHYL CHLORIDE AND METHYLENE CHLORIDE MIXTURE | UN1912 | 115 |
| METHYL CHLOROACETATE | UN2295 | 155 |
| METHYL CHLOROFORMATE | UN1238 | 155T |
| METHYL CHLOROMETHYL ETHER | UN1239 | 131T |
| METHYL 2-CHLOROPROPIONATE | UN2933 | 132 |
| METHYLCHLOROSILANE | UN2534 | 119U |
| METHYLCYCLOHEXANE | UN2296 | 128 |
| METHYLCYCLOHEXANOLS, flammable | UN2617 | 129 |
| METHYLCYCLOHEXANONE | UN2297 | 127 |
| METHYLCYCLOPENTANE | UN2298 | 128 |
| METHYL DICHLOROACETATE | UN2299 | 155 |
| METHYLDICHLOROSILANE | UN1242 | 139T |
| METHYLENE GLYCOL DINITRATE | Forbidden | |
| METHYL ETHYL KETONE | UN1193 | 127 |
| METHYL ETHYL KETONE PEROXIDE, in solution with more than 9 percent by mass active oxygen | Forbidden | |
| 2-METHYL-5-ETHYLPYRIDINE | UN2300 | 153 |
| METHYL FLUORIDE | UN2454 | 115 |
| METHYL FORMATE | UN1243 | 129 |
| 2-METHYLFURAN | UN2301 | 127 |
| a-METHYLGLUCOSIDE TETRANITRATE | Forbidden | |
| a-METHYLGLYCEROL TRINITRATE | Forbidden | |
| 2-METHYL-2-HEPTANETHIOL | UN3023 | 131T |
| 5-METHYLHEXAN-2-ONE | UN2302 | 127 |
| METHYLHYDRAZINE | UN1244 | 131T |
| METHYL IODIDE | UN2644 | 151T |
| METHYL ISOBUTYL CARBINOL | UN2053 | 129 |
| METHYL ISOBUTYL KETONE | UN1245 | 127 |
| METHYL ISOBUTYL KETONE PEROXIDE, in solution with more than 9 percent by mass active oxygen | Forbidden | |
| METHYL ISOCYANATE | UN2480 | 155T |
| METHYL ISOPROPENYL KETONE, STABILIZED | UN1246 | 127P |
| METHYL ISOTHIOCYANATE | UN2477 | 131T |
| METHYL ISOVALERATE | UN2400 | 130 |
| METHYL MAGNESIUM BROMIDE IN ETHYL ETHER | UN1928 | 135 |
| METHYL MERCAPTAN | UN1064 | 117T |
| METHYL METHACRYLATE MONOMER, STABILIZED | UN1247 | 129P |
| 4-METHYLMORPHOLINE | UN2535 | 132 |
| N-METHYLMORPHOLINE | UN2535 | 132 |
| METHYL NITRAMINE (DRY) | Forbidden | |
| METHYL NITRATE | Forbidden | |
| METHYL NITRITE | UN2455 | 116 |
| METHYL ORTHOSILICATE | UN2606 | 155T |
| METHYLPENTADIENE | UN2461 | 127 |
| 2-METHYLPENTAN-2-OL | UN2560 | 129 |
| METHYLPHENYLDICHLOROSILANE | UN2437 | 156T |
| METHYL PICRIC ACID (HEAVY METAL SALTS OF) | Forbidden | |
| 1-METHYLPIPERIDINE | UN2399 | 132 |
| METHYL PROPIONATE | UN1248 | 129 |
| METHYL PROPYL ETHER | UN2612 | 127 |
| METHYL PROPYL KETONE | UN1249 | 127 |
| METHYLTETRAHYDROFURAN | UN2536 | 127 |
| METHYL TRICHLOROACETATE | UN2533 | 156 |
| METHYLTRICHLOROSILANE | UN1250 | 155T |

| Description | UN # | ERG # |
|---|---|---|
| METHYL TRIMETHYLOL METHANE TRINITRATE | Forbidden | |
| alpha-METHYLVALERALDEHYDE | UN2367 | 130 |
| METHYL VINYL KETONE, STABILIZED | UN1251 | 131PT |
| MINES with bursting charge | UN0136 | 112 |
| MINES with bursting charge | UN0137 | 112 |
| MINES with bursting charge | UN0138 | 112 |
| MINES with bursting charge | UN0294 | 112 |
| MOLTEN SULFUR | UN2448 | 133 |
| MOLTEN SULPHUR | UN2448 | 133 |
| MOLYBDENUM PENTACHLORIDE | UN2508 | 156 |
| MONOCHLOROACETONE (UNSTABILIZED) | Forbidden | |
| MONONITROTOLUIDINES | UN2660 | 153 |
| MORPHOLINE | UN2054 | 132 |
| MOTOR FUEL ANTI-KNOCK MIXTURE | UN1649 | 131 |
| MOTOR FUEL ANTI-KNOCK MIXTURE with a flash point that is equal to or less than 60.5 °C | UN1649 | 131 |
| MOTOR SPIRIT | UN1203 | 128 |
| MUSK XYLENE | UN2956 | 149 |
| NAPHTHALENE, CRUDE | UN1334 | 133 |
| NAPHTHALENE DIOZONIDE | Forbidden | |
| NAPHTHALENE, MOLTEN | UN2304 | 133 |
| NAPHTHALENE, REFINED | UN1334 | 133 |
| alpha-NAPHTHYLAMINE | UN2077 | 153 |
| beta-NAPHTHYLAMINE | UN1650 | 153 |
| NAPHTHYL AMINE PERCHLORATE | Forbidden | |
| NAPHTHYLTHIOUREA | UN1651 | 153 |
| NAPHTHYLUREA | UN1652 | 153 |
| NATURAL GAS, COMPRESSED with high methane content | UN1971 | 115 |
| NATURAL GAS, REFRIGERATED LIQUID with high methane content | UN1972 | 115 |
| NEON, COMPRESSED | UN1065 | 121 |
| NEON, REFRIGERATED LIQUID | UN1913 | 120 |
| NICKEL CARBONYL | UN1259 | 131T |
| NICKEL CYANIDE | UN1653 | 151 |
| NICKEL NITRATE | UN2725 | 140 |
| NICKEL NITRITE | UN2726 | 140 |
| NICKEL PICRATE | Forbidden | |
| NICOTINE | UN1654 | 151 |
| NICOTINE COMPOUND, LIQUID, N.O.S. | UN3144 | 151 |
| NICOTINE COMPOUND, SOLID, N.O.S. | UN1655 | 151 |
| NICOTINE HYDROCHLORIDE, liquid | UN1656 | 151 |
| NICOTINE HYDROCHLORIDE, solid | UN1656 | 151 |
| NICOTINE HYDROCHLORIDE SOLUTION | UN1656 | 151 |
| NICOTINE PREPARATION, LIQUID, N.O.S. | UN3144 | 151 |
| NICOTINE PREPARATION, SOLID, N.O.S. | UN1655 | 151 |
| NICOTINE SALICYLATE | UN1657 | 151 |
| NICOTINE SULFATE, SOLID | UN1658 | 151 |
| NICOTINE SULFATE, SOLUTION | UN1658 | 151 |
| NICOTINE SULPHATE, SOLID | UN1658 | 151 |
| NICOTINE SULPHATE, SOLUTION | UN1658 | 151 |
| NICOTINE TARTRATE | UN1659 | 151 |
| NITRATED PAPER, UNSTABLE | Forbidden | |
| NITRATES, INORGANIC, AQUEOUS SOLUTION, N.O.S. | UN3218 | 140 |
| NITRATES, INORGANIC, N.O.S. | UN1477 | 140 |
| NITRATES OF DIAZONIUM COMPOUNDS | Forbidden | |
| NITRATING ACID MIXTURE, SPENT, with more than 50 per cent nitric acid | UN1826 | 157 |
| NITRATING ACID MIXTURE, SPENT, with not more than 50 per cent nitric acid | UN1826 | 157 |
| NITRATING ACID MIXTURE with more than 50 per cent nitric acid | UN1796 | 157 |
| NITRATING ACID MIXTURE with not more than 50 per cent nitric acid | UN1796 | 157 |

Schedule 3

| Description | UN # | ERG # |
|---|---|---|
| NITRIC ACID, other than red fuming, with more than 70 per cent nitric acid | UN2031 | 157 |
| NITRIC ACID, other than red fuming, with not more than 70 per cent nitric acid | UN2031 | 157 |
| NITRIC ACID, RED FUMING | UN2032 | 157T |
| NITRIC OXIDE AND DINITROGEN TETROXIDE MIXTURE | UN1975 | 124T |
| NITRIC OXIDE AND NITROGEN DIOXIDE MIXTURE | UN1975 | 124T |
| NITRIC OXIDE, COMPRESSED | UN1660 | 124T |
| NITRILES, FLAMMABLE, TOXIC, N.O.S. | UN3273 | 131 |
| NITRILES, TOXIC, FLAMMABLE, N.O.S. | UN3275 | 131T |
| NITRILES, TOXIC, liquid, N.O.S. | UN3276 | 151T |
| NITRILES, TOXIC, LIQUID, N.O.S. (ICAO terminology) | UN3276 | 151T |
| NITRILES, TOXIC, solid, N.O.S. | UN3276 | 151T |
| NITRILES, TOXIC, SOLID, N.O.S. (ICAO terminology) | UN3276 | 151T |
| NITRITES, INORGANIC, AQUEOUS SOLUTION, N.O.S. | UN3219 | 140 |
| NITRITES, INORGANIC MIXTURES WITH AMMONIUM COMPOUNDS | Forbidden | |
| NITRITES, INORGANIC, N.O.S. | UN2627 | 140 |
| N-NITROANILINE | Forbidden | |
| NITROANILINES, (o-,m-,p-) | UN1661 | 153 |
| NITROANISOLES, LIQUID | UN2730 | 152 |
| NITROANISOLES, SOLID | UN2730 | 152 |
| NITROBENZENE | UN1662 | 152 |
| m-NITROBENZENE DIAZONIUM PERCHLORATE | Forbidden | |
| NITROBENZENESULFONIC ACID | UN2305 | 153 |
| NITROBENZENESULPHONIC ACID | UN2305 | 153 |
| 5-NITROBENZOTRIAZOL | UN0385 | 112 |
| NITROBENZOTRIFLUORIDES | UN2306 | 152 |
| NITROBROMOBENZENES, LIQUID | UN2732 | 152 |
| NITROBROMOBENZENES, SOLID | UN2732 | 152 |
| NITROCELLULOSE, dry or wetted with less than 25 per cent water (or alcohol), by mass | UN0340 | 112 |
| NITROCELLULOSE MEMBRANE FILTERS, with not more than 12.6 percent nitrogen, by dry mass | UN3270 | 133 |
| NITROCELLULOSE, MIXTURE, WITHOUT PIGMENT with not more than 12.6 per cent nitrogen, by dry mass | UN2557 | 133 |
| NITROCELLULOSE, MIXTURE, WITHOUT PLASTICIZER with not more than 12.6 per cent nitrogen, by dry mass | UN2557 | 133 |
| NITROCELLULOSE, MIXTURE, WITH PIGMENT with not more than 12.6 per cent nitrogen, by dry mass | UN2557 | 133 |
| NITROCELLULOSE, MIXTURE, WITH PLASTICIZER with not more than 12.6 per cent nitrogen, by dry mass | UN2557 | 133 |
| NITROCELLULOSE, PLASTICIZED with not less than 18 per cent plasticizing substance, by mass | UN0343 | 112 |
| NITROCELLULOSE SOLUTION, FLAMMABLE with not more than 12.6 per cent nitrogen, by dry mass, and not more than 55 per cent nitrocellulose | UN2059 | 127 |
| NITROCELLULOSE, unmodified or plasticized with less than 18 per cent plasticizing substance, by mass | UN0341 | 112 |
| NITROCELLULOSE, WETTED with not less than 25 per cent alcohol, by mass | UN0342 | 112 |
| NITROCELLULOSE WITH ALCOHOL, not less than 25 per cent alcohol, by mass, and not more than 12.6 per cent nitrogen, by dry mass | UN2556 | 113 |
| NITROCELLULOSE WITH WATER, not less than 25 per cent water, by mass | UN2555 | 113 |
| 3-NITRO-4-CHLOROBENZOTRIFLUORIDE | UN2307 | 152 |
| NITROCRESOLS | UN2446 | 153 |
| 6-NITRO-4-DIAZOTOLUENE-3-SULFONIC ACID (DRY) | Forbidden | |

| Description | UN # | ERG # |
|---|---|---|
| 6-NITRO-4-DIAZOTOLUENE-3-SULPHONIC ACID (DRY) | Forbidden | |
| NITROETHANE | UN2842 | 129 |
| NITROETHYLENE POLYMER | Forbidden | |
| NITROETHYL NITRATE | Forbidden | |
| NITROGEN, COMPRESSED | UN1066 | 121 |
| NITROGEN DIOXIDE | UN1067 | 124T |
| NITROGEN, REFRIGERATED LIQUID | UN1977 | 120 |
| NITROGEN TRICHLORIDE | Forbidden | |
| NITROGEN TRIFLUORIDE, COMPRESSED | UN2451 | 122 |
| NITROGEN TRIIODIDE | Forbidden | |
| NITROGEN TRIIODIDE MONOAMINE | Forbidden | |
| NITROGEN TRIOXIDE | UN2421 | 124T |
| NITROGLYCERIN, DESENSITIZED with not less than 40 per cent non-volatile water-insoluble phlegmatizer, by mass | UN0143 | 112 |
| NITROGLYCERIN, LIQUID, NOT DESENSITIZED | Forbidden | |
| NITROGLYCERIN MIXTURE, DESENSITIZED, LIQUID, FLAMMABLE, N.O.S. with not more than 30 per cent nitroglycerin, by mass | UN3343 | 113 |
| NITROGLYCERIN MIXTURE, DESENSITIZED, LIQUID, N.O.S. with not more than 30 per cent nitroglycerin, by mass | UN3357 | 113 |
| NITROGLYCERIN MIXTURE, DESENSITIZED, SOLID, N.O.S. with more than 2 per cent but not more than 10 per cent nitroglycerin, by mass | UN3319 | 113 |
| NITROGLYCERIN, SOLUTION IN ALCOHOL with more than 1 per cent but not more than 5 per cent nitroglycerin | UN3064 | 127 |
| NITROGLYCERIN, SOLUTION IN ALCOHOL with more than 1 per cent but not more than 10 per cent nitroglycerin | UN0144 | 112 |
| NITROGLYCERIN, SOLUTION IN ALCOHOL with not more than 1 per cent nitroglycerin | UN1204 | 127 |
| NITROGUANIDINE, dry or wetted with less than 20 per cent water, by mass | UN0282 | 112 |
| NITROGUANIDINE NITRATE | Forbidden | |
| NITROGUANIDINE, WETTED with not less than 20 per cent water, by mass | UN1336 | 113 |
| 1-NITRO HYDANTOIN | Forbidden | |
| NITROHYDROCHLORIC ACID | UN1798 | 157 |
| NITRO ISOBUTANE TRIOL TRINITRATE | Forbidden | |
| NITROMANNITE, (DRY) | Forbidden | |
| NITROMANNITE, WETTED with not less than 40 per cent water, or mixture of alcohol and water, by mass | UN0133 | 112 |
| NITROMETHANE | UN1261 | 129 |
| N-NITRO-N-METHYLGLYCOLAMIDE NITRATE | Forbidden | |
| 2-NITRO-2-METHYLPROPANOL NITRATE | Forbidden | |
| NITRONAPHTHALENE | UN2538 | 133 |
| NITROPHENOLS (o-,m-,p-) | UN1663 | 153 |
| m-NITROPHENYLDINITRO METHANE | Forbidden | |
| NITROPROPANES | UN2608 | 129 |
| NITROSILANES | Forbidden | |
| p-NITROSODIMETHYLANILINE | UN1369 | 135 |
| NITROSTARCH, dry or wetted with less than 20 per cent water, by mass | UN0146 | 112 |
| NITROSTARCH, WETTED with not less than 20 per cent water, by mass | UN1337 | 113 |
| NITROSUGARS | Forbidden | |
| NITROSYL CHLORIDE | UN1069 | 125T |
| NITROSYLSULFURIC ACID, LIQUID | UN2308 | 157 |
| NITROSYLSULFURIC ACID, SOLID | UN2308 | 157 |
| NITROSYLSULPHURIC ACID, LIQUID | UN2308 | 157 |
| NITROSYLSULPHURIC ACID, SOLID | UN2308 | 157 |
| NITROTOLUENES, LIQUID | UN1664 | 152 |
| NITROTOLUENES, SOLID | UN1664 | 152 |
| NITROTOLUIDINES | UN2660 | 153 |

| Description | UN # | ERG # |
|---|---|---|
| NITROTRIAZOLONE | UN0490 | 112 |
| NITRO UREA | UN0147 | 112 |
| NITROUS OXIDE | UN1070 | 122 |
| NITROUS OXIDE, REFRIGERATED LIQUID | UN2201 | 122 |
| NITROXYLENES, LIQUID | UN1665 | 152 |
| NITROXYLENES, SOLID | UN1665 | 152 |
| NONANES | UN1920 | 128 |
| NONYLTRICHLOROSILANE | UN1799 | 156T |
| 2,5-NORBORNADIENE, STABILIZED | UN2251 | 127P |
| NTO | UN0490 | 112 |
| OCTADECYLTRICHLOROSILANE | UN1800 | 156T |
| OCTADIENE | UN2309 | 128P |
| 1,7-OCTADIENE-3,5-DIYNE-1,8-DIMETHOXY-9-OCTADECYNOIC ACID | Forbidden | |
| OCTAFLUOROBUT-2-ENE | UN2422 | 126 |
| OCTAFLUOROCYCLOBUTANE | UN1976 | 126 |
| OCTAFLUOROPROPANE | UN2424 | 126 |
| OCTANES | UN1262 | 128 |
| OCTOGEN, DESENSITIZED | UN0484 | 112 |
| OCTOGEN, DRY or unphlegmatized | Forbidden | |
| OCTOGEN WETTED with not less than 15 per cent water, by mass | UN0226 | 112 |
| OCTOL, dry or wetted with less than 15 per cent water, by mass | UN0266 | 112 |
| OCTOLITE, dry or wetted with less than 15 per cent water, by mass | UN0266 | 112 |
| OCTONAL | UN0496 | 112 |
| OCTYL ALDEHYDES | UN1191 | 129 |
| OCTYLTRICHLOROSILANE | UN1801 | 156T |
| OIL GAS, COMPRESSED | UN1071 | 119T |
| ORGANIC PEROXIDE TYPE A, LIQUID OR SOLID | Forbidden | |
| ORGANIC PEROXIDE TYPE B, LIQUID | UN3101 | 146 |
| ORGANIC PEROXIDE TYPE B, LIQUID, TEMPERATURE CONTROLLED | UN3111 | 148 |
| ORGANIC PEROXIDE TYPE B, SOLID | UN3102 | 146 |
| ORGANIC PEROXIDE TYPE B, SOLID, TEMPERATURE CONTROLLED | UN3112 | 148 |
| ORGANIC PEROXIDE TYPE C, LIQUID | UN3103 | 146 |
| ORGANIC PEROXIDE TYPE C, LIQUID, TEMPERATURE CONTROLLED | UN3113 | 148 |
| ORGANIC PEROXIDE TYPE C, SOLID | UN3104 | 146 |
| ORGANIC PEROXIDE TYPE C, SOLID, TEMPERATURE CONTROLLED | UN3114 | 148 |
| ORGANIC PEROXIDE TYPE D, LIQUID | UN3105 | 145 |
| ORGANIC PEROXIDE TYPE D, LIQUID, TEMPERATURE CONTROLLED | UN3115 | 148 |
| ORGANIC PEROXIDE TYPE D, SOLID | UN3106 | 145 |
| ORGANIC PEROXIDE TYPE D, SOLID, TEMPERATURE CONTROLLED | UN3116 | 148 |
| ORGANIC PEROXIDE TYPE E, LIQUID | UN3107 | 145 |
| ORGANIC PEROXIDE TYPE E, LIQUID, TEMPERATURE CONTROLLED | UN3117 | 148 |
| ORGANIC PEROXIDE TYPE E, SOLID | UN3108 | 145 |
| ORGANIC PEROXIDE TYPE E, SOLID, TEMPERATURE CONTROLLED | UN3118 | 148 |
| ORGANIC PEROXIDE TYPE F, LIQUID | UN3109 | 145 |
| ORGANIC PEROXIDE TYPE F, LIQUID, TEMPERATURE CONTROLLED | UN3119 | 148 |
| ORGANIC PEROXIDE TYPE F, SOLID | UN3110 | 145 |
| ORGANIC PEROXIDE TYPE F, SOLID, TEMPERATURE CONTROLLED | UN3120 | 148 |
| ORGANIC PIGMENTS, SELF-HEATING | UN3313 | 135 |
| ORGANOARSENIC COMPOUND, N.O.S., liquid | UN3280 | 151T |
| ORGANOARSENIC COMPOUND, N.O.S., solid | UN3280 | 151T |
| ORGANOCHLORINE PESTICIDE, LIQUID, FLAMMABLE, TOXIC, flash point less than 23 °C | UN2762 | 131 |

| Description | UN # | ERG # |
|---|---|---|
| ORGANOCHLORINE PESTICIDE, LIQUID, TOXIC | UN2996 | 151 |
| ORGANOCHLORINE PESTICIDE, LIQUID, TOXIC, FLAMMABLE, flash point not less than 23 °C | UN2995 | 131 |
| ORGANOCHLORINE PESTICIDE, SOLID, TOXIC | UN2761 | 151 |
| ORGANOMETALLIC COMPOUND DISPERSION, WATER-REACTIVE, FLAMMABLE, N.O.S. | UN3207 | 138 |
| ORGANOMETALLIC COMPOUND SOLUTION, WATER-REACTIVE, FLAMMABLE, N.O.S. | UN3207 | 138 |
| ORGANOMETALLIC COMPOUND, TOXIC, N.O.S., liquid | UN3282 | 151 |
| ORGANOMETALLIC COMPOUND, TOXIC, N.O.S., solid | UN3282 | 151 |
| ORGANOMETALLIC COMPOUND, WATER-REACTIVE, FLAMMABLE, N.O.S. | UN3207 | 138 |
| ORGANOPHOSPHORUS COMPOUND, TOXIC, FLAMMABLE, N.O.S. | UN3279 | 131T |
| ORGANOPHOSPHORUS COMPOUND, TOXIC, N.O.S., liquid | UN3278 | 151T |
| ORGANOPHOSPHORUS COMPOUND, TOXIC, N.O.S., solid | UN3278 | 151T |
| ORGANOPHOSPHORUS PESTICIDE, LIQUID, FLAMMABLE, TOXIC, flash point less than 23 °C | UN2784 | 131 |
| ORGANOPHOSPHORUS PESTICIDE, LIQUID, TOXIC | UN3018 | 152 |
| ORGANOPHOSPHORUS PESTICIDE, LIQUID, TOXIC, FLAMMABLE, flash point not less than 23 °C | UN3017 | 131 |
| ORGANOPHOSPHORUS PESTICIDE, SOLID, TOXIC | UN2783 | 152 |
| ORGANOTIN COMPOUND, LIQUID, N.O.S. | UN2788 | 153 |
| ORGANOTIN COMPOUND, SOLID, N.O.S. | UN3146 | 153 |
| ORGANOTIN PESTICIDE, LIQUID, FLAMMABLE, TOXIC, flash point less than 23 °C | UN2787 | 131 |
| ORGANOTIN PESTICIDE, LIQUID, TOXIC | UN3020 | 153 |
| ORGANOTIN PESTICIDE, LIQUID, TOXIC, FLAMMABLE, flash point not less than 23 °C | UN3019 | 131 |
| ORGANOTIN PESTICIDE, SOLID, TOXIC | UN2786 | 153 |
| OSMIUM TETROXIDE | UN2471 | 154 |
| OXIDIZING LIQUID, CORROSIVE, N.O.S. | UN3098 | 140 |
| OXIDIZING LIQUID, N.O.S. | UN3139 | 140 |
| OXIDIZING LIQUID, TOXIC, N.O.S. | UN3099 | 142 |
| OXIDIZING SOLID, CORROSIVE, N.O.S. | UN3085 | 140 |
| OXIDIZING SOLID, FLAMMABLE, N.O.S. | UN3137 | 140 |
| OXIDIZING SOLID, N.O.S. | UN1479 | 140 |
| OXIDIZING SOLID, SELF-HEATING, N.O.S. | UN3100 | 135 |
| OXIDIZING SOLID, TOXIC, N.O.S. | UN3087 | 141 |
| OXIDIZING SOLID, WATER-REACTIVE, N.O.S. | UN3121 | 144 |
| OXYGEN, COMPRESSED | UN1072 | 122 |
| OXYGEN DIFLUORIDE, COMPRESSED | UN2190 | 124T |
| OXYGEN GENERATOR, CHEMICAL | UN3356 | 140 |
| OXYGEN, REFRIGERATED LIQUID | UN1073 | 122 |
| PAINT (including paint, lacquer, enamel, stain, shellac, varnish, polish, liquid filler and liquid lacquer base) with not more than 20 per cent nitrocellulose by mass if the nitrogen content of the nitrocellulose is not more than 12.6 per cent by mass | UN1263 | 128 |
| PAINT (including paint, lacquer, enamel, stain, shellac, varnish, polish, liquid filler and liquid lacquer base) with not more than 20 per cent nitrocellulose by mass if the nitrogen content of the nitrocellulose is not more than 12.6 per cent by mass | UN3066 | 153 |
| PAINT RELATED MATERIAL (including paint thinning or reducing compound) with not more than 20 per cent nitrocellulose by mass if the nitrogen content of the nitrocellulose is not more than 12.6 per cent by mass | UN1263 | 138 |

Schedule 3

| Description | UN # | ERG # |
|---|---|---|
| PAINT RELATED MATERIAL (including paint thinning or reducing compound) with not more than 20 per cent nitrocellulose by mass if the nitrogen content of the nitrocellulose is not more than 12.6 per cent by mass | UN3066 | 153 |
| PAPER, UNSATURATED OIL TREATED, incompletely dried (including carbon paper) | UN1379 | 133 |
| PAINT, flammable, corrosive | UN3469 | 132 |
| PAINT, corrosive, flammable | UN3470 | 132 |
| PARAFORMALDEHYDE | UN2213 | 133 |
| PARALDEHYDE | UN1264 | 129 |
| PENTABORANE | UN1380 | 135T |
| PENTACHLOROETHANE | UN1669 | 151 |
| PENTACHLOROPHENOL | UN3155 | 154 |
| PENTAERYTHRITE TETRANITRATE, DESENSITIZED with not less than 15 per cent phlegmatizer, by mass | UN0150 | 112 |
| PENTAERYTHRITE TETRANITRATE, (DRY) | Forbidden | |
| PENTAERYTHRITE TETRANITRATE MIXTURE, DESENSITIZED, SOLID, N.O.S. with more than 10 per cent but not more than 20 per cent pentaerythrite tetranitrate (PETN), by mass | UN3344 | 113 |
| PENTAERYTHRITE TETRANITRATE, WETTED with not less than 25 per cent water, by mass | UN0150 | 112 |
| PENTAERYTHRITE TETRANITRATE with not less than 7 per cent wax, by mass | UN0411 | 112 |
| PENTAERYTHRITOL TETRANITRATE, DESENSITIZED with not less than 15 per cent phlegmatizer, by mass | UN0150 | 112 |
| PENTAERYTHRITOL TETRANITRATE (DRY) | Forbidden | |
| PENTAERYTHRITOL TETRANITRATE, WETTED with not less than 25 per cent water, by mass | UN0150 | 112 |
| PENTAERYTHRITOL TETRANITRATE with not less than 7 per cent wax, by mass | UN0411 | 112 |
| PENTAFLUOROETHANE | UN3220 | 126 |
| PENTAMETHYLHEPTANE | UN2286 | 128 |
| PENTANE-2,4-DIONE | UN2310 | 131 |
| PENTANES, liquid | UN1265 | 128 |
| PENTANITROANILINE (DRY) | Forbidden | |
| PENTANOLS | UN1105 | 129 |
| 1-PENTENE | UN1108 | 127 |
| 1-PENTOL | UN2705 | 153P |
| PENTOLITE, dry or wetted with less than 15 per cent water, by mass | UN0151 | 112 |
| PERCHLORATES, INORGANIC, AQUEOUS SOLUTION, N.O.S. | UN3211 | 140 |
| PERCHLORATES, INORGANIC, N.O.S. | UN1481 | 140 |
| PERCHLORIC ACID with more than 50 per cent but not more than 72 per cent acid, by mass | UN1873 | 143 |
| PERCHLORIC ACID with more than 72 per cent acid, by mass | Forbidden | |
| PERCHLORIC ACID with not more than 50 per cent acid, by mass | UN1802 | 140 |
| PERCHLOROMETHYL MERCAPTAN | UN1670 | 157T |
| PERCHLORYL FLUORIDE | UN3083 | 124T |
| PERFLUORO(ETHYLVINYL ETHER) | UN3154 | 115 |
| PERFLUORO(METHYLVINYL ETHER) | UN3153 | 115 |
| PERFUMERY PRODUCTS with flammable solvents | UN1266 | 127 |
| PERMANGANATES, INORGANIC, AQUEOUS SOLUTION, N.O.S. | UN3214 | 140 |
| PERMANGANATES, INORGANIC, N.O.S. | UN1482 | 140 |
| PEROXIDES, INORGANIC, N.O.S. | UN1483 | 140 |
| PEROXYACETIC ACID, with more than 43 percent and with more than 6 percent hydrogen peroxide | Forbidden | |
| PERSULFATES, INORGANIC, AQUEOUS SOLUTION, N.O.S. | UN3216 | 140 |
| PERSULFATES, INORGANIC, N.O.S. | UN3215 | 140 |
| PERSULPHATES, INORGANIC, AQUEOUS SOLUTION, N.O.S. | UN3216 | 140 |

| Description | UN # | ERG # |
|---|---|---|
| PERSULPHATES, INORGANIC, N.O.S. | UN3215 | 140 |
| PESTICIDE, LIQUID, FLAMMABLE, TOXIC, N.O.S., flash point less than 23 °C | UN3021 | 131 |
| PESTICIDE, LIQUID, TOXIC, FLAMMABLE, N.O.S., flash point not less than 23 °C | UN2903 | 131 |
| PESTICIDE, LIQUID, TOXIC, N.O.S. | UN2902 | 151 |
| PESTICIDE, SOLID, TOXIC, N.O.S. | UN2588 | 151 |
| PETN, DESENSITIZED with not less than 15 per cent phlegmatizer, by mass | UN0150 | 112 |
| PETN, WETTED with not less than 25 per cent water, by mass | UN0150 | 112 |
| PETN with not less than 7 per cent wax, by mass | UN0411 | 112 |
| PETROL | UN1203 | 128 |
| PETROLEUM CRUDE OIL | UN1267 | 128 |
| PETROLEUM DISTILLATES, N.O.S. | UN1268 | 128 |
| PETROLEUM GASES, LIQUEFIED | UN1075 | 115 |
| PETROLEUM PRODUCTS, N.O.S. | UN1268 | 128 |
| PHENACYL BROMIDE | UN2645 | 153 |
| PHENETIDINES | UN2311 | 153 |
| PHENOLATES, LIQUID | UN2904 | 154 |
| PHENOLATES, SOLID | UN2905 | 154 |
| PHENOL, MOLTEN | UN2312 | 153 |
| PHENOL, SOLID | UN1671 | 153 |
| PHENOL SOLUTION | UN2821 | 153 |
| PHENOLSULFONIC ACID, LIQUID | UN1803 | 153 |
| PHENOLSULPHONIC ACID, LIQUID | UN1803 | 153 |
| PHENOXYACETIC ACID DERIVATIVE PESTICIDE, LIQUID, FLAMMABLE, TOXIC, flash point less than 23 °C | UN3346 | 131 |
| PHENOXYACETIC ACID DERIVATIVE PESTICIDE, LIQUID, TOXIC | UN3348 | 153 |
| PHENOXYACETIC ACID DERIVATIVE PESTICIDE, LIQUID, TOXIC, FLAMMABLE, flash point not less than 23 °C | UN3347 | 131 |
| PHENOXYACETIC ACID DERIVATIVE PESTICIDE, SOLID, TOXIC | UN3345 | 153 |
| PHENYLACETONITRILE, LIQUID | UN2470 | 152 |
| PHENYLACETYL CHLORIDE | UN2577 | 156 |
| PHENYLCARBYLAMINE CHLORIDE | UN1672 | 151 |
| PHENYL CHLOROFORMATE | UN2746 | 156 |
| m-PHENYLENE DIAMINEDIPERCHLORATE (DRY) | Forbidden | |
| PHENYLENEDIAMINES (o-,m-,p-) | UN1673 | 153 |
| PHENYLHYDRAZINE | UN2572 | 153 |
| PHENYL ISOCYANATE | UN2487 | 155T |
| PHENYL MERCAPTAN | UN2337 | 131T |
| PHENYLMERCURIC ACETATE | UN1674 | 151 |
| PHENYLMERCURIC COMPOUND, N.O.S. | UN2026 | 151 |
| PHENYLMERCURIC HYDROXIDE | UN1894 | 151 |
| PHENYLMERCURIC NITRATE | UN1895 | 151 |
| PHENYLPHOSPHORUS DICHLORIDE | UN2798 | 137 |
| PHENYLPHOSPHORUS THIODICHLORIDE | UN2799 | 137 |
| PHENYLTRICHLOROSILANE | UN1804 | 156T |
| PHOSGENE | UN1076 | 125T |
| 9-PHOSPHABICYCLONONANES | UN2940 | 135 |
| PHOSPHINE | UN2199 | 119T |
| PHOSPHORIC ACID, LIQUID | UN1805 | 154 |
| PHOSPHORIC ACID, SOLID | UN1805 | 154 |
| PHOSPHOROUS ACID | UN2834 | 154 |
| PHOSPHORUS, AMORPHOUS | UN1338 | 133 |
| PHOSPHORUS HEPTASULFIDE, free from yellow and white phosphorus | UN1339 | 139 |
| PHOSPHORUS HEPTASULPHIDE, free from yellow and white phosphorus | UN1339 | 139 |
| PHOSPHORUS OXYBROMIDE | UN1939 | 137 |
| PHOSPHORUS OXYBROMIDE, MOLTEN | UN2576 | 137 |
| PHOSPHORUS OXYCHLORIDE | UN1810 | 137T |
| PHOSPHORUS PENTABROMIDE | UN2691 | 137T |

| Description | UN # | ERG # |
|---|---|---|
| PHOSPHORUS PENTACHLORIDE | UN1806 | 137T |
| PHOSPHORUS PENTAFLUORIDE, COMPRESSED | UN2198 | 125T |
| PHOSPHORUS PENTASULFIDE, free from yellow and white phosphorus | UN1340 | 139T |
| PHOSPHORUS PENTASULPHIDE, free from yellow and white phosphorus | UN1340 | 139T |
| PHOSPHORUS PENTOXIDE | UN1807 | 137 |
| PHOSPHORUS SESQUISULFIDE, free from yellow and white phosphorus | UN1341 | 139 |
| PHOSPHORUS SESQUISULPHIDE, free from yellow and white phosphorus | UN1341 | 139 |
| PHOSPHORUS TRIBROMIDE | UN1808 | 137 |
| PHOSPHORUS TRICHLORIDE | UN1809 | 137T |
| PHOSPHORUS TRIOXIDE | UN2578 | 157 |
| PHOSPHORUS TRISULFIDE, free from yellow and white phosphorus | UN1343 | 139 |
| PHOSPHORUS TRISULPHIDE, free from yellow and white phosphorus | UN1343 | 139 |
| PHOSPHORUS, WHITE, DRY | UN1381 | 136 |
| PHOSPHORUS, WHITE, IN SOLUTION | UN1381 | 136 |
| PHOSPHORUS, WHITE, MOLTEN | UN2447 | 136 |
| PHOSPHORUS (WHITE OR RED) AND A CHLORATE, MIXTURES OF | Forbidden | |
| PHOSPHORUS, WHITE, UNDER WATER | UN1381 | 136 |
| PHOSPHORUS, YELLOW, DRY | UN1381 | 136 |
| PHOSPHORUS, YELLOW, IN SOLUTION | UN1381 | 136 |
| PHOSPHORUS, YELLOW, UNDER WATER | UN1381 | 136 |
| PHTHALIC ANHYDRIDE with more than 0.05 per cent of maleic anhydride | UN2214 | 156 |
| PICOLINES | UN2313 | 130 |
| PICRAMIDE | UN0153 | 112 |
| PICRIC ACID, dry or wetted with less than 30 per cent water, by mass | UN0154 | 112 |
| PICRITE, dry or wetted with less than 20 per cent water, by mass | UN0282 | 112 |
| PICRITE, WETTED with not less than 20 per cent water, by mass | UN1336 | 113 |
| PICRYL CHLORIDE | UN0155 | 112 |
| alpha-PINENE | UN2368 | 127 |
| PINE OIL | UN1272 | 129 |
| PIPERAZINE | UN2579 | 153 |
| PIPERIDINE | UN2401 | 132 |
| PLASTICS MOULDING COMPOUND in dough, sheet or extruded rope form evolving flammable vapour | UN3314 | 171 |
| PLASTICS, NITROCELLULOSE-BASED, SELF-HEATING, N.O.S. | UN2006 | 135 |
| POLYAMINES, FLAMMABLE, CORROSIVE, N.O.S. | UN2733 | 132 |
| POLYAMINES, LIQUID, CORROSIVE, FLAMMABLE, N.O.S. | UN2734 | 132 |
| POLYAMINES, LIQUID, CORROSIVE, N.O.S. | UN2735 | 153 |
| POLYAMINES, SOLID, CORROSIVE, N.O.S. | UN3259 | 154 |
| POLYCHLORINATED BIPHENYLS (PCB) regulated only when the concentration is more than 50 ppm by mass | UN2315 | 171 |
| POLYESTER RESIN KIT | UN3269 | 127 |
| POLYHALOGENATED BIPHENYLS, LIQUID regulated only when the concentration is more than 50 ppm by mass | UN3151 | 171 |
| POLYHALOGENATED BIPHENYLS, SOLID regulated only when the concentration is more than 50 ppm by mass | UN3152 | 171 |
| POLYHALOGENATED TERPHENYLS, LIQUID regulated only when the concentration is more than 50 ppm by mass | UN3151 | 171 |
| POLYHALOGENATED TERPHENYLS, SOLID regulated only when the concentration is more than 50 ppm by mass | UN3152 | 171 |
| POLYMERIC BEADS, EXPANDABLE, evolving flammable vapour | UN2211 | 133 |
| POTASSIUM | UN2257 | 138 |
| POTASSIUM ARSENATE | UN1677 | 151 |

| Description | UN # | ERG # |
|---|---|---|
| POTASSIUM ARSENITE | UN1678 | 154 |
| POTASSIUM BOROHYDRIDE | UN1870 | 138 |
| POTASSIUM BROMATE | UN1484 | 140 |
| POTASSIUM CARBONYL | Forbidden | |
| POTASSIUM CHLORATE | UN1485 | 140 |
| POTASSIUM CHLORATE, AQUEOUS SOLUTION | UN2427 | 140 |
| POTASSIUM CUPROCYANIDE | UN1679 | 157 |
| POTASSIUM CYANIDE | UN1680 | 157T |
| POTASSIUM DITHIONITE | UN1929 | 135 |
| POTASSIUM FLUORIDE | UN1812 | 154 |
| POTASSIUM FLUOROACETATE | UN2628 | 151 |
| POTASSIUM FLUOROSILICATE | UN2655 | 151 |
| POTASSIUM HYDROGENDIFLUORIDE, LIQUID (IMO terminology) | UN1811 | 154 |
| POTASSIUM HYDROGENDIFLUORIDE, solid | UN1811 | 154 |
| POTASSIUM HYDROGENDIFLUORIDE, SOLID (ICAO/IMO terminology) | UN1811 | 154 |
| POTASSIUM HYDROGENDIFLUORIDE, solution | UN1811 | 154 |
| POTASSIUM HYDROGENDIFLUORIDE, SOLUTION (ICAO/IMO terminology) | UN1811 | 154 |
| POTASSIUM HYDROGEN SULFATE | UN2509 | 154 |
| POTASSIUM HYDROGEN SULPHATE | UN2509 | 154 |
| POTASSIUM HYDROSULFITE | UN1929 | 135 |
| POTASSIUM HYDROSULPHITE | UN1929 | 135 |
| POTASSIUM HYDROXIDE, SOLID | UN1813 | 154 |
| POTASSIUM HYDROXIDE, SOLUTION | UN1814 | 154 |
| POTASSIUM METAL ALLOYS | UN1420 | 138 |
| POTASSIUM METAVANADATE | UN2864 | 151 |
| POTASSIUM MONOXIDE | UN2033 | 154 |
| POTASSIUM NITRATE | UN1486 | 140 |
| POTASSIUM NITRATE AND SODIUM NITRITE MIXTURE | UN1487 | 140 |
| POTASSIUM NITRITE | UN1488 | 140 |
| POTASSIUM PERCHLORATE | UN1489 | 140 |
| POTASSIUM PERMANGANATE | UN1490 | 140 |
| POTASSIUM PEROXIDE | UN1491 | 144 |
| POTASSIUM PERSULFATE | UN1492 | 140 |
| POTASSIUM PERSULPHATE | UN1492 | 140 |
| POTASSIUM PHOSPHIDE | UN2012 | 139T |
| POTASSIUM SODIUM ALLOYS | UN1422 | 138 |
| POTASSIUM SULFIDE, ANHYDROUS | UN1382 | 135 |
| POTASSIUM SULFIDE, HYDRATED with not less than 30 per cent water of crystallization | UN1847 | 153 |
| POTASSIUM SULFIDE with less than 30 per cent water of crystallization | UN1382 | 135 |
| POTASSIUM SULPHIDE, ANHYDROUS | UN1382 | 135 |
| POTASSIUM SULPHIDE, HYDRATED with not less than 30 per cent water of crystallization | UN1847 | 153 |
| POTASSIUM SULPHIDE with less than 30 per cent water of crystallization | UN1382 | 135 |
| POTASSIUM SUPEROXIDE | UN2466 | 143 |
| POWDER CAKE, WETTED with not less than 17 per cent alcohol, by mass | UN0433 | 112 |
| POWDER CAKE, WETTED with not less than 25 per cent water, by mass | UN0159 | 112 |
| POWDER PASTE, WETTED with not less than 17 per cent alcohol, by mass | UN0433 | 112 |
| POWDER PASTE, WETTED with not less than 25 per cent water, by mass | UN0159 | 112 |
| POWDER, SMOKELESS | UN0160 | 112 |
| POWDER, SMOKELESS | UN0161 | 112 |
| PRIMERS, CAP TYPE | UN0044 | 114 |
| PRIMERS, CAP TYPE | UN0377 | 114 |
| PRIMERS, CAP TYPE | UN0378 | 114 |
| PRIMERS, TUBULAR | UN0319 | 112 |
| PRIMERS, TUBULAR | UN0320 | 114 |

Schedule 3

| Description | UN # | ERG # |
|---|---|---|
| PRIMERS, TUBULAR | UN0376 | 114 |
| PRINTING INK, flammable, with not more than 20 per cent nitrocellulose by mass if the nitrogen content of the nitrocellulose is not more than 12.6 per cent by mass | UN1210 | 129 |
| PRINTING INK RELATED MATERIAL (including printing ink thinning or reducing compound) flammable, with not more than 20 per cent nitrocellulose by mass if the nitrogen content of the nitrocellulose is not more than 12.6 per cent by mass | UN1210 | 129 |
| PROJECTILES, inert with tracer | UN0345 | 114 |
| PROJECTILES, inert with tracer | UN0424 | 112 |
| PROJECTILES, inert with tracer | UN0425 | 114 |
| PROJECTILES with burster or expelling charge | UN0346 | 112 |
| PROJECTILES with burster or expelling charge | UN0347 | 114 |
| PROJECTILES with burster or expelling charge | UN0426 | 112 |
| PROJECTILES with burster or expelling charge | UN0427 | 114 |
| PROJECTILES with burster or expelling charge | UN0434 | 112 |
| PROJECTILES with burster or expelling charge | UN0435 | 114 |
| PROJECTILES with bursting charge | UN0167 | 112 |
| PROJECTILES with bursting charge | UN0168 | 112 |
| PROJECTILES with bursting charge | UN0169 | 112 |
| PROJECTILES with bursting charge | UN0324 | 112 |
| PROJECTILES with bursting charge | UN0344 | 114 |
| PROPADIENE, STABILIZED | UN2200 | 116P |
| PROPANE | UN1978 | 115 |
| PROPANETHIOLS | UN2402 | 130 |
| n-PROPANOL | UN1274 | 129 |
| PROPELLANT, LIQUID | UN0495 | 112 |
| PROPELLANT, LIQUID | UN0497 | 112 |
| PROPELLANT, SOLID | UN0498 | 112 |
| PROPELLANT, SOLID | UN0499 | 112 |
| PROPELLANT, SOLID | UN0501 | 114 |
| PROPIONALDEHYDE | UN1275 | 129 |
| PROPIONIC ACID | UN1848 | 132 |
| PROPIONIC ACID with not less than 90% acid | UN3463 | 132 |
| PROPIONIC ANHYDRIDE | UN2496 | 156 |
| PROPIONITRILE | UN2404 | 131 |
| PROPIONYL CHLORIDE | UN1815 | 132 |
| n-PROPYL ACETATE | UN1276 | 129 |
| PROPYL ALCOHOL, NORMAL | UN1274 | 129 |
| PROPYLAMINE | UN1277 | 132 |
| n-PROPYLBENZENE | UN2364 | 127 |
| PROPYL CHLORIDE | UN1278 | 129 |
| n-PROPYL CHLOROFORMATE | UN2740 | 155T |
| PROPYLENE | UN1077 | 115 |
| PROPYLENE CHLOROHYDRIN | UN2611 | 131 |
| 1,2-PROPYLENEDIAMINE | UN2258 | 132 |
| PROPYLENEIMINE, STABILIZED | UN1921 | 131P |
| PROPYLENE OXIDE | UN1280 | 127P |
| PROPYLENE TETRAMER | UN2850 | 128 |
| PROPYL FORMATES | UN1281 | 129 |
| n-PROPYL ISOCYANATE | UN2482 | 155T |
| n-PROPYL NITRATE | UN1865 | 131 |
| PROPYLTRICHLOROSILANE | UN1816 | 155T |
| PYRETHROID PESTICIDE, LIQUID, FLAMMABLE, TOXIC, flash point less than 23 °C | UN3350 | 131 |
| PYRETHROID PESTICIDE, LIQUID, TOXIC | UN3352 | 151 |
| PYRETHROID PESTICIDE, LIQUID, TOXIC, FLAMMABLE, flash point not less than 23 °C | UN3351 | 131 |
| PYRETHROID PESTICIDE, SOLID, TOXIC | UN3349 | 151 |

| Description | UN # | ERG # |
|---|---|---|
| PYRIDINE | UN1282 | 129 |
| PYRIDINE PERCHLORATE | Forbidden | |
| PYROPHORIC ALLOY, N.O.S. | UN1383 | 135 |
| PYROPHORIC LIQUID, INORGANIC, N.O.S. | UN3194 | 135 |
| PYROPHORIC LIQUID, ORGANIC, N.O.S. | UN2845 | 135T |
| PYROPHORIC METAL, N.O.S. | UN1383 | 135 |
| PYROPHORIC ORGANOMETALLIC COMPOUND, WATER-REACTIVE, N.O.S., liquid | UN3203 | 135 |
| PYROPHORIC ORGANOMETALLIC COMPOUND, WATER-REACTIVE, N.O.S., solid | UN3203 | 135 |
| PYROPHORIC SOLID, INORGANIC, N.O.S. | UN3200 | 135 |
| PYROPHORIC SOLID, ORGANIC, N.O.S. | UN2846 | 135 |
| PYROSULFURYL CHLORIDE | UN1817 | 137 |
| PYROSULPHURYL CHLORIDE | UN1817 | 137 |
| PYRROLIDINE | UN1922 | 132 |
| QUEBRACHITOL PENTANITRATE | | |
| QUINOLINE | UN2656 | 154 |
| RADIOACTIVE MATERIAL, EXCEPTED PACKAGE - ARTICLES | UN2911 | 161 |
| RADIOACTIVE MATERIAL, EXCEPTED PACKAGE - ARTICLES MANUFACTURED FROM DEPLETED URANIUM | UN2909 | 161 |
| RADIOACTIVE MATERIAL, EXCEPTED PACKAGE - ARTICLES MANUFACTURED FROM NATURAL THORIUM | UN2909 | 161 |
| RADIOACTIVE MATERIAL, EXCEPTED PACKAGE - ARTICLES MANUFACTURED FROM NATURAL URANIUM | UN2909 | 161 |
| RADIOACTIVE MATERIAL, EXCEPTED PACKAGE - EMPTY PACKAGING | UN2908 | 161 |
| RADIOACTIVE MATERIAL, EXCEPTED PACKAGE - INSTRUMENTS | UN2911 | 161 |
| RADIOACTIVE MATERIAL, EXCEPTED PACKAGE - LIMITED QUANTITY OF MATERIAL | UN2910 | 161 |
| RADIOACTIVE MATERIAL, LOW SPECIFIC ACTIVITY (LSA-I) non-fissile or fissile excepted | UN2912 | 162 |
| RADIOACTIVE MATERIAL, LOW SPECIFIC ACTIVITY (LSA-II), FISSILE | UN3324 | 165 |
| RADIOACTIVE MATERIAL, LOW SPECIFIC ACTIVITY (LSA-II), non-fissile or fissile excepted | UN3321 | 162 |
| RADIOACTIVE MATERIAL, LOW SPECIFIC ACTIVITY, (LSA-III), FISSILE | UN3325 | 165 |
| RADIOACTIVE MATERIAL, LOW SPECIFIC ACTIVITY (LSA-III), non-fissile or fissile excepted | UN3322 | 162 |
| RADIOACTIVE MATERIAL, SURFACE CONTAMINATED OBJECTS (SCO-I), FISSILE | UN3326 | 165 |
| RADIOACTIVE MATERIAL, SURFACE CONTAMINATED OBJECTS (SCO-I), non-fissile or fissile excepted | UN2913 | 162 |
| RADIOACTIVE MATERIAL, SURFACE CONTAMINATED OBJECTS (SCO-II), FISSILE | UN3326 | 165 |
| RADIOACTIVE MATERIAL, SURFACE CONTAMINATED OBJECTS (SCO-II), non-fissile or fissile excepted | UN2913 | 162 |
| RADIOACTIVE MATERIAL, TRANSPORTED UNDER SPECIAL ARRANGEMENT, FISSILE | UN3331 | 165 |
| RADIOACTIVE MATERIAL, TRANSPORTED UNDER SPECIAL ARRANGEMENT, non-fissile or fissile excepted | UN2919 | 163 |
| RADIOACTIVE MATERIAL, TYPE A PACKAGE, FISSILE, non-special form | UN3327 | 165 |
| RADIOACTIVE MATERIAL, TYPE A PACKAGE, non-special form, non-fissile or fissile excepted | UN2915 | 163 |
| RADIOACTIVE MATERIAL, TYPE A PACKAGE, SPECIAL FORM, FISSILE | UN3333 | 165 |
| RADIOACTIVE MATERIAL, TYPE A PACKAGE, SPECIAL FORM, non-fissile or fissile excepted | UN3332 | 164 |
| RADIOACTIVE MATERIAL, TYPE B(M) PACKAGE, FISSILE | UN3329 | 165 |

| Description | UN # | ERG # |
|---|---|---|
| RADIOACTIVE MATERIAL, TYPE B(M) PACKAGE, non-fissile or fissile excepted | UN2917 | 163 |
| RADIOACTIVE MATERIAL, TYPE B(U) PACKAGE, FISSILE | UN3328 | 165 |
| RADIOACTIVE MATERIAL, TYPE B(U) PACKAGE, non-fissile or fissile excepted | UN2916 | 163 |
| RADIOACTIVE MATERIAL, TYPE C PACKAGE, FISSILE | UN3330 | 165 |
| RADIOACTIVE MATERIAL, TYPE C PACKAGE, non-fissile or fissile excepted | UN3323 | 163 |
| RADIOACTIVE MATERIAL, URANIUM HEXAFLUORIDE, FISSILE | UN2977 | 166T |
| RADIOACTIVE MATERIAL, URANIUM HEXAFLUORIDE, non-fissile or fissile excepted | UN2978 | 166T |
| RARE GASES AND NITROGEN MIXTURE, COMPRESSED | UN1981 | 121 |
| RARE GASES AND OXYGEN MIXTURE, COMPRESSED | UN1980 | 122 |
| RARE GASES MIXTURE, COMPRESSED | UN1979 | 121 |
| RDX AND CYCLOTETRAMETHYLENETETRANITRAMINE MIXTURE, DESENSITIZED with not less than 10 per cent phelgmatizer, by mass | UN0391 | 112 |
| RDX AND CYCLOTETRAMETHYLENETETRANITRAMINE MIXTURE, WETTED with not less than 15 per cent water, by mass | UN0391 | 112 |
| RDX AND HMX MIXTURE, DESENSITIZED with not less than 10 per cent phelgmatizer, by mass | UN0391 | 112 |
| RDX AND HMX MIXTURE, WETTED with not less than 15 per cent water, by mass | UN0391 | 112 |
| RDX AND OCTOGEN MIXTURE, DESENSITIZED with not less than 10 per cent phelgmatizer, by mass | UN0391 | 112 |
| RDX AND OCTOGEN MIXTURE, WETTED with not less than 15 per cent water, by mass | UN0391 | 112 |
| RDX, DESENSITIZED | UN0483 | 112 |
| RDX, WETTED with not less than 15 per cent water, by mass | UN0072 | 112 |
| RECEPTACLES, SMALL, CONTAINING GAS without a release device, non-refillable | UN2037 | 115 |
| RECEPTACLES, SMALL, CONTAINING GAS without a release device, non-refillable | UN2037 | 115 |
| REFRIGERANT GAS, N.O.S. | UN1078 | 126 |
| REFRIGERANT GAS R 12 | UN1028 | 126 |
| REFRIGERANT GAS R 12B1 | UN1974 | 126 |
| REFRIGERANT GAS R 13 | UN1022 | 126 |
| REFRIGERANT GAS R 13B1 | UN1009 | 126 |
| REFRIGERANT GAS R 14, COMPRESSED | UN1982 | 126 |
| REFRIGERANT GAS R 21 | UN1029 | 126 |
| REFRIGERANT GAS R 22 | UN1018 | 126 |
| REFRIGERANT GAS R 23 | UN1984 | 126 |
| REFRIGERANT GAS R 32 | UN3252 | 115 |
| REFRIGERANT GAS R 40 | UN1063 | 115 |
| REFRIGERANT GAS R 41 | UN2454 | 115 |
| REFRIGERANT GAS R 114 | UN1958 | 126 |
| REFRIGERANT GAS R 115 | UN1020 | 126 |
| REFRIGERANT GAS R 116, COMPRESSED | UN2193 | 126 |
| REFRIGERANT GAS R 124 | UN1021 | 126 |
| REFRIGERANT GAS R 125 | UN3220 | 126 |
| REFRIGERANT GAS R 133a | UN1983 | 126 |
| REFRIGERANT GAS R 134a | UN3159 | 126 |
| REFRIGERANT GAS R 142b | UN2517 | 115 |
| REFRIGERANT GAS R 143a | UN2035 | 115 |
| REFRIGERANT GAS R 152a | UN1030 | 115 |
| REFRIGERANT GAS R 161 | UN2453 | 115 |
| REFRIGERANT GAS R 218 | UN2424 | 126 |
| REFRIGERANT GAS R 227 | UN3296 | 126 |
| REFRIGERANT GAS RC 318 | UN1976 | 126 |
| REFRIGERANT GAS R 404A | UN3337 | 126 |
| REFRIGERANT GAS R 407A | UN3338 | 126 |

| Description | UN # | ERG # |
|---|---|---|
| REFRIGERANT GAS R 407B | UN3339 | 126 |
| REFRIGERANT GAS R 407C | UN3340 | 126 |
| REFRIGERANT GAS R 500 | UN2602 | 126 |
| REFRIGERANT GAS R 502 | UN1973 | 126 |
| REFRIGERANT GAS R 503 | UN2599 | 126 |
| REFRIGERANT GAS R 1132a | UN1959 | 116P |
| REFRIGERANT GAS R 1216 | UN1858 | 126 |
| REFRIGERANT GAS R 1318 | UN2422 | 126 |
| REFRIGERATING MACHINES containing flammable and non-toxic liquefied gas | UN3358 | 115 |
| REFRIGERATING MACHINES containing non-flammable, non-toxic, liquefied gas or ammonia solutions (UN2672) | UN2857 | 126 |
| RELEASE DEVICES, EXPLOSIVE | UN0173 | 114 |
| RESIN SOLUTION, flammable | UN1866 | 127 |
| RESORCINOL | UN2876 | 153 |
| RIVETS, EXPLOSIVE | UN0174 | 114 |
| ROCKET MOTORS | UN0186 | 112 |
| ROCKET MOTORS | UN0280 | 112 |
| ROCKET MOTORS | UN0281 | 112 |
| ROCKET MOTORS, LIQUID FUELLED | UN0395 | 112 |
| ROCKET MOTORS, LIQUID FUELLED | UN0396 | 112 |
| ROCKET MOTORS WITH HYPERGOLIC LIQUIDS with or without expelling charge | UN0250 | 112 |
| ROCKET MOTORS WITH HYPERGOLIC LIQUIDS with or without expelling charge | UN0322 | 112 |
| ROCKETS, LINE-THROWING | UN0238 | 112 |
| ROCKETS, LINE-THROWING | UN0240 | 112 |
| ROCKETS, LINE-THROWING | UN0453 | 114 |
| ROCKETS, LIQUID FUELLED with bursting charge | UN0397 | 112 |
| ROCKETS, LIQUID FUELLED with bursting charge | UN0398 | 112 |
| ROCKETS with bursting charge | UN0180 | 112 |
| ROCKETS with bursting charge | UN0181 | 112 |
| ROCKETS with bursting charge | UN0182 | 112 |
| ROCKETS with bursting charge | UN0295 | 112 |
| ROCKETS with expelling charge | UN0436 | 112 |
| ROCKETS with expelling charge | UN0437 | 112 |
| ROCKETS with expelling charge | UN0438 | 114 |
| ROCKETS with inert head | UN0183 | 112 |
| ROCKETS with inert head | UN0502 | 112 |
| ROSIN OIL | UN1286 | 127 |
| RUBBER SCRAP powdered or granulated, not exceeding 840 microns and rubber content exceeding 45 per cent | UN1345 | 133 |
| RUBBER SHODDY powdered or granulated, not exceeding 840 microns and rubber content exceeding 45 per cent | UN1345 | 133 |
| RUBBER SOLUTION | UN1287 | 127 |
| RUBIDIUM | UN1423 | 138 |
| RUBIDIUM HYDROXIDE | UN2678 | 154 |
| RUBIDIUM HYDROXIDE SOLUTION | UN2677 | 154 |
| SAMPLES, EXPLOSIVE, other than initiating explosive | UN0190 | |
| SEAT-BELT PRETENSIONERS, COMPRESSED GAS | UN3353 | 126 |
| SEAT-BELT PRETENSIONERS, pyrotechnic | UN0503 | 114 |
| SEAT-BELT PRETENSIONERS, pyrotechnic | UN3268 | 171 |
| SEED CAKE with more than 1.5 per cent oil and not more than 11 per cent moisture | UN1386 | 135 |
| SEED CAKE with not more than 1.5 per cent oil and not more than 11 per cent moisture | UN2217 | 135 |
| SELENATES | UN2630 | 151 |
| SELENIC ACID | UN1905 | 154 |
| SELENITES | UN2630 | 151 |
| SELENIUM COMPOUND, N.O.S. | UN3283 | 151 |
| SELENIUM DISULFIDE | UN2657 | 153 |
| SELENIUM DISULPHIDE | UN2657 | 153 |

Schedule 3

| Description | UN # | ERG # |
|---|---|---|
| SELENIUM HEXAFLUORIDE | UN2194 | 125T |
| SELENIUM NITRIDE | Forbidden | |
| SELENIUM OXYCHLORIDE | UN2879 | 157 |
| SELF-HEATING LIQUID, CORROSIVE, INORGANIC, N.O.S. | UN3188 | 136 |
| SELF-HEATING LIQUID, CORROSIVE, ORGANIC, N.O.S. | UN3185 | 136 |
| SELF-HEATING LIQUID, INORGANIC, N.O.S. | UN3186 | 135 |
| SELF-HEATING LIQUID, ORGANIC, N.O.S. | UN3183 | 135 |
| SELF-HEATING LIQUID, TOXIC, INORGANIC, N.O.S. | UN3187 | 136 |
| SELF-HEATING LIQUID, TOXIC, ORGANIC, N.O.S. | UN3184 | 136 |
| SELF-HEATING SOLID, CORROSIVE, INORGANIC, N.O.S. | UN3192 | 136 |
| SELF-HEATING SOLID, CORROSIVE, ORGANIC, N.O.S. | UN3126 | 136 |
| SELF-HEATING SOLID, INORGANIC, N.O.S. | UN3190 | 135 |
| SELF-HEATING SOLID, ORGANIC, N.O.S. | UN3088 | 135 |
| SELF-HEATING SOLID, OXIDIZING, N.O.S. | UN3127 | 135 |
| SELF-HEATING SOLID, TOXIC, INORGANIC, N.O.S. | UN3191 | 136 |
| SELF-HEATING SOLID, TOXIC, ORGANIC, N.O.S. | UN3128 | 136 |
| SELF-REACTIVE LIQUID TYPE B | UN3221 | 149 |
| SELF-REACTIVE LIQUID TYPE B, TEMPERATURE CONTROLLED | UN3231 | 150 |
| SELF-REACTIVE LIQUID TYPE C | UN3223 | 149 |
| SELF-REACTIVE LIQUID TYPE C, TEMPERATURE CONTROLLED | UN3233 | 150 |
| SELF-REACTIVE LIQUID TYPE D | UN3225 | 149 |
| SELF-REACTIVE LIQUID TYPE D, TEMPERATURE CONTROLLED | UN3235 | 150 |
| SELF-REACTIVE LIQUID TYPE E | UN3227 | 149 |
| SELF-REACTIVE LIQUID TYPE E, TEMPERATURE CONTROLLED | UN3237 | 150 |
| SELF-REACTIVE LIQUID TYPE F | UN3229 | 149 |
| SELF-REACTIVE LIQUID TYPE F, TEMPERATURE CONTROLLED | UN3239 | 150 |
| SELF-REACTIVE SOLID TYPE B | UN3222 | 149 |
| SELF-REACTIVE SOLID TYPE B, TEMPERATURE CONTROLLED | UN3232 | 150 |
| SELF-REACTIVE SOLID TYPE C | UN3224 | 149 |
| SELF-REACTIVE SOLID TYPE C, TEMPERATURE CONTROLLED | UN3234 | 150 |
| SELF-REACTIVE SOLID TYPE D | UN3226 | 149 |
| SELF-REACTIVE SOLID TYPE D, TEMPERATURE CONTROLLED | UN3236 | 150 |
| SELF-REACTIVE SOLID TYPE E | UN3228 | 149 |
| SELF-REACTIVE SOLID TYPE E, TEMPERATURE CONTROLLED | UN3238 | 150 |
| SELF-REACTIVE SOLID TYPE F | UN3230 | 149 |
| SELF-REACTIVE SOLID TYPE F, TEMPERATURE CONTROLLED | UN3240 | 150 |
| SHALE OIL | UN1288 | 128 |
| SIGNAL DEVICES, HAND | UN0191 | 114 |
| SIGNAL DEVICES, HAND | UN0373 | 114 |
| SIGNALS, DISTRESS, ship | UN0194 | 112 |
| SIGNALS, DISTRESS, ship | UN0195 | 112 |
| SIGNALS, RAILWAY TRACK, EXPLOSIVE | UN0192 | 112 |
| SIGNALS, RAILWAY TRACK, EXPLOSIVE | UN0193 | 114 |
| SIGNALS, RAILWAY TRACK, EXPLOSIVE | UN0492 | 112 |
| SIGNALS, RAILWAY TRACK, EXPLOSIVE | UN0493 | 114 |
| SIGNALS, SMOKE | UN0196 | 112 |
| SIGNALS, SMOKE | UN0197 | 114 |
| SIGNALS, SMOKE | UN0313 | 112 |
| SIGNALS, SMOKE | UN0487 | 112 |
| SILANE, COMPRESSED | UN2203 | 116 |
| SILICON POWDER, AMORPHOUS | UN1346 | 170 |
| SILICON TETRACHLORIDE | UN1818 | 157T |

| Description | UN # | ERG # |
|---|---|---|
| SILICON TETRAFLUORIDE, COMPRESSED | UN1859 | 125T |
| SILVER ACETYLIDE (DRY) | Forbidden | |
| SILVER ARSENITE | UN1683 | 151 |
| SILVER AZIDE (DRY) | Forbidden | |
| SILVER CHLORITE (DRY) | Forbidden | |
| SILVER CYANIDE | UN1684 | 151 |
| SILVER FULMINATE (DRY) | Forbidden | |
| SILVER NITRATE | UN1493 | 140 |
| SILVER OXALATE (DRY) | Forbidden | |
| SILVER PICRATE (DRY) | Forbidden | |
| SILVER PICRATE, WETTED with not less than 30 per cent water, by mass | UN1347 | 113 |
| SLUDGE ACID | UN1906 | 153 |
| SODA LIME with more than 4 per cent sodium hydroxide | UN1907 | 154 |
| SODIUM | UN1428 | 138 |
| SODIUM ALUMINATE, SOLID, regulated by aircraft only | UN2812 | 154 |
| SODIUM ALUMINATE SOLUTION | UN1819 | 154 |
| SODIUM ALUMINIUM HYDRIDE | UN2835 | 138 |
| SODIUM AMMONIUM VANADATE | UN2863 | 154 |
| SODIUM ARSANILATE | UN2473 | 154 |
| SODIUM ARSENATE | UN1685 | 151 |
| SODIUM ARSENITE, AQUEOUS SOLUTION | UN1686 | 154 |
| SODIUM ARSENITE, SOLID | UN2027 | 151 |
| SODIUM AZIDE | UN1687 | 153 |
| SODIUM BOROHYDRIDE | UN1426 | 138 |
| SODIUM BOROHYDRIDE AND SODIUM HYDROXIDE SOLUTION, with not more than 12 per cent sodium borohydride and not more than 40 per cent sodium hydroxide, by mass | UN3320 | 157 |
| SODIUM BROMATE | UN1494 | 141 |
| SODIUM CACODYLATE | UN1688 | 152 |
| SODIUM CHLORATE | UN1495 | 140 |
| SODIUM CHLORATE, AQUEOUS SOLUTION | UN2428 | 140 |
| SODIUM CHLORITE more than 7 per cent available chlorine | UN1496 | 143 |
| SODIUM CHLOROACETATE | UN2659 | 151 |
| SODIUM CUPROCYANIDE, SOLID | UN2316 | 157 |
| SODIUM CUPROCYANIDE SOLUTION | UN2317 | 157 |
| SODIUM CYANIDE | UN1689 | 157T |
| SODIUM DINITRO-o-CRESOLATE, dry or wetted with less than 15 per cent water, by mass | UN0234 | 112 |
| SODIUM DINITRO-o-CRESOLATE, WETTED with not less than 15 per cent water, by mass | UN1348 | 113 |
| SODIUM DITHIONITE | UN1384 | 135T |
| SODIUM FLUORIDE | UN1690 | 154 |
| SODIUM FLUOROACETATE | UN2629 | 151 |
| SODIUM FLUOROSILICATE | UN2674 | 154 |
| SODIUM HYDRIDE | UN1427 | 138 |
| SODIUM HYDROGENDIFLUORIDE, solid | UN2439 | 154 |
| SODIUM HYDROGENDIFLUORIDE, SOLID (ICAO terminology) | UN2439 | 154 |
| SODIUM HYDROGENDIFLUORIDE, solution | UN2439 | 154 |
| SODIUM HYDROGENDIFLUORIDE, SOLUTION (ICAO terminology) | UN2439 | 154 |
| SODIUM HYDROSULFIDE with less than 25 per cent water of crystallization | UN2318 | 135 |
| SODIUM HYDROSULFIDE with not less than 25 per cent water of crystallization | UN2949 | 154 |
| SODIUM HYDROSULFITE | UN1384 | 135T |
| SODIUM HYDROSULPHIDE with less than 25 per cent water of crystallization | UN2318 | 135 |
| SODIUM HYDROSULPHIDE with not less than 25 per cent water of crystallization | UN2949 | 154 |
| SODIUM HYDROSULPHITE | UN1384 | 135T |
| SODIUM HYDROXIDE, SOLID | UN1823 | 154 |
| SODIUM HYDROXIDE SOLUTION | UN1824 | 154 |

| Description | UN # | ERG # |
|---|---|---|
| SODIUM METHYLATE | UN1431 | 138 |
| SODIUM METHYLATE SOLUTION in alcohol | UN1289 | 132 |
| SODIUM MONOXIDE | UN1825 | 157 |
| SODIUM NITRATE | UN1498 | 140 |
| SODIUM NITRATE AND POTASSIUM NITRATE MIXTURE | UN1499 | 140 |
| SODIUM NITRITE | UN1500 | 140 |
| SODIUM PENTACHLOROPHENATE | UN2567 | 154 |
| SODIUM PERCHLORATE | UN1502 | 140 |
| SODIUM PERMANGANATE | UN1503 | 140 |
| SODIUM PEROXIDE | UN1504 | 144 |
| SODIUM PEROXOBORATE, ANHYDROUS | UN3247 | 140 |
| SODIUM PERSULFATE | UN1505 | 140 |
| SODIUM PERSULPHATE | UN1505 | 140 |
| SODIUM PHOSPHIDE | UN1432 | 139T |
| SODIUM PICRAMATE, dry or wetted with less than 20 per cent water, by mass | UN0235 | 112 |
| SODIUM PICRAMATE, WETTED with not less than 20 per cent water, by mass | UN1349 | 113 |
| SODIUM PICRYL PEROXIDE | Forbidden | |
| SODIUM SULFIDE, ANHYDROUS | UN1385 | 135 |
| SODIUM SULFIDE, HYDRATED with not less than 30 per cent water | UN1849 | 153 |
| SODIUM SULFIDE with less than 30 per cent water of crystallization | UN1385 | 135 |
| SODIUM SULPHIDE, ANHYDROUS | UN1385 | 135 |
| SODIUM SULPHIDE, HYDRATED with not less than 30 per cent water | UN1849 | 153 |
| SODIUM SULPHIDE with less than 30 per cent water of crystallization | UN1385 | 135 |
| SODIUM SUPEROXIDE | UN2547 | 143 |
| SODIUM TETRANITRIDE | Forbidden | |
| SOLIDS CONTAINING CORROSIVE LIQUID, N.O.S. | UN3244 | 154 |
| SOLIDS CONTAINING FLAMMABLE LIQUID, N.O.S. | UN3175 | 133 |
| SOLIDS CONTAINING TOXIC LIQUID, N.O.S. | UN3243 | 151 |
| SOUNDING DEVICES, EXPLOSIVE | UN0204 | 112 |
| SOUNDING DEVICES, EXPLOSIVE | UN0296 | 112 |
| SOUNDING DEVICES, EXPLOSIVE | UN0374 | 112 |
| SOUNDING DEVICES, EXPLOSIVE | UN0375 | 112 |
| STANNIC CHLORIDE, ANHYDROUS | UN1827 | 137 |
| STANNIC CHLORIDE PENTAHYDRATE | UN2440 | 154 |
| STANNIC PHOSPHIDES | UN1433 | 139 |
| STIBINE | UN2676 | 119T |
| STRAW, regulated by ship only | UN1327 | 133 |
| STRAW, wet, damp or contaminated with oil, by ship only | Forbidden | |
| STRONTIUM ARSENITE | UN1691 | 151 |
| STRONTIUM CHLORATE | UN1506 | 143 |
| STRONTIUM NITRATE | UN1507 | 140 |
| STRONTIUM PERCHLORATE | UN1508 | 140 |
| STRONTIUM PEROXIDE | UN1509 | 143 |
| STRONTIUM PHOSPHIDE | UN2013 | 139T |
| STRYCHNINE | UN1692 | 151 |
| STRYCHNINE SALTS | UN1692 | 151 |
| STYPHNIC ACID, dry or wetted with less than 20 per cent water, or mixture of alcohol and water, by mass | UN0219 | 112 |
| STYPHNIC ACID, WETTED with not less than 20 per cent water, or mixture of alcohol and water, by mass | UN0394 | 112 |
| STYRENE MONOMER, STABILIZED | UN2055 | 128P |
| SUBSTANCES, EVI, N.O.S. | UN0482 | 112 |
| SUBSTANCES, EXPLOSIVE, N.O.S. | UN0357 | 112 |
| SUBSTANCES, EXPLOSIVE, N.O.S. | UN0358 | 112 |
| SUBSTANCES, EXPLOSIVE, N.O.S. | UN0359 | 112 |
| SUBSTANCES, EXPLOSIVE, N.O.S. | UN0473 | 112 |

| Description | UN # | ERG # |
|---|---|---|
| SUBSTANCES, EXPLOSIVE, N.O.S. | UN0474 | 112 |
| SUBSTANCES, EXPLOSIVE, N.O.S. | UN0475 | 112 |
| SUBSTANCES, EXPLOSIVE, N.O.S. | UN0476 | 112 |
| SUBSTANCES, EXPLOSIVE, N.O.S. | UN0477 | 112 |
| SUBSTANCES, EXPLOSIVE, N.O.S. | UN0478 | 112 |
| SUBSTANCES, EXPLOSIVE, N.O.S. | UN0479 | 114 |
| SUBSTANCES, EXPLOSIVE, N.O.S. | UN0480 | 114 |
| SUBSTANCES, EXPLOSIVE, N.O.S. | UN0481 | 114 |
| SUBSTANCES, EXPLOSIVE, N.O.S. | UN0485 | 114 |
| SUBSTANCES, EXPLOSIVE, VERY INSENSITIVE, N.O.S. | UN0482 | 112 |
| SUBSTITUTED NITROPHENOL PESTICIDE, LIQUID, FLAMMABLE, TOXIC, flash point less than 23 °C | UN2780 | 131 |
| SUBSTITUTED NITROPHENOL PESTICIDE, LIQUID, TOXIC | UN3014 | 153 |
| SUBSTITUTED NITROPHENOL PESTICIDE, LIQUID, TOXIC, FLAMMABLE, flash point not less than 23 °C | UN3013 | 131 |
| SUBSTITUTED NITROPHENOL PESTICIDE, SOLID, TOXIC | UN2779 | 153 |
| SUCROSE OCTANITRATE, (DRY) | Forbidden | |
| SULFAMIC ACID | UN2967 | 154 |
| SULFUR | UN1350 | 133 |
| SULFUR AND CHLORATE, LOOSE MIXTURES OF | Forbidden | |
| SULFUR CHLORIDES | UN1828 | 137 |
| SULFUR DIOXIDE | UN1079 | 135T |
| SULFUR HEXAFLUORIDE | UN1080 | 126 |
| SULFURIC ACID, FUMING | UN1831 | 137T |
| SULFURIC ACID, SPENT | UN1832 | 137 |
| SULFURIC ACID with more than 51 per cent acid | UN1830 | 137 |
| SULFURIC ACID with not more than 51 per cent acid | UN2796 | 157 |
| SULFUR, MOLTEN | UN2448 | 133 |
| SULFUROUS ACID | UN1833 | 154 |
| SULFUR TETRAFLUORIDE | UN2418 | 125T |
| SULFUR TRIOXIDE, STABILIZED | UN1829 | 137T |
| SULFURYL CHLORIDE | UN1834 | 137T |
| SULFURYL FLUORIDE | UN2191 | 123T |
| SULPHAMIC ACID | UN2967 | 151 |
| SULPHUR | UN1350 | 133 |
| SULPHUR AND CHLORATE, LOOSE MIXTURES OF | Forbidden | |
| SULPHUR CHLORIDES | UN1828 | 137T |
| SULPHUR DIOXIDE | UN1079 | 125T |
| SULPHUR HEXAFLUORIDE | UN1080 | 126 |
| SULPHURIC ACID, FUMING | UN1831 | 137T |
| SULPHURIC ACID, SPENT | UN1832 | 137 |
| SULPHURIC ACID with more than 51 per cent acid | UN1830 | 137 |
| SULPHURIC ACID with not more than 51 per cent acid | UN2796 | 157 |
| SULPHUR, MOLTEN | UN2448 | 133 |
| SULPHUROUS ACID | UN1833 | 154 |
| SULPHUR TETRAFLUORIDE | UN2418 | 125T |
| SULPHUR TRIOXIDE, STABILIZED | UN1829 | 137T |
| SULPHURYL CHLORIDE | UN1834 | 137T |
| SULPHURYL FLUORIDE | UN2191 | 123T |
| TARS, LIQUID, including road asphalt and oils, bitumen and cut backs | UN1999 | 130 |
| TEAR GAS CANDLES | UN1700 | 159 |
| TEAR GAS SUBSTANCE, LIQUID, N.O.S. | UN1693 | 159 |
| TEAR GAS SUBSTANCE, SOLID, N.O.S. | UN1693 | 159 |
| TELLURIUM COMPOUND, N.O.S. | UN3284 | 151 |
| TELLURIUM HEXAFLUORIDE | UN2195 | 125T |
| TERPENE HYDROCARBONS, N.O.S. | UN2319 | 128 |
| TERPINOLENE | UN2541 | 128 |

| Description | UN # | ERG # |
|---|---|---|
| TETRAAZIDO BENZENE QUINONE | Forbidden | |
| TETRABROMOETHANE | UN2504 | 159 |
| TETRACHLOROETHANE | UN1702 | 151 |
| TETRACHLOROETHYLENE | UN1897 | 160 |
| TETRAETHYLAMMONIUM PERCHLORATE (DRY) | Forbidden | |
| TETRAETHYL DITHIOPYROPHOSPHATE | UN1704 | 153 |
| TETRAETHYLENEPENTAMINE | UN2320 | 153 |
| TETRAETHYL SILICATE | UN1292 | 132 |
| 1,1,1,2-TETRAFLUOROETHANE | UN3159 | 126 |
| TETRAFLUOROETHYLENE, STABILIZED | UN1081 | 116P |
| TETRAFLUOROMETHANE, COMPRESSED | UN1982 | 126 |
| 1,2,3,6-TETRAHYDROBENZALDEHYDE | UN2498 | 132 |
| TETRAHYDROFURAN | UN2056 | 127 |
| TETRAHYDROFURFURYLAMINE | UN2943 | 129 |
| TETRAHYDROPHTHALIC ANHYDRIDES with more than 0.05 per cent of maleic anhydride | UN2698 | 156 |
| 1,2,3,6-TETRAHYDROPYRIDINE | UN2410 | 129 |
| TETRAHYDROTHIOPHENE | UN2412 | 129 |
| TETRAMETHYLAMMONIUM HYDROXIDE | UN1835 | 153 |
| TETRAMETHYLENE DIPEROXIDE DICARBAMIDE | Forbidden | |
| TETRAMETHYLSILANE | UN2749 | 130 |
| TETRANITROANILINE | UN0207 | 112 |
| TETRANITRODIGLYCERIN | Forbidden | |
| TETRANITROMETHANE | UN1510 | 143T |
| 2,3,4,6-TETRANITROPHENOL | Forbidden | |
| 2,3,4,6-TETRANITROPHENYL METHYL NITRAMINE | Forbidden | |
| 2,3,4,6-TETRANITROPHENYLNITRAMINE | Forbidden | |
| TETRANITRORESORCINAL (DRY) | Forbidden | |
| 2,3,5,6-TETRANITROSO-1,4-DINITROBENZENE | Forbidden | |
| 2,3,5,6-TETRANITROSO NITROBENZENE (DRY) | Forbidden | |
| TETRAPROPYL ORTHOTITANATE | UN2413 | 128 |
| TETRAZENE, WETTED with not less than 30 per cent water, or mixture of alcohol and water, by mass | UN0114 | 112 |
| TETRAZINE | Forbidden | |
| TETRAZOL-1-ACETIC ACID | UN0407 | 112 |
| 1H-TETRAZOLE | UN0504 | 112 |
| TETRAZOLYL AZIDE (DRY) | Forbidden | |
| TETRYL | UN0208 | 112 |
| THALLIUM CHLORATE | UN2573 | 141 |
| THALLIUM COMPOUND, N.O.S. | UN1707 | 151 |
| THALLIUM NITRATE | UN2727 | 141 |
| 4-THIAPENTANAL | UN2785 | 152 |
| THIOACETIC ACID | UN2436 | 129 |
| THIOCARBAMATE PESTICIDE, LIQUID, FLAMMABLE, TOXIC, flash point less than 23 °C | UN2772 | 131 |
| THIOCARBAMATE PESTICIDE, LIQUID, TOXIC | UN3006 | 151 |
| THIOCARBAMATE PESTICIDE, LIQUID, TOXIC, FLAMMABLE, flash point not less than 23 °C | UN3005 | 131 |
| THIOCARBAMATE PESTICIDE, SOLID, TOXIC | UN2771 | 151 |
| THIOGLYCOL | UN2966 | 153 |
| THIOGLYCOLIC ACID | UN1940 | 153 |
| THIOLACTIC ACID | UN2936 | 153 |
| THIONYL CHLORIDE | UN1836 | 137T |
| THIOPHENE | UN2414 | 130 |
| THIOPHOSGENE | UN2474 | 157T |
| THIOPHOSPHORYL CHLORIDE | UN1837 | 157 |
| THIOUREA DIOXIDE | UN3341 | 135 |
| TINCTURES, MEDICINAL | UN1293 | 127 |

| Description | UN # | ERG # |
|---|---|---|
| TITANIUM DISULFIDE | UN3174 | 135 |
| TITANIUM DISULPHIDE | UN3174 | 135 |
| TITANIUM HYDRIDE | UN1871 | 170 |
| TITANIUM POWDER, DRY | UN2546 | 135 |
| TITANIUM POWDER, WETTED with not less than 25 per cent water (a visible excess of water must be present) (a) mechanically produced, particle size less than 53 microns; (b) chemically produced, particle size less than 840 microns | UN1352 | 170 |
| TITANIUM SPONGE GRANULES | UN2878 | 170 |
| TITANIUM SPONGE POWDERS | UN2878 | 170 |
| TITANIUM TETRACHLORIDE | UN1838 | 137T |
| TITANIUM TRICHLORIDE MIXTURE | UN2869 | 157 |
| TITANIUM TRICHLORIDE MIXTURE, PYROPHORIC | UN2441 | 135 |
| TITANIUM TRICHLORIDE, PYROPHORIC | UN2441 | 135 |
| TNT AND HEXANITROSTILBENE MIXTURE | UN0388 | 112 |
| TNT AND TRINITROBENZENE MIXTURE | UN0388 | 112 |
| TNT, dry or wetted with less than 30 per cent water, by mass | UN0209 | 112 |
| TNT MIXTURE CONTAINING TRINITROBENZENE AND HEXANITROSTILBENE | UN0389 | 112 |
| TOLUENE | UN1294 | 130 |
| TOLUENE DIISOCYANATE | UN2078 | 156 |
| TOLUIDINES, LIQUID | UN1708 | 153 |
| TOLUIDINES, SOLID | UN1708 | 153 |
| 2,4-TOLUYLENEDIAMINE | UN1709 | 151 |
| TORPEDOES, LIQUID FUELLED with inert head | UN0450 | 112 |
| TORPEDOES, LIQUID FUELLED with or without bursting charge | UN0449 | 112 |
| TORPEDOES with bursting charge | UN0329 | 112 |
| TORPEDOES with bursting charge | UN0330 | 112 |
| TORPEDOES with bursting charge | UN0451 | 112 |
| TOXIC LIQUID, CORROSIVE, INORGANIC, N.O.S. | UN3289 | 154T |
| TOXIC LIQUID, CORROSIVE, ORGANIC, N.O.S. | UN2927 | 154T |
| TOXIC LIQUID, FLAMMABLE, ORGANIC, N.O.S. | UN2929 | 131T |
| TOXIC LIQUID, INORGANIC, N.O.S. | UN3287 | 151T |
| TOXIC LIQUID, ORGANIC, N.O.S. | UN2810 | 153T |
| TOXIC LIQUID, OXIDIZING, N.O.S. | UN3122 | 142T |
| TOXIC LIQUID, WATER-REACTIVE, N.O.S. | UN3123 | 139T |
| TOXIC SOLID, CORROSIVE, INORGANIC, N.O.S. | UN3290 | 154 |
| TOXIC SOLID, CORROSIVE, ORGANIC, N.O.S. | UN2928 | 154 |
| TOXIC SOLID, FLAMMABLE, ORGANIC, N.O.S. | UN2930 | 134 |
| TOXIC SOLID, INORGANIC, N.O.S. | UN3288 | 151 |
| TOXIC SOLID, ORGANIC, N.O.S. | UN2811 | 154 |
| TOXIC SOLID, OXIDIZING, N.O.S. | UN3086 | 141 |
| TOXIC SOLID, SELF-HEATING, N.O.S. | UN3124 | 136 |
| TOXIC SOLID, WATER-REACTIVE, N.O.S. | UN3125 | 139 |
| TOXINS, EXTRACTED FROM LIVING SOURCES, LIQUID, N.O.S., not containing infectious substances | UN3172 | 153 |
| TOXINS, EXTRACTED FROM LIVING SOURCES, SOLID, N.O.S., not containing infectious substances | UN3172 | 153 |
| TRACERS FOR AMMUNITION | UN0212 | 112 |
| TRACERS FOR AMMUNITION | UN0306 | 114 |
| TRIALLYLAMINE | UN2610 | 132 |
| TRIALLYL BORATE | UN2609 | 156 |
| TRIAZINE PESTICIDE, LIQUID, FLAMMABLE, TOXIC, flash point less than 23 °C | UN2764 | 131 |
| TRIAZINE PESTICIDE, LIQUID, TOXIC | UN2998 | 151 |

| Description | UN # | ERG # |
|---|---|---|
| TRIAZINE PESTICIDE, LIQUID, TOXIC, FLAMMABLE, flash point not less than 23 °C | UN2997 | 131 |
| TRIAZINE PESTICIDE, SOLID, TOXIC | UN2763 | 151 |
| TRI-(b-NITROXYETHYL) AMMONIUM NITRATE | Forbidden | |
| TRIBUTYLAMINE | UN2542 | 153 |
| TRIBUTYLPHOSPHANE | UN3254 | 135 |
| TRICHLOROACETIC ACID | UN1839 | 153 |
| TRICHLOROACETIC ACID SOLUTION | UN2564 | 153 |
| TRICHLOROACETYL CHLORIDE | UN2442 | 156T |
| TRICHLOROBENZENES, LIQUID | UN2321 | 153 |
| TRICHLOROBUTENE | UN2322 | 152 |
| 1,1,1-TRICHLOROETHANE | UN2831 | 160 |
| TRICHLOROETHYLENE | UN1710 | 160 |
| TRICHLOROISOCYANURIC ACID, DRY | UN2468 | 140 |
| TRICHLOROMETHYL PERCHLORATE | Forbidden | |
| TRICHLOROSILANE | UN1295 | 139T |
| TRICRESYL PHOSPHATE with more than 3 per cent ortho isomer | UN2574 | 151 |
| TRIETHYLAMINE | UN1296 | 132 |
| TRIETHYLENETETRAMINE | UN2259 | 153 |
| TRIETHYL PHOSPHITE | UN2323 | 129 |
| TRIFLUOROACETIC ACID | UN2699 | 154 |
| TRIFLUOROACETYL CHLORIDE | UN3057 | 125T |
| TRIFLUOROCHLOROETHYLENE, STABILIZED | UN1082 | 119PT |
| 1,1,1-TRIFLUOROETHANE | UN2035 | 115 |
| TRIFLUOROMETHANE | UN1984 | 126 |
| TRIFLUOROMETHANE, REFRIGERATED LIQUID | UN3136 | 120 |
| 2-TRIFLUOROMETHYLANILINE | UN2942 | 153 |
| 3-TRIFLUOROMETHYLANILINE | UN2948 | 153 |
| TRIFORMOXIME TRINITRATE | Forbidden | |
| TRIISOBUTYLENE | UN2324 | 128 |
| TRIISOPROPYL BORATE | UN2616 | 129 |
| TRIMETHYLACETYL CHLORIDE | UN2438 | 132T |
| TRIMETHYLAMINE, ANHYDROUS | UN1083 | 118 |
| TRIMETHYLAMINE, AQUEOUS SOLUTION, not more than 50 per cent trimethylamine, by mass | UN1297 | 132 |
| 1,3,5-TRIMETHYLBENZENE | UN2325 | 129 |
| TRIMETHYL BORATE | UN2416 | 129 |
| TRIMETHYLCHLOROSILANE | UN1298 | 155T |
| TRIMETHYLCYCLOHEXYLAMINE | UN2326 | 153 |
| TRIMETHYLENE GLYCOL DIPERCHLORATE | Forbidden | |
| TRIMETHYLHEXAMETHYLENEDIAMINES | UN2327 | 153 |
| TRIMETHYLHEXAMETHYLENE DIISOCYANATE | UN2328 | 156 |
| TRIMETHYLOL NITROMETHANE TRINITRATE | Forbidden | |
| TRIMETHYL PHOSPHITE | UN2329 | 129 |
| 1,3,5-TRIMETHYL-2,4,6-TRINITROBENZENE | Forbidden | |
| TRINITROACETIC ACID | Forbidden | |
| TRINITROACETONITRILE | Forbidden | |
| TRINITROAMINE COBALT | Forbidden | |
| TRINITROANILINE | UN0153 | 112 |
| TRINITROANISOLE | UN0213 | 112 |
| TRINITROBENZENE, dry or wetted with less than 30 per cent water, by mass | UN0214 | 112 |
| TRINITROBENZENESULFONIC ACID | UN0386 | 112 |
| TRINITROBENZENESULPHONIC ACID | UN0386 | 112 |
| TRINITROBENZENE, WETTED with not less than 30 per cent water, by mass | UN1354 | 113 |
| TRINITROBENZOIC ACID, dry or wetted with less than 30 per cent water, by mass | UN0215 | 112 |
| TRINITROBENZOIC ACID, WETTED with not less than 30 per cent water, by mass | UN1355 | 113 |
| TRINITROCHLOROBENZENE | UN0155 | 112 |

| Description | UN # | ERG # |
|---|---|---|
| TRINITRO-m-CRESOL | UN0216 | 112 |
| 2,4,6-TRINITRO-1,3-DIAZOBENZENE | Forbidden | |
| TRINITROETHANOL | Forbidden | |
| TRINITROETHYLNITRATE | Forbidden | |
| TRINITROFLUORENONE | UN0387 | 112 |
| TRINITROMETHANE | Forbidden | |
| 1,3,5-TRINITRONAPHTHALENE | Forbidden | |
| TRINITRONAPHTHALENE | UN0217 | 112 |
| TRINITROPHENETOLE | UN0218 | 112 |
| TRINITROPHENOL, dry or wetted with less than 30 per cent water, by mass | UN0154 | 112 |
| TRINITROPHENOL, WETTED with not less than 30 per cent water, by mass | UN1344 | 113 |
| 2,4,6-TRINITROPHENYL GUANIDINE (DRY) | Forbidden | |
| TRINITROPHENYLMETHYLNITRAMINE | UN0208 | 112 |
| 2,4,6-TRINITROPHENYL NITRAMINE | Forbidden | |
| 2,4,6-TRINITROPHENYL TRIMETHYLOL METHYL NITRAMINE TRINITRATE (DRY) | Forbidden | |
| TRINITRORESORCINOL, dry or wetted with less than 20 per cent water, or mixture of alcohol and water, by mass | UN0219 | 112 |
| TRINITRORESORCINOL, WETTED with not less than 20 per cent water, or mixture of alcohol and water, by mass | UN0394 | 112 |
| 2,4,6-TRINITROSO-3-METHYL NITRAMINOANISOLE | Forbidden | |
| TRINITROTETRAMINE COBALT NITRATE | Forbidden | |
| TRINITROTOLUENE AND HEXANITROSTILBENE MIXTURE | UN0388 | 112 |
| TRINITROTOLUENE AND TRINITROBENZENE MIXTURE | UN0388 | 112 |
| TRINITROTOLUENE, dry or wetted with less than 30 per cent water, by mass | UN0209 | 112 |
| TRINITROTOLUENE MIXTURE CONTAINING TRINITROBENZENE AND HEXANITROSTILBENE | UN0389 | 112 |
| TRINITROTOLUENE, WETTED with not less than 30 per cent water, by mass | UN1356 | 113 |
| 2,4,6-TRINITRO-1,3,5-TRIAZIDO BENZENE (DRY) | Forbidden | |
| TRIPROPYLAMINE | UN2260 | 132 |
| TRIPROPYLENE | UN2057 | 128 |
| TRIS-(1-AZIRIDINYL) PHOSPHINE OXIDE SOLUTION | UN2501 | 152 |
| TRIS, BIS-BIFLUORAMINO DIETHOXY PROPANE (TVOPA) | Forbidden | |
| TRITONAL | UN0390 | 112 |
| TUNGSTEN HEXAFLUORIDE | UN2196 | 125T |
| TURPENTINE | UN1299 | 128 |
| TURPENTINE SUBSTITUTE | UN1300 | 128 |
| UNDECANE | UN2330 | 128 |
| URANYL NITRATE, HEXAHYDRATE, SOLUTION | UN2980 | 162 |
| UREA HYDROGEN PEROXIDE | UN1511 | 140 |
| UREA NITRATE, dry or wetted with less than 20 per cent water, by mass | UN0220 | 112 |
| UREA NITRATE, WETTED with not less than 20 per cent water, by mass | UN1357 | 153 |
| VALERALDEHYDE | UN2058 | 129 |
| VALERYL CHLORIDE | UN2502 | 132 |
| VANADIUM COMPOUND, N.O.S. | UN3285 | 151 |
| VANADIUM OXYTRICHLORIDE | UN2443 | 137 |
| VANADIUM PENTOXIDE, non-fused form | UN2862 | 151 |
| VANADIUM TETRACHLORIDE | UN2444 | 137 |
| VANADIUM TRICHLORIDE | UN2475 | 157 |
| VANADYL SULFATE | UN2931 | 151 |
| VANADYL SULPHATE | UN2931 | 151 |
| VINYL ACETATE, STABILIZED | UN1301 | 129P |
| VINYL BROMIDE, STABILIZED | UN1085 | 116P |
| VINYL BUTYRATE, STABILIZED | UN2838 | 129P |
| VINYL CHLORIDE, STABILIZED | UN1086 | 116P |

| Description | UN # | ERG # |
|---|---|---|
| VINYL CHLOROACETATE | UN2589 | 155 |
| VINYL ETHYL ETHER, STABILIZED | UN1302 | 127P |
| VINYL FLUORIDE, STABILIZED | UN1860 | 116P |
| VINYLIDENE CHLORIDE, STABILIZED | UN1303 | 129P |
| VINYL ISOBUTYL ETHER, STABILIZED | UN1304 | 127P |
| VINYL METHYL ETHER, STABILIZED | UN1087 | 116P |
| VINYL NITRATE POLYMER | Forbidden | |
| VINYLPYRIDINES, STABILIZED | UN3073 | 131P |
| VINYLTOLUENES, STABILIZED | UN2618 | 130P |
| VINYLTRICHLOROSILANE, STABILIZED | UN1305 | 155 |
| WARHEADS, ROCKET with burster or expelling charge | UN0370 | 114 |
| WARHEADS, ROCKET with burster or expelling charge | UN0371 | 114 |
| WARHEADS, ROCKET with bursting charge | UN0286 | 112 |
| WARHEADS, ROCKET with bursting charge | UN0287 | 112 |
| WARHEADS, ROCKET with bursting charge | UN0369 | 112 |
| WARHEADS, TORPEDO with bursting charge | UN0221 | 112 |
| WATER-REACTIVE LIQUID, CORROSIVE, N.O.S. | UN3129 | 138 |
| WATER-REACTIVE LIQUID, N.O.S. | UN3148 | 138 |
| WATER-REACTIVE LIQUID, TOXIC, N.O.S. | UN3130 | 139 |
| WATER-REACTIVE SOLID, CORROSIVE, N.O.S. | UN3131 | 138 |
| WATER-REACTIVE SOLID, FLAMMABLE, N.O.S. | UN3132 | 138 |
| WATER-REACTIVE SOLID, N.O.S. | UN2813 | 138 |
| WATER-REACTIVE SOLID, OXIDIZING, N.O.S. | UN3133 | 138 |
| WATER-REACTIVE SOLID, SELF-HEATING, N.O.S. | UN3135 | 138 |
| WATER-REACTIVE SOLID, TOXIC, N.O.S. | UN3134 | 139 |
| WOOD PRESERVATIVES, LIQUID | UN1306 | 129 |
| XANTHATES | UN3342 | 135 |
| XENON, COMPRESSED | UN2036 | 121 |
| XENON, REFRIGERATED LIQUID | UN2591 | 120 |
| XYLENES | UN1307 | 130 |
| XYLENOLS | UN2261 | 153 |
| XYLIDINES, LIQUID | UN1711 | 153 |
| XYLIDINES, SOLID | UN1711 | 153 |
| XYLYL BROMIDE | UN1701 | 152 |
| p-XYLYL DIAZIDE | Forbidden | |
| ZINC AMMONIUM NITRITE | UN1512 | 140 |
| ZINC ARSENATE | UN1712 | 151 |
| ZINC ARSENATE AND ZINC ARSENITE MIXTURES | UN1712 | 151 |
| ZINC ARSENITE | UN1712 | 151 |
| ZINC ASHES | UN1435 | 138 |
| ZINC BROMATE | UN2469 | 140 |
| ZINC CHLORATE | UN1513 | 140 |
| ZINC CHLORIDE, ANHYDROUS | UN2331 | 154 |
| ZINC CHLORIDE SOLUTION | UN1840 | 154 |
| ZINC CYANIDE | UN1713 | 151 |
| ZINC DITHIONITE | UN1931 | 171T |
| ZINC DUST | UN1436 | 138 |
| ZINC FLUOROSILICATE | UN2855 | 151 |
| ZINC HYDROSULFITE | UN1931 | 171 |
| ZINC HYDROSULPHITE | UN1931 | 171 |
| ZINC NITRATE | UN1514 | 140 |
| ZINC PERMANGANATE | UN1515 | 140 |
| ZINC PEROXIDE | UN1516 | 143 |
| ZINC PHOSPHIDE | UN1714 | 139 |
| ZINC POWDER | UN1436 | 138 |
| ZINC RESINATE | UN2714 | 133 |
| ZIRCONIUM, DRY, coiled wire, finished metal sheets, strip (thinner than 254 microns but not thinner than 18 microns) | UN2858 | 151 |

| Description | UN # | ERG # |
|---|---|---|
| ZIRCONIUM, DRY, finished sheets, strip or coiled wire | UN2009 | 135 |
| ZIRCONIUM HYDRIDE | UN1437 | 138 |
| ZIRCONIUM NITRATE | UN2728 | 140 |
| ZIRCONIUM PICRAMATE, dry or wetted with less than 20 per cent water, by mass | UN0236 | 112 |
| ZIRCONIUM PICRAMATE, WETTED with not less than 20 per cent water, by mass | UN1517 | 113 |
| ZIRCONIUM POWDER, DRY | UN2008 | 135 |
| ZIRCONIUM POWDER, WETTED with not less than 25 per cent water (a visible excess of water must be present) (a) mechanically produced, particle size less than 53 microns; (b) chemically produced, particle size less than 840 microns | UN1358 | 170 |
| ZIRCONIUM SCRAP | UN1932 | 135 |
| ZIRCONIUM SUSPENDED IN A FLAMMABLE LIQUID | UN1308 | 170 |
| ZIRCONIUM TETRACHLORIDE | UN2503 | 137 |

# SCHEDULE 4

## Emergency Response Guides (ERG)

This Schedule when used in conjunction with Schedule 3 satisfies the requirements of 49CFR 172.602 with respect to the information that must accompany a shipment of dangerous goods. The information is obtained from the 2008 Emergency Response Guidebook developed by Transport Canada and the US Department of Transportation.

| Class shown on placard | Emergency Response Guide Number |
|---|---|
| DANGER | 111 |
| Explosives, 1.1, 1.2 and 1.3 | 112 |
| Explosives, 1.4 | 114 |
| Explosives, 1.5 | 112 |
| Explosives, 1.6 | 112 |
| Flammable Gases, 2.1 | 118 |
| Non-flammable and Non-toxic Gases, 2.2 | 121 |
| Oxygen, 2.2 | 122 |
| Toxic Gases, 2.3 | 123 |
| Flammable Liquids, 3 | 127 |
| Flammable Solids, 4.1 | 134 |
| Substances liable to spontaneous combustion, 4.2 | 136 |
| Water Reactive Substances, 4.3 | 139 |
| Oxidizing Substances, 5.1 | 143 |
| Organic Peroxides, 5.2 | 148 |
| Toxic Substances, 6.1 | 153 |
| Infectious Substances, 6.2 | 158 |
| Radioactive Materials, 7 | 163 |
| Corrosives, 8 | 153 |
| Miscellaneous Products, Substances and Organisms, 9 | 171 |

**How to determine the correct Emergency Response Guide**

1. Identify the dangerous goods by **UN Number from the Shipping Document** ( * See below), the placard or the adjacent orange panel.

2. Identify the **Emergency Response Guide number from Schedule 3.** (Or use the UN Number/Emergency Response Guide cross-reference at the end of this Schedule.)

3. **Read the Emergency Response Guide carefully**.

**If an Emergency Response Guide can not be found** and an incident is believed to involve dangerous goods, then Guide No.111 should be used.

**If the dangerous goods cannot be identified** by means of the Shipping Document and no UN Number is shown on the large MoC, then the Emergency Response Guides shown in the table to the left should be used.

* Note: When using the Shipping Document it is possible that:

- the words describing the dangerous goods on the Shipping Document might not be in the same order as shown in Schedule 3, which is acceptable, *for example Asbestos, White, UN2590 might be described as White Asbestos, UN2590*

- there might be prefixes added to the chemical name of the dangerous goods shown on the Shipping Document, *for example, Ethanolamine, UN2491 may be described as Monoethanolamine, UN2491*

- there might be additional descriptive text with the Shipping Name, *for example Barium Chlorate, UN1445 may be described as Barium Chlorate, wet, UN1445*

- there might be alternative spelling, particularly on consignments originating in the U.S. It should be noted that "poison" and "toxic" are used interchangeably, *for example Compressed Gas, Toxic, Oxidizing, Corrosive, N.O.S., UN3306 may be described as Compressed Gas, Poisonous, Oxidizing, Corrosive, N.O.S., UN3306.* "Stabilised" and "inhibited" are also used interchangeably, *e.g. Butadienes, Stabilized, UN1010 may be described as Butadienes, Inhibited, UN1010*

- there might be specific chemical names used in place of a generic name, *for example the Shipping Document might show Lead Fluoride, UN2811, rather than Toxic Solid, Organic, N.O.S. UN 2811*

A driver should be aware that these differences can occur but in all cases the UN Number shown must be used to identify the correct Emergency Response Guide Number.

For each UN Number there is a corresponding Emergency Response Guide Number, *for example, the Emergency Response Guide Number for Sodium Hydroxide, solution UN1824 is # 154.*

# GENERAL SAFETY PRECAUTIONS FOR SPILLS OF DANGEROUS GOODS

**Approach cautiously from upwind.** Resist the urge to rush in; fully assess the situation before you attempt to assist others.

**Secure the scene.** Without entering the immediate hazard area, isolate the area and assure the safety of people and the environment, keep people away from the scene. Allow enough room to move and remove your own equipment.

**Identify the hazards.** Obtain the necessary information from placards, labels, shipping documents, material safety data sheets, and/or knowledgeable persons on the scene. Evaluate all available information and consult the appropriate Emergency Response Guide to reduce immediate risks.

**Assess the situation.** Consider the following:

Is there a fire, a spill or a leak?

What are the weather conditions?

What is the terrain like?

Who/what is at risk: people, property or the environment?

What actions should be taken: Is an evacuation necessary? Is diking necessary? What resources (human and equipment) are required and are readily available?

What can be done immediately?

**Obtain help.** Take action to notify responsible agencies and call for assistance from qualified personnel.

## BEFORE TAKING ANY FURTHER ACTION:

**Decide on site entry.** Any efforts made to rescue persons, protect property or the environment, must be weighed against the possibility of worsening the situation. Enter the area only when wearing appropriate protective gear.

**Respond.** Respond in an appropriate manner. The first duty is to consider the safety of people in the immediate area, including your own. Do not walk into or touch spilled material. Avoid inhalation of fumes, smoke and vapors, even if no dangerous goods are known to be involved. Do not assume that gases or vapors are harmless because of lack of a smell. Odorless gases or vapors may be harmful.

## ADDITIONAL HAZARDS

The letter "**T**" following the Emergency Response Guide number indicates substances that are toxic-by-inhalation. Substances that are "toxic-by-inhalation" (TIH), require special precautions and isolation distances. These are detailed in Schedule 6 and an explanation of how to use Schedule 6 is provided on page 233.

The letter "**P**" following the Emergency Response Guide number indicates substances that may polymerize explosively when heated or involved in a fire.

Schedule 4

# Guide No. 111   Mixed Load/Unidentified Cargo

## POTENTIAL HAZARDS

**FIRE OR EXPLOSION**
- May explode from heat, shock, friction or contamination.• May react violently or explosively on contact with air, water or foam.• May be ignited by heat, sparks or flames. • Vapors may travel to source of ignition and flash back. • Containers may explode when heated. • Ruptured cylinders may rocket.

**HEALTH**
- Inhalation, ingestion or contact with substance may cause severe injury, infection, disease or death.• High concentration of gas may cause asphyxiation without warning. • Contact may cause burns to skin and eyes. • Fire or contact with water may produce irritating, toxic and/or corrosive gases. • Runoff from fire control may cause pollution.

## PUBLIC SAFETY

- CALL Emergency Response Telephone Number on Shipping Document first. If Shipping Document not available or no answer, refer to appropriate telephone number listed at the end of this book. • As an immediate precautionary measure, isolate spill or leak area for at least 100 meters (330 feet) in all directions. • Keep unauthorized personnel away. • Stay upwind. • Keep out of low areas.

**PROTECTIVE CLOTHING**
- Wear positive pressure self-contained breathing apparatus (SCBA). • Structural firefighters' protective clothing provides limited protection in fire situations ONLY; it may not be effective in spill situations.

**EVACUATION**

**Fire**
- If tank, rail car or tank truck is involved in a fire, ISOLATE for 800 meters (1/2 mile) in all directions; also, consider initial evacuation for 800 meters (1/2 mile) in all directions.

## EMERGENCY RESPONSE

**FIRE**

*CAUTION: Material may react with extinguishing agent.*

**Small Fire**
- Dry chemical, $CO_2$, water spray or regular foam.

**Large Fire**
- Water spray, fog or regular foam. • Move containers from fire area if you can do it without risk.

**Fire involving Tanks**
- Cool containers with flooding quantities of water until well after fire is out. • Do not get water inside containers. • Withdraw immediately in case of rising sound from venting safety devices or discoloration of tank. • ALWAYS stay away from tanks engulfed in fire.

**SPILL OR LEAK**

- Do not touch or walk through spilled material. • ELIMINATE all ignition sources (no smoking, flares, sparks or flames in immediate area). • All equipment used when handling the product must be grounded. • Keep combustibles (wood, paper, oil, etc.) away from spilled material. • Use water spray to reduce vapors or divert vapor cloud drift. Avoid allowing water runoff to contact spilled material. • Prevent entry into waterways, sewers, basements or confined areas.

**Small Spill**
- Take up with sand or other non-combustible absorbent material and place into containers for later disposal.

**Large Spill**
- Dike far ahead of liquid spill for later disposal.

**FIRST AID**

- Move victim to fresh air. • Call 911 or emergency medical service. • Give artificial respiration if victim is not breathing • **Do not use mouth-to-mouth method if victim ingested or inhaled the substance; give artificial respiration with the aid of a pocket mask equipped with a one-way valve or other proper respiratory medical device.** • Administer oxygen if breathing is difficult. • Remove and isolate contaminated clothing and shoes. • In case of contact with substance, immediately flush skin or eyes with running water for at least 20 minutes. • Shower and wash with soap and water. • Keep victim warm and quiet. • Effects of exposure (inhalation, ingestion or skin contact) to substance may be delayed. • Ensure that medical personnel are aware of the material(s) involved, and take precautions to protect themselves.

Schedule 4

# Guide No. 112 Explosives* - Division 1.1, 1.2, 1.3, 1.5 or 1.6; Class A or B

## POTENTIAL HAZARDS

**FIRE OR EXPLOSION**
- MAY EXPLODE AND THROW FRAGMENTS 1600 meters (1 MILE) OR MORE IF FIRE REACHES CARGO.
- For information on "Compatibility Group" letters, refer to Appendix 3.

**HEALTH**
- Fire may produce irritating, corrosive and/or toxic gases.

## PUBLIC SAFETY

- CALL Emergency Response Telephone Number on Shipping Document first. If Shipping Document not available or no answer, refer to appropriate telephone number listed at the end of this book. • Isolate spill or leak area immediately for at least 500 meters (1/3 mile) in all directions. • Move people out of line of sight of the scene and away from windows. • Keep unauthorized personnel away. • Stay upwind. • Ventilate closed spaces before entering.

**PROTECTIVE CLOTHING**
- Wear positive pressure self-contained breathing apparatus (SCBA). • Structural firefighters' protective clothing will only provide limited protection.

**EVACUATION**

**Large Spill**
- Consider initial evacuation for 800 meters (1/2 mile) in all directions.

**Fire**
- If rail car or trailer is involved in a fire and heavily encased explosives such as bombs or artillery projectiles are suspected, ISOLATE for 1600 m (1 mile) in all directions; also, initiate evacuation including emergency responders for 1600 m (1 mile) in all directions. • When heavily encased explosives are not involved, evacuate the area for 800 meters (1/2 mile) in all directions.
- For information on "Compatibility Group" letters, refer to Appendix 3.

## EMERGENCY RESPONSE

**FIRE**

**CARGO Fire**
- **DO NOT fight fire when fire reaches cargo! Cargo may EXPLODE!** • Stop all traffic and clear the area for at least 1600 meters (1 mile) in all directions and let burn. • Do not move cargo or vehicle if cargo has been exposed to heat.

**TIRE or VEHICLE Fire**
- **Use plenty of water - FLOOD it! If water is not available, use CO$_2$, dry chemical or dirt.** • If possible, and WITHOUT RISK, use unmanned hose holders or monitor nozzles from maximum distance to prevent fire from spreading to cargo area. • Pay special attention to tire fires as re-ignition may occur. Stand by with extinguisher ready.

**SPILL OR LEAK**
- ELIMINATE all ignition sources (no smoking, flares, sparks or flames in immediate area). • All equipment used when handling the product must be grounded. • Do not touch or walk through spilled material. • **DO NOT OPERATE RADIO TRANSMITTERS WITHIN 100 meters (330 feet) OF ELECTRIC DETONATORS. • DO NOT CLEAN-UP OR DISPOSE OF, EXCEPT UNDER SUPERVISION OF A SPECIALIST.**

**FIRST AID**
- Move victim to fresh air. • Call 911 or emergency medical service. • Give artificial respiration if victim is not breathing. • Administer oxygen if breathing is difficult. • Remove and isolate contaminated clothing and shoes. • In case of contact with substance, immediately flush skin or eyes with running water for at least 20 minutes. • Ensure that medical personnel are aware of the material(s) involved, and take precautions to protect themselves.

For information on "Compatibility Group" letters, refer to Appendix 3.

Schedule 4

# Guide No. 113 Flammable Solids - Toxic (Wet/Desensitized Explosive)

## POTENTIAL HAZARDS

**FIRE OR EXPLOSION**
- Flammable/combustible material. • May be ignited by heat, sparks or flames. • **DRIED OUT material may explode if exposed to heat, flame, friction or shock; Treat as an explosive (GUIDE 112).** • **Keep material wet with water or treat as an explosive (Guide 112).** • Runoff to sewer may create fire or explosion hazard.

**HEALTH**
- Some are toxic and may be fatal if inhaled, swallowed or absorbed through skin. • Contact may cause burns to skin and eyes. • Fire may produce irritating, corrosive and/or toxic gases. • Runoff from fire control or dilution water may cause pollution.

## PUBLIC SAFETY

- **CALL Emergency Response Telephone Number on Shipping Document first. If Shipping Document not available or no answer, refer to appropriate telephone number listed at the end of this book.** • Isolate spill or leak area immediately for at least 100 meters (330 feet) in all directions. • Keep unauthorized personnel away. • Stay upwind. • Ventilate closed spaces before entering.

**PROTECTIVE CLOTHING**
- Wear positive pressure self-contained breathing apparatus (SCBA). • Structural firefighters' protective clothing will only provide limited protection.

**EVACUATION**

**Large Spill**
- Consider initial evacuation for 500 meters (1/3 mile) in all directions.

**Fire**
- If tank, rail car or tank truck is involved in a fire, ISOLATE for 800 meters (1/2 mile) in all directions; also, consider initial evacuation for 800 meters (1/2 mile) in all directions.

## EMERGENCY RESPONSE

**FIRE**

**CARGO Fire**
- **DO NOT fight fire when fire reaches cargo! Cargo may EXPLODE!** • Stop all traffic and clear the area for at least 800 meters (1/2 mile) in all directions and let burn. • **Do not move cargo or vehicle if cargo has been exposed to heat.**

**TIRE or VEHICLE Fire**
- **Use plenty of water - FLOOD it! If water is not available, use $CO_2$, dry chemical or dirt.** • If possible, and WITHOUT RISK, use unmanned hose holders or monitor nozzles from maximum distance to prevent fire from spreading to cargo area. • Pay special attention to tire fires as re-ignition may occur. Stand by with extinguisher ready.

**SPILL OR LEAK**
- ELIMINATE all ignition sources (no smoking, flares, sparks or flames in immediate area). • All equipment used when handling the product must be grounded. • Do not touch or walk through spilled material.

**Small Spill**
- Flush area with flooding quantities of water.

**Large Spill**
- Wet down with water and dike for later disposal.
- **KEEP "WETTED" PRODUCT WET BY SLOWLY ADDING FLOODING QUANTITIES OF WATER.**

**FIRST AID**
- Move victim to fresh air. • Call 911 or emergency medical service. • Give artificial respiration if victim is not breathing. • Administer oxygen if breathing is difficult. • Remove and isolate contaminated clothing and shoes. • In case of contact with substance, immediately flush skin or eyes with running water for at least 20 minutes. • Ensure that medical personnel are aware of the material(s) involved, and take precautions to protect themselves.

# Guide No. 114    Explosives* - Division 1.4; Class C

## POTENTIAL HAZARDS

| | |
|---|---|
| **FIRE OR EXPLOSION** | • MAY EXPLODE AND THROW FRAGMENTS 500 meters (1/3 MILE) OR MORE IF FIRE REACHES CARGO.<br>• For information on "Compatibility Group" letters, refer to Appendix 3. |
| **HEALTH** | • Fire may produce irritating, corrosive and/or toxic gases. |

## PUBLIC SAFETY

• **CALL Emergency Response Telephone Number on Shipping Document first. If Shipping Document not available or no answer, refer to appropriate telephone number listed at the end of this book.** • Isolate spill or leak area immediately for at least 100 meters (330 feet) in all directions. • Move people out of line of sight of the scene and away from windows. • Keep unauthorized personnel away. • Stay upwind. • Ventilate closed spaces before entering.

| | |
|---|---|
| **PROTECTIVE CLOTHING** | • Wear positive pressure self-contained breathing apparatus (SCBA). • Structural firefighters' protective clothing will only provide limited protection. |
| **EVACUATION** | **Large Spill**<br>• **Consider initial evacuation for 250 meters (800 feet) in all directions.**<br>**Fire**<br>• If rail car or trailer is involved in a fire, ISOLATE for 500 meters (1/3 mile) in all directions; also initiate evacuation including emergency responders for 500 meters (1/3 mile) in all directions.<br>• **For information on "Compatibility Group" letters, refer to Appendix 3.** |

## EMERGENCY RESPONSE

| | |
|---|---|
| **FIRE** | **CARGO Fire**<br>• **DO NOT fight fire when fire reaches cargo! Cargo may EXPLODE!** • Stop all traffic and clear the area for at least 500 meters (1/3 mile) in all directions and let burn. • **Do not move cargo or vehicle if cargo has been exposed to heat.**<br>**TIRE or VEHICLE Fire**<br>• **Use plenty of water - FLOOD it! If water is not available, use $CO_2$, dry chemical or dirt.** • If possible, and WITHOUT RISK, use unmanned hose holders or monitor nozzles from maximum distance to prevent fire from spreading to cargo area. • Pay special attention to tire fires as re-ignition may occur. • Stand by with extinguisher ready. |
| **SPILL OR LEAK** | • ELIMINATE all ignition sources (no smoking, flares, sparks or flames in immediate area). • All equipment used when handling the product must be grounded. • Do not touch or walk through spilled material. • **DO NOT OPERATE RADIO TRANSMITTERS WITHIN 100 meters (330 feet) OF ELECTRIC DETONATORS.** • **DO NOT CLEAN-UP OR DISPOSE OF, EXCEPT UNDER SUPERVISION OF A SPECIALIST.** |
| **FIRST AID** | • Move victim to fresh air. • Call 911 or emergency medical service. • Give artificial respiration if victim is not breathing. **Do not use mouth-to-mouth method if victim ingested or inhaled the substance; give artificial respiration with the aid of a pocket mask equipped with a one-way valve or other proper respiratory medical device.** • Administer oxygen if breathing is difficult. • Remove and isolate contaminated clothing and shoes. • In case of contact with substance, immediately flush skin or eyes with running water for at least 20 minutes. • Shower and wash with soap and water. • Keep victim warm and quiet. • Effects of exposure (inhalation, ingestion or skin contact) to substance may be delayed. • Ensure that medical personnel are aware of the material(s) involved, and take precautions to protect themselves. |

## SUPPLEMENTAL INFORMATION

• Packages bearing the 1.4S label or packages containing material classified as 1.4S are designed or packaged in such a manner that when involved in a fire, may burn vigorously with localized detonations and projection of fragments. • Effects are usually confined to immediate vicinity of packages. • If fire threatens cargo area containing packages bearing the 1.4S label or packages containing material classified as 1.4S, consider isolating at least 15 meters (50 feet) in all directions. Fight fire with normal precautions from a reasonable distance

**For information on "Compatibility Group" letters, refer to Appendix 3.**

Schedule 4

# Guide No. 115   Gases - Flammable (Including Refrigerated Liquids)

## POTENTIAL HAZARDS

| | |
|---|---|
| **FIRE OR EXPLOSION** | • **EXTREMELY FLAMMABLE** • Will be easily ignited by heat, sparks or flames • Will form explosive mixtures with air • Vapors from liquefied gas are initially heavier than air and spread along ground • **CAUTION: Hydrogen (UN1049), Deuterium (UN1957), Hydrogen, refrigerated liquid (UN1966) and Methane (UN1971) are lighter than air and will rise.  Hydrogen and Deuterium fires are difficult to detect since they burn with an invisible flame. Use an alternate method of detection (thermal camera, broom handle, etc.)** • Vapors may travel to source of ignition and flash back • Cylinders exposed to fire may vent and release flammable gas through pressure relief devices • Containers may explode when heated • Ruptured cylinders may rocket. |
| **HEALTH** | • Vapors may cause dizziness or asphyxiation without warning. • Some may be irritating if inhaled at high concentrations. • Contact with gas or liquefied gas may cause burns, severe injury and/or frostbite. • Fire may produce irritating and/or toxic gases. |

## PUBLIC SAFETY

• **CALL Emergency Response Telephone Number on Shipping Document first. If Shipping Document not available or no answer, refer to appropriate telephone number listed at the end of this book.** • As an immediate precautionary measure, isolate spill or leak area for at least 100 meters (330 feet) in all directions. • Keep unauthorized personnel away.• Keep unauthorized personnel away. • Stay upwind. • Many gases are heavier than air and will spread along ground and collect in low or confined areas (sewers, basements, tanks). • Keep out of low areas.

| | |
|---|---|
| **PROTECTIVE CLOTHING** | • Wear positive pressure self-contained breathing apparatus (SCBA). • Structural firefighters' protective clothing will only provide limited protection. • Always wear thermal protective clothing when handling refrigerated/cryogenic liquids. |
| **EVACUATION** | **Large Spill**<br>• Consider initial downwind evacuation for at least 800 meters (1/2 mile).<br>**Fire**<br>• If tank, rail car or tank truck is involved in a fire, ISOLATE for 1600 meters (1 mile) in all directions; also, consider initial evacuation for 1600 meters (1 mile) in all directions. |

## EMERGENCY RESPONSE

| | |
|---|---|
| **FIRE** | • **DO NOT EXTINGUISH A LEAKING GAS FIRE UNLESS LEAK CAN BE STOPPED.** • **CAUTION: Hydrogen (UN1049), Deuterium (UN1957) and Hydrogen, refrigerated liquid (UN1966) burn with an invisible flame.  Hydrogen and Methane mixture, compressed (UN2034) may burn with an invisible flame.**<br>**Small Fire**<br>• Dry chemical or $CO_2$.<br>**Large Fire**<br>• Water spray or fog. • Move containers from fire area if you can do it without risk.<br>**Fire involving Tank**<br>• Fight fire from maximum distance or use unmanned hose holders or monitor nozzles • Cool containers with flooding quantities of water until well after fire is out • Do not direct water at source of leak or safety devices; icing may occur • Withdraw immediately in case of rising sound from venting safety devices or discoloration of tank. • ALWAYS stay away from tanks engulfed in fire • For massive fire, use unmanned hose holders or monitor nozzles; if this is impossible, withdraw from area and let fire burn. |
| **SPILL OR LEAK** | • ELIMINATE all ignition sources (no smoking, flares, sparks or flames in immediate area). • All equipment used when handling the product must be grounded. • Do not touch or walk through spilled material. • Stop leak if you can do it without risk. • If possible, turn leaking containers so that gas escapes rather than liquid. • Use water spray to reduce vapors or divert vapor cloud drift. Avoid allowing water runoff to contact spilled material. • Do not direct water at spill or source of leak. • Prevent spreading of vapors through sewers, ventilation systems and confined areas. • Isolate area until gas has dispersed. **CAUTION: When in contact with refrigerated/cryogenic liquids, many materials become brittle and are likely to break without warning.** |
| **FIRST AID** | • Move victim to fresh air. • Call 911 or emergency medical service. • Give artificial respiration if victim is not breathing. • Administer oxygen if breathing is difficult. • Remove and isolate contaminated clothing and shoes. • Clothing frozen to the skin should be thawed before being removed. • In case of contact with liquefied gas, thaw frosted parts with lukewarm water. • In case of burns, immediately cool affected skin for as long as possible with cold water. • Do not remove clothing if adhering to skin.       • Keep victim warm and quiet. • Ensure that medical personnel are aware of the material(s) involved, and take precautions to protect themselves. |

# Guide No. 116    Gases - Flammable (Unstable)

## POTENTIAL HAZARDS

| | |
|---|---|
| **FIRE OR EXPLOSION** | • **EXTREMELY FLAMMABLE.** • Will be easily ignited by heat, sparks or flames. • Will form explosive mixtures with air. • Silane will ignite spontaneously in air. • Those substances designated with a "**P**" may polymerize explosively when heated or involved in a fire. • Vapors from liquefied gas are initially heavier than air and spread along ground. • Vapors may travel to source of ignition and flash back. • Cylinders exposed to fire may vent and release flammable gas through pressure relief devices. • Containers may explode when heated. • Ruptured cylinders may rocket. |
| **HEALTH** | • Vapors may cause dizziness or asphyxiation without warning. • Some may be toxic if inhaled at high concentrations. • Contact with gas or liquefied gas may cause burns, severe injury and/or frostbite. • Fire may produce irritating and/or toxic gases. |

## PUBLIC SAFETY

• CALL Emergency Response Telephone Number on Shipping Document first. If Shipping Document not available or no answer, refer to appropriate telephone number listed at the end of this book. • As an immediate precautionary measure, isolate spill or leak area immediately for at least 100 meters. • (330 feet) in all directions. • Keep unauthorized personnel away. • Stay upwind. • Many gases are heavier than air and will spread along ground and collect in low or confined areas (sewers, basements, tanks). • Keep out of low areas.

| | |
|---|---|
| **PROTECTIVE CLOTHING** | • Wear positive pressure self-contained breathing apparatus (SCBA). • Structural firefighters' protective clothing will only provide limited protection. |
| **EVACUATION** | **Large Spill**<br>• Consider initial downwind evacuation for at least 800 meters (1/2 mile).<br>**Fire**<br>• If tank, rail car or tank truck is involved in a fire, ISOLATE for 1600 meters (1 mile) in all directions; also, consider initial evacuation for 1600 meters (1 mile) in all directions. |

## EMERGENCY RESPONSE

| | |
|---|---|
| **FIRE** | • **DO NOT EXTINGUISH A LEAKING GAS FIRE UNLESS LEAK CAN BE STOPPED.**<br>**Small Fire**<br>• Dry chemical or $CO_2$.<br>**Large Fire**<br>Water spray or fog. • Move containers from fire area if you can do it without risk.<br>**Fire involving Tanks**<br>• Fight fire from maximum distance or use unmanned hose holders or monitor nozzles. • Cool containers with flooding quantities of water until well after fire is out. • Do not direct water at source of leak or safety devices; icing may occur. • Withdraw immediately in case of rising sound from venting safety devices or discoloration of tank. • ALWAYS stay away from tanks engulfed in fire. • For massive fire, use unmanned hose holders or monitor nozzles; if this is impossible, withdraw from area and let fire burn. |
| **SPILL OR LEAK** | • ELIMINATE all ignition sources (no smoking, flares, sparks or flames in immediate area). • All equipment used when handling the product must be grounded. • Stop leak if you can do it without risk. • Do not touch or walk through spilled material. • Do not direct water at spill or source of leak. • Use water spray to reduce vapors or divert vapor cloud drift. Avoid allowing water runoff to contact spilled material. • If possible, turn leaking containers so that gas escapes rather than liquid. • Prevent entry into waterways, sewers, basements or confined areas. • Isolate area until gas has dispersed. |
| **FIRST AID** | • Move victim to fresh air. • Call 911 or emergency medical service. • Give artificial respiration if victim is not breathing. • Administer oxygen if breathing is difficult. • Remove and isolate contaminated clothing and shoes. • In case of contact with liquefied gas, thaw frosted parts with lukewarm water. • In case of burns, immediately cool affected skin for as long as possible with cold water. • Do not remove clothing if adhering to skin. • Keep victim warm and quiet. • Ensure that medical personnel are aware of the material(s) involved, and take precautions to protect themselves. |

Schedule 4

# Guide No. 117    Gases - Toxic - Flammable (Extreme Hazard)

## POTENTIAL HAZARDS

**HEALTH**
- **TOXIC; Extremely Hazardous.** • May be fatal if inhaled or absorbed through skin. • Initial odor may be irritating or foul and may deaden your sense of smell. • Contact with gas or liquefied gas may cause burns, severe injury and/or frostbite. • Fire will produce irritating, corrosive and/or toxic gases. • Runoff from fire control may cause pollution.

**FIRE OR EXPLOSION**
- These materials are extremely flammable. • May form explosive mixtures with air. • May be ignited by heat, sparks or flames.
- Vapors from liquefied gas are initially heavier than air and spread along ground. • Vapors may travel to source of ignition and flash back. • Runoff may create fire or explosion hazard. • Cylinders exposed to fire may vent and release flammable and toxic gas through pressure relief devices. • Containers may explode when heated. • Ruptured cylinders may rocket.

## PUBLIC SAFETY

- **CALL Emergency Response Telephone Number on Shipping Document first. If Shipping Document not available or no answer, refer to appropriate telephone number listed at the end of this book.** • As an immediate precautionary measure, isolate spill or leak area immediately for at least 100 meters. • Keep unauthorized personnel away. • Stay upwind. • Many gases are heavier than air and will spread along ground and collect in low or confined areas (sewers, basements, tanks). • Keep out of low areas. • Ventilate closed spaces before entering.

**PROTECTIVE CLOTHING**
- Wear positive pressure self-contained breathing apparatus (SCBA). • Wear chemical protective clothing that is specifically recommended by the manufacturer. It may provide little or no thermal protection. • Structural firefighters' protective clothing provides limited protection in fire situations ONLY; it is not effective in spill situations where direct contact with the substance is possible.

**EVACUATION**

**Spill**
- See Table of Initial Isolation and Protective Action Distances in Schedule 6.

**Fire**
- If tank, rail car or tank truck is involved in a fire, ISOLATE for 1600 meters (1 mile) in all directions; also, consider initial evacuation for 1600 meters (1 mile) in all directions.

## EMERGENCY RESPONSE

**FIRE**
- **DO NOT EXTINGUISH A LEAKING GAS FIRE UNLESS LEAK CAN BE STOPPED.**

**Small Fire**
Dry chemical, $CO_2$, water spray or regular foam.

**Large Fire**
- Water spray, fog or regular foam. • Move containers from fire area if you can do it without risk. • Damaged cylinders should be handled only by specialists.

**Fire involving Tanks**
- Fight fire from maximum distance or use unmanned hose holders or monitor nozzles. • Cool containers with flooding quantities of water until well after fire is out. • Do not direct water at source of leak or safety devices; icing may occur. • Withdraw immediately in case of rising sound from venting safety devices or discoloration of tank. • ALWAYS stay away from tanks engulfed in fire.

**SPILL OR LEAK**
- ELIMINATE all ignition sources (no smoking, flares, sparks or flames in immediate area). • All equipment used when handling the product must be grounded. • Fully encapsulating, vapor protective clothing should be worn for spills and leaks with no fire. Do not touch or walk through spilled material. • Stop leak if you can do it without risk. • Use water spray to reduce vapors or divert vapor cloud drift. Avoid allowing water runoff to contact spilled material. • Do not direct water at spill or source of leak. • If possible, turn leaking containers so that gas escapes rather than liquid. • Prevent entry into waterways, sewers, basements or confined areas. Isolate area until gas has dispersed. • Consider igniting spill or leak to eliminate toxic gas concerns.

**FIRST AID**
- Move victim to fresh air. • Call 911 or emergency medical service. • Give artificial respiration if victim is not breathing. • **Do not use mouth-to-mouth method if victim ingested or inhaled the substance; give artificial respiration with the aid of a pocket mask equipped with a one-way valve or other proper respiratory medical device.** • Administer oxygen if breathing is difficult. • Remove and isolate contaminated clothing and shoes. • In case of contact with substance, immediately flush skin or eyes with running water for at least 20 minutes. • In case of contact with liquefied gas, thaw frosted parts with lukewarm water. • In case of burns, immediately cool affected skin for as long as possible with cold water. • Do not remove clothing if adhering to skin. • Keep victim warm and quiet. • Keep victim under observation. • Effects of contact or inhalation may be delayed. • Ensure that medical personnel are aware of the material(s) involved, and take precautions to protect themselves.

# Guide No. 118    *Gases - Flammable - Corrosive*

## POTENTIAL HAZARDS

**FIRE OR EXPLOSION**
- **EXTREMELY FLAMMABLE.** • May be ignited by heat, sparks or flames. • May form explosive mixtures with air. • Vapors from liquefied gas are initially heavier than air and spread along ground. • Vapors may travel to source of ignition and flash back. • Some of these materials may react violently with water. • Cylinders exposed to fire may vent and release flammable gas through pressure relief devices. • Containers may explode when heated. • Ruptured cylinders may rocket.

**HEALTH**
May cause toxic effects if inhaled. • Vapors are extremely irritating. • Contact with gas or liquefied gas may cause burns, severe injury and/or frostbite. • Fire will produce irritating, corrosive and/or toxic gases. • Runoff from fire control may cause pollution.

## PUBLIC SAFETY

- **CALL Emergency Response Telephone Number on Shipping Document first. If Shipping Document not available or no answer, refer to appropriate telephone number listed at the end of this book.** • As an immediate precautionary measure, isolate spill or leak area for at least 100 meters (330 feet) in all directions. • Keep unauthorized personnel away. • Stay upwind. • Many gases are heavier than air and will spread along ground and collect in low or confined areas (sewers, basements, tanks). • Keep out of low areas. • Ventilate closed spaces before entering.

**PROTECTIVE CLOTHING**
- Wear positive pressure self-contained breathing apparatus (SCBA). • Wear chemical protective clothing that is specifically recommended by the manufacturer. It may provide little or no thermal protection. • Structural firefighters' protective clothing provides limited protection in fire situations ONLY; it is not effective in spill situations where direct contact with the substance is possible.

**EVACUATION**
**Large Spill**
- Consider initial downwind evacuation for at least 800 meters (1/2 mile).

**Fire**
- If tank, rail car or tank truck is involved in a fire, ISOLATE for 1600 meters (1 mile) in all directions; also, consider initial evacuation for 1600 meters (1 mile) in all directions.

## EMERGENCY RESPONSE

**FIRE**
- **DO NOT EXTINGUISH A LEAKING GAS FIRE UNLESS LEAK CAN BE STOPPED.**

**Small Fire**
- Dry chemical or $CO_2$.

**Large Fire**
- Water spray, fog or regular foam. • Move containers from fire area if you can do it without risk. • Damaged cylinders should be handled only by specialists.

**Fire involving Tanks**
- Fight fire from maximum distance or use unmanned hose holders or monitor nozzles. • Cool containers with flooding quantities of water until well after fire is out. • Do not direct water at source of leak or safety devices; icing may occur. • Withdraw immediately in case of rising sound from venting safety devices or discoloration of tank. • ALWAYS stay away from tanks engulfed in fire.

**SPILL OR LEAK**
- ELIMINATE all ignition sources (no smoking, flares, sparks or flames in immediate area). • All equipment used when handling the product must be grounded. • Fully encapsulating, vapor protective clothing should be worn for spills and leaks with no fire. • Do not touch or walk through spilled material. • Stop leak if you can do it without risk. • If possible, turn leaking containers so that gas escapes rather than liquid. • Use water spray to reduce vapors or divert vapor cloud drift. Avoid allowing water runoff to contact spilled material. • Do not direct water at spill or source of leak. • Isolate area until gas has dispersed.

**FIRST AID**
- Move victim to fresh air. • Call 911 or emergency medical service. • Give artificial respiration if victim is not breathing. • *Do not use mouth-to-mouth method if victim ingested or inhaled the substance; give artificial respiration with the aid of a pocket mask equipped with a one-way valve or other proper respiratory medical device.* • Administer oxygen if breathing is difficult. • Remove and isolate contaminated clothing and shoes. • In case of contact with liquefied gas, thaw frosted parts with lukewarm water. • In case of burns, immediately cool affected skin for as long as possible with cold water. • Do not remove clothing if adhering to skin. • Keep victim warm and quiet. • Keep victim under observation. • Effects of contact or inhalation may be delayed. • Ensure that medical personnel are aware of the material(s) involved, and take precautions to protect themselves.

# Guide No. 119   Gases - Toxic - Flammable

## POTENTIAL HAZARDS

**HEALTH**
- TOXIC; may be fatal if inhaled or absorbed through skin. • Contact with gas or liquefied gas may cause burns, severe injury and/or frostbite. • Fire will produce irritating, corrosive and/or toxic gases. • Runoff from fire control may cause pollution.

**FIRE OR EXPLOSION**
- Flammable; may be ignited by heat, sparks or flames. • May form explosive mixtures with air. • Those substances designated with a **"P"** may polymerize explosively when heated or involved in a fire. • Vapors from liquefied gas are initially heavier than air and spread along ground. • Vapors may travel to source of ignition and flash back. • Some of these materials may react violently with water. • Cylinders exposed to fire may vent and release toxic and flammable gas through pressure relief devices. • Containers may explode when heated. • Ruptured cylinders may rocket. • Runoff may create fire or explosion hazard.

## PUBLIC SAFETY

- **CALL Emergency Response Telephone Number on Shipping Document first. If Shipping Document not available or no answer, refer to appropriate telephone number listed at the end of this book.** • As an immediate precautionary measure, isolate spill or leak area for at least 100 meters (330 feet) in all directions. • Keep unauthorized personnel away. • Stay upwind. • Many gases are heavier than air and will spread along ground and collect in low or confined areas (sewers, basements, tanks). • Keep out of low areas. • Ventilate closed spaces before entering.

**PROTECTIVE CLOTHING**
- Wear positive pressure self-contained breathing apparatus (SCBA). • Wear chemical protective clothing that is specifically recommended by the manufacturer. It may provide little or no thermal protection. • Structural firefighters' protective clothing provides limited protection in fire situations ONLY; it may not be effective in spill situations where direct contact with the substance is possible.

**EVACUATION**

**Spill**
- See Table of Initial Isolation and Protective Action Distances in Schedule 6 for those dangerous goods marked with a "T" in Schedule 5. For those dangerous goods not marked with a "T" in Schedule 5 increase, as necessary, the minimum isolation distance of 100 meters in the downwind direction.

**Fire**
- If tank, rail car or tank truck is involved in a fire, ISOLATE for 1600 meters (1 mile) in all directions; also, consider initial evacuation for 1600 meters (1 mile) in all directions.

## EMERGENCY RESPONSE

- **DO NOT EXTINGUISH A LEAKING GAS FIRE UNLESS LEAK CAN BE STOPPED.**

**FIRE**

**Small Fire**
- Dry chemical, $CO_2$, water spray or alcohol-resistant foam.

**Large Fire**
- Water spray, fog or alcohol-resistant foam. • **FOR CHLOROSILANES, DO NOT USE WATER;** use AFFF alcohol-resistant medium expansion foam. • Move containers from fire area if you can do it without risk. • Damaged cylinders should be handled only by specialists.

**Fire involving Tanks**
- Fight fire from maximum distance or use unmanned hose holders or monitor nozzles. • Cool containers with flooding quantities of water until well after fire is out. • Do not direct water at source of leak or safety devices; icing may occur. • Withdraw immediately in case of rising sound from venting safety devices or discoloration of tank. • ALWAYS stay away from tanks engulfed in fire.

**SPILL OR LEAK**
- ELIMINATE all ignition sources (no smoking, flares, sparks or flames in immediate area). • All equipment used when handling the product must be grounded. • Fully encapsulating, vapor protective clothing should be worn for spills and leaks with no fire. • Do not touch or walk through spilled material. • Stop leak if you can do it without risk. • Do not direct water at spill or source of leak. • Use water spray to reduce vapors or divert vapor cloud drift. Avoid allowing water runoff to contact spilled material. • **FOR CHLOROSILANES,** use AFFF alcohol-resistant medium expansion foam to reduce vapors. • If possible, turn leaking containers so that gas escapes rather than liquid. • Prevent entry into waterways, sewers, basements or confined areas. • Isolate area until gas has dispersed.

**FIRST AID**
- Move victim to fresh air. • Call 911 or emergency medical service. • Give artificial respiration if victim is not breathing. • **Do not use mouth-to-mouth method if victim ingested or inhaled the substance; give artificial respiration with the aid of a pocket mask equipped with a one-way valve or other proper respiratory medical device.** • Administer oxygen if breathing is difficult. • Remove and isolate contaminated clothing and shoes. • In case of contact with substance, immediately flush skin or eyes with running water for at least 20 minutes. • In case of contact with liquefied gas, thaw frosted parts with lukewarm water. • In case of burns, immediately cool affected skin for as long as possible with cold water. • Do not remove clothing if adhering to skin. • Keep victim warm and quiet. • Keep victim under observation. • Effects of contact or inhalation may be delayed. • Ensure that medical personnel are aware of the material(s) involved, and take precautions to protect themselves.

**Schedule 4**

# Guide No. 120   Gases - Inert (Including Refrigerated Liquids)

## POTENTIAL HAZARDS

**HEALTH**
- Vapors may cause dizziness or asphyxiation without warning. • Vapors from liquefied gas are initially heavier than air and spread along ground. • Contact with gas or liquefied gas may cause burns, severe injury and/or frostbite.

**FIRE OR EXPLOSION**
- **Non-flammable gases.** • Containers may explode when heated. • Ruptured cylinders may rocket.

## PUBLIC SAFETY

- **CALL Emergency Response Telephone Number on Shipping Document first. If Shipping Document not available or no answer, refer to appropriate telephone number listed at the end of this book.** • As an immediate precautionary measure, isolate spill or leak area for at least 100 meters (330 feet) in all directions. • Keep unauthorized personnel away. • Stay upwind. • Many gases are heavier than air and will spread along ground and collect in low or confined areas (sewers, basements, tanks). • Keep out of low areas. • Ventilate closed spaces before entering.

**PROTECTIVE CLOTHING**
- Wear positive pressure self-contained breathing apparatus (SCBA). • Structural firefighters' protective clothing will only provide limited protection. • Always wear thermal protective clothing when handling refrigerated/cryogenic liquids or solids.

**EVACUATION**

**Large Spill**
- Consider initial downwind evacuation for at least 100 meters (330 feet).

**Fire**
- If tank, rail car or tank truck is involved in a fire, ISOLATE for 800 meters (1/2 mile) in all directions; also, consider initial evacuation for 800 meters (1/2 mile) in all directions.

## EMERGENCY RESPONSE

**FIRE**
- Use extinguishing agent suitable for type of surrounding fire. • Move containers from fire area if you can do it without risk. • Damaged cylinders should be handled only by specialists.

**Fire involving Tanks**
- Fight fire from maximum distance or use unmanned hose holders or monitor nozzles. • Cool containers with flooding quantities of water until well after fire is out. • Do not direct water at source of leak or safety devices; icing may occur. • Withdraw immediately in case of rising sound from venting safety devices or discoloration of tank. • ALWAYS stay away from tanks engulfed in fire.

**SPILL OR LEAK**
- Do not touch or walk through spilled material. • Stop leak if you can do it without risk. • Use water spray to reduce vapors or divert vapor cloud drift. Avoid allowing water runoff to contact spilled material. • Do not direct water at spill or source of leak. • If possible, turn leaking containers so that gas escapes rather than liquid. • Prevent entry into waterways, sewers, basements or confined areas. • Allow substance to evaporate. • Ventilate the area. **CAUTION: When in contact with refrigerated/cryogenic liquids, many materials become brittle and are likely to break without warning.**

**FIRST AID**
- Move victim to fresh air. • Call 911 or emergency medical service. • Give artificial respiration if victim is not breathing. •
Administer oxygen if breathing is difficult. • Clothing frozen to the skin should be thawed before being removed. • In case of contact with liquefied gas, thaw frosted parts with lukewarm water • Keep victim warm and quiet. • Ensure that medical personnel are aware of the material(s) involved, and take precautions to protect themselves.

# Guide No. 121  Gases - Inert

## POTENTIAL HAZARDS

**HEALTH**
- Vapors may cause dizziness or asphyxiation without warning. • Vapors from liquefied gas are initially heavier than air and spread along ground.

**FIRE OR EXPLOSION**
- Non-flammable gases. • Containers may explode when heated. • Ruptured cylinders may rocket.

## PUBLIC SAFETY

- **CALL Emergency Response Telephone Number on Shipping Document first. If Shipping Document not available or no answer, refer to appropriate telephone number listed at the end of this book.** • As an immediate precautionary measure, isolate spill or leak area for at least 100 meters (330 feet) in all directions. • Keep unauthorized personnel away. • Stay upwind. • Many gases are heavier than air and will spread along ground and collect in low or confined areas (sewers, basements, tanks). • Keep out of low areas. • Ventilate closed spaces before entering.

**PROTECTIVE CLOTHING**
- Wear positive pressure self-contained breathing apparatus (SCBA). • Structural firefighters' protective clothing will only provide limited protection.

**EVACUATION**

**Large Spill**
- Consider initial downwind evacuation for at least 100 meters (330 feet).

**Fire**
- If tank, rail car or tank truck is involved in a fire, ISOLATE for 800 meters (1/2 mile) in all directions; also, consider initial evacuation for 800 meters (1/2 mile) in all directions.

## EMERGENCY RESPONSE

**FIRE**
- Use extinguishing agent suitable for type of surrounding fire. • Move containers from fire area if you can do it without risk. • Damaged cylinders should be handled only by specialists.

**Fire involving Tanks**
- Fight fire from maximum distance or use unmanned hose holders or monitor nozzles. • Cool containers with flooding quantities of water until well after fire is out. • Do not direct water at source of leak or safety devices; icing may occur. • Withdraw immediately in case of rising sound from venting safety devices or discoloration of tank. • ALWAYS stay away from tanks engulfed in fire.

**SPILL OR LEAK**
- Do not touch or walk through spilled material. • Stop leak if you can do it without risk. • Use water spray to reduce vapors or divert vapor cloud drift. Avoid allowing water runoff to contact spilled material. • Do not direct water at spill or source of leak. • If possible, turn leaking containers so that gas escapes rather than liquid. • Prevent entry into waterways, sewers, basements or confined areas. • Allow substance to evaporate. • Ventilate the area.

**FIRST AID**
- Move victim to fresh air. • Call 911 or emergency medical service. • Give artificial respiration if victim is not breathing. • Administer oxygen if breathing is difficult. • Keep victim warm and quiet. • Ensure that medical personnel are aware of the material(s) involved, and take precautions to protect themselves.

Schedule 4

# Guide No. 122   Gases - Oxidizing (Including Refrigerated Liquids)

## POTENTIAL HAZARDS

**FIRE OR EXPLOSION**
- Substance does not burn but will support combustion. • Some may react explosively with fuels. • May ignite combustibles (wood, paper, oil, clothing, etc.). • Vapors from liquefied gas are initially heavier than air and spread along ground. • Runoff may create fire or explosion hazard. • Containers may explode when heated. • Ruptured cylinders may rocket.

**HEALTH**
- Vapors may cause dizziness or asphyxiation without warning. • Contact with gas or liquefied gas may cause burns, severe injury and/or frostbite. • Fire may produce irritating and/or toxic gases.

## PUBLIC SAFETY

- **CALL Emergency Response Telephone Number on Shipping Document first. If Shipping Document not available or no answer, refer to appropriate telephone number listed at the end of this book.** • As an immediate precautionary measure, isolate spill or leak area for at least 100 meters (330 feet) in all directions. • Keep unauthorized personnel away. • Stay upwind. • Many gases are heavier than air and will spread along ground and collect in low or confined areas (sewers, basements, tanks). • Keep out of low areas. • Ventilate closed spaces before entering.

**PROTECTIVE CLOTHING**
- Wear positive pressure self-contained breathing apparatus (SCBA). • Wear chemical protective clothing that is specifically recommended by the manufacturer. It may provide little or no thermal protection. • Structural firefighters' protective clothing provides limited protection in fire situations ONLY; it is not effective in spill situations where direct contact with the substance is possible. • Always wear thermal protective clothing when handling refrigerated/cryogenic liquids.

**EVACUATION**

**Large Spill**
- Consider initial downwind evacuation for at least 500 meters (1/3 mile).

**Fire**
- If tank, rail car or tank truck is involved in a fire, ISOLATE for 800 meters (1/2 mile) in all directions; also, consider initial evacuation for 800 meters (1/2 mile) in all directions.

## EMERGENCY RESPONSE

**FIRE**
- Use extinguishing agent suitable for type of surrounding fire.

**Small Fire**
- Dry chemical or $CO_2$.

**Large Fire**
- Water spray, fog or regular foam. • Move containers from fire area if you can do it without risk. • Damaged cylinders should be handled only by specialists.

**Fire involving Tanks**
- Fight fire from maximum distance or use unmanned hose holders or monitor nozzles. • Cool containers with flooding quantities of water until well after fire is out. • Do not direct water at source of leak or safety devices; icing may occur. • Withdraw immediately in case of rising sound from venting safety devices or discoloration of tank. • ALWAYS stay away from tanks engulfed in fire. • For massive fire, use unmanned hose holders or monitor nozzles; if this is impossible, withdraw from area and let fire burn.

**SPILL OR LEAK**
- Keep combustibles (wood, paper, oil, etc.) away from spilled material. • Do not touch or walk through spilled material. • Stop leak if you can do it without risk. • If possible, turn leaking containers so that gas escapes rather than liquid. • Do not direct water at spill or source of leak. • Use water spray to reduce vapors or divert vapor cloud drift. Avoid allowing water runoff to contact spilled material. • Prevent entry into waterways, sewers, basements or confined areas. • Allow substance to evaporate. • Isolate area until gas has dispersed. **CAUTION: When in contact with refrigerated/cryogenic liquids, many materials become brittle and are likely to break without warning.**

**FIRST AID**
- Move victim to fresh air. • Call 911 or emergency medical service. • Give artificial respiration if victim is not breathing. • Administer oxygen if breathing is difficult. • Remove and isolate contaminated clothing and shoes. • Clothing frozen to the skin should be thawed before being removed. • In case of contact with liquefied gas, thaw frosted parts with lukewarm water. • Keep victim warm and quiet. • Ensure that medical personnel are aware of the material(s) involved, and take precautions to protect themselves.

Schedule 4

# Guide No. 123  Gases - Toxic and/or Corrosive

## POTENTIAL HAZARDS

**HEALTH**
- TOXIC; may be fatal if inhaled or absorbed through skin. • Vapors may be irritating. • Contact with gas or liquefied gas may cause burns, severe injury and/or frostbite. • Fire will produce irritating, corrosive and/or toxic gases. • Runoff from fire control may cause pollution.

**FIRE OR EXPLOSION**
- Some may burn, but none ignite readily. • Cylinders exposed to fire may vent and release toxic and/or corrosive gas through pressure relief devices. • Vapors from liquefied gas are initially heavier than air and spread along ground. • Containers may explode when heated. • Ruptured cylinders may rocket.

## PUBLIC SAFETY

- CALL Emergency Response Telephone Number on Shipping Document first. If Shipping Document not available or no answer, refer to appropriate telephone number listed at the end of this book. • As an immediate precautionary measure, isolate spill or leak area for at least 100 meters (330 feet) in all directions. • Keep unauthorized personnel away. • Stay upwind. • Many gases are heavier than air and will spread along ground and collect in low or confined areas (sewers, basements, tanks). • Keep out of low areas. • Ventilate closed spaces before entering.

**PROTECTIVE CLOTHING**
- Wear positive pressure self-contained breathing apparatus (SCBA). • Wear chemical protective clothing that is specifically recommended by the manufacturer. It may provide little or no thermal protection. • Structural firefighters' protective clothing provides limited protection in fire situations ONLY; it is not effective in spill situations where direct contact with the substance is possible.

**EVACUATION**

**Spill**
- See Table of Initial Isolation and Protective Action Distances in Schedule 6 for those dangerous goods marked with a "T" in Schedule 5. For those dangerous goods not marked with a "T" in Schedule 5 increase, as necessary, the minimum isolation distance of 100 meters in the downwind direction.

**Fire**
- If tank, rail car or tank truck is involved in a fire, ISOLATE for 800 meters (1/2 mile) in all directions; also, consider initial evacuation for 800 meters (1/2 mile) in all directions.

## EMERGENCY RESPONSE

**FIRE**

**Small Fire**
- Dry chemical or $CO_2$.

**Large Fire**
- Water spray, fog or regular foam. • Do not get water inside containers. • Move containers from fire area if you can do it without risk. • Damaged cylinders should be handled only by specialists.

**Fire involving Tanks**
- Fight fire from maximum distance or use unmanned hose holders or monitor nozzles. • Cool containers with flooding quantities of water until well after fire is out. • Do not direct water at source of leak or safety devices; icing may occur. • Withdraw immediately in case of rising sound from venting safety devices or discoloration of tank. • ALWAYS stay away from tanks engulfed in fire.

**SPILL OR LEAK**
- Fully encapsulating, vapor protective clothing should be worn for spills and leaks with no fire. • Do not touch or walk through spilled material. • Stop leak if you can do it without risk. • If possible, turn leaking containers so that gas escapes rather than liquid. • Prevent entry into waterways, sewers, basements or confined areas. • Use water spray to reduce vapors or divert vapor cloud drift. Avoid allowing water runoff to contact spilled material. • Do not direct water at spill or source of leak. • Isolate area until gas has dispersed.

**FIRST AID**
- Move victim to fresh air. • Call 911 or emergency medical service. • Give artificial respiration if victim is not breathing. • **Do not use mouth-to-mouth method if victim ingested or inhaled the substance; give artificial respiration with the aid of a pocket mask equipped with a one-way valve or other proper respiratory medical device.** • Administer oxygen if breathing is difficult. • Remove and isolate contaminated clothing and shoes. • In case of contact with liquefied gas, thaw frosted parts with lukewarm water. • In case of contact with substance, immediately flush skin or eyes with running water for at least 20 minutes. • Keep victim warm and quiet. • Keep victim under observation. • Effects of contact or inhalation may be delayed. • Ensure that medical personnel are aware of the material(s) involved, and take precautions to protect themselves.

**Schedule 4**

# Guide No. 124  Gases - Toxic and/or Corrosive - Oxidizing

## POTENTIAL HAZARDS

**HEALTH**
- **TOXIC; may be fatal if inhaled or absorbed through skin.** • Fire will produce irritating, corrosive and/or toxic gases. • Contact with gas or liquefied gas may cause burns, severe injury and/or frostbite. • Runoff from fire control may cause pollution.

**FIRE OR EXPLOSION**
- Substance does not burn but will support combustion. • Vapors from liquefied gas are initially heavier than air and spread along ground. • These are strong oxidizers and will react vigorously or explosively with many materials including fuels. • May ignite combustibles (wood, paper, oil, clothing, etc.). • Some will react violently with air, moist air and/or water. • Cylinders exposed to fire may vent and release toxic and/or corrosive gas through pressure relief devices. • Containers may explode when heated. • Ruptured cylinders may rocket.

## PUBLIC SAFETY

- **CALL Emergency Response Telephone Number on Shipping Document first. If Shipping Document not available or no answer, refer to appropriate telephone number listed at the end of this book.** • As an immediate precautionary measure, isolate spill or leak area for at least 100 meters (330 feet) in all directions. • Keep unauthorized personnel away. • Stay upwind. • Many gases are heavier than air and will spread along ground and collect in low or confined areas (sewers, basements, tanks). • Keep out of low areas. • Ventilate closed spaces before entering.

**PROTECTIVE CLOTHING**
- Wear positive pressure self-contained breathing apparatus (SCBA). • Wear chemical protective clothing that is specifically recommended by the manufacturer. It may provide little or no thermal protection. • Structural firefighters' protective clothing provides limited protection in fire situations ONLY; it is not effective in spill situations where direct contact with the substance is possible.

**EVACUATION**

**Spill**
- See Table of Initial Isolation and Protective Action Distances in Schedule 6.

**Fire**
- If tank, rail car or tank truck is involved in a fire, ISOLATE for 800 meters (1/2 mile) in all directions; also, consider initial evacuation for 800 meters (1/2 mile) in all directions.

## EMERGENCY RESPONSE

**FIRE**

**Small Fire**
**Water only; no dry chemical, CO$_2$ or Halon®.**
- Contain fire and let burn. If fire must be fought, water spray or fog is recommended. • Do not get water inside containers. • Move containers from fire area if you can do it without risk. • Damaged cylinders should be handled only by specialists.

**Fire involving Tanks**
- Fight fire from maximum distance or use unmanned hose holders or monitor nozzles. • Cool containers with flooding quantities of water until well after fire is out. • Do not direct water at source of leak or safety devices; icing may occur. • Withdraw immediately in case of rising sound from venting safety devices or discoloration of tank. • ALWAYS stay away from tanks engulfed in fire. • For massive fire, use unmanned hose holders or monitor nozzles; if this is impossible, withdraw from area and let fire burn.

**SPILL OR LEAK**
- Fully encapsulating, vapor protective clothing should be worn for spills and leaks with no fire. • Do not touch or walk through spilled material. • Keep combustibles (wood, paper, oil, etc.) away from spilled material. • Stop leak if you can do it without risk. • Use water spray to reduce vapors or divert vapor cloud drift. Avoid allowing water runoff to contact spilled material. • Do not direct water at spill or source of leak. • If possible, turn leaking containers so that gas escapes rather than liquid. • Prevent entry into waterways, sewers, basements or confined areas. • Isolate area until gas has dispersed. • Ventilate the area.

**FIRST AID**
- Move victim to fresh air. • Call 911 or emergency medical service. • Give artificial respiration if victim is not breathing. • **Do not use mouth-to-mouth method if victim ingested or inhaled the substance; give artificial respiration with the aid of a pocket mask equipped with a one-way valve or other proper respiratory medical device.** • Administer oxygen if breathing is difficult. • Clothing frozen to the skin should be thawed before being removed. • Remove and isolate contaminated clothing and shoes. • In case of contact with substance, immediately flush skin or eyes with running water for at least 20 minutes. • Keep victim warm and quiet. • Keep victim under observation. • Effects of contact or inhalation may be delayed. • Ensure that medical personnel are aware of the material(s) involved, and take precautions to protect themselves.

Schedule 4

# Guide No. 125  Gases - Corrosive

## POTENTIAL HAZARDS

**HEALTH**
- TOXIC; may be fatal if inhaled, ingested or absorbed through skin. • Vapors are extremely irritating and corrosive.
- Contact with gas or liquefied gas may cause burns, severe injury and/or frostbite. • Fire will produce irritating, corrosive and/or toxic gases. • Runoff from fire control may cause pollution.

**FIRE OR EXPLOSION**
- Some may burn, but none ignite readily. • Vapors from liquefied gas are initially heavier than air and spread along ground.
- Some of these materials may react violently with water. • Cylinders exposed to fire may vent and release toxic and/or corrosive gas through pressure relief devices. • Containers may explode when heated. • Ruptured cylinders may rocket.

## PUBLIC SAFETY

- CALL Emergency Response Telephone Number on Shipping Document first. If Shipping Document not available or no answer, refer to appropriate telephone number listed at the end of this book. • As an immediate precautionary measure, isolate spill or leak area for at least 100 meters (330 feet) in all directions. • Keep unauthorized personnel away. • Stay upwind. • Many gases are heavier than air and will spread along ground and collect in low or confined areas (sewers, basements, tanks). • Keep out of low areas. • Ventilate closed spaces before entering.

**PROTECTIVE CLOTHING**
- Wear positive pressure self-contained breathing apparatus (SCBA). • Wear chemical protective clothing that is specifically recommended by the manufacturer. It may provide little or no thermal protection. • Structural firefighters' protective clothing provides limited protection in fire situations ONLY; it is not effective in spill situations where direct contact with the substance is possible.

**EVACUATION**

**Spill**
- See Table of Initial Isolation and Protective Action Distances in Schedule 6 for those dangerous goods marked with a "T" in Schedule 5. For those dangerous goods not marked with a "T" in Schedule 5 increase, as necessary, the minimum isolation distance of 100 meters in the downwind direction.

**Fire**
- If tank, rail car or tank truck is involved in a fire, ISOLATE for 1600 meters (1 mile) in all directions; also, consider initial evacuation for 1600 meters (1 mile) in all directions.

## EMERGENCY RESPONSE

**FIRE**

**Small Fire**
- Dry chemical or $CO_2$.

**Large Fire**
- Water spray, fog or regular foam. • Move containers from fire area if you can do it without risk. • Do not get water inside containers. • Damaged cylinders should be handled only by specialists.

**Fire involving Tanks**
- Fight fire from maximum distance or use unmanned hose holders or monitor nozzles. • Cool containers with flooding quantities of water until well after fire is out. • Do not direct water at source of leak or safety devices; icing may occur. • Withdraw immediately in case of rising sound from venting safety devices or discoloration of tank. • ALWAYS stay away from tanks engulfed in fire.

**SPILL OR LEAK**
- Fully encapsulating, vapor protective clothing should be worn for spills and leaks with no fire. • Do not touch or walk through spilled material. • Stop leak if you can do it without risk. • If possible, turn leaking containers so that gas escapes rather than liquid. • Prevent entry into waterways, sewers, basements or confined areas. • Do not direct water at spill or source of leak. • Use water spray to reduce vapors or divert vapor cloud drift. Avoid allowing water runoff to contact spilled material. • Isolate area until gas has dispersed.

**FIRST AID**
- Move victim to fresh air. • Call 911 or emergency medical service. • Give artificial respiration if victim is not breathing. • **Do not use mouth-to-mouth method if victim ingested or inhaled the substance; give artificial respiration with the aid of a pocket mask equipped with a one-way valve or other proper respiratory medical device.** • Administer oxygen if breathing is difficult. • Remove and isolate contaminated clothing and shoes. • In case of contact with liquefied gas, thaw frosted parts with lukewarm water. • In case of contact with substance, immediately flush skin or eyes with running water for at least 20 minutes. • **In case of contact with Hydrogen fluoride, anhydrous (UN1052)**, flush skin and eyes with water for 5 minutes; then, for skin exposures rub on a calcium/jelly combination; for eyes flush with a water/calcium solution for 15 minutes. • Keep victim warm and quiet. • Keep victim under observation. • Effects of contact or inhalation may be delayed. • Ensure that medical personnel are aware of the material(s) involved, and take precautions to protect themselves.

# Guide No. 126  Gases - Compressed or Liquefied (Including Refrigerant Gases)

| | |
|---|---|
| **FIRE OR EXPLOSION** | • Some may burn, but none ignite readily. • Containers may explode when heated. • Ruptured cylinders may rocket. |
| **HEALTH** | • Vapors may cause dizziness or asphyxiation without warning. • Vapors from liquefied gas are initially heavier than air and spread along ground. • Contact with gas or liquefied gas may cause burns, severe injury and/or frostbite. • Fire may produce irritating, corrosive and/or toxic gases. |

## PUBLIC SAFETY

• **CALL Emergency Response Telephone Number on Shipping Document first. If Shipping Document not available or no answer, refer to appropriate telephone number listed at the end of this book.** • As an immediate precautionary measure, isolate spill or leak area for at least 100 meters (330 feet) in all directions. • Keep unauthorized personnel away. • Stay upwind. • Many gases are heavier than air and will spread along ground and collect in low or confined areas (sewers, basements, tanks). • Keep out of low areas. • Ventilate closed spaces before entering.

| | |
|---|---|
| **PROTECTIVE CLOTHING** | • Wear positive pressure self-contained breathing apparatus (SCBA). • Wear chemical protective clothing that is specifically recommended by the manufacturer. It may provide little or no thermal protection. • Structural firefighters' protective clothing will only provide limited protection. |
| **EVACUATION** | **Large Spill**<br>• Consider initial downwind evacuation for at least 500 meters (1/3 mile).<br>**Fire**<br>• If tank, rail car or tank truck is involved in a fire, ISOLATE for 800 meters (1/2 mile) in all directions; also, consider initial evacuation for 800 meters (1/2 mile) in all directions. |

## EMERGENCY RESPONSE

| | |
|---|---|
| **FIRE** | • Use extinguishing agent suitable for type of surrounding fire.<br>**Small Fire**<br>• Dry chemical or $CO_2$.<br>**Large Fire**<br>• Water spray, fog or regular foam. • Move containers from fire area if you can do it without risk. • Damaged cylinders should be handled only by specialists.<br>**Fire involving Tanks**<br>• Fight fire from maximum distance or use unmanned hose holders or monitor nozzles. • Cool containers with flooding quantities of water until well after fire is out. • Do not direct water at source of leak or safety devices; icing may occur. • Withdraw immediately in case of rising sound from venting safety devices or discoloration of tank. • ALWAYS stay away from tanks engulfed in fire. • Some of these materials, if spilled, may evaporate leaving a flammable residue. |
| **SPILL OR LEAK** | • Do not touch or walk through spilled material. • Stop leak if you can do it without risk. • Do not direct water at spill or source of leak. • Use water spray to reduce vapors or divert vapor cloud drift. Avoid allowing water runoff to contact spilled material.<br>• If possible, turn leaking containers so that gas escapes rather than liquid. • Prevent entry into waterways, sewers, basements or confined areas. • Allow substance to evaporate. • Ventilate the area. |
| **FIRST AID** | • Move victim to fresh air. • Call 911 or emergency medical service. • Give artificial respiration if victim is not breathing.<br>• Administer oxygen if breathing is difficult. • Remove and isolate contaminated clothing and shoes. • In case of contact with liquefied gas, thaw frosted parts with lukewarm water. • Keep victim warm and quiet. • Ensure that medical personnel are aware of the material(s) involved, and take precautions to protect themselves. |

Schedule 4

# Guide No. 127    Flammable Liquids (Polar/Water-Miscible)

## POTENTIAL HAZARDS

**FIRE OR EXPLOSION**

- **HIGHLY FLAMMABLE: Will be easily ignited by heat, sparks or flames.** • Vapors may form explosive mixtures with air. • Vapors may travel to source of ignition and flash back. • Most vapors are heavier than air. They will spread along ground and collect in low or confined areas (sewers, basements, tanks). • Vapor explosion hazard indoors, outdoors or in sewers. • Those substances designated with a "P" may polymerize explosively when heated or involved in a fire. • Runoff to sewer may create fire or explosion hazard. • Containers may explode when heated. • Many liquids are lighter than water.

**HEALTH**

- Inhalation or contact with material may irritate or burn skin and eyes. • Fire may produce irritating, corrosive and/or toxic gases. • Vapors may cause dizziness or suffocation. • Runoff from fire control may cause pollution.

## PUBLIC SAFETY

- **CALL Emergency Response Telephone Number on Shipping Document first. If Shipping Document not available or no answer, refer to appropriate telephone number listed at the end of this book.** • As an immediate precautionary measure, isolate spill or leak area for at least 50 meters (150 feet) in all directions. • Keep unauthorized personnel away. • Stay upwind. • Keep out of low areas. • Ventilate closed spaces before entering.

**PROTECTIVE CLOTHING**

- Wear positive pressure self-contained breathing apparatus (SCBA). • Structural firefighters' protective clothing will only provide limited protection.

**EVACUATION**

**Large Spill**
- Consider initial downwind evacuation for at least 300 meters (1000 feet).

**Fire**
- If tank, rail car or tank truck is involved in a fire, ISOLATE for 800 meters (1/2 mile) in all directions; also, consider initial evacuation for 800 meters (1/2 mile) in all directions.

## EMERGENCY RESPONSE

**FIRE**

**CAUTION: All these products have a very low flash point: Use of water spray when fighting fire may be inefficient.**

**Small Fire**
- Dry chemical, $CO_2$, water spray or alcohol-resistant foam.

**Large Fire**
- Water spray, fog or alcohol-resistant foam. • Use water spray or fog; do not use straight streams. • Move containers from fire area if you can do it without risk.

**Fire involving Tanks or Car/Trailer Loads**
- Fight fire from maximum distance or use unmanned hose holders or monitor nozzles. • Cool containers with flooding quantities of water until well after fire is out. • Withdraw immediately in case of rising sound from venting safety devices or discoloration of tank. • ALWAYS stay away from tanks engulfed in fire. • For massive fire, use unmanned hose holders or monitor nozzles; if this is impossible, withdraw from area and let fire burn.

**SPILL OR LEAK**

- ELIMINATE all ignition sources (no smoking, flares, sparks or flames in immediate area). • All equipment used when handling the product must be grounded. • Do not touch or walk through spilled material. • Stop leak if you can do it without risk. • Prevent entry into waterways, sewers, basements or confined areas. • A vapor suppressing foam may be used to reduce vapors. • Absorb or cover with dry earth, sand or other non-combustible material and transfer to containers. • Use clean non-sparking tools to collect absorbed material.

**Large Spill**
- Dike far ahead of liquid spill for later disposal. • Water spray may reduce vapor; but may not prevent ignition in closed spaces.

**FIRST AID**

- Move victim to fresh air. • Call 911 or emergency medical service. • Give artificial respiration if victim is not breathing. • Administer oxygen if breathing is difficult. • Remove and isolate contaminated clothing and shoes. • In case of contact with substance, immediately flush skin or eyes with running water for at least 20 minutes. • Wash skin with soap and water. • In case of burns, immediately cool affected skin for as long as possible with cold water. • Do not remove clothing if adhering to skin. • Keep victim warm and quiet. • Ensure that medical personnel are aware of the material(s) involved, and take precautions to protect themselves.

# Guide No. 128   Flammable Liquids (Non-Polar/Water-Immiscible)

## POTENTIAL HAZARDS

**FIRE OR EXPLOSION**

- **HIGHLY FLAMMABLE: Will be easily ignited by heat, sparks or flames.** • Vapors may form explosive mixtures with air. • Vapors may travel to source of ignition and flash back. • Most vapors are heavier than air. They will spread along ground and collect in low or confined areas (sewers, basements, tanks). • Vapor explosion hazard indoors, outdoors or in sewers. • Those substances designated with a **"P"** may polymerize explosively when heated or involved in a fire. • Runoff to sewer may create fire or explosion hazard. • Containers may explode when heated. • Many liquids are lighter than water. • Substance may be transported hot. • **If molten aluminum is involved, refer to GUIDE 169.**

**HEALTH**

- Inhalation or contact with material may irritate or burn skin and eyes. • Fire may produce irritating, corrosive and/or toxic gases. • Vapors may cause dizziness or suffocation. • Runoff from fire control or dilution water may cause pollution.

## PUBLIC SAFETY

- **CALL Emergency Response Telephone Number on Shipping Document first. If Shipping Document not available or no answer, refer to appropriate telephone number listed at the end of this book.** • As an immediate precautionary measure, isolate spill or leak area for at least 50 meters (150 feet) in all directions. • Keep unauthorized personnel away. • Stay upwind. • Keep out of low areas. • Ventilate closed spaces before entering.

**PROTECTIVE CLOTHING**

- Wear positive pressure self-contained breathing apparatus (SCBA). • Structural firefighters' protective clothing will only provide limited protection.

**EVACUATION**

**Large Spill**
- Consider initial downwind evacuation for at least 300 meters (1000 feet).

**Fire**
- If tank, rail car or tank truck is involved in a fire, ISOLATE for 800 meters (1/2 mile) in all directions; also, consider initial evacuation for 800 meters (1/2 mile) in all directions.

## EMERGENCY RESPONSE

**FIRE**

CAUTION: All these products have a very low flash point: Use of water spray when fighting fire may be inefficient.
CAUTION: For mixtures containing alcohol or polar solvent, alcohol-resistant foam may be more effective
**Small Fire**
- Dry chemical, $CO_2$, water spray or regular foam.
**Large Fire**
- Water spray, fog or regular foam. • Use water spray or fog; do not use straight streams. • Move containers from fire area if you can do it without risk.
**Fire involving Tanks or Car/Trailer Loads**
- Fight fire from maximum distance or use unmanned hose holders or monitor nozzles. • Cool containers with flooding quantities of water until well after fire is out. • Withdraw immediately in case of rising sound from venting safety devices or discoloration of tank. • ALWAYS stay away from tanks engulfed in fire. • For massive fire, use unmanned hose holders or monitor nozzles; if this is impossible, withdraw from area and let fire burn.

**SPILL OR LEAK**

- ELIMINATE all ignition sources (no smoking, flares, sparks or flames in immediate area). • All equipment used when handling the product must be grounded. • Do not touch or walk through spilled material. • Stop leak if you can do it without risk. • Prevent entry into waterways, sewers, basements or confined areas. • A vapor suppressing foam may be used to reduce vapors. • Absorb or cover with dry earth, sand or other non-combustible material and transfer to containers. • Use clean non-sparking tools to collect absorbed material.
**Large Spill**
- Dike far ahead of liquid spill for later disposal. • Water spray may reduce vapor; but may not prevent ignition in closed spaces.

**FIRST AID**

- Move victim to fresh air. • Call 911 or emergency medical service. • Give artificial respiration if victim is not breathing. • Administer oxygen if breathing is difficult. • Remove and isolate contaminated clothing and shoes. • In case of contact with substance, immediately flush skin or eyes with running water for at least 20 minutes. • Wash skin with soap and water. • Keep victim warm and quiet. • Ensure that medical personnel are aware of the material(s) involved, and take precautions to protect themselves.

# Guide No. 129  Flammable Liquids (Polar/Water-Miscible/Noxious)

## POTENTIAL HAZARDS

**FIRE OR EXPLOSION**
- **HIGHLY FLAMMABLE: Will be easily ignited by heat, sparks or flames.** • Vapors may form explosive mixtures with air. • Vapors may travel to source of ignition and flash back. • Most vapors are heavier than air. They will spread along ground and collect in low or confined areas (sewers, basements, tanks). • Vapor explosion hazard indoors, outdoors or in sewers. • Those substances designated with a "P" may polymerize explosively when heated or involved in a fire. • Runoff to sewer may create fire or explosion hazard. • Containers may explode when heated. • Many liquids are lighter than water.

**HEALTH**
- May cause toxic effects if inhaled or absorbed through skin. • Inhalation or contact with material may irritate or burn skin and eyes. • Fire will produce irritating, corrosive and/or toxic gases. • Vapors may cause dizziness or suffocation. • Runoff from fire control or dilution water may cause pollution.

## PUBLIC SAFETY

- **CALL Emergency Response Telephone Number on Shipping Document first. If Shipping Document not available or no answer, refer to appropriate telephone number listed at the end of this book.** • As an immediate precautionary measure, isolate spill or leak area for at least 50 meters (150 feet) in all directions. • Keep unauthorized personnel away. • Stay upwind. • Keep out of low areas. • Ventilate closed spaces before entering.

**PROTECTIVE CLOTHING**
- Wear positive pressure self-contained breathing apparatus (SCBA). • Structural firefighters' protective clothing will only provide limited protection.

**EVACUATION**
**Large Spill**
- Consider initial downwind evacuation for at least 300 meters (1000 feet).
**Fire**
- If tank, rail car or tank truck is involved in a fire, ISOLATE for 800 meters (1/2 mile) in all directions; also, consider initial evacuation for 800 meters (1/2 mile) in all directions.

## EMERGENCY RESPONSE

**FIRE**
CAUTION: All these products have a very low flash point: Use of water spray when fighting fire may be inefficient.
**Small Fire**
- Dry chemical, $CO_2$, water spray or alcohol-resistant foam. • **Do not use dry chemical extinguishers to control fires involving nitromethane or nitroethane.**
**Large Fire**
- Water spray, fog or alcohol-resistant foam. • **Do not use straight streams.** • Move containers from fire area if you can do it without risk.
**Fire involving Tanks or Car/Trailer Loads**
- Fight fire from maximum distance or use unmanned hose holders or monitor nozzles. • Cool containers with flooding quantities of water until well after fire is out. • Withdraw immediately in case of rising sound from venting safety devices or discoloration of tank. • ALWAYS stay away from tanks engulfed in fire. • For massive fire, use unmanned hose holders or monitor nozzles; if this is impossible, withdraw from area and let fire burn.

**SPILL OR LEAK**
- ELIMINATE all ignition sources (no smoking, flares, sparks or flames in immediate area). • All equipment used when handling the product must be grounded. • Do not touch or walk through spilled material. • Stop leak if you can do it without risk. • Prevent entry into waterways, sewers, basements or confined areas. • A vapor suppressing foam may be used to reduce vapors. • Absorb or cover with dry earth, sand or other non-combustible material and transfer to containers. • Use clean non-sparking tools to collect absorbed material.
**Large Spill**
- Dike far ahead of liquid spill for later disposal. • Water spray may reduce vapor; but may not prevent ignition in closed spaces.

**FIRST AID**
- Move victim to fresh air. • Call 911 or emergency medical service. • Give artificial respiration if victim is not breathing. • Administer oxygen if breathing is difficult. • Remove and isolate contaminated clothing and shoes. • In case of contact with substance, immediately flush skin or eyes with running water for at least 20 minutes. • Wash skin with soap and water. • Keep victim warm and quiet. • In case of burns, immediately cool affected skin for as long as possible with cold water. • Do not remove clothing if adhering to skin. • Effects of exposure (inhalation, ingestion or skin contact) to substance may be delayed. • Ensure that medical personnel are aware of the material(s) involved, and take precautions to protect themselves.

Schedule 4

# Guide No. 130 Flammable Liquids (Non-Polar/Water-Immiscible/Noxious)

## POTENTIAL HAZARDS

**FIRE OR EXPLOSION**
- **HIGHLY FLAMMABLE: Will be easily ignited by heat, sparks or flames.** • Vapors may form explosive mixtures with air. • Vapors may travel to source of ignition and flash back. • Most vapors are heavier than air. They will spread along ground and collect in low or confined areas (sewers, basements, tanks). • Vapor explosion hazard indoors, outdoors or in sewers. • Those substances designated with a **"P"** may polymerize explosively when heated or involved in a fire. • Runoff to sewer may create fire or explosion hazard. • Containers may explode when heated. • Many liquids are lighter than water.

**HEALTH**
- May cause toxic effects if inhaled or absorbed through skin. • Inhalation or contact with material may irritate or burn skin and eyes. • Fire will produce irritating, corrosive and/or toxic gases. • Vapors may cause dizziness or suffocation. • Runoff from fire control or dilution water may cause pollution.

## PUBLIC SAFETY

- **CALL Emergency Response Telephone Number on Shipping Document first. If Shipping Document not available or no answer, refer to appropriate telephone number listed at the end of this book.** • As an immediate precautionary measure, isolate spill or leak area for at least 50 meters (150 feet) in all directions. • Keep unauthorized personnel away. • Stay upwind. • Keep out of low areas. • Ventilate closed spaces before entering.

**PROTECTIVE CLOTHING**
- Wear positive pressure self-contained breathing apparatus (SCBA). • Structural firefighters' protective clothing will only provide limited protection.

**EVACUATION**

**Large Spill**
- Consider initial downwind evacuation for at least 300 meters (1000 feet).

**Fire**
- If tank, rail car or tank truck is involved in a fire, ISOLATE for 800 meters (1/2 mile) in all directions; also, consider initial evacuation for 800 meters (1/2 mile) in all directions.

## EMERGENCY RESPONSE

**FIRE**

CAUTION: All these products have a very low flash point: Use of water spray when fighting fire may be inefficient.

**Small Fire**
- Dry chemical, $CO_2$, water spray or regular foam.

**Large Fire**
- Water spray, fog or regular foam. • **Do not use straight streams.** • Move containers from fire area if you can do it without risk.

**Fire involving Tanks or Car/Trailer Loads**
- Fight fire from maximum distance or use unmanned hose holders or monitor nozzles. • Cool containers with flooding quantities of water until well after fire is out. • Withdraw immediately in case of rising sound from venting safety devices or discoloration of tank. • ALWAYS stay away from tanks engulfed in fire. • For massive fire, use unmanned hose holders or monitor nozzles; if this is impossible, withdraw from area and let fire burn.

**SPILL OR LEAK**
- ELIMINATE all ignition sources (no smoking, flares, sparks or flames in immediate area). • All equipment used when handling the product must be grounded. • Do not touch or walk through spilled material. • Stop leak if you can do it without risk. • Prevent entry into waterways, sewers, basements or confined areas. • A vapor suppressing foam may be used to reduce vapors. • Absorb or cover with dry earth, sand or other non-combustible material and transfer to containers. • Use clean non-sparking tools to collect absorbed material.

**Large Spill**
- Dike far ahead of liquid spill for later disposal. • Water spray may reduce vapor; but may not prevent ignition in closed spaces.

**FIRST AID**
- Move victim to fresh air. • Call 911 or emergency medical service. • Give artificial respiration if victim is not breathing. • Administer oxygen if breathing is difficult. • Remove and isolate contaminated clothing and shoes. • In case of contact with substance, immediately flush skin or eyes with running water for at least 20 minutes. • Wash skin with soap and water. • Keep victim warm and quiet. • In case of burns, immediately cool affected skin for as long as possible with cold water. • Do not remove clothing if adhering to skin. • Effects of exposure (inhalation, ingestion or skin contact) to substance may be delayed. • Ensure that medical personnel are aware of the material(s) involved, and take precautions to protect themselves.

Schedule 4

# Guide No. 131  Flammable Liquids – Toxic

## POTENTIAL HAZARDS

**HEALTH**

- **TOXIC; may be fatal if inhaled, ingested or absorbed through skin.** • Inhalation or contact with some of these materials will irritate or burn skin and eyes. • Fire will produce irritating, corrosive and/or toxic gases. • Vapors may cause dizziness or suffocation. • Runoff from fire control or dilution water may cause pollution.

**FIRE OR EXPLOSION**

- **HIGHLY FLAMMABLE: Will be easily ignited by heat, sparks or flames.** • Vapors may form explosive mixtures with air. • Vapors may travel to source of ignition and flash back. • Most vapors are heavier than air. They will spread along ground and collect in low or confined areas (sewers, basements, tanks). • Vapor explosion and poison hazard indoors, outdoors or in sewers. • Those substances designated with a **"P"** may polymerize explosively when heated or involved in a fire. • Runoff to sewer may create fire or explosion hazard. • Containers may explode when heated. • Many liquids are lighter than water.

## PUBLIC SAFETY

- **CALL Emergency Response Telephone Number on Shipping Document first. If Shipping Document not available or no answer, refer to appropriate telephone number listed at the end of this book.** • As an immediate precautionary measure, isolate spill or leak area for at least 50 meters (150 feet) in all directions. • Keep unauthorized personnel away. • Stay upwind. • Keep out of low areas. • Ventilate closed spaces before entering.

**PROTECTIVE CLOTHING**

- Wear positive pressure self-contained breathing apparatus (SCBA). • Wear chemical protective clothing that is specifically recommended by the manufacturer. It may provide little or no thermal protection. • Structural firefighters' protective clothing provides limited protection in fire situations ONLY; it is not effective in spill situations where direct contact with the substance is possible.

**EVACUATION**

**Spill**

- See Table of Initial Isolation and Protective Action Distances in Schedule 6 for those dangerous goods marked with a "T" in Schedule 5. For those dangerous goods not marked with a "T" in Schedule 5 increase, as necessary, the minimum isolation distance of 50 meters in the downwind direction.

**Fire**

- If tank, rail car or tank truck is involved in a fire, ISOLATE for 800 meters (1/2 mile) in all directions; also, consider initial evacuation for 800 meters (1/2 mile) in all directions.

## EMERGENCY RESPONSE

**FIRE**

**CAUTION: All these products have a very low flash point: Use of water spray when fighting fire may be inefficient.**

**Small Fire**

- Dry chemical, $CO_2$, water spray or alcohol-resistant foam.

**Large Fire**

- Water spray, fog or alcohol-resistant foam. • Move containers from fire area if you can do it without risk. • Dike fire control water for later disposal; do not scatter the material. • Use water spray or fog; do not use straight streams.

**Fire involving Tanks or Car/Trailer Loads**

- Fight fire from maximum distance or use unmanned hose holders or monitor nozzles. • Cool containers with flooding quantities of water until well after fire is out. • Withdraw immediately in case of rising sound from venting safety devices or discoloration of tank. • ALWAYS stay away from tanks engulfed in fire. • For massive fire, use unmanned hose holders or monitor nozzles; if this is impossible, withdraw from area and let fire burn.

**SPILL OR LEAK**

- Fully encapsulating, vapor protective clothing should be worn for spills and leaks with no fire. • ELIMINATE all ignition sources (no smoking, flares, sparks or flames in immediate area). • All equipment used when handling the product must be grounded.
- Do not touch or walk through spilled material. • Stop leak if you can do it without risk. • Prevent entry into waterways, sewers, basements or confined areas. • A vapor suppressing foam may be used to reduce vapors.

**Small Spill**

- Absorb with earth, sand or other non-combustible material and transfer to containers for later disposal. • Use clean non-sparking tools to collect absorbed material.

**Large Spill**

- Dike far ahead of liquid spill for later disposal. • Water spray may reduce vapor; but may not prevent ignition in closed spaces.

**FIRST AID**

- Move victim to fresh air. • Call 911 or emergency medical service. • Give artificial respiration if victim is not breathing. • **Do not use mouth-to-mouth method if victim ingested or inhaled the substance; give artificial respiration with the aid of a pocket mask equipped with a one-way valve or other proper respiratory medical device.** • Administer oxygen if breathing is difficult. • Remove and isolate contaminated clothing and shoes. • In case of contact with substance, immediately flush skin or eyes with running water for at least 20 minutes. • Wash skin with soap and water. • Keep victim warm and quiet. • In case of burns, immediately cool affected skin for as long as possible with cold water. • Do not remove clothing if adhering to skin. • Effects of exposure (inhalation, ingestion or skin contact) to substance may be delayed. • Ensure that medical personnel are aware of the material(s) involved, and take precautions to protect themselves.

# Guide No. 132    Flammable Liquids - Corrosive

## POTENTIAL HAZARDS

| | |
|---|---|
| **FIRE OR EXPLOSION** | • **Flammable/combustible material.** • May be ignited by heat, sparks or flames. • Vapors may form explosive mixtures with air. • Vapors may travel to source of ignition and flash back. • Most vapors are heavier than air. They will spread along ground and collect in low or confined areas (sewers, basements, tanks). • Vapor explosion hazard indoors, outdoors or in sewers. • Those substances designated with a **"P"** may polymerize explosively when heated or involved in a fire. • Runoff to sewer may create fire or explosion hazard. • Containers may explode when heated. • Many liquids are lighter than water. |
| **HEALTH** | • May cause toxic effects if inhaled or ingested/swallowed. • Contact with substance may cause severe burns to skin and eyes. • Fire will produce irritating, corrosive and/or toxic gases. • Vapors may cause dizziness or suffocation. • Runoff from fire control or dilution water may cause pollution. |

## PUBLIC SAFETY

• CALL Emergency Response Telephone Number on Shipping Document first. If Shipping Document not available or no answer, refer to appropriate telephone number listed at the end of this book. • As an immediate precautionary measure, isolate spill or leak area for at least 50 meters (150 feet) in all directions.• Keep unauthorized personnel away. • Stay upwind. • Keep out of low areas. • Ventilate closed spaces before entering.

| | |
|---|---|
| **PROTECTIVE CLOTHING** | • Wear positive pressure self-contained breathing apparatus (SCBA). • Wear chemical protective clothing that is specifically recommended by the manufacturer. It may provide little or no thermal protection. • Structural firefighters' protective clothing provides limited protection in fire situations ONLY; it is not effective in spill situations where direct contact with the substance is possible. |
| **EVACUATION** | **Large Spill**<br>• See Table of Initial Isolation and Protective Action Distances in Schedule 6 for those dangerous goods marked with a "T" in Schedule 5. For those dangerous goods not marked with a "T" in Schedule 5 increase, as necessary, the minimum isolation distance of 50 meters in the downwind direction.<br>**Fire**<br>• If tank, rail car or tank truck is involved in a fire, ISOLATE for 800 meters (1/2 mile) in all directions; also, consider initial evacuation for 800 meters (1/2 mile) in all directions. |

## EMERGENCY RESPONSE

| | |
|---|---|
| **FIRE** | • **Some of these materials may react violently with water.**<br>**Small Fire**<br>• Dry chemical, $CO_2$, water spray or alcohol-resistant foam.<br>**Large Fire**<br>• Water spray, fog or alcohol-resistant foam. • Move containers from fire area if you can do it without risk. • Dike fire control water for later disposal; do not scatter the material. • Do not get water inside containers.<br>**Fire involving Tanks or Car/Trailer Loads**<br>• Fight fire from maximum distance or use unmanned hose holders or monitor nozzles. • Cool containers with flooding quantities of water until well after fire is out. • Withdraw immediately in case of rising sound from venting safety devices or discoloration of tank. • ALWAYS stay away from tanks engulfed in fire. • For massive fire, use unmanned hose holders or monitor nozzles; if this is impossible, withdraw from area and let fire burn. |
| **SPILL OR LEAK** | • Fully encapsulating, vapor protective clothing should be worn for spills and leaks with no fire. • ELIMINATE all ignition sources (no smoking, flares, sparks or flames in immediate area). • All equipment used when handling the product must be grounded.<br>• Do not touch or walk through spilled material. • Stop leak if you can do it without risk. • Prevent entry into waterways, sewers, basements or confined areas. • A vapor suppressing foam may be used to reduce vapors. • Absorb with earth, sand or other non-combustible material and transfer to containers (except for Hydrazine). • Use clean non-sparking tools to collect absorbed material.<br>**Large Spill**<br>• Dike far ahead of liquid spill for later disposal. • Water spray may reduce vapor; but may not prevent ignition in closed spaces. |
| **FIRST AID** | • Move victim to fresh air. • Call 911 or emergency medical service. • Give artificial respiration if victim is not breathing. • **Do not use mouth-to-mouth method if victim ingested or inhaled the substance; give artificial respiration with the aid of a pocket mask equipped with a one-way valve or other proper respiratory medical device.** • Administer oxygen if breathing is difficult. • Remove and isolate contaminated clothing and shoes. • In case of contact with substance, immediately flush skin or eyes with running water for at least 20 minutes. • In case of burns, immediately cool affected skin for as long as possible with cold water. • Do not remove clothing if adhering to skin. • Keep victim warm and quiet. • Effects of exposure (inhalation, ingestion or skin contact) to substance may be delayed. • Ensure that medical personnel are aware of the material(s) involved, and take precautions to protect themselves. |

Schedule 4

# Guide No. 133    Flammable Solids

## POTENTIAL HAZARDS

**FIRE OR EXPLOSION**
- Flammable/combustible material. • May be ignited by friction, heat, sparks or flames. • Some may burn rapidly with flare burning effect. • Powders, dusts, shavings, borings, turnings or cuttings may explode or burn with explosive violence. • Substance may be transported in a molten form at a temperature that may be above its flash point. • May re-ignite after fire is extinguished.

**HEALTH**
- Fire may produce irritating and/or toxic gases. • Contact may cause burns to skin and eyes. • Contact with molten substance may cause severe burns to skin and eyes. • Runoff from fire control may cause pollution.

## PUBLIC SAFETY

- CALL Emergency Response Telephone Number on Shipping Document first. If Shipping Document not available or no answer, refer to appropriate telephone number listed at the end of this book. • As an immediate precautionary measure, isolate spill or leak area for at least 25 meters (75 feet) in all directions. • Keep unauthorized personnel away. • Stay upwind. • Keep out of low areas.

**PROTECTIVE CLOTHING**
- Wear positive pressure self-contained breathing apparatus (SCBA). • Structural firefighters' protective clothing will only provide limited protection.

**EVACUATION**
**Large Spill**
- Consider initial downwind evacuation for at least 100 meters (330 feet).
**Fire**
- If tank, rail car or tank truck is involved in a fire, ISOLATE for 800 meters (1/2 mile) in all directions; also, consider initial evacuation for 800 meters (1/2 mile) in all directions.

## EMERGENCY RESPONSE

**FIRE**
**Small Fire**
- Dry chemical, $CO_2$, sand, earth, water spray or regular foam.
**Large Fire**
- Water spray, fog or regular foam. • Move containers from fire area if you can do it without risk.
**Fire Involving Metal Pigments or Pastes (e.g. "Aluminum Paste")**
- Aluminum Paste fires should be treated as a combustible metal fire. Use DRY sand, graphite powder, dry sodium chloride based extinguishers, G-1® or Met-L-X® powder. Also, see GUIDE 170
**Fire involving Tanks or Car/Trailer Loads**
- Cool containers with flooding quantities of water until well after fire is out. • For massive fire, use unmanned hose holders or monitor nozzles; if this is impossible, withdraw from area and let fire burn. • Withdraw immediately in case of rising sound from venting safety devices or discoloration of tank. • ALWAYS stay away from tanks engulfed in fire.

**SPILL OR LEAK**
- ELIMINATE all ignition sources (no smoking, flares, sparks or flames in immediate area). • Do not touch or walk through spilled material.
**Small Dry Spill**
- With clean shovel place material into clean, dry container and cover loosely; move containers from spill area.
**Large Spill**
- Wet down with water and dike for later disposal. • Prevent entry into waterways, sewers, basements or confined areas.

**FIRST AID**
- Move victim to fresh air. • Call 911 or emergency medical service. • Give artificial respiration if victim is not breathing. • Administer oxygen if breathing is difficult. • Remove and isolate contaminated clothing and shoes. • In case of contact with substance, immediately flush skin or eyes with running water for at least 20 minutes. • Removal of solidified molten material from skin requires medical assistance. • Keep victim warm and quiet. • Ensure that medical personnel are aware of the material(s) involved, and take precautions to protect themselves.

# Guide No. 134   Flammable Solids - Toxic and/or Corrosive

## POTENTIAL HAZARDS

| | |
|---|---|
| **FIRE OR EXPLOSION** | • Flammable/combustible material. • May be ignited by heat, sparks or flames. • When heated, vapors may form explosive mixtures with air: indoors, outdoors, and sewers explosion hazards. • Contact with metals may evolve flammable hydrogen gas. • Containers may explode when heated. |
| **HEALTH** | • **TOXIC; inhalation, ingestion, or skin contact with material may cause severe injury or death.** • Fire will produce irritating, corrosive and/or toxic gases. • Runoff from fire control or dilution water may be corrosive and/or toxic and cause pollution. |

## PUBLIC SAFETY

• **CALL Emergency Response Telephone Number on Shipping Document first. If Shipping Document not available or no answer, refer to appropriate telephone number listed at the end of this book.** • As an immediate precautionary measure, isolate spill or leak area for at least 25 meters (75 feet) in all directions. • Stay upwind. • Keep unauthorized personnel away. • Keep out of low areas. • Ventilate enclosed areas.

| | |
|---|---|
| **PROTECTIVE CLOTHING** | • Wear positive pressure self-contained breathing apparatus (SCBA). • Wear chemical protective clothing that is specifically recommended by the manufacturer. It may provide little or no thermal protection. • Structural firefighters' protective clothing provides limited protection in fire situations ONLY; it is not effective in spill situations where direct contact with the substance is possible. |
| **EVACUATION** | **Large Spill**<br>• Consider initial downwind evacuation for at least 100 meters (330 feet).<br>**Fire**<br>• If tank, rail car or tank truck is involved in a fire, ISOLATE for 800 meters (1/2 mile) in all directions; also, consider initial evacuation for 800 meters (1/2 mile) in all directions. |

## EMERGENCY RESPONSE

| | |
|---|---|
| **FIRE** | **Small Fire**<br>• Dry chemical, $CO_2$, water spray or alcohol-resistant foam.<br>**Large Fire**<br>• Water spray, fog or alcohol-resistant foam. • Move containers from fire area if you can do it without risk. • Use water spray or fog; do not use straight streams. • Do not get water inside containers. • Dike fire control water for later disposal; do not scatter the material.<br>**Fire involving Tanks or Car/Trailer Loads**<br>• Fight fire from maximum distance or use unmanned hose holders or monitor nozzles. • Cool containers with flooding quantities of water until well after fire is out. • Withdraw immediately in case of rising sound from venting safety devices or discoloration of tank. • ALWAYS stay away from tanks engulfed in fire. |
| **SPILL OR LEAK** | • Fully encapsulating, vapor protective clothing should be worn for spills and leaks with no fire. • ELIMINATE all ignition sources (no smoking, flares, sparks or flames in immediate area). • Stop leak if you can do it without risk. • Do not touch damaged containers or spilled material unless wearing appropriate protective clothing. • Prevent entry into waterways, sewers, basements or confined areas. • Use clean non-sparking tools to collect material and place it into loosely covered plastic containers for later disposal. |
| **FIRST AID** | • Move victim to fresh air. • Call 911 or emergency medical service. • Give artificial respiration if victim is not breathing. • **Do not use mouth-to-mouth method if victim ingested or inhaled the substance; give artificial respiration with the aid of a pocket mask equipped with a one-way valve or other proper respiratory medical device.** • Administer oxygen if breathing is difficult. • Remove and isolate contaminated clothing and shoes. • In case of contact with substance, immediately flush skin or eyes with running water for at least 20 minutes. • For minor skin contact, avoid spreading material on unaffected skin. • Keep victim warm and quiet. • Effects of exposure (inhalation, ingestion or skin contact) to substance may be delayed. • Ensure that medical personnel are aware of the material(s) involved, and take precautions to protect themselves. |

**Schedule 4**

# Guide No. 135  Substances - Spontaneously Combustible

## POTENTIAL HAZARDS

**FIRE OR EXPLOSION**
- Flammable/combustible material. • May ignite on contact with moist air or moisture. • May burn rapidly with flare-burning effect. • Some react vigorously or explosively on contact with water. • Some may decompose explosively when heated or involved in a fire. • May re-ignite after fire is extinguished. • Runoff may create fire or explosion hazard. • Containers may explode when heated.

**HEALTH**
- Fire will produce irritating, corrosive and/or toxic gases. • Inhalation of decomposition products may cause severe injury or death. • Contact with substance may cause severe burns to skin and eyes. • Runoff from fire control may cause pollution.

## PUBLIC SAFETY

- CALL Emergency Response Telephone Number on Shipping Document first. If Shipping Document not available or no answer, refer to appropriate telephone number listed at the end of this book. • As an immediate precautionary measure, isolate spill or leak area in all directions for at least 50 meters (150 feet) for liquids and at least 25 meters (75 feet) for solids. • Stay upwind. • Keep unauthorized personnel away. • Keep out of low areas.

**PROTECTIVE CLOTHING**
- Wear positive pressure self-contained breathing apparatus (SCBA). • Wear chemical protective clothing that is specifically recommended by the manufacturer. It may provide little or no thermal protection. • Structural firefighters' protective clothing will only provide limited protection.

**EVACUATION**

**Spill**
- See Table of Initial Isolation and Protective Action Distances in Schedule 6 for those dangerous goods marked with a "T" in Schedule 5. For those dangerous goods not marked with a "T" in Schedule 5 increase, as necessary, the minimum isolation distance of at 50 meters for liquids and 25 meters for solids in the downwind direction.

**Fire**
- If tank, rail car or tank truck is involved in a fire, ISOLATE for 800 meters (1/2 mile) in all directions; also, consider initial evacuation for 800 meters (1/2 mile) in all directions.

## EMERGENCY RESPONSE

**FIRE**
- DO NOT USE WATER, CO$_2$ OR FOAM ON MATERIAL ITSELF. • Some of these materials may react violently with water. EXCEPTION: For Xanthates, UN3342 and for Dithionite (Hydrosulphite/Hydrosulphite) UN1384, UN1923 and UN1929, USE FLOODING AMOUNTS OF WATER for SMALL AND LARGE fires to stop the reaction. Smothering will not work for these materials they do not need air to burn.

**Small Fire**
- Dry chemical, soda ash, lime or DRY sand, EXCEPT for UN1384, UN1923 and UN1929.

**Large Fire**
- DRY sand, dry chemical, soda ash or lime, EXCEPT for UN1384, UN1923 and UN1929, or withdraw from area and let fire burn. • Move containers from fire area if you can do it without risk.

**Fire involving Tanks or Car/Trailer Loads**
- Fight fire from maximum distance or use unmanned hose holders or monitor nozzles. • Do not get water inside containers or in contact with substance. • Cool containers with flooding quantities of water until well after fire is out. • Withdraw immediately in case of rising sound from venting safety devices or discoloration of tank. • ALWAYS stay away from tanks engulfed in fire.

**SPILL OR LEAK**
- Fully encapsulating, vapor protective clothing should be worn for spills and leaks with no fire. • ELIMINATE all ignition sources (no smoking, flares, sparks or flames in immediate area). • Do not touch or walk through spilled material. • Stop leak if you can do it without risk.

**Small Spill**
EXCEPTION: For spills of Xanthates, UN3342 and for Dithionite (Hydrosulfite/Hydrosulphite), UN1384, UN1923 and UN1929, dissolve in 5 parts water and collect for proper disposal.
- Cover with DRY earth, DRY sand, or other non-combustible material followed with plastic sheet to minimize spreading or contact with rain. • Use clean non-sparking tools to collect material and place it into loosely covered plastic containers for later disposal. • Prevent entry into waterways, sewers, basements or confined areas.

**FIRST AID**
- Move victim to fresh air. • Call 911 or emergency medical service. • Give artificial respiration if victim is not breathing. • Administer oxygen if breathing is difficult. • Remove and isolate contaminated clothing and shoes. • In case of contact with substance, immediately flush skin or eyes with running water for at least 20 minutes. • Keep victim warm and quiet. • Ensure that medical personnel are aware of the material(s) involved, and take precautions to protect themselves.

Schedule 4

# Guide No. 136 Substances - Spontaneously Combustible - Toxic (Air-Reactive)

## POTENTIAL HAZARDS

**FIRE OR EXPLOSION**

• Extremely flammable; will ignite itself if exposed to air. • Burns rapidly, releasing dense, white, irritating fumes. • Substance may be transported in a molten form. • May re-ignite after fire is extinguished. • Corrosive substances in contact with metals may produce flammable hydrogen gas. • Containers may explode when heated.

**HEALTH**

• Fire will produce irritating, corrosive and/or toxic gases. • **TOXIC; ingestion of substance or inhalation of decomposition products will cause severe injury or death.** • Contact with substance may cause severe burns to skin and eyes. • Some effects may be experienced due to skin absorption. • Runoff from fire control may be corrosive and/or toxic and cause pollution.

## PUBLIC SAFETY

• **CALL Emergency Response Telephone Number on Shipping Document first. If Shipping Document not available or no answer, refer to appropriate telephone number listed at the end of this book.** • As an immediate precautionary measure, isolate spill or leak area in all directions for at least 50 meters (150 feet) for liquids and at least 25 meters (75 feet) for solids. • Stay upwind. • Keep unauthorized personnel away. • Keep out of low areas.

**PROTECTIVE CLOTHING**

• Wear positive pressure self-contained breathing apparatus (SCBA). • Wear chemical protective clothing that is specifically recommended by the manufacturer. It may provide little or no thermal protection. • Structural firefighters' protective clothing provides limited protection in fire situations ONLY; it is not effective in spill situations where direct contact with the substance is possible. • **For Phosphorus (UN1381): Special aluminized protective clothing should be worn when direct contact with the substance is possible.**

**EVACUATION**

**Spill**

• Consider initial downwind evacuation for at least 300 meters (1000 feet).

**Fire**

• If tank, rail car or tank truck is involved in a fire, ISOLATE for 800 meters (1/2 mile) in all directions; also, consider initial evacuation for 800 meters (1/2 mile) in all directions.

## EMERGENCY RESPONSE

**FIRE**

**Small Fire**

• Water spray, wet sand or wet earth.

**Large Fire**

• Water spray or fog. • **Do not scatter spilled material with high pressure water streams.** • Move containers from fire area if you can do it without risk.

**Fire involving Tanks or Car/Trailer Loads**

• Fight fire from maximum distance or use unmanned hose holders or monitor nozzles. • Cool containers with flooding quantities of water until well after fire is out. • Withdraw immediately in case of rising sound from venting safety devices or discoloration of tank. • ALWAYS stay away from tanks engulfed in fire.

**SPILL OR LEAK**

• Fully encapsulating, vapor protective clothing should be worn for spills and leaks with no fire. • ELIMINATE all ignition sources (no smoking, flares, sparks or flames in immediate area). • Do not touch or walk through spilled material. • Do not touch damaged containers or spilled material unless wearing appropriate protective clothing. • Stop leak if you can do it without risk.

**Small Spill**

• Cover with water, sand or earth. Shovel into metal container and keep material under water.

**Large Spill**

• Dike for later disposal and cover with wet sand or earth. • Prevent entry into waterways, sewers, basements or confined areas.

**FIRST AID**

• Move victim to fresh air. • Call 911 or emergency medical service. • Give artificial respiration if victim is not breathing. • Administer oxygen if breathing is difficult. • In case of contact with substance, keep exposed skin areas immersed in water or covered with wet bandages until medical attention is received. • Removal of solidified molten material from skin requires medical assistance. • Remove and isolate contaminated clothing and shoes at the site and place in metal container filled with water. Fire hazard if allowed to dry. • Effects of exposure (inhalation, ingestion or skin contact) to substance may be delayed. • Keep victim warm and quiet. • Ensure that medical personnel are aware of the material(s) involved, and take precautions to protect themselves.

Schedule 4

# Guide No. 137    Substances - Water-Reactive - Corrosive

## POTENTIAL HAZARDS

**HEALTH**
- CORROSIVE and/or TOXIC; inhalation, ingestion or contact (skin, eyes) with vapors, dusts or substance may cause severe injury, burns, or death. • Fire will produce irritating, corrosive and/or toxic gases. • Reaction with water may generate much heat which will increase the concentration of fumes in the air. • Contact with molten substance may cause severe burns to skin and eyes. • Runoff from fire control or dilution water may cause pollution.

**FIRE OR EXPLOSION**
- EXCEPT FOR ACETIC ANHYDRIDE (UN1715), THAT IS FLAMMABLE, some of these materials may burn, but none ignite readily. • May ignite combustibles (wood, paper, oil, clothing, etc.). • Substance will react with water (some violently), releasing corrosive and/or toxic gases and runoff. • Flammable/toxic gases may accumulate in confined areas (basement, tanks, hopper/tank cars, etc.) • Contact with metals may evolve flammable hydrogen gas. • Containers may explode when heated or if contaminated with water. • Substance may be transported in a molten form.

## PUBLIC SAFETY

- **CALL Emergency Response Telephone Number on Shipping Document first. If Shipping Document not available or no answer, refer to appropriate telephone number listed at the end of this book.** • As an immediate precautionary measure, isolate spill or leak area in all direction for at least 50 meters (150 feet) for liquids and at least 25 meters (75 feet) for solids. • Keep unauthorized personnel away. • Stay upwind. • Keep out of low areas. • Ventilate enclosed areas.

**PROTECTIVE CLOTHING**
- Wear positive pressure self-contained breathing apparatus (SCBA). • Wear chemical protective clothing that is specifically recommended by the manufacturer. It may provide little or no thermal protection. • Structural firefighters' protective clothing provides limited protection in fire situations ONLY; it is not effective in spill situations where direct contact with the substance is possible.

**EVACUATION**
**Spill**
- See Table of Initial Isolation and Protective Action Distances in Schedule 6 for those dangerous goods marked with a "T" in Schedule 5. For those dangerous goods not marked with a "T" in Schedule 5 increase, as necessary, the minimum isolation distance of at 50 meters for liquids and 25 meters for solids in the downwind direction.
**Fire**
- If tank, rail car or tank truck is involved in a fire, ISOLATE for 800 meters (1/2 mile) in all directions; also, consider initial evacuation for 800 meters (1/2 mile) in all directions.

## EMERGENCY RESPONSE

**FIRE**
- **When material is not involved in fire: do not use water on material itself.**
**Small Fire**
- Dry chemical or $CO_2$. • Move containers from fire area if you can do it without risk.
**Large Fire**
- Flood fire area with large quantities of water, while knocking down vapors with water fog. If insufficient water supply: knock dow vapors only.
**Fire involving Tanks or Car/Trailer Loads**
- Cool containers with flooding quantities of water until well after fire is out. • Do not get water inside containers. • Withdraw immediately in case of rising sound from venting safety devices or discoloration of tank. • ALWAYS stay away from tanks engulfed in fire.

**SPILL OR LEAK**
- Fully encapsulating, vapor protective clothing should be worn for spills and leaks with no fire. • Do not touch damaged containers or spilled material unless wearing appropriate protective clothing. • Stop leak if you can do it without risk. • Use water spray to reduce vapors; do not put water directly on leak, spill area or inside container. • Keep combustibles (wood, paper, oil, etc.) away from spilled material.
**Small Spill**
- Cover with DRY earth, DRY sand, or other non-combustible material followed with plastic sheet to minimize spreading or conta with rain. • Use clean non-sparking tools to collect material and place it into loosely covered plastic containers for later disposal. • Prevent entry into waterways, sewers, basements or confined areas.

**FIRST AID**
- Move victim to fresh air. • Call 911 or emergency medical service. • Give artificial respiration if victim is not breathing. • **Do no use mouth-to-mouth method if victim ingested or inhaled the substance; give artificial respiration with the aid of a pocket mask equipped with a one-way valve or other proper respiratory medical device.** • Administer oxygen if breathing is difficult. • Remove and isolate contaminated clothing and shoes. • In case of contact with substance, immediately flush skin or eyes with running water for at least 20 minutes. • For minor skin contact, avoid spreading material on unaffected skin. • Remova of solidified molten material from skin requires medical assistance. • Keep victim warm and quiet. • Effects of exposure (inhalation, ingestion or skin contact) to substance may be delayed. • Ensure that medical personnel are aware of the material(s) involved, and take precautions to protect themselves.

Schedule 4

# Guide No. 138   Substances - Water-Reactive (Emitting Flammable Gases)

## POTENTIAL HAZARDS

**FIRE OR EXPLOSION**
- Produce flammable gases on contact with water. • May ignite on contact with water or moist air. • Some react vigorously or explosively on contact with water. • May be ignited by heat, sparks or flames. • May re-ignite after fire is extinguished. • Some are transported in highly flammable liquids. • Runoff may create fire or explosion hazard.

**HEALTH**
- Inhalation or contact with vapors, substance, or decomposition products may cause severe injury or death. • May produce corrosive solutions on contact with water. • Fire will produce irritating, corrosive and/or toxic gases. • Runoff from fire control may cause pollution.

## PUBLIC SAFETY

- CALL Emergency Response Telephone Number on Shipping Document first. If Shipping Document not available or no answer, refer to appropriate telephone number listed at the end of this book. • As an immediate precautionary measure, isolate spill or leak area in all directions for at least 50 meters (150 feet) for liquids and at least 25 meters (75 feet) for solids. • Keep unauthorized personnel away. • Stay upwind. • Keep out of low areas. • Ventilate the area before entry.

**PROTECTIVE CLOTHING**
- Wear positive pressure self-contained breathing apparatus (SCBA). • Wear chemical protective clothing that is specifically recommended by the manufacturer. It may provide little or no thermal protection. • Structural firefighters' protective clothing provides limited protection in fire situations ONLY; it is not effective in spill situations where direct contact with the substance is possible.

**EVACUATION**

**Large Spill**
- See Table of Initial Isolation and Protective Action Distances in Schedule 6 for those dangerous goods marked with a "T" in Schedule 5. For those dangerous goods not marked with a "T" in Schedule 5 increase, as necessary, the minimum isolation distance of at 50 meters for liquids and 25 meters for solids in the downwind direction.

**Fire**
- If tank, rail car or tank truck is involved in a fire, ISOLATE for 800 meters (1/2 mile) in all directions; also, consider initial evacuation for 800 meters (1/2 mile) in all directions.

## EMERGENCY RESPONSE

**FIRE**
- DO NOT USE WATER OR FOAM.

**Small Fire**
- Dry chemical, soda ash, lime or sand.

**Large Fire**
- DRY sand, dry chemical, soda ash or lime or withdraw from area and let fire burn. • Move containers from fire area if you can do it without risk.

**Fire Involving Metals or Powders (Aluminum, Lithium, Magnesium, etc.)**
- Use dry chemical, DRY sand, sodium chloride powder, graphite powder or Met-L-X® powder; in addition, for Lithium you may use Lith-X® powder or copper powder. Also, see GUIDE 170.

**Fire involving Tanks or Car/Trailer Loads**
- Fight fire from maximum distance or use unmanned hose holders or monitor nozzles. • Do not get water inside containers. • Cool containers with flooding quantities of water until well after fire is out. • Withdraw immediately in case of rising sound from venting safety devices or discoloration of tank. • ALWAYS stay away from tanks engulfed in fire.

**SPILL OR LEAK**
- ELIMINATE all ignition sources (no smoking, flares, sparks or flames in immediate area). • Do not touch or walk through spilled material. • Stop leak if you can do it without risk. • Use water spray to reduce vapors or divert vapor cloud drift. Avoid allowing water runoff to contact spilled material. • **DO NOT GET WATER on spilled substance or inside containers.**

**Small Spill**
- Cover with DRY earth, DRY sand, or other non-combustible material followed with plastic sheet to minimize spreading or contact with rain. • Dike for later disposal; do not apply water unless directed to do so.

**Powder Spill**
- Cover powder spill with plastic sheet or tarp to minimize spreading and keep powder dry. • **DO NOT CLEAN-UP OR DISPOSE OF, EXCEPT UNDER SUPERVISION OF A SPECIALIST.**

**FIRST AID**
- Move victim to fresh air. • Call 911 or emergency medical service. • Give artificial respiration if victim is not breathing. • Administer oxygen if breathing is difficult. • Remove and isolate contaminated clothing and shoes. • In case of contact with substance, wipe from skin immediately; flush skin or eyes with running water for at least 20 minutes. • Keep victim warm and quiet. • Ensure that medical personnel are aware of the material(s) involved, and take precautions to protect themselves.

**Schedule 4**

# Guide No. 139 Substances - Water-Reactive (Emitting Flammable And Toxic Gases)

## POTENTIAL HAZARDS

**FIRE OR EXPLOSION**

- Produce flammable and toxic gases on contact with water. • May ignite on contact with water or moist air. • Some react vigorous or explosively on contact with water. • May be ignited by heat, sparks or flames. • May re-ignite after fire is extinguished. • Some are transported in highly flammable liquids. • Runoff may create fire or explosion hazard.

**HEALTH**

- Highly toxic: contact with water produces toxic gas, may be fatal if inhaled. • Inhalation or contact with vapors, substance, or decomposition products may cause severe injury or death. • May produce corrosive solutions on contact with water. • Fire will produc irritating, corrosive and/or toxic gases. • Containers may explode when heated. • Runoff from fire control may cause pollution.

## PUBLIC SAFETY

- CALL Emergency Response Telephone Number on Shipping Document first. **If Shipping Document not available or no answer, refer to appropriate telephone number listed at the end of this book.** • As an immediate precautionary measure, isolate spill or leak area in all direction for at least 50 meters (150 feet) for liquids and at least 25 meters (75 feet) for solids. • Keep unauthorized personnel away. • Stay upwind. • Keep out of low areas. • Ventilate the area before entry.

**PROTECTIVE CLOTHING**

- Wear positive pressure self-contained breathing apparatus (SCBA). • Wear chemical protective clothing that is specifically recommended by the manufacturer. It may provide little or no thermal protection. • Structural firefighters' protective clothing provides limited protection in fire situations ONLY; it is not effective where direct contact with the substance is possible.

**EVACUATION**

**Large Spill**

- See Table of Initial Isolation and Protective Action Distances in Schedule 6 for those dangerous goods marked with a "T" in Schedule 5. For those dangerous goods not marked with a "T" in Schedule 5 increase, as necessary, the minimum isolation distance of at 50 meters for liquids and 25 meters for solids in the downwind direction.

**Fire**

- If tank, rail car or tank truck is involved in a fire, ISOLATE for 800 meters (1/2 mile) in all directions; also, consider initial evacuation for 800 meters (1/2 mile) in all directions.

## EMERGENCY RESPONSE

**FIRE**

- **DO NOT USE WATER OR FOAM. (FOAM MAY BE USED FOR CHLOROSILANES, SEE BELOW)**

**Small Fire**

- Dry chemical, soda ash, lime or sand.

**Large Fire**

- DRY sand, dry chemical, soda ash or lime or withdraw from area and let fire burn. • **FOR CHLOROSILANES, DO NOT USE WATER; use AFFF alcohol-resistant medium expansion foam; DO NOT USE dry chemicals, soda ash or lime on chlorosilan fires (large or small) as they may release large quantities of hydrogen gas which may explode.** • Move containers from fire area if you can do it without risk.

**Fire involving Tanks or Car/Trailer Loads**

- Fight fire from maximum distance or use unmanned hose holders or monitor nozzles. • Cool containers with flooding quantities of water until well after fire is out. • Do not get water inside containers. • Withdraw immediately in case of rising sound from venting safety devices or discoloration of tank. • ALWAYS stay away from tanks engulfed in fire.

**SPILL OR LEAK**

- Fully encapsulating, vapor protective clothing should be worn for spills and leaks with no fire. • ELIMINATE all ignition sources (no smoking, flares, sparks or flames in immediate area). • Do not touch or walk through spilled material. • Stop leak if you can do it without risk. • **DO NOT GET WATER on spilled substance or inside containers.** • Use water spray to reduce vapors or divert vapor cloud drift. Avoid allowing water runoff to contact spilled material. • **FOR CHLOROSILANES, use AFFF alcohol-resistant medium expansion foam to reduce vapors.**

**Small Spill**

- Cover with DRY earth, DRY sand, or other non-combustible material followed with plastic sheet to minimize spreading or contact with rain. • Dike for later disposal; do not apply water unless directed to do so.

**Powder Spill**

- Cover powder spill with plastic sheet or tarp to minimize spreading and keep powder dry. • **DO NOT CLEAN-UP OR DISPOSE OF EXCEPT UNDER SUPERVISION OF A SPECIALIST.**

**FIRST AID**

- Move victim to fresh air. • Call 911 or emergency medical service. • Give artificial respiration if victim is not breathing. • **Do not us mouth-to-mouth method if victim ingested or inhaled the substance; give artificial respiration with the aid of a pocket mask equipped with a one-way valve or other proper respiratory medical device.** • Administer oxygen if breathing is difficult. • Remove and isolate contaminated clothing and shoes. • In case of contact with substance, wipe from skin immediately; flush skin or eyes with running water for at least 20 minutes. • Keep victim warm and quiet. • Ensure that medical personnel are aware of the material(s) involved, and take precautions to protect themselves.

Schedule 4

# Guide No. 140  Oxidizers

## POTENTIAL HAZARDS

**FIRE OR EXPLOSION**
- These substances will accelerate burning when involved in a fire. • Some may decompose explosively when heated or involved in a fire. • May explode from heat or contamination. • Some will react explosively with hydrocarbons (fuels). • May ignite combustibles (wood, paper, oil, clothing, etc.). • Containers may explode when heated. • Runoff may create fire or explosion hazard.

**HEALTH**
- Inhalation, ingestion or contact (skin, eyes) with vapors or substance may cause severe injury, burns, or death. • Fire may produce irritating, corrosive and/or toxic gases. • Runoff from fire control or dilution water may cause pollution.

## PUBLIC SAFETY

- **CALL Emergency Response Telephone Number on Shipping Document first. If Shipping Document not available or no answer, refer to appropriate telephone number listed at the end of this book.** • As an immediate precautionary measure, isolate spill or leak area in all directions for at least 50 meters (150 feet) for liquids and at least 25 meters (75 feet) for solids. • Keep unauthorized personnel away. • Stay upwind. • Keep out of low areas. • Ventilate closed spaces before entering.

**PROTECTIVE CLOTHING**
- Wear positive pressure self-contained breathing apparatus (SCBA). • Wear chemical protective clothing that is specifically recommended by the manufacturer. It may provide little or no thermal protection. • Structural firefighters' protective clothing will only provide limited protection.

**EVACUATION**
**Large Spill**
- Consider initial downwind evacuation for at least 100 meters (330 feet).
**Fire**
- If tank, rail car or tank truck is involved in a fire, ISOLATE for 800 meters (1/2 mile) in all directions; also, consider initial evacuation for 800 meters (1/2 mile) in all directions.

## EMERGENCY RESPONSE

**FIRE**
**Small Fire**
- Use water. Do not use dry chemicals or foams. $CO_2$ or Halon® may provide limited control.
**Large Fire**
- Flood fire area with water from a distance. • Move containers from fire area if you can do it without risk. • Do not move cargo or vehicle if cargo has been exposed to heat. • Fight fire from maximum distance or use unmanned hose holders or monitor nozzles. • Cool containers with flooding quantities of water until well after fire is out. • ALWAYS stay away from tanks engulfed in fire. • For massive fire, use unmanned hose holders or monitor nozzles; if this is impossible, withdraw from area and let fire burn.

**SPILL OR LEAK**
- Keep combustibles (wood, paper, oil, etc.) away from spilled material. • Do not touch damaged containers or spilled material unless wearing appropriate protective clothing. • Stop leak if you can do it without risk. • Do not get water inside containers.
**Small Dry Spill**
- With clean shovel place material into clean, dry container and cover loosely; move containers from spill area.
**Small Liquid Spill**
- Use a non-combustible material like vermiculite, sand or earth to soak up the product and place into a container for later disposal.
**Large Spill**
- Dike far ahead of liquid spill for later disposal. • **Following product recovery, flush area with water.**

**FIRST AID**
- Move victim to fresh air. • Call 911 or emergency medical service. • Give artificial respiration if victim is not breathing. • Administer oxygen if breathing is difficult. • Remove and isolate contaminated clothing and shoes. • Contaminated clothing may be a fire risk when dry. • In case of contact with substance, immediately flush skin or eyes with running water for at least 20 minutes. • Keep victim warm and quiet. • Ensure that medical personnel are aware of the material(s) involved, and take precautions to protect themselves.

Schedule 4

# Guide No. 141    Oxidizers - Toxic (Solid)

## POTENTIAL HAZARDS

**FIRE OR EXPLOSION**
- These substances will accelerate burning when involved in a fire. • May explode from heat or contamination. • Some may burn rapidly. • Some will react explosively with hydrocarbons (fuels). • May ignite combustibles (wood, paper, oil, clothing, etc.). • Containers may explode when heated. • Runoff may create fire or explosion hazard.

**HEALTH**
- Toxic by ingestion. • Inhalation of dust is toxic. • Fire may produce irritating, corrosive and/or toxic gases. • Contact with substance may cause severe burns to skin and eyes. • Runoff from fire control or dilution water may cause pollution.

## PUBLIC SAFETY

- **CALL Emergency Response Telephone Number on Shipping Document first. If Shipping Document not available or no answer, refer to appropriate telephone number listed at the end of this book.** • As an immediate precautionary measure, isolate spill or leak area in all directions for at least 50 meters (150 feet) for liquids and at least 25 meters (75 feet) for solids. • Keep unauthorized personnel away. • Stay upwind. • Keep out of low areas. • Ventilate closed spaces before entering.

**PROTECTIVE CLOTHING**
- Wear positive pressure self-contained breathing apparatus (SCBA). • Wear chemical protective clothing that is specifically recommended by the manufacturer. It may provide little or no thermal protection. • Structural firefighters' protective clothing will only provide limited protection.

**EVACUATION**

**Large Spill**
- Consider initial downwind evacuation for at least 100 meters (330 feet).

**Fire**
- If tank, rail car or tank truck is involved in a fire, ISOLATE for 800 meters (1/2 mile) in all directions; also, consider initial evacuation for 800 meters (1/2 mile) in all directions.

## EMERGENCY RESPONSE

**FIRE**

**Small Fire**
- Use water. Do not use dry chemicals or foams. $CO_2$ or Halon® may provide limited control.

**Large Fire**
- Flood fire area with water from a distance. • Move containers from fire area if you can do it without risk. • Do not move cargo or vehicle if cargo has been exposed to heat. • Fight fire from maximum distance or use unmanned hose holders or monitor nozzles. • Cool containers with flooding quantities of water until well after fire is out. • ALWAYS stay away from tanks engulfed in fire. • For massive fire, use unmanned hose holders or monitor nozzles; if this is impossible, withdraw from area and let fire burn.

**SPILL OR LEAK**
- Keep combustibles (wood, paper, oil, etc.) away from spilled material. • Do not touch damaged containers or spilled material unless wearing appropriate protective clothing. • Stop leak if you can do it without risk.

**Small Dry Spill**
- With clean shovel place material into clean, dry container and cover loosely; move containers from spill area.

**Large Spill**
- Dike far ahead of spill for later disposal.

**FIRST AID**
- Move victim to fresh air. • Call 911 or emergency medical service. • Give artificial respiration if victim is not breathing. • Administer oxygen if breathing is difficult. • Remove and isolate contaminated clothing and shoes. • Contaminated clothing may be a fire risk when dry. • In case of contact with substance, immediately flush skin or eyes with running water for at least 20 minutes. • Keep victim warm and quiet. • Ensure that medical personnel are aware of the material(s) involved, and take precautions to protect themselves.

## POTENTIAL HAZARDS

**FIRE OR EXPLOSION**
- These substances will accelerate burning when involved in a fire. • May explode from heat or contamination. • Some will react explosively with hydrocarbons (fuels). • May ignite combustibles (wood, paper, oil, clothing, etc.). • Containers may explode when heated. • Runoff may create fire or explosion hazard.

**HEALTH**
- TOXIC; inhalation, ingestion or contact (skin, eyes) with vapors or substance may cause severe injury, burns or death. • Fire may produce irritating, corrosive and/or toxic gases. • Toxic/flammable fumes may accumulate in confined areas (basement, tanks, hopper/tank cars, etc.). • Runoff from fire control or dilution water may cause pollution.

## PUBLIC SAFETY

- **CALL Emergency Response Telephone Number on Shipping Document first. If Shipping Document not available or no answer, refer to appropriate telephone number listed at the end of this book.** • As an immediate precautionary measure, isolate spill or leak area for at least 50 meters (150 feet) in all directions. • Keep unauthorized personnel away. • Stay upwind. • Keep out of low areas. • Ventilate closed spaces before entering.

**PROTECTIVE CLOTHING**
- Wear positive pressure self-contained breathing apparatus (SCBA). • Wear chemical protective clothing that is specifically recommended by the manufacturer. It may provide little or no thermal protection. • Structural firefighters' protective clothing provides limited protection in fire situations ONLY; it is not effective in spill situations where direct contact with the substance is possible.

**EVACUATION**

**Spill**
- See Table of Initial Isolation and Protective Action Distances in Schedule 6 for those dangerous goods marked with a "T" in Schedule 5. For those dangerous goods not marked with a "T" in Schedule 5 increase, as necessary, the minimum isolation distance of 50 meters in the downwind direction.

**Fire**
- If tank, rail car or tank truck is involved in a fire, ISOLATE for 800 meters (1/2 mile) in all directions; also, consider initial evacuation for 800 meters (1/2 mile) in all directions.

## EMERGENCY RESPONSE

**FIRE**

**Small Fire**
- Use water. Do not use dry chemicals or foams. $CO_2$ or Halon® may provide limited control.

**Large Fire**
- Flood fire area with water from a distance. • Do not move cargo or vehicle if cargo has been exposed to heat. • Move containers from fire area if you can do it without risk.

**Fire involving Tanks or Car/Trailer Loads**
- Fight fire from maximum distance or use unmanned hose holders or monitor nozzles. • Cool containers with flooding quantities of water until well after fire is out. • ALWAYS stay away from tanks engulfed in fire. • For massive fire, use unmanned hose holders or monitor nozzles; if this is impossible, withdraw from area and let fire burn.

**SPILL OR LEAK**
- Keep combustibles (wood, paper, oil, etc.) away from spilled material. • Fully encapsulating, vapor protective clothing should be worn for spills and leaks with no fire. • Do not touch damaged containers or spilled material unless wearing appropriate protective clothing. • Stop leak if you can do it without risk. • Use water spray to reduce vapors or divert vapor cloud drift. • Do not get water inside containers.

**Small Liquid Spill**
- Use a non-combustible material like vermiculite, sand or earth to soak up the product and place into a container for later disposal.

**Large Spill**
- Dike far ahead of liquid spill for later disposal.

**FIRST AID**
- Move victim to fresh air. • Call 911 or emergency medical service. • Give artificial respiration if victim is not breathing. • **Do not use mouth-to-mouth method if victim ingested or inhaled the substance; give artificial respiration with the aid of a pocket mask equipped with a one-way valve or other proper respiratory medical device.** • Administer oxygen if breathing is difficult. • Remove and isolate contaminated clothing and shoes. • Contaminated clothing may be a fire risk when dry. • In case of contact with substance, immediately flush skin or eyes with running water for at least 20 minutes. • Keep victim warm and quiet.
- Ensure that medical personnel are aware of the material(s) involved, and take precautions to protect themselves.

**Schedule 4**

# Guide No. 143    Oxidizers (Unstable)

## POTENTIAL HAZARDS

**FIRE OR EXPLOSION**
- May explode from friction, heat or contamination. • These substances will accelerate burning when involved in a fire. • May ignite combustibles (wood, paper, oil, clothing, etc.). • Some will react explosively with hydrocarbons (fuels). • Containers may explode when heated. • Runoff may create fire or explosion hazard.

**HEALTH**
- TOXIC; inhalation, ingestion or contact (skin, eyes) with vapors, dusts or substance may cause severe injury, burns or death. Fire may produce irritating and/or toxic gases. • Toxic fumes or dust may accumulate in confined areas (basement, tanks, hopper/tank cars, etc.). • Runoff from fire control or dilution water may cause pollution.

## PUBLIC SAFETY

- CALL Emergency Response Telephone Number on Shipping Document first. If Shipping Document not available or no answer, refer to appropriate telephone number listed at the end of this book. • As an immediate precautionary measure, isolate spill or leak area in all directions for at least 50 meters (150 feet) for liquids and at least 25 meters (75 feet) for solids. • Keep unauthorized personnel away. • Stay upwind. • Keep out of low areas. • Ventilate closed spaces before entering.

**PROTECTIVE CLOTHING**
- Wear positive pressure self-contained breathing apparatus (SCBA). • Wear chemical protective clothing that is specifically recommended by the manufacturer. It may provide little or no thermal protection. • Structural firefighters' protective clothing provides limited protection in fire situations ONLY; it is not effective in spill situations where direct contact with the substance is possible.

**EVACUATION**

**Spill**
- See Table of Initial Isolation and Protective Action Distances in Schedule 6 for those dangerous goods marked with a "T" in Schedule 5. For those dangerous goods not marked with a "T" in Schedule 5 increase, as necessary, the minimum isolation distance of at 50 meters for liquids and 25 meters for solids in the downwind direction.

**Fire**
- If tank, rail car or tank truck is involved in a fire, ISOLATE for 800 meters (1/2 mile) in all directions; also, consider initial evacuation for 800 meters (1/2 mile) in all directions.

## EMERGENCY RESPONSE

**FIRE**

**Small Fire**
- Use water. Do not use dry chemicals or foams. $CO_2$ or Halon® may provide limited control.

**Large Fire**
- Flood fire area with water from a distance. • Do not move cargo or vehicle if cargo has been exposed to heat. Move containers from fire area if you can do it without risk. • Do not get water inside containers: a violent reaction may occur.

**Fire involving Tanks or Car/Trailer Loads**

Cool containers with flooding quantities of water until well after fire is out. • Dike fire-control water for later disposal.• ALWAYS stay away from tanks engulfed in fire. • For massive fire, use unmanned hose holders or monitor nozzles; if this is impossible, withdraw from area and let fire burn.

**SPILL OR LEAK**
- Keep combustibles (wood, paper, oil, etc.) away from spilled material. • Do not touch damaged containers or spilled material unless wearing appropriate protective clothing. • Use water spray to reduce vapors or divert vapor cloud drift. • Prevent entry into waterways, sewers, basements or confined areas.

**Small Spill**
- Flush area with flooding quantities of water.

**Large Spill**
- DO NOT CLEAN-UP OR DISPOSE OF, EXCEPT UNDER SUPERVISION OF A SPECIALIST.

**FIRST AID**
- Move victim to fresh air. • Call 911 or emergency medical service. • Give artificial respiration if victim is not breathing. • Administer oxygen if breathing is difficult. • Remove and isolate contaminated clothing and shoes. • Contaminated clothing may be a fire risk when dry. • In case of contact with substance, immediately flush skin or eyes with running water for at least 20 minutes. • Keep victim warm and quiet. • Ensure that medical personnel are aware of the material(s) involved, and take precautions to protect themselves.

# Guide No. 144 Oxidizers (Water-Reactive)

## POTENTIAL HAZARDS

**FIRE OR EXPLOSION**
- May ignite combustibles (wood, paper, oil, clothing, etc.). • React vigorously and/or explosively with water. • Produce toxic and/or corrosive substances on contact with water. • Flammable/toxic gases may accumulate in tanks and hopper cars. • Some may produce flammable hydrogen gas upon contact with metals. • Containers may explode when heated. • Runoff may create fire or explosion hazard.

**HEALTH**
- TOXIC; inhalation or contact with vapor, substance, or decomposition products may cause severe injury or death. • Fire will produce irritating, corrosive and/or toxic gases. • Runoff from fire control or dilution water may cause pollution.

## PUBLIC SAFETY

- **CALL Emergency Response Telephone Number on Shipping Document first. If Shipping Document not available or no answer, refer to appropriate telephone number listed at the end of this book.** • As an immediate precautionary measure, isolate spill or leak area in all directions for at least 50 meters (150 feet) for liquids and at least 25 meters (75 feet) for solids. • Keep unauthorized personnel away. • Stay upwind. • Keep out of low areas. • Ventilate closed spaces before entering.

**PROTECTIVE CLOTHING**
- Wear positive pressure self-contained breathing apparatus (SCBA). • Wear chemical protective clothing that is specifically recommended by the manufacturer. It may provide little or no thermal protection. • Structural firefighters' protective clothing provides limited protection in fire situations ONLY; it is not effective in spill situations where direct contact with the substance is possible.

**EVACUATION**

**Spill**
- See Table of Initial Isolation and Protective Action Distances in Schedule 6 for those dangerous goods marked with a "T" in Schedule 5. For those dangerous goods not marked with a "T" in Schedule 5 increase, as necessary, the minimum isolation distance of at 50 meters for liquids and 25 meters for solids in the downwind direction.

**Fire**
- If tank, rail car or tank truck is involved in a fire, ISOLATE for 800 meters (1/2 mile) in all directions; also, consider initial evacuation for 800 meters (1/2 mile) in all directions

## EMERGENCY RESPONSE

**FIRE**
- **DO NOT USE WATER OR FOAM.**

**Small Fire**
- Dry chemical, soda ash or lime.

**Large Fire**
- DRY sand, dry chemical, soda ash or lime or withdraw from area and let fire burn. • Do not move cargo or vehicle if cargo has been exposed to heat.• Move containers from fire area if you can do it without risk.

**Fire involving Tanks or Car/Trailer Loads**
- Fight fire from maximum distance or use unmanned hose holders or monitor nozzles. • Cool containers with flooding quantities of water until well after fire is out. • Withdraw immediately in case of rising sound from venting safety devices or discoloration of tank. ALWAYS stay away from tanks engulfed in fire.

**SPILL OR LEAK**
- ELIMINATE all ignition sources (no smoking, flares, sparks or flames in immediate area). • Do not touch damaged containers or spilled material unless wearing appropriate protective clothing. • Stop leak if you can do it without risk. • Use water spray to reduce vapors or divert vapor cloud drift. Avoid allowing water runoff to contact spilled material. • **DO NOT GET WATER on spilled substance or inside containers.**

**Small Spill**
- Cover with DRY earth, DRY sand, or other non-combustible material followed with plastic sheet to minimize spreading or contact with rain.

**Large Spill**
- **DO NOT CLEAN-UP OR DISPOSE OF, EXCEPT UNDER SUPERVISION OF A SPECIALIST.**

**FIRST AID**
- Move victim to fresh air. • Call 911 or emergency medical service. • Give artificial respiration if victim is not breathing. • **Do not use mouth-to-mouth method if victim ingested or inhaled the substance; give artificial respiration with the aid of a pocket mask equipped with a one-way valve or other proper respiratory medical device.** • Administer oxygen if breathing is difficult. • Remove and isolate contaminated clothing and shoes. • Contaminated clothing may be a fire risk when dry. • In case of contact with substance, immediately flush skin or eyes with running water for at least 20 minutes. • Keep victim warm and quiet. • Keep victim under observation. • Effects of contact or inhalation may be delayed. • Ensure that medical personnel are aware of the material(s) involved, and take precautions to protect themselves.

Schedule 4

# Guide No. 145　Organic Peroxides (Heat and Contamination Sensitive)

## POTENTIAL HAZARDS

**FIRE OR EXPLOSION**
- May explode from heat or contamination. • May ignite combustibles (wood, paper, oil, clothing, etc.). • May be ignited by heat, sparks or flames. • May burn rapidly with flare-burning effect. • Containers may explode when heated. • Runoff may create fire or explosion hazard.

**HEALTH**
- Fire may produce irritating, corrosive and/or toxic gases. • Ingestion or contact (skin, eyes) with substance may cause severe injury or burns. • Runoff from fire control or dilution water may cause pollution.

## PUBLIC SAFETY

- CALL Emergency Response Telephone Number on Shipping Document first. If Shipping Document not available or no answer, refer to appropriate telephone number listed at the end of this book. • As an immediate precautionary measure, isolate spill or leak area in all directions for at least 50 meters (150 feet) for liquids and at least 25 meters (75 feet) for solids. • Keep unauthorized personnel away. • Stay upwind. • Keep out of low areas.

**PROTECTIVE CLOTHING**
- Wear positive pressure self-contained breathing apparatus (SCBA). • Wear chemical protective clothing that is specifically recommended by the manufacturer. It may provide little or no thermal protection. • Structural firefighters' protective clothing will only provide limited protection.

**EVACUATION**

**Large Spill**
- Consider initial evacuation for at least 250 meters (800 feet).

**Fire**
- If tank, rail car or tank truck is involved in a fire, ISOLATE for 800 meters (1/2 mile) in all directions; also, consider initial evacuation for 800 meters (1/2 mile) in all directions.

## EMERGENCY RESPONSE

**FIRE**

**Small Fire**
- Water spray or fog is preferred; if water not available use dry chemical, $CO_2$ or regular foam.

**Large Fire**
- Flood fire area with water from a distance. • Use water spray or fog; do not use straight streams. • Move containers from fire area if you can do it without risk. • Do not move cargo or vehicle if cargo has been exposed to heat. • Fight fire from maximum distance or use unmanned hose holders or monitor nozzles. • Cool containers with flooding quantities of water until well after fire is out. • ALWAYS stay away from tanks engulfed in fire. • For massive fire, use unmanned hose holders or monitor nozzles; if this is impossible, withdraw from area and let fire burn.

**Fire involving Tanks or Car/Trailer Loads**
- Fight fire from maximum distance or use unmanned hose holders or monitor nozzles. • Cool containers with flooding quantities of water until well after fire is out. • ALWAYS stay away from tanks engulfed in fire. • For massive fire, use unmanned hose holders or monitor nozzles; if this is impossible, withdraw from area and let fire burn.

**SPILL OR LEAK**
- ELIMINATE all ignition sources (no smoking, flares, sparks or flames in immediate area). • Keep combustibles (wood, paper, oil, etc.) away from spilled material. • Do not touch damaged containers or spilled material unless wearing appropriate protective clothing. • Keep substance wet using water spray. • Stop leak if you can do it without risk.

**Small Spill**
- Take up with inert, damp, non-combustible material using clean non-sparking tools and place into loosely covered plastic containers for later disposal.

**Large Spill**
- Wet down with water and dike for later disposal. • Prevent entry into waterways, sewers, basements or confined areas.
- **DO NOT CLEAN-UP OR DISPOSE OF, EXCEPT UNDER SUPERVISION OF A SPECIALIST.**

**FIRST AID**
- Move victim to fresh air. • Call 911 or emergency medical service. • Give artificial respiration if victim is not breathing. • Administer oxygen if breathing is difficult. • Remove and isolate contaminated clothing and shoes. • Contaminated clothing may be a fire risk when dry. • Remove material from skin immediately. • In case of contact with substance, immediately flush skin or eyes with running water for at least 20 minutes. • Keep victim warm and quiet. • Ensure that medical personnel are aware of the material(s) involved, and take precautions to protect themselves.

# Guide No. 146　Organic Peroxides (Heat, Contamination and Friction Sensitive)

## POTENTIAL HAZARDS

**FIRE OR EXPLOSION**
- May explode from heat, shock, friction or contamination. • May ignite combustibles (wood, paper, oil, clothing, etc.). • May be ignited by heat, sparks or flames. • May burn rapidly with flare-burning effect. • Containers may explode when heated. • Runoff may create fire or explosion hazard.

**HEALTH**
- Fire may produce irritating, corrosive and/or toxic gases. • Ingestion or contact (skin, eyes) with substance may cause severe injury or burns. • Runoff from fire control or dilution water may cause pollution.

## PUBLIC SAFETY

- **CALL Emergency Response Telephone Number on Shipping Document first. If Shipping Document not available or no answer, refer to appropriate telephone number listed at the end of this book.** • As an immediate precautionary measure, isolate spill or leak area in all directions for at least 50 meters (150 feet) for liquids and at least 25 meters (75 feet) for solids. • Keep unauthorized personnel away. • Stay upwind. • Keep out of low areas.

**PROTECTIVE CLOTHING**
- Wear positive pressure self-contained breathing apparatus (SCBA). • Wear chemical protective clothing that is specifically recommended by the manufacturer. It may provide little or no thermal protection. • Structural firefighters' protective clothing will only provide limited protection.

**EVACUATION**

**Large Spill**
- Consider initial evacuation for at least 250 meters (800 feet).

**Fire**
- If tank, rail car or tank truck is involved in a fire, ISOLATE for 800 meters (1/2 mile) in all directions; also, consider initial evacuation for 800 meters (1/2 mile) in all directions.

## EMERGENCY RESPONSE

**FIRE**

**Small Fire**
- Water spray or fog is preferred; if water not available use dry chemical, $CO_2$ or regular foam.

**Large Fire**
- Flood fire area with water from a distance. • Use water spray or fog; do not use straight streams. • Do not move cargo or vehicle if cargo has been exposed to heat. • Move containers from fire area if you can do it without risk.

**Fire involving Tanks or Car/Trailer Loads**
- Fight fire from maximum distance or use unmanned hose holders or monitor nozzles. • Cool containers with flooding quantities of water until well after fire is out. • ALWAYS stay away from tanks engulfed in fire. • For massive fire, use unmanned hose holders or monitor nozzles; if this is impossible, withdraw from area and let fire burn.

**SPILL OR LEAK**
- ELIMINATE all ignition sources (no smoking, flares, sparks or flames in immediate area). • Keep combustibles (wood, paper, oil, etc.) away from spilled material. • Do not touch damaged containers or spilled material unless wearing appropriate protective clothing. • Keep substance wet using water spray. • Stop leak if you can do it without risk.

**Small Spill**
- Take up with inert, damp, non-combustible material using clean non-sparking tools and place into loosely covered plastic containers for later disposal.

**Large Spill**
- Wet down with water and dike for later disposal. • Prevent entry into waterways, sewers, basements or confined areas.
- **DO NOT CLEAN-UP OR DISPOSE OF, EXCEPT UNDER SUPERVISION OF A SPECIALIST.**

**FIRST AID**
- Move victim to fresh air. • Call 911 or emergency medical service. • Give artificial respiration if victim is not breathing. • Administer oxygen if breathing is difficult. • Remove and isolate contaminated clothing and shoes. • Contaminated clothing may be a fire risk when dry. • Remove material from skin immediately. • In case of contact with substance, immediately flush skin or eyes with running water for at least 20 minutes. • Keep victim warm and quiet. • Ensure that medical personnel are aware of the material(s) involved, and take precautions to protect themselves.

Schedule 4

# Guide No. 147   LITHIUM ION BATTERIES

## POTENTIAL HAZARDS

**FIRE OR EXPLOSION**
- Lithium ion batteries contain flammable liquid electrolyte that may vent, ignite and produce sparks when subjected to high temperatures (> 150 °C (302 °F)), when damaged or abused (e.g., mechanical damage or electrical overcharging). • May burn rapidly with flare-burning effect. • May ignite other batteries in close proximity.

**HEALTH**
- Contact with battery electrolyte may be irritating to skin, eyes and mucous membranes. • Fire will produce irritating, corrosive and/or toxic gases. • Burning batteries may produce toxic hydrogen fluoride gas (see GUIDE 125). • Fumes may cause dizziness or suffocation.

## PUBLIC SAFETY

- **CALL Emergency Response Telephone Number on Shipping Document first. If Shipping Document not available or no answer, refer to appropriate telephone number listed at the end of this book.** • As an immediate precautionary measure, isolate spill or leak area for at least 25 meters (75 feet) in all directions. • Keep unauthorized personnel away. • Stay upwind. • Keep out of low areas. • Ventilate closed spaces before entering.

**PROTECTIVE CLOTHING**
- Wear positive pressure self-contained breathing apparatus (SCBA). • Structural firefighters' protective clothing will only provide limited protection.

**EVACUATION**

**Large Spill**
- Consider initial evacuation for at least 100 meters (330 feet).

**Fire**
- If rail car or trailer is involved in a fire, ISOLATE for 500 meters (1/3 mile) in all directions; also initiate evacuation including emergency responders for 500 meters (1/3 mile) in all directions.

## EMERGENCY RESPONSE

**FIRE**

**Small Fire**
· Dry chemical, CO2, water spray or regular foam.

**Large Fire**
- Water spray, fog or regular foam. • Move containers from fire area if you can do it without risk.

**SPILL OR LEAK**
- ELIMINATE all ignition sources (no smoking, flares, sparks or flames in immediate area). • Do not touch or walk through spilled material. • Absorb with earth, sand or other non-combustible material. • Leaking batteries and contaminated absorbent material should be placed in metal containers

**FIRST AID**
- Move victim to fresh air. • Call 911 or emergency medical service. • Give artificial respiration if victim is not breathing. • Administer oxygen if breathing is difficult. • Remove and isolate contaminated clothing and shoes. • Contaminated clothing may be a fire risk when dry. • Remove material from skin immediately. • In case of contact with substance, immediately flush skin or eyes with running water for at least 20 minutes. • Keep victim warm and quiet. • Ensure that medical personnel are aware of the material(s) involved, and take precautions to protect themselves.

# Guide No. 148    Organic Peroxides (Heat and Contamination Sensitive/Temperature Controlled)

## POTENTIAL HAZARDS

**FIRE OR EXPLOSION**
- May explode from heat, contamination or loss of temperature control. • These materials are particularly sensitive to temperature rises. • Above a given "Control Temperature" they decompose violently and catch fire. • May ignite combustibles (wood, paper, oil, clothing, etc.). • May ignite spontaneously if exposed to air. • May be ignited by heat, sparks or flames. • May burn rapidly with flare-burning effect. • Containers may explode when heated. • Runoff may create fire or explosion hazard.

**HEALTH**
- Fire may produce irritating, corrosive and/or toxic gases. • Ingestion or contact (skin, eyes) with substance may cause severe injury or burns. • Runoff from fire control or dilution water may cause pollution.

## PUBLIC SAFETY

- CALL Emergency Response Telephone Number on Shipping Document first. If Shipping Document not available or no answer, refer to appropriate telephone number listed at the end of this book. • As an immediate precautionary measure, isolate spill or leak area in all directions for at least 50 meters (150 feet) for liquids and at least 25 meters (75 feet) for solids. • Keep unauthorized personnel away. • Stay upwind. • Keep out of low areas. • DO NOT allow the substance to warm up. Obtain liquid nitrogen, dry ice or ice for cooling. If none can be obtained, evacuate the area immediately.

**PROTECTIVE CLOTHING**
- Wear positive pressure self-contained breathing apparatus (SCBA). • Wear chemical protective clothing that is specifically recommended by the manufacturer. It may provide little or no thermal protection. • Structural firefighters' protective clothing will only provide limited protection.

**EVACUATION**

**Large Spill**
- Consider initial evacuation for at least 250 meters (800 feet).

**Fire**
- If tank, rail car or tank truck is involved in a fire, ISOLATE for 800 meters (1/2 mile) in all directions; also, consider initial evacuation for 800 meters (1/2 mile) in all directions.

## EMERGENCY RESPONSE

**FIRE**
- The temperature of the substance must be maintained at or below the "Control Temperature" at all times.

**Small Fire**
- Water spray or fog is preferred; if water not available use dry chemical, $CO_2$ or regular foam.

**Large Fire**
- Flood fire area with water from a distance. • Use water spray or fog; do not use straight streams. • Move containers from fire area if you can do it without risk. • Do not move cargo or vehicle if cargo has been exposed to heat. • Fight fire from maximum distance or use unmanned hose holders or monitor nozzles. • Cool containers with flooding quantities of water until well after fire is out. • BEWARE OF POSSIBLE CONTAINER EXPLOSION. • ALWAYS stay away from tanks engulfed in fire. • For massive fire, use unmanned hose holders or monitor nozzles; if this is impossible, withdraw from area and let fire burn.

**SPILL OR LEAK**
- ELIMINATE all ignition sources (no smoking, flares, sparks or flames in immediate area). • Keep combustibles (wood, paper, oil, etc.) away from spilled material. • Do not touch or walk through spilled material. • Stop leak if you can do it without risk.

**Small Spill**
- Take up with inert, damp, non-combustible material using clean non-sparking tools and place into loosely covered plastic containers for later disposal.

**Large Spill**
- Dike far ahead of liquid spill for later disposal. • Prevent entry into waterways, sewers, basements or confined areas. • DO NOT CLEAN-UP OR DISPOSE OF, EXCEPT UNDER SUPERVISION OF A SPECIALIST.

**FIRST AID**
- Move victim to fresh air. • Call 911 or emergency medical service. • Give artificial respiration if victim is not breathing. • Administer oxygen if breathing is difficult. • Remove and isolate contaminated clothing and shoes. • Contaminated clothing may be a fire risk when dry. • Remove material from skin immediately. • In case of contact with substance, immediately flush skin or eyes with running water for at least 20 minutes. • Keep victim warm and quiet. • Ensure that medical personnel are aware of the material(s) involved, and take precautions to protect themselves.

Schedule 4

# Guide No. 149 Substances (Self-Reactive)

## POTENTIAL HAZARDS

**FIRE OR EXPLOSION**
- Self-decomposition or self-ignition may be triggered by heat, chemical reaction, friction or impact. • May be ignited by heat, sparks or flames. • Some may decompose explosively when heated or involved in a fire. • May burn violently. Decomposition may be self-accelerating and produce large amounts of gases. • Vapors or dust may form explosive mixtures with air.

**HEALTH**
- Inhalation or contact with vapors, substance, or decomposition products may cause severe injury or death. • May produce irritating, toxic and/or corrosive gases. • Runoff from fire control may cause pollution.

## PUBLIC SAFETY

- **CALL Emergency Response Telephone Number on Shipping Document first. If Shipping Document not available or no answer, refer to appropriate telephone number listed at the end of this book.** • As an immediate precautionary measure, isolate spill or leak area in all directions for at least 50 meters (150 feet) for liquids and at least 25 meters (75 feet) for solids. • Keep unauthorized personnel away. • Stay upwind. • Keep out of low areas.

**PROTECTIVE CLOTHING**
- Wear positive pressure self-contained breathing apparatus (SCBA). • Wear chemical protective clothing that is specifically recommended by the manufacturer. It may provide little or no thermal protection. • Structural firefighters' protective clothing will only provide limited protection.

**EVACUATION**
**Large Spill**
- Consider initial downwind evacuation for at least 250 meters (800 feet).
**Fire**
- If tank, rail car or tank truck is involved in a fire, ISOLATE for 800 meters (1/2 mile) in all directions; also, consider initial evacuation for 800 meters (1/2 mile) in all directions.

## EMERGENCY RESPONSE

**FIRE**
**Small Fire**
- Dry chemical, $CO_2$, water spray or regular foam.
**Large Fire**
- Flood fire area with water from a distance. • Move containers from fire area if you can do it without risk.
**Fire involving Tanks or Car/Trailer Loads**
- **BEWARE OF POSSIBLE CONTAINER EXPLOSION.** • Fight fire from maximum distance or use unmanned hose holders or monitor nozzles. • Cool containers with flooding quantities of water until well after fire is out. • Withdraw immediately in case of rising sound from venting safety devices or discoloration of tank. • ALWAYS stay away from tanks engulfed in fire.

**SPILL OR LEAK**
- ELIMINATE all ignition sources (no smoking, flares, sparks or flames in immediate area). • Do not touch or walk through spilled material. • Stop leak if you can do it without risk.
**Small Spill**
- Take up with inert, damp, non-combustible material using clean non-sparking tools and place into loosely covered plastic containers for later disposal. • Prevent entry into waterways, sewers, basements or confined areas.

**FIRST AID**
- Move victim to fresh air. • Call 911 or emergency medical service. • Give artificial respiration if victim is not breathing. • Administer oxygen if breathing is difficult. • Remove and isolate contaminated clothing and shoes. • In case of contact with substance, immediately flush skin or eyes with running water for at least 20 minutes. • Keep victim warm and quiet. • Ensure that medical personnel are aware of the material(s) involved, and take precautions to protect themselves.

## POTENTIAL HAZARDS

**FIRE OR EXPLOSION**
- Self-decomposition or self-ignition may be triggered by heat, chemical reaction, friction or impact. • Self-accelerating decomposition may occur if the specific control temperature is not maintained. • These materials are particularly sensitive to temperature rises. • Above a given "Control Temperature" they decompose violently and catch fire. • May be ignited by heat, sparks or flames. • Some may decompose explosively when heated or involved in a fire. • May burn violently. Decomposition may be self-accelerating and produce large amounts of gases. • Vapors or dust may form explosive mixtures with air.

**HEALTH**
- Inhalation or contact with vapors, substance, or decomposition products may cause severe injury or death. • May produce irritating, toxic and/or corrosive gases. • Runoff from fire control may cause pollution.

## PUBLIC SAFETY

- CALL Emergency Response Telephone Number on Shipping Document first. If Shipping Document not available or no answer, refer to appropriate telephone number listed at the end of this book. • As an immediate precautionary measure, isolate spill or leak area in all directions for at least 50 meters (150 feet) for liquids and at least 25 meters (75 feet) for solids. • Keep unauthorized personnel away. • Stay upwind. • Keep out of low areas. • **DO NOT allow the substance to warm up. Obtain liquid nitrogen, dry ice or ice for cooling. If none can be obtained, evacuate the area immediately.**

**PROTECTIVE CLOTHING**
- Wear positive pressure self-contained breathing apparatus (SCBA). • Wear chemical protective clothing that is specifically recommended by the manufacturer. It may provide little or no thermal protection. • Structural firefighters' protective clothing will only provide limited protection.

**EVACUATION**
**Large Spill**
- Consider initial downwind evacuation for at least 250 meters (800 feet).

**Fire**
- If tank, rail car or tank truck is involved in a fire, ISOLATE for 800 meters (1/2 mile) in all directions; also, consider initial evacuation for 800 meters (1/2 mile) in all directions.

## EMERGENCY RESPONSE

**FIRE**
- The temperature of the substance must be maintained at or below the "Control Temperature" at all times.

**Small Fire**
- Dry chemical, $CO_2$, water spray or regular foam.

**Large Fire**
- Flood fire area with water from a distance. • Move containers from fire area if you can do it without risk.

**Fire involving Tanks or Car/Trailer Loads**
- BEWARE OF POSSIBLE CONTAINER EXPLOSION. • Fight fire from maximum distance or use unmanned hose holders or monitor nozzles. • Cool containers with flooding quantities of water until well after fire is out. • Withdraw immediately in case of rising sound from venting safety devices or discoloration of tank. • ALWAYS stay away from tanks engulfed in fire.

**SPILL OR LEAK**
- ELIMINATE all ignition sources (no smoking, flares, sparks or flames in immediate area). • Do not touch or walk through spilled material. • Stop leak if you can do it without risk.

**Small Spill**
- Take up with inert, damp, non-combustible material using clean non-sparking tools and place into loosely covered plastic containers for later disposal. • Prevent entry into waterways, sewers, basements or confined areas. • **DO NOT CLEAN-UP OR DISPOSE OF, EXCEPT UNDER SUPERVISION OF A SPECIALIST.**

**FIRST AID**
- Move victim to fresh air. • Call 911 or emergency medical service. • Give artificial respiration if victim is not breathing. • Administer oxygen if breathing is difficult. • Remove and isolate contaminated clothing and shoes. • In case of contact with substance, immediately flush skin or eyes with running water for at least 20 minutes. • Keep victim warm and quiet. • Ensure that medical personnel are aware of the material(s) involved, and take precautions to protect themselves.

**Schedule 4**

# Guide No. 151    Substances - Toxic (Non-Combustible)

## POTENTIAL HAZARDS

**HEALTH**
- **Highly toxic,** may be fatal if inhaled, swallowed or absorbed through skin. • Avoid any skin contact. • Effects of contact or inhalation may be delayed. • Fire may produce irritating, corrosive and/or toxic gases. • Runoff from fire control or dilution water may be corrosive and/or toxic and cause pollution.

**FIRE OR EXPLOSION**
- Non-combustible, substance itself does not burn but may decompose upon heating to produce corrosive and/or toxic fumes.
- Containers may explode when heated. • Runoff may pollute waterways.

## PUBLIC SAFETY

- **CALL Emergency Response Telephone Number on Shipping Document first. If Shipping Document not available or no answer, refer to appropriate telephone number listed at the end of this book.** • As an immediate precautionary measure, isolate spill or leak area in all directions for at least 50 meters (150 feet) for liquids and at least 25 meters (75 feet) for solids. • Keep unauthorized personnel away. • Stay upwind. • Keep out of low areas.

**PROTECTIVE CLOTHING**
- Wear positive pressure self-contained breathing apparatus (SCBA). • Wear chemical protective clothing that is specifically recommended by the manufacturer. It may provide little or no thermal protection. • Structural firefighters' protective clothing provides limited protection in fire situations ONLY; it is not effective in spill situations where direct contact with the substance is possible.

**EVACUATION**

**Spill**
- See Table of Initial Isolation and Protective Action Distances in Schedule 6 for those dangerous goods marked with a "T" in Schedule 5. For those dangerous goods not marked with a "T" in Schedule 5 increase, as necessary, the minimum isolation distance of at 50 meters for liquids and 25 meters for solids in the downwind direction.

**Fire**
- If tank, rail car or tank truck is involved in a fire, ISOLATE for 800 meters (1/2 mile) in all directions; also, consider initial evacuation for 800 meters (1/2 mile) in all directions.

## EMERGENCY RESPONSE

**FIRE**

**Small Fire**
- Dry chemical, $CO_2$ or water spray.

**Large Fire**
- Water spray, fog or regular foam. • Move containers from fire area if you can do it without risk. • Dike fire control water for later disposal; do not scatter the material. • Use water spray or fog; do not use straight streams.

**Fire involving Tanks or Car/Trailer Loads**
- Fight fire from maximum distance or use unmanned hose holders or monitor nozzles. • Do not get water inside containers.
- Cool containers with flooding quantities of water until well after fire is out. • Withdraw immediately in case of rising sound from venting safety devices or discoloration of tank. • ALWAYS stay away from tanks engulfed in fire. • For massive fire, use unmanned hose holders or monitor nozzles; if this is impossible, withdraw from area and let fire burn.

**SPILL OR LEAK**
- Do not touch damaged containers or spilled material unless wearing appropriate protective clothing. • Stop leak if you can do it without risk. • Prevent entry into waterways, sewers, basements or confined areas. • Cover with plastic sheet to prevent spreading. • Absorb or cover with dry earth, sand or other non-combustible material and transfer to containers. • **DO NOT GET WATER INSIDE CONTAINERS.**

**FIRST AID**
- Move victim to fresh air. • Call 911 or emergency medical service. • Give artificial respiration if victim is not breathing. • **Do not use mouth-to-mouth method if victim ingested or inhaled the substance; give artificial respiration with the aid of a pocket mask equipped with a one-way valve or other proper respiratory medical device.** • Administer oxygen if breathing is difficult. • Remove and isolate contaminated clothing and shoes. • In case of contact with substance, immediately flush skin or eyes with running water for at least 20 minutes. • For minor skin contact, avoid spreading material on unaffected skin. • Keep victim warm and quiet. • Effects of exposure (inhalation, ingestion or skin contact) to substance may be delayed. • Ensure that medical personnel are aware of the material(s) involved, and take precautions to protect themselves.

**Schedule 4**

# Guide No. 152   Substances - Toxic (Combustible)

## POTENTIAL HAZARDS

**HEALTH**
- Highly toxic, may be fatal if inhaled, swallowed or absorbed through skin. • Contact with molten substance may cause severe burns to skin and eyes. • Avoid any skin contact. • Effects of contact or inhalation may be delayed. • Fire may produce irritating, corrosive and/or toxic gases. • Runoff from fire control or dilution water may be corrosive and/or toxic and cause pollution.

**FIRE OR EXPLOSION**
- Combustible material: may burn but does not ignite readily. • Containers may explode when heated. • Runoff may pollute waterways. • Substance may be transported in a molten form.

## PUBLIC SAFETY

- **CALL Emergency Response Telephone Number on Shipping Document first. If Shipping Document not available or no answer, refer to appropriate telephone number listed at the end of this book.** • As an immediate precautionary measure, isolate spill or leak area in all directions for at least 50 meters (150 feet) for liquids and at least 25 meters (75 feet) for solids. • Keep unauthorized personnel away. • Stay upwind. • Keep out of low areas.

**PROTECTIVE CLOTHING**
- Wear positive pressure self-contained breathing apparatus (SCBA). • Wear chemical protective clothing that is specifically recommended by the manufacturer. It may provide little or no thermal protection. • Structural firefighters' protective clothing provides limited protection in fire situations ONLY; it is not effective in spill situations where direct contact with the substance is possible.

**EVACUATION**

**Spill**
- See Table of Initial Isolation and Protective Action Distances in Schedule 6 for those dangerous goods marked with a "T" in Schedule 5. For those dangerous goods not marked with a "T" in Schedule 5 increase, as necessary, the minimum isolation distance of at 50 meters for liquids and 25 meters for solids in the downwind direction.

**Fire**
- If tank, rail car or tank truck is involved in a fire, ISOLATE for 800 meters (1/2 mile) in all directions; also, consider initial evacuation for 800 meters (1/2 mile) in all directions.

## EMERGENCY RESPONSE

**FIRE**

**Small Fire**
- Dry chemical, $CO_2$ or water spray.

**Large Fire**
- Water spray, fog or regular foam. • Move containers from fire area if you can do it without risk. • Dike fire control water for later disposal; do not scatter the material. • Use water spray or fog; do not use straight streams.

**Fire involving Tanks or Car/Trailer Loads**
- Fight fire from maximum distance or use unmanned hose holders or monitor nozzles. • Do not get water inside containers.
- Cool containers with flooding quantities of water until well after fire is out. • Withdraw immediately in case of rising sound from venting safety devices or discoloration of tank. • ALWAYS stay away from tanks engulfed in fire. • For massive fire, use unmanned hose holders or monitor nozzles; if this is impossible, withdraw from area and let fire burn.

**SPILL OR LEAK**
- Eliminate all ignition sources (no smoking, flares, sparks or flame in immediate area). • Do not touch damaged containers or spilled material unless wearing appropriate protective clothing. • Stop leak if you can do it without risk. • Prevent entry into waterways, sewers, basements or confined areas. • Cover with plastic sheet to prevent spreading. • Absorb or cover with dry earth, sand or other non-combustible material and transfer to containers. • **DO NOT GET WATER INSIDE CONTAINERS.**

**FIRST AID**
- Move victim to fresh air. • Call 911 or emergency medical service. • Give artificial respiration if victim is not breathing. • **Do not use mouth-to-mouth method if victim ingested or inhaled the substance; give artificial respiration with the aid of a pocket mask equipped with a one-way valve or other proper respiratory medical device.** • Administer oxygen if breathing is difficult. • Remove and isolate contaminated clothing and shoes. • In case of contact with substance, immediately flush skin or eyes with running water for at least 20 minutes. • For minor skin contact, avoid spreading material on unaffected skin. • Keep victim warm and quiet. • Effects of exposure (inhalation, ingestion or skin contact) to substance may be delayed. • Ensure that medical personnel are aware of the material(s) involved, and take precautions to protect themselves.

Schedule 4

# Guide No. 153   Substances - Toxic and/or Corrosive (Combustible)

## POTENTIAL HAZARDS

**HEALTH**

- **TOXIC**; inhalation, ingestion, or skin contact with material may cause severe injury or death. • Contact with molten substance may cause severe burns to skin and eyes. • Avoid any skin contact. • Effects of contact or inhalation may be delayed. • Fire may produce irritating, corrosive and/or toxic gases. • Runoff from fire control or dilution water may be corrosive and/or toxic and cause pollution.

**FIRE OR EXPLOSION**

Combustible material: may burn but does not ignite readily. • When heated, vapors may form explosive mixtures with air: indoors, outdoors, and sewers explosion hazards. • Those substances designated with a **"P"** may polymerize explosively when heated or involved in a fire. • Contact with metals may evolve flammable hydrogen gas. • Containers may explode when heated. • Runoff may pollute waterways. • Substance may be transported in a molten form.

## PUBLIC SAFETY

- **CALL Emergency Response Telephone Number on Shipping Document first. If Shipping Document not available or no answer, refer to appropriate telephone number listed at the end of this book.** • As an immediate precautionary measure, isolate spill or leak area in all directions for at least 50 meters (150 feet) for liquids and at least 25 meters (75 feet) for solids. • Keep unauthorized personnel away. • Stay upwind. • Keep out of low areas. • Ventilate enclosed areas.

**PROTECTIVE CLOTHING**

- Wear positive pressure self-contained breathing apparatus (SCBA). • Wear chemical protective clothing that is specifically recommended by the manufacturer. It may provide little or no thermal protection. • Structural firefighters' protective clothing provides limited protection in fire situations ONLY; it is not effective in spill situations.

**EVACUATION**

**Spill**
- See Table of Initial Isolation and Protective Action Distances in Schedule 6 for those dangerous goods marked with a "T" in Schedule 5. For those dangerous goods not marked with a "T" in Schedule 5 increase, as necessary, the minimum isolation distance of at least 50 meters for liquids and 25 meters for solids in the downwind direction.

**Fire**
- If tank, rail car or tank truck is involved in a fire, ISOLATE for 800 meters (1/2 mile) in all directions; also, consider initial evacuation for 800 meters (1/2 mile) in all directions.

## EMERGENCY RESPONSE

**FIRE**

**Small Fire**
- Dry chemical, $CO_2$ or water spray.

**Large Fire**
- Dry chemical, $CO_2$, alcohol-resistant foam or water spray. • Move containers from fire area if you can do it without risk. • Dike fire control water for later disposal; do not scatter the material.

**Fire involving Tanks or Car/Trailer Loads**
- Fight fire from maximum distance or use unmanned hose holders or monitor nozzles. • Do not get water inside containers.
- Cool containers with flooding quantities of water until well after fire is out. • Withdraw immediately in case of rising sound from venting safety devices or discoloration of tank. • ALWAYS stay away from tanks engulfed in fire.

**SPILL OR LEAK**

- ELIMINATE all ignition sources (no smoking, flares, sparks or flames in immediate area). • Do not touch damaged containers or spilled material unless wearing appropriate protective clothing. • Stop leak if you can do it without risk. • Prevent entry into waterways, sewers, basements or confined areas. • Absorb or cover with dry earth, sand or other non-combustible material and transfer to containers. • **DO NOT GET WATER INSIDE CONTAINERS.**

**FIRST AID**

- Move victim to fresh air. • Call 911 or emergency medical service. • Give artificial respiration if victim is not breathing. • **Do not use mouth-to-mouth method if victim ingested or inhaled the substance; give artificial respiration with the aid of a pocket mask equipped with a one-way valve or other proper respiratory medical device.** • Administer oxygen if breathing is difficult. • Remove and isolate contaminated clothing and shoes. • In case of contact with substance, immediately flush skin or eyes with running water for at least 20 minutes. • For minor skin contact, avoid spreading material on unaffected skin. • Keep victim warm and quiet. • Effects of exposure (inhalation, ingestion or skin contact) to substance may be delayed. • Ensure that medical personnel are aware of the material(s) involved, and take precautions to protect themselves.

# Guide No. 154 Substances - Toxic and/or Corrosive (Non-Combustible)

## POTENTIAL HAZARDS

**HEALTH**
- **TOXIC**; inhalation, ingestion, or skin contact with material may cause severe injury or death. • Contact with molten substance may cause severe burns to skin and eyes. • Avoid any skin contact. • Effects of contact or inhalation may be delayed. • Fire may produce irritating, corrosive and/or toxic gases. • Runoff from fire control or dilution water may be corrosive and/or toxic and cause pollution.

**FIRE OR EXPLOSION**
- Non-combustible, substance itself does not burn but may decompose upon heating to produce corrosive and/or toxic fumes. • Some are oxidizers and may ignite combustibles (wood, paper, oil, clothing, etc.). • Contact with metals may evolve flammable hydrogen gas. • Containers may explode when heated.

## PUBLIC SAFETY

- **CALL Emergency Response Telephone Number on Shipping Document first. If Shipping Document not available or no answer, refer to appropriate telephone number listed at the end of this book.** • As an immediate precautionary measure, isolate spill or leak area in all directions for at least 50 meters (150 feet) for liquids and at least 25 meters (75 feet) for solids. • Keep unauthorized personnel away. • Stay upwind. • Keep out of low areas. • Ventilate enclosed areas.

**PROTECTIVE CLOTHING**
- Wear positive pressure self-contained breathing apparatus (SCBA). • Wear chemical protective clothing that is specifically recommended by the manufacturer. It may provide little or no thermal protection. • Structural firefighters' protective clothing provides limited protection in fire situations ONLY; it is not effective in spill situations where direct contact with the substance is possible.

**EVACUATION**

Spill
- See Table of Initial Isolation and Protective Action Distances in Schedule 6 for those dangerous goods marked with a "T" in Schedule 5. For those dangerous goods not marked with a "T" in Schedule 5 increase, as necessary, the minimum isolation distance of at 50 meters for liquids and 25 meters for solids in the downwind direction.

Fire
- If tank, rail car or tank truck is involved in a fire, ISOLATE for 800 meters (1/2 mile) in all directions; also, consider initial evacuation for 800 meters (1/2 mile) in all directions.

## EMERGENCY RESPONSE

**FIRE**

Small Fire
- Dry chemical, $CO_2$ or water spray.

Large Fire
- Dry chemical, $CO_2$, alcohol-resistant foam or water spray. • Move containers from fire area if you can do it without risk. • Dike fire control water for later disposal; do not scatter the material.

Fire involving Tanks or Car/Trailer Loads
- Fight fire from maximum distance or use unmanned hose holders or monitor nozzles. • Do not get water inside containers.
- Cool containers with flooding quantities of water until well after fire is out. • Withdraw immediately in case of rising sound from venting safety devices or discoloration of tank. • ALWAYS stay away from tanks engulfed in fire.

**SPILL OR LEAK**
- ELIMINATE all ignition sources (no smoking, flares, sparks or flames in immediate area). • Do not touch damaged containers or spilled material unless wearing appropriate protective clothing. • Stop leak if you can do it without risk. • Prevent entry into waterways, sewers, basements or confined areas. • Absorb or cover with dry earth, sand or other non-combustible material and transfer to containers. • **DO NOT GET WATER INSIDE CONTAINERS.**

**FIRST AID**
- Move victim to fresh air. • Call 911 or emergency medical service. • Give artificial respiration if victim is not breathing. • **Do not use mouth-to-mouth method if victim ingested or inhaled the substance; give artificial respiration with the aid of a pocket mask equipped with a one-way valve or other proper respiratory medical device.** • Administer oxygen if breathing is difficult. • Remove and isolate contaminated clothing and shoes. • In case of contact with substance, immediately flush skin or eyes with running water for at least 20 minutes. • For minor skin contact, avoid spreading material on unaffected skin. • Keep victim warm and quiet. • Effects of exposure (inhalation, ingestion or skin contact) to substance may be delayed. • Ensure that medical personnel are aware of the material(s) involved, and take precautions to protect themselves.

# Guide No. 155   Substances - Toxic and/or Corrosive (Flammable/Water-Sensitive)

## POTENTIAL HAZARDS

**FIRE OR EXPLOSION**
- HIGHLY FLAMMABLE: Will be easily ignited by heat, sparks or flames. • Vapors form explosive mixtures with air: indoors, outdoors, and sewers explosion hazards. • Most vapors are heavier than air. They will spread along ground and collect in low or confined areas (sewers, basements, tanks). • Vapors may travel to source of ignition and flash back. • Those designated with a "P" may polymerize when heated or involved in a fire. • Substance will react with water (some violently) releasing flammable, toxic or corrosive gases and runoff. • Contact with metals may evolve flammable hydrogen gas. • Containers may explode when heated or if contaminated with water.

**HEALTH**
- TOXIC; inhalation, ingestion or contact (skin, eyes) with vapors, dusts or substance may cause severe injury, burns or death. • **Bromoacetates and chloroacetates are extremely irritating/lachrymators.** • Reaction with water or moist air will release toxic, corrosive or flammable gases. • Reaction with water may generate much heat which will increase the concentration of fumes in the air. • Fire will produce irritating, corrosive and/or toxic gases. • Runoff from fire control or dilution water may be corrosive and/or toxic and cause pollution.

## PUBLIC SAFETY

- CALL Emergency Response Telephone Number on Shipping Document first. If Shipping Document not available or no answer, refer to appropriate telephone number listed at the end of this book. • As an immediate precautionary measure, isolate spill or leak area in all directions for at least 50 meters (150 feet) for liquids and at least 25 meters (75 feet) for solids. • Keep unauthorized personnel away. • Stay upwind. • Keep out of low areas. • Ventilate enclosed areas.

**PROTECTIVE CLOTHING**
- Wear positive pressure self-contained breathing apparatus (SCBA). • Wear chemical protective clothing that is specifically recommended by the manufacturer. It may provide little or no thermal protection. • Structural firefighters' protective clothing provides limited protection in fire situations ONLY; it is not effective where direct contact with the substance is possible.

**EVACUATION**

Spill
- See Table of Initial Isolation and Protective Action Distances in Schedule 6 for those dangerous goods marked with a "T" in Schedule 5. For those dangerous goods not marked with a "T" in Schedule 5 increase, as necessary, the minimum isolation distance of at 50 meters for liquids and 25 meters for solids in the downwind direction.

Fire
- If tank, rail car or tank truck is involved in a fire, ISOLATE for 800 meters (1/2 mile) in all directions; also, consider initial evacuation for 800 meters (1/2 mile) in all directions.

## EMERGENCY RESPONSE

**FIRE**
- Note: Most foams will react with the material and release corrosive/toxic gases. **CAUTION: For Acetyl chloride(UN1717), use $CO_2$ or dry chemical only.**

**Small Fire** • $CO_2$, dry chemical, dry sand, alcohol-resistant foam.

**Large Fire** • Water spray, fog or alcohol-resistant foam. • **FOR CHLOROSILANES, DO NOT USE WATER;** use AFFF alcohol-resistant medium expansion foam. • Move containers from fire area if you can do it without risk. • Use water spray or fog; not straight streams.

**Fire involving Tanks or Car/Trailer Loads**
- Fight fire from maximum distance or use unmanned hose holders or monitor nozzles. • Do not get water inside containers.
- Cool containers with flooding quantities of water until well after fire is out. • Withdraw immediately in case of rising sound from venting safety devices or discoloration of tank. • ALWAYS stay away from tanks engulfed in fire.

**SPILL OR LEAK**
- ELIMINATE all ignition sources (no smoking, flares, sparks or flames in immediate area). • All equipment used when handling the product must be grounded. • Do not touch damaged containers or spilled material unless wearing appropriate protective clothing. • Stop leak if you can do it without risk. • A vapor suppressing foam may be used to reduce vapors. • **FOR CHLOROSILANES, use AFFF alcohol-resistant medium expansion foam to reduce vapors.** • **DO NOT GET WATER on spilled substance or inside containers.** • Use water spray to reduce vapors or divert vapor cloud drift. Avoid allowing water runoff to contact spilled material. • Prevent entry into waterways, sewers, basements or confined areas.

**Small Spill**
- Cover with DRY earth, DRY sand, or other non-combustible material followed with plastic sheet to minimize spreading or contact with rain.
- Use clean non-sparking tools to collect material and place it into loosely covered plastic containers for later disposal.

**FIRST AID**
- Move victim to fresh air. • Call 911 or emergency medical service. • Give artificial respiration if victim is not breathing. • **Do not use mouth-to-mouth method if victim ingested or inhaled the substance; give artificial respiration with the aid of a pocket mask equipped with a one-way valve or other proper respiratory medical device.** • Administer oxygen if breathing is difficult. • Remove and isolate contaminated clothing and shoes. • In case of contact with substance, immediately flush skin or eyes with running water for at least 20 minutes. • For minor skin contact, avoid spreading material on unaffected skin. • Keep victim warm and quiet. • Effects of exposure (inhalation, ingestion or skin contact) to substance may be delayed. • Ensure that medical personnel are aware of the material(s) involved, and take precautions to protect themselves.

# Guide No. 156   Substances - Toxic and/or Corrosive (Combustible/Water-Sensitive)

## POTENTIAL HAZARDS

**FIRE OR EXPLOSION**

• Combustible material: may burn but does not ignite readily. • Substance will react with water (some violently) releasing flammable, toxic or corrosive gases and runoff. • When heated, vapors may form explosive mixtures with air: indoors, outdoors, and sewers explosion hazards. • Most vapors are heavier than air. They will spread along ground and collect in low or confined areas (sewers, basements, tanks). • Vapors may travel to source of ignition and flash back. • Contact with metals may evolve flammable hydrogen gas. • Containers may explode when heated or if contaminated with water.

**HEALTH**

• TOXIC; inhalation, ingestion or contact (skin, eyes) with vapors, dusts or substance may cause severe injury, burns or death. • Contact with molten substance may cause severe burns to skin and eyes. • Reaction with water or moist air will release toxic, corrosive or flammable gases. • Reaction with water may generate much heat which will increase the concentration of fumes in the air. • Fire will produce irritating, corrosive and/or toxic gases. • Runoff from fire control or dilution water may be corrosive and/or toxic and cause pollution.

## PUBLIC SAFETY

• CALL Emergency Response Telephone Number on Shipping Document first. If Shipping Document not available or no answer, refer to appropriate telephone number listed at the end of this book. • As an immediate precautionary measure, isolate spill or leak area in all directions for at least 50 meters (150 feet) for liquids and at least 25 meters (75 feet) for solids. • Keep unauthorized personnel away. • Stay upwind. • Keep out of low areas. • Ventilate enclosed areas.

**PROTECTIVE CLOTHING**

• Wear positive pressure self-contained breathing apparatus (SCBA). • Wear chemical protective clothing that is specifically recommended by the manufacturer. It may provide little or no thermal protection. • Structural firefighters' protective clothing provides limited protection in fire situations ONLY; it is not effective where direct contact with the substance is possible.

**EVACUATION**

**Spill**

• See Table of Initial Isolation and Protective Action Distances in Schedule 6 for those dangerous goods marked with a "T" in Schedule 5. For those dangerous goods not marked with a "T" in Schedule 5 increase, as necessary, the minimum isolation distance of at 50 meters for liquids and 25 meters for solids in the downwind direction.

**Fire**

• If tank, rail car or tank truck is involved in a fire, ISOLATE for 800 meters (1/2 mile) in all directions; also, consider initial evacuation for 800 meters (1/2 mile) in all directions.

## EMERGENCY RESPONSE

**FIRE**

• Note: Most foams will react with the material and release corrosive/toxic gases.

**Small Fire**

• CO$_2$, dry chemical, dry sand, alcohol-resistant foam.

**Large Fire**

• Water spray, fog or alcohol-resistant foam. • **FOR CHLOROSILANES, DO NOT USE WATER;** use AFFF alcohol-resistant medium expansion foam. • Move containers from fire area if you can do it without risk. • Use water spray or fog; not straight streams.

**Fire involving Tanks or Car/Trailer Loads**

• Fight fire from maximum distance or use unmanned hose holders or monitor nozzles. • Do not get water inside containers. • Cool containers with flooding quantities of water until well after fire is out. • Withdraw immediately in case of rising sound from venting safety devices or discoloration of tank. • ALWAYS stay away from tanks engulfed in fire.

**SPILL OR LEAK**

• ELIMINATE all ignition sources (no smoking, flares, sparks or flames in immediate area). • All equipment used when handling the product must be grounded. • Do not touch damaged containers or spilled material unless wearing appropriate protective clothing. • Stop leak if you can do it without risk. • A vapor suppressing foam may be used to reduce vapors. • **FOR CHLOROSILANES, use AFFF** alcohol-resistant medium expansion foam to reduce vapors. • **DO NOT GET WATER on spilled substance or inside containers.** • Use water spray to reduce vapors or divert vapor cloud drift. Avoid allowing water runoff to contact spilled material. • Prevent entry into waterways, sewers, basements or confined areas.

**Small Spill**

• Cover with DRY earth, DRY sand, or other non-combustible material followed with plastic sheet to minimize spreading or contact with rain. • Use clean non-sparking tools to collect material and place it into loosely covered plastic containers for later disposal.

**FIRST AID**

• Move victim to fresh air. • Call 911 or emergency medical service. • Give artificial respiration if victim is not breathing. • **Do not use mouth-to-mouth method if victim ingested or inhaled the substance; give artificial respiration with the aid of a pocket mask equipped with a one-way valve or other proper respiratory medical device.** • Administer oxygen if breathing is difficult. • Remove and isolate contaminated clothing and shoes. • In case of contact with substance, immediately flush skin or eyes with running water for at least 20 minutes. • For minor skin contact, avoid spreading material on unaffected skin. • Keep victim warm and quiet. • Effects of exposure (inhalation, ingestion or skin contact) to substance may be delayed. • Ensure that medical personnel are aware of the material(s) involved, and take precautions to protect themselves.

Schedule 4

# Guide No. 157    Substances - Toxic and/or Corrosive (Non-Combustible/Water-Sensitive)

## POTENTIAL HAZARDS

**HEALTH**

- **TOXIC**; inhalation, ingestion or contact (skin, eyes) with vapors, dusts or substance may cause severe injury, burns or death.
- Reaction with water or moist air will release toxic, corrosive or flammable gases. • Reaction with water may generate much heat which will increase the concentration of fumes in the air. • Fire will produce irritating, corrosive and/or toxic gases. • Runoff from fire control or dilution water may be corrosive and/or toxic and cause pollution.

**FIRE OR EXPLOSION**

- Non-combustible, substance itself does not burn but may decompose upon heating to produce corrosive and/or toxic fumes.
- Vapors may accumulate in confined areas (basement, tanks, hopper/tank cars, etc.). • Substance will react with water (some violently), releasing corrosive and/or toxic gases. • Reaction with water may generate much heat which will increase the concentration of fumes in the air. • Contact with metals may evolve flammable hydrogen gas. • Containers may explode when heated or if contaminated with water.

## PUBLIC SAFETY

- **CALL Emergency Response Telephone Number on Shipping Document first. If Shipping Document not available or no answer, refer to appropriate telephone number listed at the end of this book.** • As an immediate precautionary measure, isolate spill or leak area in all direction for at least 50 meters (150 feet) for liquids and at least 25 meters (75 feet) for solids. • Keep unauthorized personnel away. • Stay upwind. • Keep out of low areas. • Ventilate enclosed areas.

**PROTECTIVE CLOTHING**

- Wear positive pressure self-contained breathing apparatus (SCBA). • Wear chemical protective clothing that is specifically recommended by the manufacturer. It may provide little or no thermal protection. • Structural firefighters' protective clothing provides limited protection in fire situations ONLY; it is not effective in spill situations where direct contact with the substance is possible.

**EVACUATION**

**Spill**

- See Table of Initial Isolation and Protective Action Distances in Schedule 6 for those dangerous goods marked with a "T" in Schedule 5. For those dangerous goods not marked with a "T" in Schedule 5 increase, as necessary, the minimum isolation distance of at 50 meters for liquids and 25 meters for solids in the downwind direction.

**Fire**

- If tank, rail car or tank truck is involved in a fire, ISOLATE for 800 meters (1/2 mile) in all directions; also, consider initial evacuation for 800 meters (1/2 mile) in all directions.

## EMERGENCY RESPONSE

**FIRE**

- Note: Most foams will react with the material and release corrosive/toxic gases.

**Small Fire**

- $CO_2$ (except for Cyanides), dry chemical, dry sand, alcohol-resistant foam.

**Large Fire**

- Water spray, fog or alcohol-resistant foam. • Move containers from fire area if you can do it without risk. • Use water spray or fog; do not use straight streams. • Dike fire control water for later disposal; do not scatter the material.

**Fire involving Tanks or Car/Trailer Loads**

- Fight fire from maximum distance or use unmanned hose holders or monitor nozzles. • Do not get water inside containers.
- Cool containers with flooding quantities of water until well after fire is out. • Withdraw immediately in case of rising sound from venting safety devices or discoloration of tank. • ALWAYS stay away from tanks engulfed in fire.

**SPILL OR LEAK**

- ELIMINATE all ignition sources (no smoking, flares, sparks or flames in immediate area). • All equipment used when handling the product must be grounded. • Do not touch damaged containers or spilled material unless wearing appropriate protective clothing. • Stop leak if you can do it without risk. • A vapor suppressing foam may be used to reduce vapors. • **DO NOT GET WATER INSIDE CONTAINERS.** • Use water spray to reduce vapors or divert vapor cloud drift. Avoid allowing water runoff to contact spilled material. • Prevent entry into waterways, sewers, basements or confined areas.

**Small Spill**

- Cover with DRY earth, DRY sand, or other non-combustible material followed with plastic sheet to minimize spreading or contact with rain. • Use clean non-sparking tools to collect material and place it into loosely covered plastic containers for later disposal.

**FIRST AID**

- Move victim to fresh air. • Call 911 or emergency medical service. • Give artificial respiration if victim is not breathing. • **Do not use mouth-to-mouth method if victim ingested or inhaled the substance; give artificial respiration with the aid of a pocket mask equipped with a one-way valve or other proper respiratory medical device.** • Administer oxygen if breathing is difficult. • Remove and isolate contaminated clothing and shoes. • In case of contact with substance, immediately flush skin or eyes with running water for at least 20 minutes. • For minor skin contact, avoid spreading material on unaffected skin. • Keep victim warm and quiet. • Effects of exposure (inhalation, ingestion or skin contact) to substance may be delayed. • Ensure that medical personnel are aware of the material(s) involved, and take precautions to protect themselves.

Schedule 4

# Guide No. 158    Infectious Substances

## POTENTIAL HAZARDS

**HEALTH**
- Inhalation or contact with substance may cause infection, disease, or death. • Runoff from fire control may cause pollution.
- **Note: Damaged packages containing solid $CO_2$ as a refrigerant may produce water or frost from condensation of air. Do not touch this liquid as it could be contaminated by the contents of the parcel.**

**FIRE OR EXPLOSION**
- Some of these materials may burn, but none ignite readily. • Some may be transported in flammable liquids.

## PUBLIC SAFETY

- **CALL Emergency Response Telephone Number on Shipping Document first. If Shipping Document not available or no answer, refer to appropriate telephone number listed at the end of this book.** • As an immediate precautionary measure, isolate spill or leak area for at least 25 meters (75 feet) in all directions. • Keep unauthorized personnel away. • Stay upwind. • Obtain identity of substance involved.

**PROTECTIVE CLOTHING**
- Wear positive pressure self-contained breathing apparatus (SCBA). • Structural firefighters' protective clothing will only provide limited protection.

## EMERGENCY RESPONSE

**FIRE**

**Small Fire**
- Dry chemical, soda ash, lime or sand.

**Large Fire**
- Use extinguishing agent suitable for type of surrounding fire. • Move containers from fire area if you can do it without risk. • Do not scatter spilled material with high pressure water streams.

**SPILL OR LEAK**
- Do not touch or walk through spilled material. • Do not touch damaged containers or spilled material unless wearing appropriate protective clothing. • Absorb with earth, sand or other non-combustible material. • Cover damaged package or spilled material with damp towel or rag and keep wet with liquid bleach or other disinfectant. • **DO NOT CLEAN-UP OR DISPOSE OF, EXCEPT UNDER SUPERVISION OF A SPECIALIST.**

**FIRST AID**
- Move victim to a safe isolated area. • **CAUTION: Victim may be a source of contamination.** • Call 911 or emergency medical service. • Remove and isolate contaminated clothing and shoes. • In case of contact with substance, immediately flush skin or eyes with running water for at least 20 minutes. • Effects of exposure (inhalation, ingestion or skin contact) to substance may be delayed. • **For further assistance, contact your local Poison Control Center.** • Ensure that medical personnel are aware of the material(s) involved, and take precautions to protect themselves.

Schedule 4

# Guide No. 159    Substances (Irritating)

## POTENTIAL HAZARDS

**HEALTH**
- Inhalation of vapors or dust is extremely irritating. • May cause burning of eyes and flow of tears. • May cause coughing, diffic breathing and nausea. • Brief exposure effects last only a few minutes. • Exposure in an enclosed area may be very harmful.
- Fire will produce irritating, corrosive and/or toxic gases. • Runoff from fire control or dilution water may cause pollution.

**FIRE OR EXPLOSION**
- Some of these materials may burn, but none ignite readily. • Containers may explode when heated.

## PUBLIC SAFETY

- **CALL Emergency Response Telephone Number on Shipping Document first. If Shipping Document not available or no answer, refer to appropriate telephone number listed at the end of this book.** • As an immediate precautionary measure, isolate spill or leak area in all directio for at least 50 meters (150 feet) for liquids and at least 25 meters (75 feet) for solids. • Keep unauthorized personnel away. • Stay upwind. • Keep out of low areas. • Ventilate closed spaces before entering.

**PROTECTIVE CLOTHING**
- Wear positive pressure self-contained breathing apparatus (SCBA). • Wear chemical protective clothing that is specifically recommended by the manufacturer. It may provide little or no thermal protection. • Structural firefighters' protective clothing provides limited protection in fire situations ONLY; it is not effective in spill situations where direct contact with the substance is possible.

**EVACUATION**

**Large Spill**
- See Table of Initial Isolation and Protective Action Distances in Schedule 6 for those dangerous goods marked with a "T" in Schedule 5. For those dangerous goods not marked with a "T" in Schedule 5 increase, as necessary, the minimum isolation distance of at 50 meters for liquids and 25 meters for solids in the downwind direction.

**Fire**
- If tank, rail car or tank truck is involved in a fire, ISOLATE for 800 meters (1/2 mile) in all directions; also, consider initial evacuation for 800 meters (1/2 mile) in all directions.

## EMERGENCY RESPONSE

**FIRE**

**Small Fire**
- Dry chemical, $CO_2$, water spray or regular foam.

**Large Fire**
- Water spray, fog or regular foam. • Move containers from fire area if you can do it without risk. • Dike fire control water for late disposal; do not scatter the material.

**Fire involving Tanks or Car/Trailer Loads**
- Fight fire from maximum distance or use unmanned hose holders or monitor nozzles. • Do not get water inside containers.
- Cool containers with flooding quantities of water until well after fire is out. • Withdraw immediately in case of rising sound from venting safety devices or discoloration of tank. • ALWAYS stay away from tanks engulfed in fire. • For massive fire, use unmanned hose holders or monitor nozzles; if this is impossible, withdraw from area and let fire burn.

**SPILL OR LEAK**
- Do not touch or walk through spilled material. • Stop leak if you can do it without risk. • Fully encapsulating, vapor protective clothing should be worn for spills and leaks with no fire.

**Small Spill**
- Take up with sand or other non-combustible absorbent material and place into containers for later disposal.

**Large Spill**
- Dike far ahead of liquid spill for later disposal. • Prevent entry into waterways, sewers, basements or confined areas.

**FIRST AID**
- Move victim to fresh air. • Call 911 or emergency medical service. • Give artificial respiration if victim is not breathing. • **Do n use mouth-to-mouth method if victim ingested or inhaled the substance; induce artificial respiration with the aid of a pocket mask equipped with a one-way valve or other proper respiratory medical device.** • Administer oxygen if breathing difficult. • Remove and isolate contaminated clothing and shoes. • In case of contact with substance, immediately flush skin or eyes with running water for at least 20 minutes. • For minor skin contact, avoid spreading material on unaffected skin. • Keep victim warm and quiet. • Effects should disappear after individual has been exposed to fresh air for approximately 10 minutes.
- Ensure that medical personnel are aware of the material(s) involved, and take precautions to protect themselves.

Schedule 4

# Guide No. 160    Halogenated Solvents

## POTENTIAL HAZARDS

**HEALTH**
- Toxic by ingestion. • Vapors may cause dizziness or suffocation. • Exposure in an enclosed area may be very harmful. • Contact may irritate or burn skin and eyes. • Fire may produce irritating and/or toxic gases. • Runoff from fire control or dilution water may cause pollution.

**FIRE OR EXPLOSION**
- Some of these materials may burn, but none ignite readily. • Most vapors are heavier than air. • Air/vapor mixtures may explode when ignited. • Container may explode in heat of fire.

## PUBLIC SAFETY

- **CALL Emergency Response Telephone Number on Shipping Document first. If Shipping Document not available or no answer, refer to appropriate telephone number listed at the end of this book.** • As an immediate precautionary measure, isolate spill or leak area for at least 50 meters (150 feet) in all directions.. • Keep unauthorized personnel away. • Stay upwind. • Many gases are heavier than air and will spread along ground and collect in low or confined areas (sewers, basements, tanks). • Keep out of low areas. • Ventilate closed spaces before entering.

**PROTECTIVE CLOTHING**
- Wear positive pressure self-contained breathing apparatus (SCBA). • Wear chemical protective clothing that is specifically recommended by the manufacturer. It may provide little or no thermal protection. • Structural firefighters' protective clothing will only provide limited protection.

**EVACUATION**

**Large Spill**
- Consider initial downwind evacuation for at least 100 meters (330 feet).

**Fire**
- If tank, rail car or tank truck is involved in a fire, ISOLATE for 800 meters (1/2 mile) in all directions; also, consider initial evacuation for 800 meters (1/2 mile) in all directions.

## EMERGENCY RESPONSE

**FIRE**

**Small Fire**
- Dry chemical, $CO_2$ or water spray.

**Large Fire**
- Dry chemical, CO2, alcohol-resistant foam or water spray.• Move containers from fire area if you can do it without risk.• Dike fire-control water for later disposal; do not scatter the material.

**Fire involving Tanks or Car/Trailer Loads**
- Fight fire from maximum distance or use unmanned hose holders or monitor nozzles. • Cool containers with flooding quantities of water until well after fire is out. • Withdraw immediately in case of rising sound from venting safety devices or discoloration of tank. • **ALWAYS stay away from tanks engulfed in fire.**

**SPILL OR LEAK**
- ELIMINATE all ignition sources (no smoking, flares, sparks or flames in immediate area). • Stop leak if you can do it without risk.

**Small Liquid Spill**
- Take up with sand, earth or other non-combustible absorbent material.

**Large Spill**
- Dike far ahead of liquid spill for later disposal. • Prevent entry into waterways, sewers, basements or confined areas.

**FIRST AID**
- Move victim to fresh air. • Call 911 or emergency medical service. • Give artificial respiration if victim is not breathing. • Administer oxygen if breathing is difficult. • Remove and isolate contaminated clothing and shoes. • In case of contact with substance, immediately flush skin or eyes with running water for at least 20 minutes. • For minor skin contact, avoid spreading material on unaffected skin. • Wash skin with soap and water. • Keep victim warm and quiet. • Ensure that medical personnel are aware of the material(s) involved, and take precautions to protect themselves.

# Guide No. 161   Radioactive Materials (Low Level Radiation)

## POTENTIAL HAZARDS

**HEALTH**
- Radiation presents minimal risk to transport workers, emergency response personnel, and the public during transportation accidents. • Packaging durability increases as potential hazard of radioactive content increases. • Very low levels of contained radioactive materials and low radiation levels outside packages result in low risks to people. Damaged packages may release measurable amounts of radioactive material, but the resulting risks are expected to be low. • Some radioactive materials cannot be detected by commonly available instruments. • Packages do not have RADIOACTIVE I, II, or III labels. Some may have EMPTY labels or may have the word "Radioactive" in the package marking.

**FIRE OR EXPLOSION**
- Some of these materials may burn, but most do not ignite readily. • Many have cardboard outer packaging; content (physically large or small) can be of many different physical forms. • Radioactivity does not change flammability or other properties of materials.

## PUBLIC SAFETY

- **CALL Emergency Response Telephone Number on Shipping Document first. If Shipping Document not available or no answer, refer to appropriate telephone number listed at the end of this book.** • **Priorities for rescue, life-saving, first aid, and fire control and other hazard are higher than the priority for measuring radiation levels.** • Radiation Authority must be notified of accident conditions. Radiation Authority is usually responsible for decisions about radiological consequences and closure of emergencies. • As an immediate precautionary measure, isolate spill or leak area for at least 25 meters (75 feet) in all directions. • Stay upwind. • Keep unauthorized personnel away. • Detain or isolate uninjured persons or equipment suspected to be contaminated; delay decontamination and cleanup until instructions are received from Radiation Authority.

**PROTECTIVE CLOTHING**
- Positive pressure self-contained breathing apparatus (SCBA) and structural firefighters' protective clothing will provide adequate protection.

**EVACUATION**

**Large Spill**
- Consider initial downwind evacuation for at least 100 meters (330 feet).

**Fire**
- When a large quantity of this material is involved in a major fire, consider an initial evacuation distance of 300 meters (1000 feet) in all directions.

## EMERGENCY RESPONSE

**FIRE**
- Presence of radioactive material will not influence the fire control processes and should not influence selection of techniques.
- Move containers from fire area if you can do it without risk. • Do not move damaged packages; move undamaged packages out of fire zone.

**Small Fire**
- Dry chemical, $CO_2$, water spray or regular foam.

**Large Fire**
- Water spray, fog (flooding amounts).

**SPILL OR LEAK**
- Do not touch damaged packages or spilled material. • Cover liquid spill with sand, earth or other non-combustible absorbent material. • Cover powder spill with plastic sheet or tarp to minimize spreading.

**FIRST AID**
- Call 911 or emergency medical service. • Medical problems take priority over radiological concerns. • Use first aid treatment according to the nature of the injury. • Do not delay care and transport of a seriously injured person. • Give artificial respiration if victim is not breathing. • Administer oxygen if breathing is difficult. • In case of contact with substance, immediately flush skin or eyes with running water for at least 20 minutes. • Injured persons contaminated by contact with released material are not a serious hazard to health care personnel, equipment or facilities. • Ensure that medical personnel are aware of the material(s) involved, take precautions to protect themselves and prevent spread of contamination.

# Guide No. 162    Radioactive Materials (Low to Moderate Level Radiation)

## POTENTIAL HAZARDS

**HEALTH**

- Radiation presents minimal risk to transport workers, emergency response personnel, and the public during transportation accidents. • Packaging durability increases as potential hazard of radioactive content increases. • Undamaged packages are safe. Contents of damaged packages may cause higher external radiation exposure, or both external and internal radiation exposure if contents are released. • Low radiation hazard when material is inside container. If material is released from package or bulk container, hazard will vary from low to moderate. Level of hazard will depend on the type and amount of radioactivity, the kind of material it is in, and/or the surfaces it is on. • Some material may be released from packages during accidents of moderate severity but risks to people are not great. • Released radioactive materials or contaminated objects usually will be visible if packaging fails. • Some exclusive use shipments of bulk and packaged materials will not have "RADIOACTIVE" labels.
- Placards, markings, and Shipping Documents provide identification. • Some packages may have a "RADIOACTIVE" label and a second hazard label. The second hazard is usually greater than the radiation hazard; so follow this Guide as well as the response Guide for the second hazard class label. • Some radioactive materials cannot be detected by commonly available instruments.
- Runoff from control of cargo fire may cause low-level pollution.

**FIRE OR EXPLOSION**

- Some of these materials may burn, but most do not ignite readily. • Uranium and Thorium metal cuttings may ignite spontaneously if exposed to air (see Guide 136). • Nitrates are oxidizers and may ignite other combustibles (see Guide 141).

## PUBLIC SAFETY

• **CALL Emergency Response Telephone Number on Shipping Document first. If Shipping Document not available or no answer, refer to appropriate telephone number listed at the end of this book. • Priorities for rescue, life-saving, first aid, and fire control and other hazards are higher than the priority for measuring radiation levels.** • Radiation Authority must be notified of accident conditions. Radiation Authority is usually responsible for decisions about radiological consequences and closure of emergencies. • As an immediate precautionary measure, isolate spill or leak area for at least 25 meters (75 feet) in all directions. • Stay upwind. • Keep unauthorized personnel away. • Detain or isolate uninjured persons or equipment suspected to be contaminated; delay decontamination and cleanup until instructions are received from Radiation Authority.

**PROTECTIVE CLOTHING**

- Positive pressure self-contained breathing apparatus (SCBA) and structural firefighters' protective clothing will provide adequate protection.

**EVACUATION**

**Large Spill**
- Consider initial downwind evacuation for at least 100 meters (330 feet).

**Fire**
- When a large quantity of this material is involved in a major fire, consider an initial evacuation distance of 300 meters (1000 feet) in all directions.

## EMERGENCY RESPONSE

**FIRE**

- Presence of radioactive material will not influence the fire control processes and should not influence selection of techniques.
- Move containers from fire area if you can do it without risk. • Do not move damaged packages; move undamaged packages out of fire zone.

**Small Fire**
- Dry chemical, $CO_2$, water spray or regular foam.

**Large Fire**
- Water spray, fog (flooding amounts). • Dike fire-control water for later disposal.

**SPILL OR LEAK**

- Do not touch damaged packages or spilled material. • Cover liquid spill with sand, earth or other non-combustible absorbent material. • Dike to collect large liquid spills. • Cover powder spill with plastic sheet or tarp to minimize spreading.

**FIRST AID**

- Call 911 or emergency medical service. • Medical problems take priority over radiological concerns. • Use first aid treatment according to the nature of the injury. • Do not delay care and transport of a seriously injured person. • Give artificial respiration if victim is not breathing. • Administer oxygen if breathing is difficult. • In case of contact with substance, wipe from skin immediately; flush skin or eyes with running water for at least 20 minutes. • Injured persons contaminated by contact with released material are not a serious hazard to health care personnel, equipment or facilities. • Ensure that medical personnel are aware of the material(s) involved, take precautions to protect themselves and prevent spread of contamination.

Schedule 4

# Guide No. 163　Radioactive Materials (Low to High Level Radiation)

## POTENTIAL HAZARDS

| | |
|---|---|
| **HEALTH** | • Radiation presents minimal risk to transport workers, emergency response personnel, and the public during transportation accidents. • Packaging durability increases as potential hazard of radioactive content increases. • Undamaged packages are safe. Contents of damaged packages may cause higher external radiation exposure, or both external and internal radiation exposure if contents are released. • Type A packages (cartons, boxes, drums, articles, etc.) identified as "Type A" by marking o packages or by Shipping Documents contain non-life endangering amounts. Partial releases might be expected if "Type A" packages are damaged in moderately severe accidents. • Type B packages, and the rarely occurring Type C packages, (large and small, usually metal) contain the most hazardous amounts. They can be identified by package markings or by Shipping Documents. Life threatening conditions may exist only if contents are released or package shielding fails. Because of design, evaluation, and testing of packages, these conditions would be expected only for accidents of utmost severity. • The rarely occurring "Special Arrangement" shipments may be of Type A, Type B or Type C packages. Package type will be marked on packages, and shipment details will be on Shipping Documents. • Radioactive White-I labels indicate radiation levels outside single, isolated, undamaged packages are very low (less than 0.005 mSv/h (0.5 mrem/h)). • Radioactive Yellow-II and Yellow-II labeled packages have higher radiation levels. The transport index (TI) on the label identifies the maximum radiation level in mrem/h one meter from a single, isolated, undamaged package. • Some radioactive materials cannot be detected by commonly available instruments. • Water from cargo fire control may cause pollution. |
| **FIRE OR EXPLOSION** | • Some of these materials may burn, but most do not ignite readily. • Radioactivity does not change flammability or other properties of materials. • Type B packages are designed and evaluated to withstand total engulfment in flames at temperatures 800 degrees C (1475 degrees F) for a period of 30 minutes. |

## PUBLIC SAFETY

**• CALL Emergency Response Telephone Number on Shipping Paper first. If Shipping Paper not available or no answer, refer to appropriate telephone number listed on the inside back cover. • Priorities for rescue, life-saving, first aid, fire control and other hazards are higher than the priority for measuring radiation levels.** • Radiation Authority must be notified of accident conditions. Radiation Authority is usually responsible for  decisions about radiological consequences and closure of emergencies. • As an immediate precautionary measure, isolat spill or leak area for at least 25 meters (75 feet) in all directions. • Stay upwind. • Keep unauthorized personnel away. • Detain or isolate uninjure persons or equipment suspected to be contaminated; delay decontamination and cleanup until instructions are received from Radiation Authority.

| | |
|---|---|
| **PROTECTIVE CLOTHING** | • Positive pressure self-contained breathing apparatus (SCBA) and structural firefighters' protective clothing will provide adequa protection against internal radiation exposure, but not external radiation exposure. |
| **EVACUATION** | **Large Spill**<br>• Consider initial downwind evacuation for at least 100 meters (330 feet).<br>**Fire**<br>• When a large quantity of this material is involved in a major fire, consider an initial evacuation distance of 300 meters (1000 fe in all directions. |

## EMERGENCY RESPONSE

| | |
|---|---|
| **FIRE** | • Presence of radioactive material will not influence the fire control processes and should not influence selection of techniques.<br>• Move containers from fire area if you can do it without risk. • Do not move damaged packages; move undamaged packages o of fire zone.<br>**Small Fire**<br>• Dry chemical, $CO_2$, water spray or regular foam.<br>**Large Fire**<br>• Water spray, fog (flooding amounts). • Dike fire-control water for later disposal. |
| **SPILL OR LEAK** | • Do not touch damaged packages or spilled material. • Damp surfaces on undamaged or slightly damaged packages are seldo an indication of packaging failure. Most packaging for liquid content have inner containers and/or inner absorbent materials.<br>• Cover liquid spill with sand, earth or other non-combustible absorbent material. |
| **FIRST AID** | • Call 911 or emergency medical service. • Medical problems take priority over radiological concerns. • Use first aid treatment according to the nature of the injury. • Do not delay care and transport of a seriously injured person. • Give artificial respiration i victim is not breathing. • Administer oxygen if breathing is difficult. • In case of contact with substance, immediately flush skin or eyes with running water for at least 20 minutes. • Injured persons contaminated by contact with released material are not a serious hazard to health care personnel, equipment or facilities. • Ensure that medical personnel are aware of the material(s) involved, take precautions to protect themselves and prevent spread of contamination. |

Schedule 4

# Guide No. 164    Radioactive Materials (Special Form / Low to High Level External Radiation)

## POTENTIAL HAZARDS

**HEALTH**

• Radiation presents minimal risk to transport workers, emergency response personnel, and the public during transportation accidents. • Packaging durability increases as potential hazard of radioactive content increases. • Undamaged packages are safe. Contents of damaged packages may cause external radiation exposure, and much higher external exposure if contents (source capsules) are released. • Contamination and internal radiation hazards are not expected, but not impossible. • Type A packages (cartons, boxes, drums, articles, etc.) identified as "Type A" by marking on packages or by Shipping Documents contain non-life endangering amounts. Radioactive sources may be released if "Type A" packages are damaged in moderately severe accidents. • Type B packages, and the rarely occurring Type C packages, (large and small, usually metal) contain the most hazardous amounts. They can be identified by package markings or by Shipping Documents. Life threatening conditions may exist only if contents are released or package shielding fails. Because of design, evaluation, and testing of packages, these conditions would be expected only for accidents of utmost severity. • Radioactive White-I labels indicate radiation levels outside single, isolated, undamaged packages are very low (less than 0.005 mSv/h (0.5 mrem/h)). • Radioactive Yellow-II and Yellow-III labeled packages have higher radiation levels. The transport index (TI) on the label identifies the maximum radiation level in mrem/h one meter from a single, isolated, undamaged package. • Radiation from the package contents, usually in durable metal capsules, can be detected by most radiation instruments. • Water from cargo fire control is not expected to cause pollution.

**FIRE OR EXPLOSION**

• Packagings can burn completely without risk of content loss from sealed source capsule. • Radioactivity does not change flammability or other properties of materials. • Radioactive source capsules and Type B packages are designed and evaluated to withstand total engulfment in flames at temperatures of 800 degrees C (1475 degrees F) for a period of 30 minutes.

## PUBLIC SAFETY

• CALL Emergency Response Telephone Number on Shipping Document first. If Shipping Document not available or no answer, refer to appropriate telephone number listed at the end of this book. • Priorities for rescue, life-saving, first aid, and fire control and other hazards are higher than the priority for measuring radiation levels. • Radiation Authority must be notified of accident conditions. Radiation Authority is usually responsible for decisions about radiological consequences and closure of emergencies. • As an immediate precautionary measure, isolate spill or leak area for at least 25 meters (75 feet) in all directions. • Stay upwind. • Keep unauthorized personnel away. • Delay final cleanup until instructions or advice is received from Radiation Authority.

**PROTECTIVE CLOTHING**

• Positive pressure self-contained breathing apparatus (SCBA) and structural firefighters' protective clothing will provide adequate protection against internal radiation exposure, but not external radiation exposure.

**EVACUATION**

**Large Spill**

• Consider initial downwind evacuation for at least 100 meters (330 feet).

**Fire**

• When a large quantity of this material is involved in a major fire, consider an initial evacuation distance of 300 meters (1000 feet) in all directions.

## EMERGENCY RESPONSE

**FIRE**

• Presence of radioactive material will not influence the fire control processes and should not influence selection of techniques. • Move containers from fire area if you can do it without risk. • Do not move damaged packages; move undamaged packages out of fire zone.

**Small Fire**

• Dry chemical, $CO_2$, water spray or regular foam.

**Large Fire**

• Water spray, fog (flooding amounts).

**SPILL OR LEAK**

• Do not touch damaged packages or spilled material. • Damp surfaces on undamaged or slightly damaged packages are seldom an indication of packaging failure. Contents are seldom liquid. Content is usually a metal capsule, easily seen if released from package. • If source capsule is identified as being out of package, **DO NOT TOUCH**. Stay away and await advice from Radiation Authority.

**FIRST AID**

• Medical problems take priority over radiological concerns. • Use first aid treatment according to the nature of the injury. • Do not delay care and transport of a seriously injured person. • Persons exposed to special form sources are not likely to be contaminated with radioactive material. • Give artificial respiration if victim is not breathing. • Administer oxygen if breathing is difficult. • Injured persons contaminated by contact with released material are not a serious hazard to health care personnel, equipment or facilities. • Ensure that medical personnel are aware of the material(s) involved, take precautions to protect themselves and prevent spread of contamination.

**Schedule 4**

# Guide No. 165 Radioactive Materials (Fissile/Low to High Level Radiation)

## POTENTIAL HAZARDS

| | |
|---|---|
| **HEALTH** | • Radiation presents minimal risk to transport workers, emergency response personnel, and the public during transportation accidents. • Packaging durability increases as potential radiation and criticality hazards of the content increase. • Undamaged packages are safe. Contents of damaged packages may cause higher external radiation exposure, or both external and internal radiation exposure if contents are released. • Type AF or IF packages, identified by package markings, do not contain life-threatening amounts of material. External radiation levels are low and packages are designed, evaluated, and tested to control releases and to prevent a fission chain reaction under severe transport conditions. • Type B(U)F, B(M)F and CF packages (identified by markings on packages or Shipping Documents) contain potentially life endangering amounts. Because of design, evaluation, and testing of packages, fission chain reactions are prevented and releases are not expected to be life endangering in all accidents except those of utmost severity. • The rarely occurring "Special Arrangement" shipments may be of Type AF, BF or CF packages. Package type will be marked on packages, and shipment details will be on Shipping Documents. • The transport index (TI) shown on labels or a Shipping Document might not indicate the radiation level at one meter from a single, isolated, undamaged package; instead, it might relate to controls needed during transport because of the fissile properties of the material. • Some radioactive materials cannot be detected by commonly available instruments. • Water from cargo fire control is not expected to cause pollution. |
| **FIRE OR EXPLOSION** | • These materials are seldom flammable. Packages are designed to withstand Fire without damage to contents. • Radioactivity does not change flammability or other properties of materials. • Type AF, IF, B(U)F, B(M)F and CF packages are designed and evaluated to withstand total engulfment in flames at temperatures of 800 degrees C (1475 degrees F) for a period of 30 minutes. |

## PUBLIC SAFETY

• CALL Emergency Response Telephone Number on Shipping Document first. If Shipping Document not available or no answer, refer to appropriate telephone number listed at the end of this book. • Priorities for rescue, life-saving, first aid, and fire control and other hazards are higher than the priority for measuring radiation levels. • Radiation Authority must be notified of accident conditions. Radiation Authority is usually responsible for decisions about radiological consequences and closure of emergencies. • Isolate spill or leak area immediately for at least 50 meters (80 to 160 feet) in all directions. • Stay upwind. • Keep unauthorized personnel away. • Detain or isolate uninjured persons or equipment suspected to be contaminated; delay decontamination and cleanup until instructions are received from Radiation Authority.

| | |
|---|---|
| **PROTECTIVE CLOTHING** | • Positive pressure self-contained breathing apparatus (SCBA) and structural firefighters' protective clothing will provide adequate protection against internal radiation exposure, but not external radiation exposure. |
| **EVACUATION** | **Large Spill**<br>• Consider initial downwind evacuation for at least 100 meters (330 feet).<br>**Fire**<br>• When a large quantity of this material is involved in a major fire, consider an initial evacuation distance of 300 meters (1000 feet) in all directions. |

## EMERGENCY RESPONSE

| | |
|---|---|
| **FIRE** | • Presence of radioactive material will not influence the fire control processes and should not influence selection of techniques. • Move containers from fire area if you can do it without risk. • Do not move damaged packages; move undamaged packages out of fire zone.<br>**Small Fire**<br>• Dry chemical, $CO_2$, water spray or regular foam.<br>**Large Fire**<br>• Water spray, fog (flooding amounts). |
| **SPILL OR LEAK** | • Do not touch damaged packages or spilled material. • Damp surfaces on undamaged or slightly damaged packages are seldom an indication of packaging failure. Most packaging for liquid content have inner containers and/or inner absorbent materials.<br>**Liquid Spill**<br>• Package contents are seldom liquid. If any radioactive contamination resulting from a liquid release is present, it probably will be low-level. |
| **FIRST AID** | • Call 911 or emergency medical service • Medical problems take priority over radiological concerns. • Use first aid treatment according to the nature of the injury. • Do not delay care and transport of a seriously injured person. • Give artificial respiration if victim is not breathing. • Administer oxygen if breathing is difficult. • In case of contact with substance, immediately flush skin or eyes with running water for at least 20 minutes. • Injured persons contaminated by contact with released material are not a serious hazard to health care personnel, equipment or facilities. • Ensure that medical personnel are aware of the material(s) involved, take precautions to protect themselves and prevent spread of contamination. |

# Guide No. 166    Radioactive Materials - Corrosive (Uranium Hexafluoride/Water-Sensitive)

## POTENTIAL HAZARDS

**HEALTH**
- Radiation presents minimal risk to transport workers, emergency response personnel, and the public during transportation accidents. • Packaging durability increases as potential radiation and criticality hazards of the content increase. • Chemical hazard greatly exceeds radiation hazard. • Substance reacts with water and water vapor in air to form toxic and corrosive hydrogen fluoride gas and an extremely irritating and corrosive, white-colored, water-soluble residue. • If inhaled, may be fatal. • Direct contact causes burns to skin, eyes, and respiratory tract. • Low-level radioactive material; very low radiation hazard to people. • Runoff from control of cargo fire may cause low-level pollution.

**FIRE OR EXPLOSION**
- Substance does not burn. • The material may react violently with fuels. • Containers in protective overpacks (horizontal cylindrical shape with short legs for tie-downs), are identified with "AF", "B(U)F" or H(U) on Shipping Documents or by markings on the overpacks. They are designed and evaluated to withstand severe conditions including total engulfment in flames at temperatures of 800 degrees C (1475 degrees F). • Bare filled cylinders, identified with UN2978 as part of the marking, (may also be marked H(U) or H(M), may rupture in heat of engulfing fire; bare empty (except for residue) cylinders will not rupture in Fire. • The material may react violently with fuels. • Radioactivity does not change flammability or other properties of materials.

## PUBLIC SAFETY

- **CALL Emergency Response Telephone Number on Shipping Document first. If Shipping Document not available or no answer, refer to appropriate telephone number listed at the end of this book. • Priorities for rescue, life-saving, first aid, and fire control and other hazards are higher than the priority for measuring radiation levels.** • Radiation Authority must be notified of accident conditions. Radiation Authority is usually responsible for decisions about radiological consequences and closure of emergencies. • As an immediate precautionary measure, isolate spill or leak area for at least 25 meters (75 feet) in all directions. • Stay upwind. • Keep unauthorized personnel away. • Detain or isolate uninjured persons or equipment suspected to be contaminated; delay decontamination and cleanup until instructions are received from Radiation Authority.

**PROTECTIVE CLOTHING**
- Wear positive pressure self-contained breathing apparatus (SCBA). • Wear chemical protective clothing that is specifically recommended by the manufacturer. It may provide little or no thermal protection. • Structural firefighters' protective clothing provides limited protection in fire situations ONLY; it is not effective in spill situations where direct contact with the substance is possible.

**EVACUATION**
**Large Spill**
- See Table of Initial Isolation and Protective Action Distances in Schedule 6.

**Fire**
- When a large quantity of this material is involved in a major fire, consider an initial evacuation distance of 300 meters (1000 feet) in all directions.

## EMERGENCY RESPONSE

**FIRE**
- DO NOT USE WATER OR FOAM ON MATERIAL ITSELF. • Move containers from fire area if you can do it without risk.
**Small Fire**
- Dry chemical or $CO_2$.
**Large Fire**
- Water spray, fog or regular foam. • Cool containers with flooding quantities of water until well after fire is out. • If this is impossible, withdraw from area and let fire burn. • ALWAYS stay away from tanks engulfed in fire.

**SPILL OR LEAK**
- Do not touch damaged packages or spilled material. • Without fire or smoke, leak will be evident by visible and irritating vapors and residue forming at the point of release. • Use fine water spray to reduce vapors; do not put water directly on point of material release from container. • Residue buildup may self-seal small leaks. • Dike far ahead of spill to collect runoff water.

**FIRST AID**
- Call 911 or emergency medical service. • Medical problems take priority over radiological concerns. • Use first aid treatment according to the nature of the injury. • Do not delay care and transport of a seriously injured person. • Give artificial respiration if victim is not breathing. • Administer oxygen if breathing is difficult. • In case of contact with substance, immediately flush skin or eyes with running water for at least 20 minutes. • Effects of exposure (inhalation, ingestion or skin contact) to substance may be delayed. • Injured persons contaminated by contact with released material are not a serious hazard to health care personnel, equipment or facilities. • Ensure that medical personnel are aware of the material(s) involved, take precautions to protect themselves and prevent spread of contamination.

**Schedule 4**

# Guide No. 167  Fluorine (Refrigerated Liquid)

## POTENTIAL HAZARDS

**HEALTH**

• **TOXIC; may be fatal if inhaled.** • Vapors are extremely irritating. • Contact with gas or liquefied gas will cause burns, severe injury and/or frostbite. • Vapors from liquefied gas are initially heavier than air and spread along ground. • Runoff from fire cont may cause pollution.

**FIRE OR EXPLOSION**

• Substance does not burn but will support combustion. • This is a strong oxidizer and will react vigorously or explosively with many materials including fuels. • May ignite combustibles (wood, paper, oil, clothing, etc.). • Vapor explosion and poison hazar indoors, outdoors or in sewers. • Containers may explode when heated. • Ruptured cylinders may rocket.

## PUBLIC SAFETY

• **CALL Emergency Response Telephone Number on Shipping Document first. If Shipping Document not available or no answer, refer t appropriate telephone number listed at the end of this book.** • As an immediate precautionary measure, isolate spill or leak area for at least 1 meters (330 feet) in all directions. • Keep unauthorized personnel away. • Stay upwind. • Many gases are heavier than air and will spread along ground and collect in low or confined areas (sewers, basements, tanks). • Keep out of low areas. • Ventilate closed spaces before entering.

**PROTECTIVE CLOTHING**

• Wear positive pressure self-contained breathing apparatus (SCBA). • Wear chemical protective clothing that is specifically recommended by the manufacturer. It may provide little or no thermal protection. • Structural firefighters' protective clothing provides limited protection in fire situations ONLY; it is not effective in spill situations where direct contact with the substance is possible. • Always wear thermal protective clothing when handling refrigerated/cryogenic liquids.

**EVACUATION**

**Spill**

• See Table of Initial Isolation and Protective Action Distances in Schedule 6.

**Fire**

• If tank, rail car or tank truck is involved in a fire, ISOLATE for 1600 meters (1 mile) in all directions; also, consider initial evacuation for 1600 meters (1 mile) in all directions.

## EMERGENCY RESPONSE

**FIRE**

**Small Fire**

• Dry chemical, soda ash, lime or sand.

**Large Fire**

• Water spray, fog (flooding amounts). • Do not get water inside containers. • Move containers from fire area if you can do it without risk.

**Fire involving Tanks**

• Fight fire from maximum distance or use unmanned hose holders or monitor nozzles. • Cool containers with flooding quantitie of water until well after fire is out. • Do not direct water at source of leak or safety devices; icing may occur. • Withdraw immediately in case of rising sound from venting safety devices or discoloration of tank. • ALWAYS stay away from tanks engulfed in fire. • For massive fire, use unmanned hose holders or monitor nozzles; if this is impossible, withdraw from area an let fire burn.

**SPILL OR LEAK**

• Do not touch or walk through spilled material. • If you have not donned special protective clothing approved for this material, not expose yourself to any risk of this material touching you. • **Do not direct water at spill or source of leak.** • A fine water spray remotely directed to the edge of the spill pool can be used to direct and maintain a hot flare fire which will burn the spilled material in a controlled manner. • Keep combustibles (wood, paper, oil, etc.) away from spilled material. • Stop leak if you can it without risk. • Use water spray to reduce vapors or divert vapor cloud drift. Avoid allowing water runoff to contact spilled material. • If possible, turn leaking containers so that gas escapes rather than liquid. • Prevent entry into waterways, sewers, basements or confined areas. • Isolate area until gas has dispersed. • Ventilate the area.

**FIRST AID**

• Move victim to fresh air. • Call 911 or emergency medical service. • Give artificial respiration if victim is not breathing. • Administer oxygen if breathing is difficult. • Clothing frozen to the skin should be thawed before being removed. • Remove an isolate contaminated clothing and shoes. • In case of contact with substance, immediately flush skin or eyes with running water for at least 20 minutes. • Keep victim warm and quiet. • Keep victim under observation. • Effects of contact or inhalation may b delayed. • Ensure that medical personnel are aware of the material(s) involved, and take precautions to protect themselves.

# Guide No. 168 Carbon Monoxide (Refrigerated Liquid)

## POTENTIAL HAZARDS

**HEALTH**
- **TOXIC; Extremely Hazardous.** • Inhalation extremely dangerous; may be fatal. • Contact with gas or liquefied gas may cause burns, severe injury and/or frostbite. • Odorless, will not be detected by sense of smell.

**FIRE OR EXPLOSION**
- **EXTREMELY FLAMMABLE.** • May be ignited by heat, sparks or flames. • Flame may be invisible. • Containers may explode when heated. • Vapor explosion and poison hazard indoors, outdoors or in sewers. • Vapors from liquefied gas are initially heavier than air and spread along ground. • Vapors may travel to source of ignition and flash back. • Runoff may create fire or explosion hazard.

## PUBLIC SAFETY

- **CALL Emergency Response Telephone Number on Shipping Document first. If Shipping Document not available or no answer, refer to appropriate telephone number listed at the end of this book.** • As an immediate precautionary measure, isolate spill or leak area for at least 100 meters (330 feet) in all directions. • Keep unauthorized personnel away. • Stay upwind. • Many gases are heavier than air and will spread along ground and collect in low or confined areas (sewers, basements, tanks). • Keep out of low areas. • Ventilate closed spaces before entering.

**PROTECTIVE CLOTHING**
- Wear positive pressure self-contained breathing apparatus (SCBA). • Wear chemical protective clothing that is specifically recommended by the manufacturer. It may provide little or no thermal protection. • Structural firefighters' protective clothing provides limited protection in fire situations ONLY; it is not effective in spill situations where direct contact with the substance is possible. • Always wear thermal protective clothing when handling refrigerated/cryogenic liquids.

**EVACUATION**

**Spill**
- See Table of Initial Isolation and Protective Action Distances in Schedule 6.

**Fire**
- If tank, rail car or tank truck is involved in a fire, ISOLATE for 800 meters (1/2 mile) in all directions; also, consider initial evacuation for 800 meters (1/2 mile) in all directions.

## EMERGENCY RESPONSE

**FIRE**
- **DO NOT EXTINGUISH A LEAKING GAS FIRE UNLESS LEAK CAN BE STOPPED.**

**Small Fire**
- Dry chemical, $CO_2$ or water spray.

**Large Fire**
- Water spray, fog or regular foam. • Move containers from fire area if you can do it without risk.

**Fire involving Tanks**
- Fight fire from maximum distance or use unmanned hose holders or monitor nozzles. • Cool containers with flooding quantities of water until well after fire is out. • Do not direct water at source of leak or safety devices; icing may occur. • Withdraw immediately in case of rising sound from venting safety devices or discoloration of tank. • ALWAYS stay away from tanks engulfed in fire.

**SPILL OR LEAK**
- ELIMINATE all ignition sources (no smoking, flares, sparks or flames in immediate area). • All equipment used when handling the product must be grounded. • Fully encapsulating, vapor protective clothing should be worn for spills and leaks with no fire.
- Do not touch or walk through spilled material. • Stop leak if you can do it without risk. • Use water spray to reduce vapors or divert vapor cloud drift. Avoid allowing water runoff to contact spilled material. • Do not direct water at spill or source of leak.
- If possible, turn leaking containers so that gas escapes rather than liquid. • Prevent entry into waterways, sewers, basements or confined areas. • Isolate area until gas has dispersed.

**FIRST AID**
- Move victim to fresh air. • Call 911 or emergency medical service. • Give artificial respiration if victim is not breathing.
- Administer oxygen if breathing is difficult. • Remove and isolate contaminated clothing and shoes. • In case of contact with substance, immediately flush skin or eyes with running water for at least 20 minutes. • In case of contact with liquefied gas, thaw frosted parts with lukewarm water. • Keep victim warm and quiet. • Keep victim under observation. • Effects of contact or inhalation may be delayed. • Ensure that medical personnel are aware of the material(s) involved, and take precautions to protect themselves.

# Guide No. 169  Aluminum (Molten)

## POTENTIAL HAZARDS

**FIRE OR EXPLOSION**
- Substance is transported in molten form at a temperature above 705°C (1300°F). • Violent reaction with water; contact may cause an explosion or may produce a flammable gas. • Will ignite combustible materials (wood, paper, oil, debris, etc.). • Contact with nitrates or other oxidizers may cause an explosion. • Contact with containers or other materials, including cold, wet or dirty tools, may cause an explosion. • Contact with concrete will cause spalling and small pops.

**HEALTH**
- Contact causes severe burns to skin and eyes. • Fire may produce irritating and/or toxic gases.

## PUBLIC SAFETY

- CALL Emergency Response Telephone Number on Shipping Document first. **If Shipping Document not available or no answer, refer to appropriate telephone number listed at the end of this book.** • As an immediate precautionary measure, isolate spill or leak area for at least 50 meters (150 feet) in all directions. • Keep unauthorized personnel away. • Ventilate closed spaces before entering.

**PROTECTIVE CLOTHING**
- Wear positive pressure self-contained breathing apparatus (SCBA). • Wear flame retardant structural firefighters' protective clothing, including faceshield, helmet and gloves, this will provide limited thermal protection.

## EMERGENCY RESPONSE

**FIRE**
- **Do Not Use Water, except in life threatening situations and then only in a fine spray. • Do not use halogenated extinguishing agents or foam.** • Move combustibles out of path of advancing pool if you can do so without risk. • Extinguish fires started by molten material by using appropriate method for the burning material; keep water, halogenated extinguishing agents and foam away from the molten material.

**SPILL OR LEAK**
- Do not touch or walk through spilled material. • Do not attempt to stop leak, due to danger of explosion. • Keep combustibles (wood, paper, oil, etc.) away from spilled material. • Substance is very fluid, spreads quickly, and may splash. Do not try to stop with shovels or other objects. • Dike far ahead of spill; use dry sand to contain the flow of material. • Where possible allow molten material to solidify naturally. • Avoid contact even after material solidifies. Molten, heated and cold aluminum look alike; do not touch unless you know it is cold. • Clean up under the supervision of an expert after material has solidified.

**FIRST AID**
- Move victim to fresh air. • Call 911 or emergency medical service. • Give artificial respiration if victim is not breathing. • Administer oxygen if breathing is difficult. • For severe burns, immediate medical attention is required. • Removal of solidified molten material from skin requires medical assistance. • Remove and isolate contaminated clothing and shoes. • In case of contact with substance, immediately flush skin or eyes with running water for at least 20 minutes. • Keep victim warm and quiet.

# Guide No. 170  Metals (Powders, Dusts, Shavings, Borings, Turnings, or Cuttings, etc.)

## POTENTIAL HAZARDS

**FIRE OR EXPLOSION**
- May react violently or explosively on contact with water. • Some are transported in flammable liquids. • May be ignited by friction, heat, sparks or flames. • Some of these materials will burn with intense heat. • Dusts or fumes may form explosive mixtures in air. • Containers may explode when heated. • May re-ignite after fire is extinguished.

**HEALTH**
- Oxides from metallic fires are a severe health hazard. • Inhalation or contact with substance or decomposition products may cause severe injury or death. • Fire may produce irritating, corrosive and/or toxic gases. • Runoff from fire control or dilution water may cause pollution.

## PUBLIC SAFETY

- **CALL Emergency Response Telephone Number on Shipping Document first. If Shipping Document not available or no answer, refer to appropriate telephone number listed at the end of this book.** • As an immediate precautionary measure, isolate spill or leak area for at least 25 meters (75 feet) in all directions. • Stay upwind. • Keep unauthorized personnel away.

**PROTECTIVE CLOTHING**
- Wear positive pressure self-contained breathing apparatus (SCBA). • Structural firefighters' protective clothing will only provide limited protection.

**EVACUATION**

**Large Spill**
- Consider initial downwind evacuation for at least 50 meters (160 feet).

**Fire**
- If tank, rail car or tank truck is involved in a fire, ISOLATE for 800 meters (1/2 mile) in all directions; also, consider initial evacuation for 800 meters (1/2 mile) in all directions.

## EMERGENCY RESPONSE

**FIRE**
- **DO NOT USE WATER, FOAM OR CO₂.** • Dousing metallic fires with water may generate hydrogen gas, an extremely dangerous explosion hazard, particularly if fire is in a confined environment (i.e., building, cargo hold, etc.). • Use DRY sand, graphite powder, dry sodium chloride based extinguishers, G-1 or Met-L-X powder. • Confining and smothering metal fires is preferable rather than applying water. • Move containers from fire area if you can do it without risk.

**Fire involving Tanks or Car/Trailer Loads**
- If impossible to extinguish, protect surroundings and allow fire to burn itself out.

**SPILL OR LEAK**
- ELIMINATE all ignition sources (no smoking, flares, sparks or flames in immediate area). • Do not touch or walk through spilled material. • Stop leak if you can do it without risk. • Prevent entry into waterways, sewers, basements or confined areas.

**FIRST AID**
- Move victim to fresh air. • Call 911 or emergency medical service. • Give artificial respiration if victim is not breathing. • Administer oxygen if breathing is difficult. • Remove and isolate contaminated clothing and shoes. • In case of contact with substance, immediately flush skin or eyes with running water for at least 20 minutes. • Keep victim warm and quiet. • Ensure that medical personnel are aware of the material(s) involved, and take precautions to protect themselves.

# Guide No. 171    Substances (Low to Moderate Hazard)

## POTENTIAL HAZARDS

**FIRE OR EXPLOSION**
- Some may burn but none ignite readily. • Those substances designated with a "**P**" may polymerize explosively when heated or involved in a fire. • Containers may explode when heated. • Some may be transported hot.

**HEALTH**
- Inhalation of material may be harmful. • Contact may cause burns to skin and eyes. • Inhalation of Asbestos dust may have a damaging effect on the lungs. • Fire may produce irritating, corrosive and/or toxic gases. • Some liquids produce vapors that may cause dizziness or suffocation. • Runoff from fire control may cause pollution.

## PUBLIC SAFETY

- **CALL Emergency Response Telephone Number on Shipping Document first. If Shipping Document not available or no answer, refer to appropriate telephone number listed at the end of this book.** • As an immediate precautionary measure, isolate spill or leak area in all direction for at least 50 meters (150 feet) for liquids and at least 25 meters (75 feet) for solids. • Keep unauthorized personnel away. • Stay upwind.

**PROTECTIVE CLOTHING**
- Wear positive pressure self-contained breathing apparatus (SCBA). • Structural firefighters' protective clothing will only provide limited protection.

**EVACUATION**

**Spill**
- See Table of Initial Isolation and Protective Action Distances in Schedule 6 for those dangerous goods marked with a "T" in Schedule 5. For those dangerous goods not marked with a "T" in Schedule 5 increase, as necessary, the minimum isolation distance of at 50 meters for liquids and 25 meters for solids in the downwind direction.

**Fire**
- If tank, rail car or tank truck is involved in a fire, ISOLATE for 800 meters (1/2 mile) in all directions; also, consider initial evacuation for 800 meters (1/2 mile) in all directions.

## EMERGENCY RESPONSE

**FIRE**

**Small Fire**
- Dry chemical, $CO_2$, water spray or regular foam.

**Large Fire**
- Water spray, fog or regular foam. • Move containers from fire area if you can do it without risk. • Do not scatter spilled material with high pressure water streams. • Dike fire-control water for later disposal.

**Fire involving Tanks**
- Cool containers with flooding quantities of water until well after fire is out. • Withdraw immediately in case of rising sound from venting safety devices or discoloration of tank. • ALWAYS stay away from tanks engulfed in fire.

**SPILL OR LEAK**
- Do not touch or walk through spilled material. • Stop leak if you can do it without risk. • Prevent dust cloud. • Avoid inhalation of asbestos dust.

**Small Dry Spill**
- With clean shovel place material into clean, dry container and cover loosely; move containers from spill area.

**Small Spill**
- Take up with sand or other non-combustible absorbent material and place into containers for later disposal.

**Large Spill**
- Dike far ahead of liquid spill for later disposal. • Cover powder spill with plastic sheet or tarp to minimize spreading. • Prevent entry into waterways, sewers, basements or confined areas.

**FIRST AID**
- Move victim to fresh air. • Call 911 or emergency medical service. • Give artificial respiration if victim is not breathing. • Administer oxygen if breathing is difficult. • Remove and isolate contaminated clothing and shoes. • In case of contact with substance, immediately flush skin or eyes with running water for at least 20 minutes. • Ensure that medical personnel are aware of the material(s) involved, and take precautions to protect themselves.

Schedule 4

# Guide No. 172    Gallium and Mercury

## POTENTIAL HAZARDS

**HEALTH**
• Inhalation of vapors or contact with substance will result in contamination and potential harmful effects. • Fire will produce irritating, corrosive and/or toxic gases.

**FIRE OR EXPLOSION**
• Non-combustible, substance itself does not burn but may react upon heating to produce corrosive and/or toxic fumes. • Runoff may pollute waterways.

## PUBLIC SAFETY

• **CALL Emergency Response Telephone Number on Shipping Document first. If Shipping Document not available or no answer, refer to appropriate telephone number listed at the end of this book.** • As an immediate precautionary measure, isolate spill or leak area for at least 50 meters (150 feet) in all directions. • Stay upwind. • Keep unauthorized personnel away.

**PROTECTIVE CLOTHING**
• Wear positive pressure self-contained breathing apparatus (SCBA). • Structural firefighters' protective clothing will only provide limited protection.

**EVACUATION**
**Large Spill**
• Consider initial downwind evacuation for at least 100 meters (330 feet).
**Fire**
• When any large container is involved in a fire, consider initial evacuation for 500 meters (1/3 mile) in all directions.

## EMERGENCY RESPONSE

**FIRE**
• Use extinguishing agent suitable for type of surrounding fire. • **Do not direct water at the heated metal.**

**SPILL OR LEAK**
• Do not touch or walk through spilled material. • Do not touch damaged containers or spilled material unless wearing appropriate protective clothing. • Stop leak if you can do it without risk. • Prevent entry into waterways, sewers, basements or confined areas. • Do not use steel or aluminum tools or equipment. • Cover with earth, sand, or other non-combustible material followed with plastic sheet to minimize spreading or contact with rain. • For mercury, use a mercury spill kit. • Mercury spill areas may be subsequently treated with calcium sulphide/calcium sulfide or with sodium thiosulphate/sodium thiosulfate wash to neutralize any residual mercury.

**FIRST AID**
• Move victim to fresh air. • Call 911 or emergency medical service. • Give artificial respiration if victim is not breathing. • Administer oxygen if breathing is difficult. • Remove and isolate contaminated clothing and shoes. • In case of contact with substance, immediately flush skin or eyes with running water for at least 20 minutes. • Keep victim warm and quiet. • Ensure that medical personnel are aware of the material(s) involved, and take precautions to protect themselves.

**Schedule 4**

# SCHEDULE 5

## UN Number/Emergency Response Guide (ERG) Cross Reference

The letter "T" following the ERG number indicates substances that are toxic-by-inhalation (TIH). (When TIH substances are spilled, isolation and protective action distances may be involved. These are shown in Schedule 6 along with an explanation of their application on page 233.)

**In an emergency involving Dangerous Goods shown with a "T"** <u>and also involving a fire</u>, **refer to the information under the PUBLIC SAFETY heading in the appropriate ERG. In an emergency involving Dangerous Goods shown with a "T"** <u>but no fire is involved</u>, **refer to the Initial Isolation and Protective Action Distances shown in Schedule 6.**

The letter "P" following the ERG number indicates substances that may polymerize explosively when heated or involved in a fire.

| UN # | Guide | UN # | Guide | UN # | Guide | UN # | Guide | UN # | Guide | UN # | Guide |
|------|-------|------|-------|------|-------|------|-------|------|-------|------|-------|
| UN0004 | 112 | UN0081 | 112 | UN0173 | 114 | UN0248 | 112 | UN0318 | 112 | UN0364 | 112 |
| UN0005 | 112 | UN0082 | 112 | UN0174 | 114 | UN0249 | 112 | UN0319 | 112 | UN0365 | 114 |
| UN0006 | 112 | UN0083 | 112 | UN0180 | 112 | UN0250 | 112 | UN0320 | 114 | UN0366 | 114 |
| UN0007 | 112 | UN0084 | 112 | UN0181 | 112 | UN0254 | 112 | UN0321 | 112 | UN0367 | 114 |
| UN0009 | 112 | UN0092 | 112 | UN0182 | 112 | UN0255 | 114 | UN0322 | 112 | UN0368 | 114 |
| UN0010 | 112 | UN0093 | 112 | UN0183 | 112 | UN0257 | 114 | UN0323 | 114 | UN0369 | 112 |
| UN0012 | 114 | UN0094 | 112 | UN0186 | 112 | UN0266 | 112 | UN0324 | 112 | UN0370 | 114 |
| UN0014 | 114 | UN0099 | 112 | UN0191 | 114 | UN0267 | 114 | UN0325 | 114 | UN0371 | 114 |
| UN0015 | 112 | UN0101 | 112 | UN0192 | 112 | UN0268 | 112 | UN0326 | 112 | UN0372 | 112 |
| UN0016 | 112 | UN0102 | 112 | UN0193 | 114 | UN0271 | 112 | UN0327 | 112 | UN0373 | 114 |
| UN0018 | 112 | UN0103 | 114 | UN0194 | 112 | UN0272 | 112 | UN0328 | 112 | UN0374 | 112 |
| UN0019 | 112 | UN0104 | 114 | UN0195 | 112 | UN0275 | 112 | UN0329 | 112 | UN0375 | 112 |
| UN0020 | 112 | UN0105 | 114 | UN0196 | 112 | UN0276 | 114 | UN0330 | 112 | UN0376 | 112 |
| UN0021 | 112 | UN0106 | 112 | UN0197 | 114 | UN0277 | 112 | UN0331 | 112 | UN0377 | 112 |
| UN0027 | 112 | UN0107 | 112 | UN0204 | 112 | UN0278 | 114 | UN0332 | 112 | UN0378 | 114 |
| UN0028 | 112 | UN0110 | 114 | UN0207 | 112 | UN0279 | 112 | UN0333 | 112 | UN0379 | 114 |
| UN0029 | 112 | UN0113 | 112 | UN0208 | 112 | UN0280 | 112 | UN0334 | 112 | UN0380 | 112 |
| UN0030 | 112 | UN0114 | 112 | UN0209 | 112 | UN0281 | 112 | UN0335 | 112 | UN0381 | 112 |
| UN0033 | 112 | UN0118 | 112 | UN0212 | 112 | UN0282 | 112 | UN0336 | 114 | UN0382 | 112 |
| UN0034 | 112 | UN0121 | 112 | UN0213 | 112 | UN0283 | 112 | UN0337 | 112 | UN0383 | 114 |
| UN0035 | 112 | UN0124 | 112 | UN0214 | 112 | UN0284 | 112 | UN0338 | 114 | UN0384 | 112 |
| UN0037 | 112 | UN0129 | 112 | UN0215 | 112 | UN0285 | 112 | UN0339 | 114 | UN0385 | 112 |
| UN0038 | 112 | UN0130 | 112 | UN0216 | 112 | UN0286 | 112 | UN0340 | 112 | UN0386 | 112 |
| UN0039 | 112 | UN0131 | 114 | UN0217 | 112 | UN0287 | 112 | UN0341 | 112 | UN0387 | 112 |
| UN0042 | 112 | UN0132 | 112 | UN0218 | 112 | UN0288 | 112 | UN0342 | 112 | UN0388 | 112 |
| UN0043 | 112 | UN0133 | 112 | UN0219 | 112 | UN0289 | 114 | UN0343 | 112 | UN0389 | 112 |
| UN0044 | 114 | UN0135 | 112 | UN0220 | 112 | UN0290 | 112 | UN0344 | 114 | UN0390 | 112 |
| UN0048 | 112 | UN0136 | 112 | UN0221 | 112 | UN0291 | 112 | UN0345 | 114 | UN0391 | 112 |
| UN0049 | 112 | UN0137 | 112 | UN0222 | 112 | UN0292 | 112 | UN0346 | 112 | UN0392 | 112 |
| UN0050 | 112 | UN0138 | 112 | UN0223 | 112 | UN0293 | 112 | UN0347 | 114 | UN0393 | 112 |
| UN0054 | 112 | UN0143 | 112 | UN0224 | 112 | UN0294 | 112 | UN0348 | 114 | UN0394 | 112 |
| UN0055 | 114 | UN0144 | 112 | UN0225 | 112 | UN0295 | 112 | UN0349 | 114 | UN0395 | 112 |
| UN0056 | 112 | UN0146 | 112 | UN0226 | 112 | UN0296 | 112 | UN0350 | 114 | UN0396 | 112 |
| UN0059 | 112 | UN0147 | 112 | UN0234 | 112 | UN0297 | 114 | UN0351 | 114 | UN0397 | 112 |
| UN0060 | 112 | UN0150 | 112 | UN0235 | 112 | UN0299 | 112 | UN0352 | 114 | UN0398 | 112 |
| UN0065 | 112 | UN0151 | 112 | UN0236 | 112 | UN0300 | 114 | UN0353 | 114 | UN0399 | 112 |
| UN0066 | 114 | UN0153 | 112 | UN0237 | 114 | UN0301 | 114 | UN0354 | 112 | UN0400 | 112 |
| UN0070 | 114 | UN0154 | 112 | UN0238 | 112 | UN0303 | 114 | UN0355 | 112 | UN0401 | 112 |
| UN0072 | 112 | UN0155 | 112 | UN0240 | 112 | UN0305 | 112 | UN0356 | 112 | UN0402 | 112 |
| UN0073 | 112 | UN0159 | 112 | UN0241 | 112 | UN0306 | 114 | UN0357 | 112 | UN0403 | 114 |
| UN0074 | 112 | UN0160 | 112 | UN0242 | 112 | UN0312 | 114 | UN0358 | 112 | UN0404 | 114 |
| UN0075 | 112 | UN0161 | 112 | UN0243 | 112 | UN0313 | 112 | UN0359 | 112 | UN0405 | 114 |
| UN0076 | 112 | UN0167 | 112 | UN0244 | 112 | UN0314 | 112 | UN0360 | 112 | UN0406 | 112 |
| UN0077 | 112 | UN0168 | 112 | UN0245 | 112 | UN0315 | 112 | UN0361 | 114 | UN0407 | 112 |
| UN0078 | 112 | UN0169 | 112 | UN0246 | 112 | UN0316 | 112 | UN0362 | 114 | UN0408 | 112 |
| UN0079 | 112 | UN0171 | 112 | UN0247 | 112 | UN0317 | 114 | UN0363 | 114 | UN0409 | 112 |

Schedule 5

| UN # | Guide | UN # | Guide | UN # | Guide | UN # | Guide | UN # | Guide | UN # | Guide |
|---|---|---|---|---|---|---|---|---|---|---|---|
| UN0410 | 114 | UN0477 | 112 | UN1045 | 124T | UN1130 | 128 | UN1207 | 129 | UN1299 | 128 |
| UN0411 | 112 | UN0478 | 112 | UN1046 | 121 | UN1131 | 131 | UN1208 | 128 | UN1300 | 128 |
| UN0412 | 114 | UN0479 | 114 | UN1048 | 125T | UN1133 | 128 | UN1210 | 129 | UN1301 | 129P |
| UN0413 | 112 | UN0480 | 114 | UN1049 | 115 | UN1134 | 130 | UN1212 | 129 | UN1302 | 127P |
| UN0414 | 112 | UN0481 | 114 | UN1050 | 125T | UN1135 | 131T | UN1213 | 129 | UN1303 | 129P |
| UN0415 | 112 | UN0482 | 112 | UN1051 | 117T | UN1136 | 128 | UN1214 | 132 | UN1304 | 127P |
| UN0417 | 112 | UN0483 | 112 | UN1052 | 125T | UN1139 | 127 | UN1216 | 128 | UN1305 | 155 |
| UN0418 | 112 | UN0484 | 112 | UN1053 | 117T | UN1143 | 131PT | UN1218 | 130P | UN1306 | 129 |
| UN0419 | 112 | UN0485 | 114 | UN1055 | 115 | UN1144 | 127 | UN1219 | 129 | UN1307 | 130 |
| UN0420 | 112 | UN0486 | 112 | UN1056 | 121 | UN1145 | 128 | UN1220 | 129 | UN1308 | 170 |
| UN0421 | 112 | UN0487 | 112 | UN1057 | 115 | UN1146 | 128 | UN1221 | 132 | UN1309 | 170 |
| UN0424 | 112 | UN0488 | 112 | UN1058 | 121 | UN1147 | 130 | UN1222 | 130 | UN1310 | 113 |
| UN0425 | 114 | UN0489 | 112 | UN1060 | 116P | UN1148 | 129 | UN1223 | 128 | UN1312 | 133 |
| UN0426 | 112 | UN0490 | 112 | UN1061 | 118 | UN1149 | 127 | UN1224 | 127 | UN1313 | 133 |
| UN0427 | 114 | UN0491 | 114 | UN1062 | 123T | UN1150 | 130P | UN1228 | 131 | UN1314 | 133 |
| UN0428 | 112 | UN0492 | 112 | UN1063 | 115 | UN1152 | 130 | UN1229 | 129 | UN1318 | 133 |
| UN0429 | 112 | UN0493 | 114 | UN1064 | 117T | UN1153 | 127 | UN1230 | 131 | UN1320 | 113 |
| UN0430 | 112 | UN0494 | 114 | UN1065 | 121 | UN1154 | 132 | UN1231 | 129 | UN1321 | 113 |
| UN0431 | 114 | UN0495 | 112 | UN1066 | 121 | UN1155 | 127 | UN1233 | 129 | UN1322 | 113 |
| UN0432 | 114 | UN0496 | 112 | UN1067 | 124T | UN1156 | 127 | UN1234 | 127 | UN1323 | 170 |
| UN0433 | 112 | UN0497 | 112 | UN1069 | 125T | UN1157 | 127 | UN1235 | 132 | UN1324 | 133 |
| UN0434 | 112 | UN0498 | 112 | UN1070 | 122 | UN1158 | 132 | UN1237 | 129 | UN1325 | 133 |
| UN0435 | 114 | UN0499 | 112 | UN1071 | 119T | UN1159 | 127 | UN1238 | 155T | UN1326 | 170 |
| UN0436 | 112 | UN0500 | 114 | UN1072 | 122 | UN1160 | 129 | UN1239 | 131T | UN1327 | 133 |
| UN0437 | 112 | UN0501 | 114 | UN1073 | 122 | UN1161 | 129 | UN1242 | 139T | UN1328 | 133 |
| UN0438 | 114 | UN0502 | 112 | UN1075 | 115 | UN1162 | 155T | UN1243 | 129 | UN1330 | 133 |
| UN0439 | 112 | UN0503 | 114 | UN1076 | 125T | UN1163 | 131T | UN1244 | 131T | UN1331 | 133 |
| UN0440 | 114 | UN0504 | 112 | UN1077 | 115 | UN1164 | 130 | UN1245 | 127 | UN1332 | 133 |
| UN0441 | 114 | UN1001 | 116 | UN1078 | 126 | UN1165 | 127 | UN1246 | 127P | UN1333 | 170 |
| UN0442 | 112 | UN1002 | 122 | UN1079 | 135T | UN1166 | 127 | UN1247 | 129P | UN1334 | 133 |
| UN0443 | 112 | UN1003 | 122 | UN1080 | 126 | UN1167 | 131P | UN1248 | 129 | UN1336 | 113 |
| UN0444 | 114 | UN1005 | 125T | UN1081 | 116P | UN1169 | 127 | UN1249 | 127 | UN1337 | 113 |
| UN0445 | 114 | UN1006 | 121 | UN1082 | 119PT | UN1170 | 127 | UN1250 | 155T | UN1338 | 133 |
| UN0446 | 114 | UN1008 | 125T | UN1083 | 118 | UN1171 | 127 | UN1251 | 131PT | UN1339 | 139 |
| UN0447 | 112 | UN1009 | 126 | UN1085 | 116P | UN1172 | 129 | UN1259 | 131T | UN1340 | 139T |
| UN0448 | 114 | UN1010 | 116P | UN1086 | 116P | UN1173 | 129 | UN1261 | 129 | UN1341 | 139 |
| UN0449 | 112 | UN1011 | 115 | UN1087 | 116P | UN1175 | 129 | UN1262 | 128 | UN1343 | 139 |
| UN0450 | 112 | UN1012 | 115 | UN1088 | 127 | UN1176 | 129 | UN1263 | 128 | UN1344 | 113 |
| UN0451 | 112 | UN1013 | 120 | UN1089 | 129 | UN1177 | 129 | UN1264 | 129 | UN1345 | 133 |
| UN0452 | 114 | UN1014 | 122 | UN1090 | 127 | UN1178 | 129 | UN1265 | 128 | UN1346 | 170 |
| UN0453 | 114 | UN1015 | 126 | UN1091 | 127 | UN1179 | 127 | UN1266 | 127 | UN1347 | 113 |
| UN0454 | 114 | UN1016 | 119T | UN1092 | 131PT | UN1180 | 129 | UN1267 | 128 | UN1348 | 113 |
| UN0455 | 114 | UN1017 | 124T | UN1093 | 131P | UN1181 | 155 | UN1268 | 128 | UN1349 | 113 |
| UN0456 | 114 | UN1018 | 126 | UN1098 | 131T | UN1182 | 155T | UN1272 | 129 | UN1350 | 133 |
| UN0457 | 112 | UN1020 | 126 | UN1099 | 131 | UN1183 | 139 | UN1274 | 129 | UN1352 | 170 |
| UN0458 | 112 | UN1021 | 126 | UN1100 | 131 | UN1184 | 129 | UN1275 | 129 | UN1353 | 133 |
| UN0459 | 114 | UN1022 | 126 | UN1104 | 129 | UN1185 | 131PT | UN1276 | 129 | UN1354 | 113 |
| UN0460 | 114 | UN1023 | 119T | UN1105 | 129 | UN1188 | 127 | UN1277 | 132 | UN1355 | 113 |
| UN0461 | 112 | UN1026 | 119T | UN1106 | 132 | UN1189 | 129 | UN1278 | 129 | UN1356 | 113 |
| UN0462 | 112 | UN1027 | 115 | UN1107 | 129 | UN1190 | 127 | UN1279 | 130 | UN1357 | 153 |
| UN0463 | 112 | UN1028 | 126 | UN1108 | 127 | UN1191 | 129 | UN1280 | 127P | UN1358 | 170 |
| UN0464 | 112 | UN1029 | 126 | UN1109 | 129 | UN1192 | 129 | UN1281 | 129 | UN1360 | 139T |
| UN0465 | 112 | UN1030 | 115 | UN1110 | 127 | UN1193 | 127 | UN1282 | 129 | UN1361 | 133 |
| UN0466 | 112 | UN1032 | 118 | UN1111 | 130 | UN1194 | 131 | UN1286 | 127 | UN1362 | 133 |
| UN0467 | 112 | UN1033 | 115 | UN1112 | 140 | UN1195 | 129 | UN1287 | 127 | UN1363 | 135 |
| UN0468 | 112 | UN1035 | 115 | UN1113 | 129 | UN1196 | 155 | UN1288 | 128 | UN1364 | 133 |
| UN0469 | 112 | UN1036 | 118 | UN1114 | 130 | UN1197 | 127 | UN1289 | 132 | UN1365 | 133 |
| UN0470 | 112 | UN1037 | 115 | UN1120 | 115 | UN1198 | 132 | UN1292 | 132 | UN1366 | 135 |
| UN0471 | 114 | UN1038 | 115 | UN1123 | 129 | UN1199 | 132P | UN1293 | 127 | UN1369 | 135 |
| UN0472 | 114 | UN1039 | 115 | UN1125 | 132 | UN1201 | 127 | UN1294 | 130 | UN1370 | 135 |
| UN0473 | 112 | UN1040 | 119PT | UN1126 | 129 | UN1202 | 128 | UN1295 | 139T | UN1373 | 133 |
| UN0474 | 112 | UN1041 | 115 | UN1127 | 130 | UN1203 | 128 | UN1296 | 132 | UN1374 | 133 |
| UN0475 | 112 | UN1043 | 125 | UN1128 | 129 | UN1204 | 127 | UN1297 | 132 | UN1376 | 135 |
| UN0476 | 112 | UN1044 | 126 | UN1129 | 129 | UN1206 | 128 | UN1298 | 155T | UN1378 | 170 |

Schedule 5

| UN # | Guide | UN # | Guide | UN # | Guide | UN # | Guide | UN # | Guide | UN # | Guide |
|---|---|---|---|---|---|---|---|---|---|---|---|
| UN1379 | 133 | UN1457 | 140 | UN1554 | 154 | UN1627 | 141 | UN1704 | 153 | UN1775 | 154 |
| UN1380 | 135T | UN1458 | 140 | UN1555 | 151 | UN1629 | 151 | UN1707 | 151 | UN1776 | 154 |
| UN1381 | 136 | UN1459 | 140 | UN1556 | 152T | UN1630 | 151 | UN1708 | 153 | UN1777 | 137T |
| UN1382 | 135 | UN1461 | 140 | UN1557 | 152 | UN1631 | 154 | UN1709 | 151 | UN1778 | 154 |
| UN1383 | 135 | UN1462 | 143 | UN1558 | 152 | UN1634 | 154 | UN1710 | 160 | UN1779 | 153 |
| UN1384 | 135T | UN1463 | 141 | UN1559 | 151 | UN1636 | 154 | UN1711 | 153 | UN1780 | 156 |
| UN1385 | 135 | UN1465 | 140 | UN1560 | 157T | UN1637 | 151 | UN1712 | 151 | UN1781 | 156 |
| UN1386 | 135 | UN1466 | 140 | UN1561 | 151 | UN1638 | 151 | UN1713 | 151 | UN1782 | 154 |
| UN1389 | 138 | UN1467 | 143 | UN1562 | 152 | UN1639 | 151 | UN1714 | 139 | UN1783 | 153 |
| UN1390 | 139 | UN1469 | 141 | UN1564 | 154 | UN1640 | 151 | UN1715 | 137 | UN1784 | 156T |
| UN1391 | 138 | UN1470 | 141 | UN1565 | 157 | UN1641 | 151 | UN1716 | 156T | UN1786 | 157 |
| UN1392 | 138 | UN1471 | 140 | UN1566 | 154 | UN1642 | 151 | UN1717 | 132T | UN1787 | 154 |
| UN1393 | 138 | UN1472 | 143 | UN1567 | 134 | UN1643 | 151 | UN1718 | 153 | UN1788 | 154 |
| UN1394 | 138 | UN1473 | 140 | UN1569 | 131T | UN1644 | 151 | UN1719 | 154 | UN1789 | 157 |
| UN1395 | 139 | UN1474 | 140 | UN1570 | 152 | UN1645 | 151 | UN1722 | 155T | UN1790 | 157 |
| UN1396 | 138 | UN1475 | 140 | UN1571 | 113 | UN1646 | 151 | UN1723 | 132 | UN1791 | 154 |
| UN1397 | 139T | UN1476 | 140 | UN1572 | 151 | UN1647 | 151T | UN1724 | 155T | UN1792 | 157 |
| UN1398 | 138 | UN1477 | 140 | UN1573 | 151 | UN1648 | 131 | UN1725 | 137T | UN1793 | 153 |
| UN1400 | 138 | UN1479 | 140 | UN1574 | 151 | UN1649 | 131 | UN1726 | 137 | UN1794 | 154 |
| UN1401 | 138 | UN1481 | 140 | UN1575 | 157 | UN1650 | 153 | UN1727 | 154 | UN1796 | 157 |
| UN1402 | 138 | UN1482 | 140 | UN1577 | 153 | UN1651 | 153 | UN1728 | 155T | UN1798 | 157 |
| UN1403 | 138 | UN1483 | 140 | UN1578 | 152 | UN1652 | 153 | UN1729 | 156 | UN1799 | 156T |
| UN1404 | 138 | UN1484 | 140 | UN1579 | 153 | UN1653 | 151 | UN1730 | 157 | UN1800 | 156T |
| UN1405 | 138 | UN1485 | 140 | UN1580 | 154T | UN1654 | 151 | UN1731 | 157 | UN1801 | 156T |
| UN1407 | 138 | UN1486 | 140 | UN1581 | 123T | UN1655 | 151 | UN1732 | 157T | UN1802 | 140 |
| UN1408 | 139 | UN1487 | 140 | UN1582 | 119T | UN1656 | 151 | UN1733 | 157 | UN1803 | 153 |
| UN1409 | 138 | UN1488 | 140 | UN1583 | 154T | UN1657 | 151 | UN1736 | 137 | UN1804 | 156T |
| UN1410 | 138 | UN1489 | 140 | UN1585 | 151 | UN1658 | 151 | UN1737 | 156 | UN1805 | 154 |
| UN1411 | 138 | UN1490 | 140 | UN1586 | 151 | UN1659 | 151 | UN1738 | 156 | UN1806 | 137T |
| UN1413 | 138 | UN1491 | 144 | UN1587 | 151 | UN1660 | 124T | UN1739 | 137 | UN1807 | 137 |
| UN1414 | 138 | UN1492 | 140 | UN1588 | 157 | UN1661 | 153 | UN1740 | 154 | UN1808 | 137 |
| UN1415 | 138 | UN1493 | 140 | UN1589 | 125T | UN1662 | 152 | UN1741 | 125T | UN1809 | 137T |
| UN1417 | 138 | UN1494 | 141 | UN1590 | 153 | UN1663 | 153 | UN1742 | 157 | UN1810 | 137T |
| UN1418 | 138 | UN1495 | 140 | UN1591 | 152 | UN1664 | 152 | UN1743 | 157 | UN1811 | 154 |
| UN1419 | 139T | UN1496 | 143 | UN1593 | 160 | UN1665 | 152 | UN1744 | 144T | UN1812 | 154 |
| UN1420 | 138 | UN1498 | 140 | UN1594 | 152 | UN1669 | 151 | UN1745 | 124T | UN1813 | 154 |
| UN1421 | 138 | UN1499 | 140 | UN1595 | 156T | UN1670 | 157T | UN1746 | 144T | UN1814 | 154 |
| UN1422 | 138 | UN1500 | 140 | UN1596 | 153 | UN1671 | 153 | UN1747 | 155T | UN1815 | 132 |
| UN1423 | 138 | UN1502 | 140 | UN1597 | 152 | UN1672 | 151 | UN1748 | 140 | UN1816 | 155T |
| UN1426 | 138 | UN1503 | 140 | UN1598 | 153 | UN1673 | 153 | UN1749 | 124T | UN1817 | 137 |
| UN1427 | 138 | UN1504 | 144 | UN1599 | 153 | UN1674 | 151 | UN1750 | 153 | UN1818 | 157T |
| UN1428 | 138 | UN1505 | 140 | UN1600 | 152 | UN1677 | 151 | UN1751 | 153 | UN1819 | 154 |
| UN1431 | 138 | UN1506 | 143 | UN1601 | 151 | UN1678 | 154 | UN1752 | 156T | UN1823 | 154 |
| UN1432 | 139T | UN1507 | 140 | UN1602 | 151 | UN1679 | 157 | UN1753 | 156 | UN1824 | 154 |
| UN1433 | 139T | UN1508 | 140 | UN1603 | 155 | UN1680 | 157T | UN1754 | 137T | UN1825 | 157 |
| UN1435 | 138 | UN1509 | 143 | UN1604 | 132 | UN1683 | 151 | UN1755 | 154 | UN1826 | 157 |
| UN1436 | 138 | UN1510 | 143T | UN1605 | 154T | UN1684 | 151 | UN1756 | 154 | UN1827 | 137 |
| UN1437 | 138 | UN1511 | 140 | UN1606 | 151 | UN1685 | 151 | UN1757 | 154 | UN1828 | 137T |
| UN1438 | 140 | UN1512 | 140 | UN1607 | 151 | UN1686 | 154 | UN1758 | 137T | UN1829 | 137T |
| UN1439 | 141 | UN1513 | 140 | UN1608 | 151 | UN1687 | 153 | UN1759 | 154 | UN1830 | 137 |
| UN1442 | 143 | UN1514 | 140 | UN1611 | 151 | UN1688 | 152 | UN1760 | 154 | UN1831 | 137T |
| UN1444 | 140 | UN1515 | 140 | UN1612 | 123T | UN1689 | 157T | UN1761 | 154 | UN1832 | 137 |
| UN1445 | 141 | UN1516 | 143 | UN1613 | 154T | UN1690 | 154 | UN1762 | 156 | UN1833 | 154 |
| UN1446 | 141 | UN1517 | 113 | UN1614 | 131T | UN1691 | 151 | UN1763 | 156T | UN1834 | 137T |
| UN1447 | 141 | UN1541 | 155T | UN1616 | 151 | UN1692 | 151 | UN1764 | 153 | UN1835 | 153 |
| UN1448 | 141 | UN1544 | 151 | UN1617 | 151 | UN1693 | 159 | UN1765 | 156 | UN1836 | 137T |
| UN1449 | 141 | UN1545 | 155 | UN1618 | 151 | UN1694 | 159T | UN1766 | 156T | UN1837 | 157 |
| UN1450 | 141 | UN1546 | 151 | UN1620 | 151 | UN1695 | 153T | UN1767 | 155T | UN1838 | 137T |
| UN1451 | 140 | UN1547 | 153 | UN1621 | 151 | UN1697 | 153T | UN1768 | 154 | UN1839 | 153 |
| UN1452 | 140 | UN1548 | 153 | UN1622 | 151 | UN1698 | 154T | UN1769 | 156T | UN1840 | 154 |
| UN1453 | 140 | UN1549 | 157 | UN1623 | 151 | UN1699 | 151 | UN1770 | 153 | UN1841 | 171 |
| UN1454 | 140 | UN1550 | 151 | UN1624 | 154 | UN1700 | 159 | UN1771 | 156T | UN1843 | 141 |
| UN1455 | 140 | UN1551 | 151 | UN1625 | 141 | UN1701 | 152 | UN1773 | 157 | UN1845 | 120 |
| UN1456 | 140 | UN1553 | 154 | UN1626 | 157 | UN1702 | 151 | UN1774 | 154 | UN1846 | 151 |

Schedule 5

| UN # | Guide | UN # | Guide | UN # | Guide | UN # | Guide | UN # | Guide | UN # | Guide |
|---|---|---|---|---|---|---|---|---|---|---|---|
| UN1847 | 153 | UN1951 | 120 | UN2022 | 153 | UN2204 | 119T | UN2278 | 128 | UN2344 | 130 |
| UN1848 | 132 | UN1952 | 126 | UN2023 | 131P | UN2205 | 153 | UN2279 | 151 | UN2345 | 129 |
| UN1849 | 153 | UN1953 | 119T | UN2024 | 151 | UN2206 | 155 | UN2280 | 153 | UN2346 | 127 |
| UN1851 | 151 | UN1954 | 115 | UN2025 | 151 | UN2208 | 140 | UN2281 | 156 | UN2347 | 130 |
| UN1854 | 135 | UN1955 | 123T | UN2026 | 151 | UN2209 | 132 | UN2282 | 129 | UN2348 | 129P |
| UN1855 | 135 | UN1956 | 126 | UN2027 | 151 | UN2210 | 135 | UN2283 | 130P | UN2350 | 127 |
| UN1858 | 126 | UN1957 | 115 | UN2028 | 153 | UN2211 | 133 | UN2284 | 131 | UN2351 | 129 |
| UN1859 | 125T | UN1958 | 126 | UN2029 | 132 | UN2212 | 171 | UN2285 | 156 | UN2352 | 127P |
| UN1860 | 116P | UN1959 | 116P | UN2030 | 153 | UN2213 | 133 | UN2286 | 128 | UN2353 | 132 |
| UN1862 | 129 | UN1961 | 115 | UN2031 | 157 | UN2214 | 156 | UN2287 | 128 | UN2354 | 131 |
| UN1863 | 128 | UN1962 | 116P | UN2032 | 157T | UN2215 | 156 | UN2288 | 128 | UN2356 | 129 |
| UN1865 | 131 | UN1963 | 120 | UN2033 | 154 | UN2216 | 171 | UN2289 | 153 | UN2357 | 132 |
| UN1866 | 127 | UN1964 | 115 | UN2034 | 115 | UN2217 | 135 | UN2290 | 156 | UN2358 | 128P |
| UN1868 | 134 | UN1965 | 115 | UN2035 | 115 | UN2218 | 132P | UN2291 | 151 | UN2359 | 132 |
| UN1869 | 138 | UN1966 | 115 | UN2036 | 121 | UN2219 | 129 | UN2293 | 127 | UN2360 | 131P |
| UN1870 | 138 | UN1967 | 123T | UN2037 | 115 | UN2222 | 127 | UN2294 | 153 | UN2361 | 132 |
| UN1871 | 170 | UN1968 | 126 | UN2038 | 152 | UN2224 | 152 | UN2295 | 155 | UN2362 | 130 |
| UN1872 | 141 | UN1969 | 115 | UN2044 | 115 | UN2225 | 156 | UN2296 | 128 | UN2363 | 130 |
| UN1873 | 143 | UN1970 | 120 | UN2045 | 129 | UN2226 | 156 | UN2297 | 127 | UN2364 | 127 |
| UN1884 | 157 | UN1971 | 115 | UN2046 | 130 | UN2227 | 129P | UN2298 | 128 | UN2366 | 127 |
| UN1885 | 153 | UN1972 | 115 | UN2047 | 132 | UN2232 | 153T | UN2299 | 155 | UN2367 | 130 |
| UN1886 | 156 | UN1973 | 126 | UN2048 | 129 | UN2233 | 152 | UN2300 | 153 | UN2368 | 127 |
| UN1887 | 160 | UN1974 | 126 | UN2049 | 130 | UN2234 | 130 | UN2301 | 127 | UN2370 | 128 |
| UN1888 | 151 | UN1975 | 124T | UN2050 | 127 | UN2235 | 153 | UN2302 | 127 | UN2371 | 128 |
| UN1889 | 157 | UN1976 | 126 | UN2051 | 132 | UN2236 | 156 | UN2303 | 128 | UN2372 | 129 |
| UN1891 | 131 | UN1977 | 120 | UN2052 | 128 | UN2237 | 153 | UN2304 | 133 | UN2373 | 127 |
| UN1892 | 151T | UN1978 | 115 | UN2053 | 129 | UN2238 | 130 | UN2305 | 153 | UN2374 | 127 |
| UN1894 | 151 | UN1979 | 121 | UN2054 | 132 | UN2239 | 153 | UN2306 | 152 | UN2375 | 129 |
| UN1895 | 151 | UN1980 | 122 | UN2055 | 128P | UN2240 | 154 | UN2307 | 152 | UN2376 | 127 |
| UN1897 | 160 | UN1981 | 121 | UN2056 | 127 | UN2241 | 128 | UN2308 | 157 | UN2377 | 127 |
| UN1898 | 156T | UN1982 | 126 | UN2057 | 128 | UN2242 | 128 | UN2309 | 128P | UN2378 | 131 |
| UN1902 | 153 | UN1983 | 126 | UN2058 | 129 | UN2243 | 130 | UN2310 | 131 | UN2379 | 132 |
| UN1903 | 153 | UN1984 | 126 | UN2059 | 127 | UN2244 | 129 | UN2311 | 153 | UN2380 | 127 |
| UN1905 | 154 | UN1986 | 131 | UN2067 | 140 | UN2245 | 127 | UN2312 | 153 | UN2381 | 130 |
| UN1906 | 153 | UN1987 | 127 | UN2068 | 140 | UN2246 | 128 | UN2313 | 130 | UN2382 | 131T |
| UN1907 | 154 | UN1988 | 131 | UN2069 | 140 | UN2247 | 128 | UN2315 | 171 | UN2383 | 132 |
| UN1908 | 154 | UN1989 | 129 | UN2070 | 143 | UN2248 | 132 | UN2316 | 157 | UN2384 | 127 |
| UN1910 | 157 | UN1990 | 129 | UN2071 | 140 | UN2249 | 153 | UN2317 | 157 | UN2385 | 129 |
| UN1911 | 119T | UN1991 | 131P | UN2072 | 140 | UN2250 | 156 | UN2318 | 135 | UN2386 | 132 |
| UN1912 | 115 | UN1992 | 131 | UN2073 | 125 | UN2251 | 127P | UN2319 | 128 | UN2387 | 130 |
| UN1913 | 120 | UN1993 | 128 | UN2074 | 153P | UN2252 | 127 | UN2320 | 153 | UN2388 | 130 |
| UN1914 | 130 | UN1994 | 131T | UN2075 | 153 | UN2253 | 153 | UN2321 | 153 | UN2389 | 127 |
| UN1915 | 127 | UN1999 | 130 | UN2076 | 153 | UN2254 | 133 | UN2322 | 152 | UN2390 | 129 |
| UN1916 | 152 | UN2000 | 133 | UN2077 | 153 | UN2256 | 130 | UN2323 | 129 | UN2391 | 129 |
| UN1917 | 129P | UN2001 | 133 | UN2078 | 156 | UN2257 | 138 | UN2324 | 128 | UN2392 | 129 |
| UN1918 | 130 | UN2002 | 135 | UN2079 | 154 | UN2258 | 132 | UN2325 | 129 | UN2393 | 132 |
| UN1919 | 129P | UN2003 | 135 | UN2186 | 125T | UN2259 | 153 | UN2326 | 153 | UN2394 | 129 |
| UN1920 | 128 | UN2004 | 135T | UN2187 | 120 | UN2260 | 132 | UN2327 | 153 | UN2395 | 132 |
| UN1921 | 131P | UN2005 | 135 | UN2188 | 119T | UN2261 | 153 | UN2328 | 156 | UN2396 | 131P |
| UN1922 | 132 | UN2006 | 135 | UN2189 | 119T | UN2262 | 156 | UN2329 | 129 | UN2397 | 127 |
| UN1923 | 135T | UN2008 | 135 | UN2190 | 124T | UN2263 | 128 | UN2330 | 128 | UN2398 | 127 |
| UN1928 | 135 | UN2009 | 135 | UN2191 | 123T | UN2264 | 132 | UN2331 | 154 | UN2399 | 132 |
| UN1929 | 135 | UN2010 | 138 | UN2192 | 119T | UN2265 | 129 | UN2332 | 129 | UN2400 | 130 |
| UN1931 | 171T | UN2011 | 139T | UN2193 | 126 | UN2266 | 132 | UN2333 | 131 | UN2401 | 132 |
| UN1932 | 135 | UN2012 | 139T | UN2194 | 125T | UN2267 | 156 | UN2334 | 131T | UN2402 | 130 |
| UN1935 | 157 | UN2013 | 139T | UN2195 | 125T | UN2269 | 153 | UN2335 | 131 | UN2403 | 129P |
| UN1938 | 156 | UN2014 | 140 | UN2196 | 125T | UN2270 | 132 | UN2336 | 131 | UN2404 | 131 |
| UN1939 | 137 | UN2015 | 143 | UN2197 | 125T | UN2271 | 127 | UN2337 | 131T | UN2405 | 129 |
| UN1940 | 153 | UN2016 | 151 | UN2198 | 125T | UN2272 | 153 | UN2338 | 131 | UN2406 | 131 |
| UN1941 | 171 | UN2017 | 159 | UN2199 | 119T | UN2273 | 153 | UN2339 | 130 | UN2407 | 155T |
| UN1942 | 140 | UN2018 | 152 | UN2200 | 116P | UN2274 | 153 | UN2340 | 130 | UN2409 | 129 |
| UN1944 | 133 | UN2019 | 152 | UN2201 | 122 | UN2275 | 129 | UN2341 | 130 | UN2410 | 129 |
| UN1945 | 133 | UN2020 | 153 | UN2202 | 117T | UN2276 | 132 | UN2342 | 130 | UN2411 | 131 |
| UN1950 | 126 | UN2021 | 153 | UN2203 | 116 | UN2277 | 129P | UN2343 | 130 | UN2412 | 129 |

**Schedule 5**

| UN # | Guide | UN # | Guide | UN # | Guide | UN # | Guide | UN # | Guide | UN # | Guide |
|---|---|---|---|---|---|---|---|---|---|---|---|
| UN2413 | 128 | UN2487 | 155T | UN2578 | 157 | UN2668 | 131T | UN2749 | 130 | UN2834 | 154 |
| UN2414 | 130 | UN2488 | 155T | UN2579 | 153 | UN2669 | 152 | UN2750 | 153 | UN2835 | 138 |
| UN2416 | 129 | UN2490 | 153 | UN2580 | 154 | UN2670 | 157 | UN2751 | 155 | UN2837 | 154 |
| UN2417 | 125T | UN2491 | 153 | UN2581 | 154 | UN2671 | 153 | UN2752 | 127 | UN2838 | 129P |
| UN2418 | 125T | UN2493 | 132 | UN2582 | 154 | UN2672 | 154 | UN2753 | 153 | UN2839 | 153 |
| UN2419 | 116 | UN2495 | 144T | UN2583 | 153 | UN2673 | 151 | UN2754 | 153 | UN2840 | 129 |
| UN2420 | 125T | UN2496 | 156 | UN2584 | 153 | UN2674 | 154 | UN2757 | 151 | UN2841 | 131 |
| UN2421 | 124T | UN2498 | 132 | UN2585 | 153 | UN2676 | 119T | UN2758 | 131 | UN2842 | 129 |
| UN2422 | 126 | UN2501 | 152 | UN2586 | 153 | UN2677 | 154 | UN2759 | 151 | UN2844 | 138 |
| UN2424 | 126 | UN2502 | 132 | UN2587 | 153 | UN2678 | 154 | UN2760 | 131 | UN2845 | 135T |
| UN2426 | 140 | UN2503 | 137 | UN2588 | 151 | UN2679 | 154 | UN2761 | 151 | UN2846 | 135 |
| UN2427 | 140 | UN2504 | 159 | UN2589 | 155 | UN2680 | 154 | UN2762 | 131 | UN2849 | 153 |
| UN2428 | 140 | UN2505 | 154 | UN2590 | 171 | UN2681 | 154 | UN2763 | 151 | UN2850 | 128 |
| UN2429 | 140 | UN2506 | 154 | UN2591 | 120 | UN2682 | 157 | UN2764 | 131 | UN2851 | 157 |
| UN2430 | 153 | UN2507 | 154 | UN2599 | 126 | UN2683 | 132 | UN2771 | 151 | UN2852 | 113 |
| UN2431 | 153 | UN2508 | 156 | UN2600 | 119T | UN2684 | 132 | UN2772 | 131 | UN2853 | 151 |
| UN2432 | 153 | UN2509 | 154 | UN2601 | 115 | UN2685 | 132 | UN2775 | 151 | UN2854 | 151 |
| UN2433 | 153 | UN2511 | 153 | UN2602 | 126 | UN2686 | 132 | UN2776 | 131 | UN2855 | 151 |
| UN2434 | 156 | UN2512 | 152 | UN2603 | 131 | UN2687 | 133 | UN2777 | 151 | UN2856 | 151 |
| UN2435 | 156 | UN2513 | 156 | UN2604 | 132 | UN2688 | 159 | UN2778 | 131 | UN2857 | 126 |
| UN2436 | 129 | UN2514 | 129 | UN2605 | 155T | UN2689 | 153 | UN2779 | 153 | UN2858 | 151 |
| UN2437 | 156T | UN2515 | 159 | UN2606 | 155T | UN2690 | 152 | UN2780 | 131 | UN2859 | 154 |
| UN2438 | 132T | UN2516 | 151 | UN2607 | 129P | UN2691 | 137T | UN2781 | 151 | UN2861 | 151 |
| UN2439 | 154 | UN2517 | 115 | UN2608 | 129 | UN2692 | 157T | UN2782 | 131 | UN2862 | 151 |
| UN2440 | 154 | UN2518 | 153 | UN2609 | 156 | UN2693 | 154 | UN2783 | 152 | UN2863 | 154 |
| UN2441 | 135 | UN2520 | 130P | UN2610 | 132 | UN2698 | 156 | UN2784 | 131 | UN2864 | 151 |
| UN2442 | 156T | UN2521 | 131PT | UN2611 | 131 | UN2699 | 154 | UN2785 | 152 | UN2865 | 154 |
| UN2443 | 137 | UN2522 | 153P | UN2612 | 127 | UN2705 | 153P | UN2786 | 153 | UN2869 | 157 |
| UN2444 | 137 | UN2524 | 129 | UN2614 | 129 | UN2707 | 128 | UN2787 | 131 | UN2870 | 135 |
| UN2445 | 135 | UN2525 | 156 | UN2615 | 127 | UN2709 | 128 | UN2788 | 153 | UN2871 | 170 |
| UN2446 | 153 | UN2526 | 132 | UN2616 | 129 | UN2710 | 127 | UN2789 | 132 | UN2872 | 159 |
| UN2447 | 136 | UN2527 | 129P | UN2617 | 129 | UN2713 | 153 | UN2790 | 153 | UN2873 | 153 |
| UN2448 | 133 | UN2528 | 129 | UN2618 | 130P | UN2714 | 133 | UN2793 | 170 | UN2874 | 153 |
| UN2451 | 122 | UN2529 | 132 | UN2619 | 132 | UN2715 | 133 | UN2794 | 154 | UN2875 | 151 |
| UN2452 | 116P | UN2531 | 153P | UN2620 | 130 | UN2716 | 153 | UN2795 | 154 | UN2876 | 153 |
| UN2453 | 115 | UN2533 | 156 | UN2621 | 127 | UN2717 | 133 | UN2796 | 157 | UN2878 | 170 |
| UN2454 | 115 | UN2534 | 119T | UN2622 | 131P | UN2719 | 141 | UN2797 | 154 | UN2879 | 157 |
| UN2455 | 116 | UN2535 | 132 | UN2623 | 133 | UN2720 | 141 | UN2798 | 137 | UN2880 | 140 |
| UN2456 | 130P | UN2536 | 127 | UN2624 | 138 | UN2721 | 141 | UN2799 | 137 | UN2881 | 135 |
| UN2457 | 128 | UN2538 | 133 | UN2626 | 140 | UN2722 | 140 | UN2800 | 154 | UN2900 | 158 |
| UN2458 | 130 | UN2541 | 128 | UN2627 | 140 | UN2723 | 140 | UN2801 | 154 | UN2901 | 124T |
| UN2459 | 127 | UN2542 | 153 | UN2628 | 151 | UN2724 | 140 | UN2802 | 154 | UN2902 | 151 |
| UN2460 | 127 | UN2545 | 135 | UN2629 | 151 | UN2725 | 140 | UN2803 | 172 | UN2903 | 131 |
| UN2461 | 127 | UN2546 | 135 | UN2630 | 151 | UN2726 | 140 | UN2805 | 138 | UN2904 | 154 |
| UN2463 | 138 | UN2547 | 143 | UN2642 | 154 | UN2727 | 141 | UN2806 | 138T | UN2905 | 154 |
| UN2464 | 141 | UN2548 | 124T | UN2643 | 155 | UN2728 | 140 | UN2807 | 171 | UN2907 | 133 |
| UN2465 | 140 | UN2552 | 151 | UN2644 | 151T | UN2729 | 152 | UN2809 | 172 | UN2908 | 161 |
| UN2466 | 143 | UN2554 | 129P | UN2645 | 153 | UN2730 | 152 | UN2810 | 153T | UN2909 | 161 |
| UN2468 | 140 | UN2555 | 113 | UN2646 | 151T | UN2732 | 152 | UN2811 | 154 | UN2910 | 161 |
| UN2469 | 140 | UN2556 | 113 | UN2647 | 153 | UN2732 | 152 | UN2812 | 154 | UN2911 | 161 |
| UN2470 | 152 | UN2557 | 133 | UN2648 | 154 | UN2733 | 132 | UN2813 | 138 | UN2912 | 162 |
| UN2471 | 154 | UN2558 | 131 | UN2649 | 153 | UN2734 | 132 | UN2814 | 158 | UN2913 | 162 |
| UN2473 | 154 | UN2560 | 129 | UN2650 | 153 | UN2735 | 153 | UN2815 | 153 | UN2915 | 163 |
| UN2474 | 157T | UN2561 | 127 | UN2651 | 153 | UN2738 | 153 | UN2817 | 154 | UN2916 | 163 |
| UN2475 | 157 | UN2564 | 153 | UN2653 | 156 | UN2739 | 156 | UN2818 | 154 | UN2917 | 163 |
| UN2477 | 131T | UN2565 | 153 | UN2655 | 151 | UN2740 | 155T | UN2819 | 153 | UN2919 | 163 |
| UN2478 | 155 | UN2567 | 154 | UN2656 | 154 | UN2741 | 141 | UN2820 | 153 | UN2920 | 132 |
| UN2480 | 155T | UN2570 | 154 | UN2657 | 153 | UN2742 | 155T | UN2821 | 153 | UN2921 | 134 |
| UN2481 | 155T | UN2571 | 156 | UN2659 | 151 | UN2743 | 155T | UN2822 | 153 | UN2922 | 154 |
| UN2482 | 155T | UN2572 | 153 | UN2660 | 153 | UN2744 | 155 | UN2823 | 153 | UN2923 | 154 |
| UN2483 | 155T | UN2573 | 141 | UN2661 | 153 | UN2745 | 157 | UN2826 | 155T | UN2924 | 132 |
| UN2484 | 155T | UN2574 | 151 | UN2662 | 153 | UN2746 | 156 | UN2829 | 153 | UN2925 | 134 |
| UN2485 | 155T | UN2576 | 137 | UN2664 | 160 | UN2747 | 156 | UN2830 | 139 | UN2926 | 134 |
| UN2486 | 155T | UN2577 | 156 | UN2667 | 131 | UN2748 | 156 | UN2831 | 160 | UN2927 | 154T |

Schedule 5

| UN # | Guide | UN # | Guide | UN # | Guide | UN # | Guide | UN # | Guide | UN # | Guide |
|---|---|---|---|---|---|---|---|---|---|---|---|
| UN2928 | 154 | UN3028 | 154 | UN3123 | 139T | UN3188 | 136 | UN3262 | 154 | UN3327 | 165 |
| UN2929 | 131T | UN3048 | 157T | UN3124 | 136 | UN3189 | 135 | UN3263 | 154 | UN3328 | 165 |
| UN2930 | 134 | UN3049 | 138T | UN3125 | 139 | UN3190 | 135 | UN3264 | 154 | UN3329 | 165 |
| UN2931 | 151 | UN3050 | 138 | UN3126 | 136 | UN3191 | 136 | UN3265 | 153 | UN3330 | 165 |
| UN2933 | 132 | UN3051 | 135 | UN3127 | 135 | UN3192 | 136 | UN3266 | 154 | UN3331 | 165 |
| UN2934 | 132 | UN3052 | 135T | UN3128 | 136 | UN3194 | 135 | UN3267 | 153 | UN3332 | 164 |
| UN2935 | 132 | UN3053 | 135 | UN3129 | 138 | UN3200 | 135 | UN3268 | 171 | UN3333 | 165 |
| UN2936 | 153 | UN3054 | 131 | UN3130 | 139 | UN3203 | 135 | UN3269 | 127 | UN3336 | 130 |
| UN2937 | 153 | UN3055 | 154 | UN3131 | 138 | UN3205 | 135 | UN3270 | 133 | UN3337 | 126 |
| UN2940 | 135 | UN3056 | 129 | UN3132 | 138 | UN3206 | 136 | UN3271 | 127 | UN3338 | 126 |
| UN2941 | 153 | UN3057 | 125T | UN3133 | 138 | UN3207 | 138 | UN3272 | 127 | UN3339 | 126 |
| UN2942 | 153 | UN3064 | 127 | UN3134 | 139 | UN3208 | 138 | UN3273 | 131 | UN3340 | 126 |
| UN2943 | 129 | UN3065 | 127 | UN3135 | 138 | UN3209 | 138 | UN3274 | 127 | UN3341 | 135 |
| UN2945 | 132 | UN3066 | 153 | UN3136 | 120 | UN3210 | 140 | UN3275 | 131T | UN3342 | 135 |
| UN2946 | 153 | UN3070 | 126 | UN3137 | 140 | UN3211 | 140 | UN3276 | 151T | UN3343 | 113 |
| UN2947 | 155 | UN3071 | 131 | UN3138 | 116 | UN3212 | 140 | UN3277 | 154 | UN3344 | 113 |
| UN2948 | 153 | UN3072 | 171 | UN3139 | 140 | UN3213 | 140 | UN3278 | 151T | UN3345 | 153 |
| UN2949 | 154 | UN3073 | 131P | UN3140 | 151 | UN3214 | 140 | UN3279 | 131T | UN3346 | 131 |
| UN2950 | 138 | UN3076 | 138 | UN3141 | 157 | UN3215 | 140 | UN3280 | 151T | UN3347 | 131 |
| UN2956 | 149 | UN3077 | 171 | UN3142 | 151 | UN3216 | 140 | UN3281 | 151T | UN3348 | 153 |
| UN2965 | 139 | UN3078 | 138 | UN3143 | 151 | UN3218 | 140 | UN3282 | 151 | UN3349 | 151 |
| UN2966 | 153 | UN3079 | 131PT | UN3143 | 151 | UN3219 | 140 | UN3283 | 151 | UN3350 | 131 |
| UN2967 | 154 | UN3080 | 155 | UN3144 | 151 | UN3220 | 126 | UN3284 | 151 | UN3351 | 131 |
| UN2968 | 135 | UN3082 | 171 | UN3145 | 153 | UN3221 | 149 | UN3285 | 151 | UN3352 | 151 |
| UN2969 | 171 | UN3083 | 124T | UN3146 | 153 | UN3222 | 149 | UN3286 | 131 | UN3353 | 126 |
| UN2977 | 166T | UN3084 | 140 | UN3147 | 154 | UN3223 | 149 | UN3287 | 151T | UN3354 | 115 |
| UN2978 | 166T | UN3085 | 140 | UN3148 | 138 | UN3224 | 149 | UN3288 | 151 | UN3355 | 119T |
| UN2983 | 129P | UN3086 | 141 | UN3149 | 140 | UN3225 | 149 | UN3289 | 154T | UN3356 | 140 |
| UN2984 | 140 | UN3087 | 141 | UN3150 | 115 | UN3226 | 149 | UN3290 | 154 | UN3357 | 113 |
| UN2985 | 155T | UN3088 | 135 | UN3151 | 171 | UN3227 | 149 | UN3292 | 138 | UN3358 | 115 |
| UN2986 | 155T | UN3089 | 170 | UN3152 | 171 | UN3228 | 149 | UN3293 | 152 | UN3373 | 158 |
| UN2987 | 156T | UN3090 | 138 | UN3153 | 115 | UN3229 | 149 | UN3294 | 131T | UN3412* | 153 |
| UN2988 | 139T | UN3091 | 138 | UN3154 | 115 | UN3230 | 149 | UN3295 | 128 | UN3463* | 132 |
| UN2989 | 133 | UN3092 | 129 | UN3155 | 154 | UN3231 | 150 | UN3296 | 126 | UN3468* | 115 |
| UN2990 | 171 | UN3093 | 140 | UN3156 | 122 | UN3232 | 150 | UN3297 | 126 | UN3469* | 132 |
| UN2991 | 131 | UN3094 | 138 | UN3157 | 122 | UN3233 | 150 | UN3298 | 126 | UN3470* | 132 |
| UN2992 | 151 | UN3095 | 136 | UN3158 | 120 | UN3234 | 150 | UN3299 | 126 | UN3471* | 154 |
| UN2993 | 131 | UN3096 | 138 | UN3159 | 126 | UN3235 | 150 | UN3300 | 119PT | UN3472* | 153 |
| UN2994 | 151 | UN3097 | 140 | UN3160 | 119T | UN3236 | 150 | UN3301 | 136 | UN3473* | 128 |
| UN2995 | 131 | UN3098 | 140 | UN3161 | 115 | UN3237 | 150 | UN3302 | 132 | UN3474* | 113 |
| UN2996 | 151 | UN3099 | 142 | UN3162 | 123T | UN3238 | 150 | UN3303 | 124T | UN3475 | 127 |
| UN2997 | 131 | UN3100 | 135 | UN3163 | 126 | UN3239 | 150 | UN3304 | 123T | UN3476* | 138 |
| UN2998 | 151 | UN3101 | 146 | UN3164 | 126 | UN3240 | 150 | UN3305 | 119T | UN3477* | 153 |
| UN3005 | 131 | UN3102 | 146 | UN3165 | 131 | UN3241 | 133 | UN3306 | 124T | UN3478* | 115 |
| UN3006 | 151 | UN3103 | 146 | UN3166 | 128 | UN3242 | 171 | UN3307 | 124T | UN3479* | 115 |
| UN3009 | 131 | UN3104 | 146 | UN3167 | 115 | UN3243 | 151 | UN3308 | 123T | UN3480* | 147 |
| UN3010 | 151 | UN3105 | 145 | UN3168 | 119 | UN3244 | 154 | UN3309 | 119T | UN3481* | 147 |
| UN3011 | 131 | UN3106 | 145 | UN3169 | 123 | UN3245 | 171 | UN3310 | 124T | | |
| UN3012 | 151 | UN3107 | 145 | UN3170 | 138 | UN3246 | 156T | UN3311 | 122 | | |
| UN3013 | 131 | UN3108 | 145 | UN3171 | 154 | UN3247 | 140 | UN3312 | 115 | | |
| UN3014 | 153 | UN3109 | 145 | UN3172 | 153 | UN3248 | 131 | UN3313 | 135 | | |
| UN3015 | 131 | UN3110 | 145 | UN3174 | 135 | UN3249 | 151 | UN3314 | 171 | | |
| UN3016 | 151 | UN3111 | 148 | UN3175 | 133 | UN3250 | 153 | UN3315 | 151 | | |
| UN3017 | 131 | UN3112 | 148 | UN3176 | 133 | UN3251 | 133 | UN3316 | 171 | | |
| UN3018 | 152 | UN3113 | 148 | UN3178 | 133 | UN3252 | 115 | UN3317 | 113 | | |
| UN3019 | 131 | UN3114 | 148 | UN3179 | 134 | UN3253 | 154 | UN3318 | 125T | | |
| UN3020 | 153 | UN3115 | 148 | UN3180 | 134 | UN3254 | 135 | UN3319 | 113 | | |
| UN3021 | 131 | UN3116 | 148 | UN3181 | 133 | UN3255 | 135 | UN3320 | 157 | | |
| UN3022 | 127P | UN3117 | 148 | UN3182 | 170 | UN3256 | 128 | UN3321 | 162 | | |
| UN3023 | 131T | UN3118 | 148 | UN3183 | 135 | UN3257 | 128 | UN3322 | 162 | | |
| UN3024 | 131 | UN3119 | 148 | UN3184 | 136 | UN3258 | 171 | UN3323 | 163 | | |
| UN3025 | 131 | UN3120 | 148 | UN3185 | 136 | UN3259 | 154 | UN3324 | 165 | | |
| UN3026 | 151 | UN3121 | 144 | UN3186 | 135 | UN3260 | 154 | UN3325 | 165 | | |
| UN3027 | 151 | UN3122 | 142T | UN3187 | 136 | UN3261 | 154 | UN3326 | 165 | | |

*The UN Numbers are not included in Schedule 1.

Schedule 5

# SCHEDULE 6

## Initial Isolation and Protective Action Distances

**Important note to reader: This schedule is an abbreviated version of the information provided in the 2004 Emergency Response Guidebook. For detailed information refer to the full text.**

These Initial Isolation and Protective Action Distances are suggested to protect people from vapors resulting from spills involving dangerous goods which are considered toxic-by-inhalation (TIH), or which produce toxic gases upon contact with water. **This information is provided as initial guidance until technically qualified emergency response personnel are available. The distances indicate the areas likely to be affected during the first 30 minutes after materials are spilled and could increase with time.**

The **Initial Isolation Zone** defines an area SURROUNDING the incident in which persons may be exposed to dangerous (upwind) and life threatening (downwind) concentrations of material. The **Protective Action Zone** defines an area DOWNWIND from the incident in which persons may become incapacitated and unable to take protective action and/or incur serious or irreversible health effects. The Table provides specific guidance for small and large spills occurring day or night.

### Factors That May Change the Protective Action Distances

**Each ERG** clearly indicates under the section EVACUATION – Fire, the evacuation distance required to protect against fragmentation hazard of a large container. If the material becomes involved in a **FIRE**, the toxic hazard may become less important than the fire or explosion hazard.

If more than one tank car, cargo tank, portable tank, or large cylinder involved in the incident is leaking, LARGE SPILL distances may need to be increased.

For a material with a Protective Action Distance of 11.0+ km, the actual distance may be larger in certain atmospheric conditions.

Initial Isolation and Protective Action Distances are derived from historical data on transportation incidents and the use of statistical models. For worst case scenarios involving the instantaneous release of the entire contents of a package, the distances may need to be increased by multiplying the distances shown below by a factor of two.

Dangerous goods that are considered toxic by inhalation (TIH) are assigned a Hazard Zone depending on the toxicity, described by the letters A to D and shown on the Shipping Document. (Hazard Zone information is only provided for Dangerous Goods originating in or destined for the U.S.) It is possible for different dangerous goods described by the same UN Number to have different Hazard Zone classifications, and these may require a different Isolation and Protective Action Distances. In these cases the Hazard Zone is shown in column 2 of the Table together with the corresponding Protective Action Distances.

### Materials that react with water

Materials which react with water to produce large amounts of toxic gases are included in the Table of Initial Isolation and Protective Action Distances. Note that some water-reactive materials, which are also TIH (e.g., Bromine trifluoride (UN1746), Thionyl chloride (UN1836), etc.) produce additional TIH materials when spilled in water. For these materials, two entries are provided in the Table of Initial Isolation and Protective Action Distances (i.e., for **spills on land, which are identified by the letter L in Column 2 of the Table**, and for **spills in water, which are identified by the letter W in Column 2 of the Table**). If it is not clear whether the spill is on land or in water, or in cases where the spill occurs both on land and in water choose the larger Protective Action Distance.

## How to use this Schedule

Identify the dangerous goods using the UN Number shown on the Shipping Document.

For **Small Spills** (from a Small MoC or a small leak from a large MoC)
- First **ISOLATE** in all directions the distance (in metres) shown in **Column 2**
- Then **PROTECT** persons downwind the distance (in metres) shown in **Column 3** during the **DAY** and **Column 4** during the **NIGHT**

For **Large Spills** (from a large MoC or many small MoC)
- First **ISOLATE** in all directions the distance (in metres) shown in **Column 5**
- Then **PROTECT** persons downwind the distance (in metres) shown in **Column 6** during the **DAY** and **Column 7** during the **NIGHT**

*The codes shown in **Column 1** are:

**W** – means that this Schedule applies only when the dangerous goods are spilled in water
  (The TIH gases produced are listed in Schedule 7)
**L** – means that this Schedule applies only when the dangerous goods are spilled on land
**A** – identifies dangerous goods with a Hazard Zone A
**B** – identifies dangerous goods with a Hazard Zone B
**C** – identifies dangerous goods with a Hazard Zone C
**D** – identifies dangerous goods with a Hazard Zone D

| UN | 1* | 2 | 3 | 4 | 5 | 6 | 7 |
|----|----|----|----|----|----|----|----|
| 1005 |  | 30 | 100 | 200 | 150 | 800 | 2300 |
| 1008 |  | 30 | 100 | 600 | 300 | 1900 | 3000 |
| 1016 |  | 30 | 100 | 100 | 150 | 700 | 2700 |
| 1017 |  | 60 | 400 | 1600 | 600 | 3500 | 8000 |
| 1023 |  | 30 | 100 | 100 | 60 | 300 | 400 |
| 1026 |  | 30 | 200 | 900 | 150 | 1000 | 3500 |
| 1040 |  | 30 | 100 | 200 | 150 | 800 | 2500 |
| 1045 |  | 30 | 100 | 300 | 150 | 800 | 3100 |
| 1048 |  | 30 | 100 | 400 | 300 | 1500 | 4500 |
| 1050 |  | 30 | 100 | 400 | 60 | 300 | 1400 |
| 1051 |  | 100 | 300 | 1100 | 1000 | 3800 | 7200 |
| 1052 |  | 30 | 100 | 500 | 300 | 1700 | 3600 |
| 1053 |  | 300 | 100 | 400 | 300 | 2000 | 6200 |
| 1062 |  | 30 | 100 | 200 | 150 | 700 | 2200 |
| 1064 |  | 30 | 100 | 300 | 200 | 1300 | 4100 |
| 1067 |  | 30 | 100 | 400 | 400 | 1100 | 3000 |
| 1069 |  | 30 | 200 | 1100 | 800 | 4200 | 11000 |
| 1071 |  | 30 | 100 | 100 | 60 | 300 | 400 |
| 1076 |  | 200 | 1100 | 4000 | 1000 | 7500 | 11000 |
| 1079 |  | 60 | 300 | 1200 | 400 | 2100 | 5700 |
| 1082 |  | 30 | 100 | 200 | 60 | 400 | 1000 |
| 1092 |  | 100 | 1100 | 3300 | 1000 | 11000 | 11000 |
| 1098 |  | 30 | 100 | 200 | 60 | 600 | 1100 |
| 1135 |  | 30 | 200 | 300 | 60 | 700 | 1200 |
| 1143 |  | 30 | 100 | 100 | 60 | 400 | 700 |
| 1162 | W | 30 | 100 | 300 | 60 | 600 | 2000 |
| 1163 |  | 30 | 200 | 500 | 100 | 1300 | 2400 |
| 1182 |  | 30 | 100 | 200 | 60 | 400 | 700 |
| 1183 | W | 30 | 100 | 300 | 60 | 700 | 2200 |
| 1185 |  | 30 | 200 | 500 | 100 | 1100 | 2200 |

| UN | 1* | 2 | 3 | 4 | 5 | 6 | 7 |
|----|----|----|----|----|----|----|----|
| 1196 | W | 30 | 100 | 300 | 300 | 800 | 2700 |
| 1238 |  | 30 | 200 | 600 | 150 | 1200 | 2500 |
| 1239 |  | 30 | 300 | 1100 | 200 | 2500 | 5100 |
| 1242 | W | 30 | 100 | 300 | 60 | 800 | 2500 |
| 1244 |  | 30 | 300 | 700 | 150 | 1500 | 2500 |
| 1250 | W | 30 | 100 | 200 | 60 | 600 | 2000 |
| 1251 |  | 150 | 1600 | 3600 | 1000 | 11000 | 11000 |
| 1259 |  | 150 | 1400 | 4900 | 1000 | 11000 | 11000 |
| 1295 | W | 30 | 100 | 300 | 60 | 700 | 2300 |
| 1298 | W | 30 | 100 | 100 | 30 | 400 | 1200 |
| 1305 | W | 30 | 100 | 200 | 60 | 400 | 1500 |
| 1340 | W | 30 | 100 | 200 | 60 | 400 | 1500 |
| 1360 | W | 60 | 400 | 1500 | 500 | 4400 | 11000 |
| 1380 |  | 60 | 700 | 2300 | 400 | 4600 | 8900 |
| 1384 | W | 30 | 100 | 200 | 30 | 300 | 1200 |
| 1397 | W | 60 | 500 | 1900 | 600 | 5700 | 11000 |
| 1412 | W | 30 | 100 | 100 | 30 | 3600 | 1000 |
| 1419 | W | 60 | 400 | 1700 | 600 | 5300 | 11000 |
| 1432 | W | 30 | 300 | 1200 | 400 | 3500 | 10600 |
| 1510 |  | 30 | 200 | 400 | 60 | 600 | 1000 |
| 1541 | W | 30 | 100 | 100 | 100 | 300 | 1000 |
| 1556 |  | 30 | 200 | 500 | 150 | 700 | 2200 |
| 1560 |  | 30 | 200 | 300 | 100 | 1100 | 1800 |
| 1569 |  | 30 | 200 | 800 | 100 | 1100 | 2300 |
| 1580 |  | 30 | 400 | 1000 | 150 | 1900 | 3300 |
| 1581 |  | 30 | 100 | 600 | 300 | 2100 | 5900 |
| 1582 |  | 30 | 100 | 400 | 60 | 400 | 1700 |
| 1583 |  | 30 | 400 | 1000 | 150 | 1900 | 3300 |
| 1589 |  | 60 | 400 | 1500 | 600 | 4100 | 8000 |
| 1595 |  | 30 | 100 | 200 | 60 | 500 | 700 |

Schedule 6

| UN | 1* | 2 | 3 | 4 | 5 | 6 | 7 |
|---|---|---|---|---|---|---|---|
| 1605 | | 30 | 100 | 100 | 30 | 300 | 500 |
| 1612 | | 100 | 800 | 2700 | 400 | 3500 | 8100 |
| 1613 | | 30 | 100 | 100 | 100 | 500 | 1100 |
| 1614 | | 60 | 200 | 600 | 150 | 600 | 1700 |
| 1647 | | 30 | 100 | 200 | 150 | 700 | 2200 |
| 1660 | | 30 | 100 | 600 | 100 | 600 | 2200 |
| 1670 | | 30 | 200 | 400 | 100 | 800 | 1400 |
| 1680 | W | 30 | 100 | 200 | 100 | 300 | 1200 |
| 1689 | W | 30 | 100 | 200 | 100 | 400 | 1400 |
| 1694 | | 30 | 100 | 400 | 100 | 600 | 2700 |
| 1695 | | 30 | 200 | 300 | 60 | 600 | 1100 |
| 1697 | | 30 | 100 | 200 | 60 | 300 | 1400 |
| 1698 | | 30 | 100 | 300 | 60 | 300 | 1400 |
| 1699 | | 30 | 100 | 600 | 200 | 1000 | 3800 |
| 1716 | W | 30 | 100 | 300 | 60 | 600 | 1700 |
| 1717 | W | 30 | 100 | 300 | 100 | 900 | 2800 |
| 1722 | | 100 | 1200 | 2800 | 600 | 7800 | 11000 |
| 1724 | W | 30 | 100 | 200 | 60 | 600 | 1900 |
| 1725 | W | 30 | 100 | 300 | 30 | 400 | 1200 |
| 1726 | W | 30 | 100 | 300 | 60 | 600 | 2100 |
| 1728 | W | 30 | 100 | 200 | 60 | 600 | 1900 |
| 1732 | W | 30 | 100 | 500 | 150 | 1200 | 4000 |
| 1741 | L | 30 | 100 | 300 | 100 | 600 | 1500 |
| 1741 | W | 30 | 100 | 500 | 100 | 1300 | 3900 |
| 1744 | A | 60 | 600 | 1800 | 300 | 3100 | 6600 |
| 1744 | B | 30 | 500 | 1100 | 60 | 900 | 1700 |
| 1745 | L | 30 | 200 | 900 | 150 | 1500 | 3200 |
| 1745 | W | 30 | 200 | 1000 | 240 | 2200 | 6600 |
| 1746 | L | 30 | 100 | 100 | 30 | 300 | 500 |
| 1746 | W | 30 | 100 | 500 | 100 | 1100 | 3900 |
| 1747 | W | 30 | 100 | 100 | 30 | 400 | 1200 |
| 1749 | | 60 | 400 | 1800 | 400 | 2700 | 7200 |
| 1752 | L | 30 | 300 | 700 | 150 | 1400 | 2300 |
| 1752 | W | 30 | 100 | 100 | 30 | 300 | 900 |
| 1753 | W | 30 | 100 | 100 | 30 | 300 | 1000 |
| 1754 | L | 30 | 100 | 100 | 30 | 300 | 400 |
| 1754 | W | 30 | 100 | 500 | 60 | 100 | 2500 |
| 1754[1] | L | 60 | 400 | 1000 | 300 | 2900 | 5700 |
| 1754[1] | W | 30 | 100 | 500 | 60 | 100 | 2900 |
| 1758 | W | 30 | 100 | 100 | 30 | 200 | 800 |
| 1762 | W | 30 | 100 | 200 | 30 | 400 | 1400 |
| 1763 | W | 30 | 100 | 300 | 30 | 400 | 1400 |
| 1765 | W | 30 | 100 | 100 | 30 | 300 | 1000 |
| 1766 | W | 30 | 100 | 200 | 60 | 700 | 2200 |
| 1767 | W | 30 | 100 | 100 | 30 | 400 | 1100 |
| 1769 | W | 30 | 100 | 100 | 30 | 200 | 600 |
| 1771 | W | 30 | 100 | 200 | 60 | 500 | 1400 |
| 1777 | W | 30 | 100 | 100 | 30 | 200 | 800 |
| 1781 | W | 30 | 100 | 100 | 30 | 200 | 700 |

| UN | 1* | 2 | 3 | 4 | 5 | 6 | 7 |
|---|---|---|---|---|---|---|---|
| 1784 | W | 30 | 100 | 200 | 60 | 500 | 1500 |
| 1799 | W | 30 | 100 | 200 | 60 | 500 | 1600 |
| 1800 | W | 30 | 100 | 200 | 30 | 400 | 1400 |
| 1801 | W | 30 | 100 | 200 | 60 | 500 | 1600 |
| 1804 | W | 30 | 100 | 200 | 60 | 500 | 1600 |
| 1806 | W | 30 | 100 | 200 | 30 | 400 | 1600 |
| 1808 | W | 30 | 100 | 300 | 60 | 600 | 2000 |
| 1809 | L | 30 | 200 | 700 | 150 | 1500 | 3000 |
| 1809 | W | 30 | 100 | 400 | 60 | 800 | 2800 |
| 1810 | L | 30 | 300 | 500 | 100 | 1100 | 2000 |
| 1810 | W | 30 | 100 | 300 | 60 | 700 | 2300 |
| 1815 | W | 30 | 100 | 100 | 30 | 300 | 800 |
| 1816 | W | 30 | 100 | 200 | 60 | 600 | 2000 |
| 1818 | W | 30 | 100 | 300 | 100 | 900 | 2900 |
| 1828 | L | 30 | 100 | 200 | 60 | 700 | 1200 |
| 1828 | W | 30 | 100 | 200 | 30 | 400 | 1200 |
| 1829 | | 60 | 400 | 1000 | 300 | 2900 | 5700 |
| 1831 | | 60 | 400 | 1000 | 300 | 2900 | 5700 |
| 1834 | L | 30 | 200 | 500 | 100 | 1000 | 2100 |
| 1834 | W | 30 | 100 | 200 | 60 | 500 | 1800 |
| 1836 | L | 30 | 300 | 700 | 100 | 900 | 1900 |
| 1836 | W | 30 | 300 | 1400 | 300 | 3300 | 7500 |
| 1838 | L | 30 | 100 | 200 | 60 | 500 | 800 |
| 1838 | W | 30 | 100 | 200 | 60 | 600 | 1900 |
| 1859 | | 30 | 100 | 500 | 100 | 500 | 1900 |
| 1892 | | 30 | 100 | 300 | 150 | 800 | 1900 |
| 1898 | W | 30 | 100 | 300 | 60 | 500 | 1400 |
| 1911 | | 60 | 300 | 1200 | 300 | 1700 | 4300 |
| 1923 | W | 30 | 100 | 200 | 30 | 300 | 1200 |
| 1929 | W | 30 | 100 | 200 | 30 | 300 | 1100 |
| 1931 | W | 30 | 100 | 200 | 30 | 300 | 1100 |
| 1953 | A | 100 | 600 | 2500 | 800 | 4400 | 8900 |
| 1953 | B | 30 | 200 | 800 | 400 | 1900 | 4800 |
| 1953 | C | 30 | 100 | 300 | 300 | 1300 | 4100 |
| 1953 | D | 30 | 100 | 200 | 150 | 700 | 2700 |
| 1955 | A | 100 | 500 | 2100 | 800 | 4400 | 8900 |
| 1955 | B | 30 | 200 | 800 | 400 | 1900 | 4800 |
| 1955 | C | 30 | 100 | 400 | 200 | 1000 | 3200 |
| 1955 | D | 30 | 100 | 200 | 150 | 700 | 2700 |
| 1955[2] | | 100 | 1000 | 3400 | 500 | 4400 | 9600 |
| 1967 | | 100 | 1000 | 3400 | 500 | 4400 | 9600 |
| 1975 | | 30 | 100 | 600 | 100 | 600 | 2200 |
| 1994 | | 100 | 900 | 2100 | 500 | 5500 | 8900 |
| 2004 | W | 30 | 100 | 400 | 60 | 600 | 2300 |
| 2011 | W | 60 | 400 | 1600 | 500 | 4800 | 11+ km |
| 2012 | W | 30 | 300 | 1200 | 400 | 3100 | 9400 |
| 2013 | W | 30 | 300 | 1100 | 400 | 3000 | 9400 |

[1] When mixed with sulphur trioxide

[2] Compressed gas mixed with organic phosphate, organic phosphate compound or organic phosphorous compound.

Schedule 6

| UN | 1* | 2 | 3 | 4 | 5 | 6 | 7 |
|---|---|---|---|---|---|---|---|
| 2032 | | 30 | 100 | 300 | 150 | 600 | 1100 |
| 2186 | | 30 | 100 | 400 | 500 | 2800 | 10200 |
| 2188 | | 200 | 1100 | 4000 | 1000 | 7000 | 11+ km |
| 2189 | | 30 | 200 | 1000 | 800 | 4200 | 10300 |
| 2190 | | 800 | 5300 | 11+ km | 1000 | 11+ km | 11+ km |
| 2191 | | 30 | 100 | 500 | 300 | 1700 | 4900 |
| 2192 | | 30 | 200 | 800 | 150 | 2900 | 6400 |
| 2194 | | 60 | 400 | 1900 | 500 | 2900 | 6400 |
| 2195 | | 200 | 1200 | 4300 | 1000 | 9400 | 11+ km |
| 2196 | | 30 | 200 | 800 | 150 | 1000 | 2900 |
| 2197 | | 30 | 100 | 400 | 150 | 1000 | 3200 |
| 2198 | | 30 | 200 | 1100 | 200 | 1300 | 3800 |
| 2199 | | 100 | 600 | 2500 | 800 | 4400 | 8900 |
| 2202 | | 200 | 1300 | 4600 | 1000 | 8700 | 11+ km |
| 2204 | | 30 | 200 | 700 | 500 | 3300 | 8700 |
| 2232 | | 30 | 200 | 400 | 100 | 900 | 1500 |
| 2308 | W | 30 | 100 | 400 | 300 | 800 | 2500 |
| 2334 | | 30 | 200 | 600 | 150 | 1700 | 3000 |
| 2337 | | 30 | 100 | 100 | 30 | 300 | 500 |
| 2353 | W | 30 | 100 | 100 | 30 | 300 | 1000 |
| 2382 | | 30 | 200 | 400 | 100 | 1000 | 1700 |
| 2395 | W | 30 | 100 | 100 | 30 | 200 | 600 |
| 2407 | | 30 | 200 | 300 | 60 | 700 | 1400 |
| 2417 | | 30 | 200 | 800 | 150 | 900 | 3000 |
| 2418 | | 100 | 600 | 2600 | 800 | 4700 | 10300 |
| 2420 | | 60 | 300 | 1500 | 1000 | 8400 | 11+ km |
| 2421 | | 30 | 100 | 300 | 100 | 300 | 1200 |
| 2434 | W | 30 | 100 | 100 | 30 | 200 | 600 |
| 2435 | W | 30 | 100 | 100 | 30 | 400 | 1100 |
| 2437 | W | 30 | 100 | 100 | 30 | 200 | 600 |
| 2438 | | 30 | 100 | 300 | 60 | 600 | 1100 |
| 2442 | | 30 | 200 | 300 | 60 | 700 | 1300 |
| 2474 | | 60 | 700 | 2000 | 300 | 3100 | 5300 |
| 2477 | | 30 | 100 | 200 | 60 | 500 | 800 |
| 2480 | | 150 | 1800 | 5300 | 1000 | 11+ km | 11+ km |
| 2481 | | 150 | 1500 | 3800 | 1000 | 11+ km | 11+ km |
| 2482 | | 100 | 1200 | 2800 | 800 | 9600 | 11+ km |
| 2483 | | 100 | 1300 | 3000 | 1000 | 11+ km | 11+ km |
| 2484 | | 100 | 1100 | 2600 | 800 | 9300 | 11+ km |
| 2485 | | 60 | 80 | 1700 | 400 | 4800 | 6900 |
| 2486 | | 60 | 800 | 1800 | 400 | 4800 | 7400 |
| 2487 | | 30 | 400 | 600 | 150 | 1600 | 2500 |
| 2488 | | 30 | 300 | 400 | 100 | 1000 | 1400 |
| 2495 | W | 30 | 100 | 500 | 150 | 1200 | 4200 |
| 2521 | | 30 | 100 | 100 | 30 | 300 | 500 |
| 2534 | | 30 | 200 | 700 | 300 | 1600 | 4300 |
| 2548 | | 60 | 300 | 1400 | 400 | 2300 | 6500 |
| 2600 | | 30 | 100 | 100 | 150 | 700 | 2700 |
| 2605 | | 30 | 400 | 600 | 150 | 1600 | 2500 |
| 2606 | | 30 | 100 | 100 | 30 | 300 | 500 |
| 2644 | | 30 | 100 | 200 | 100 | 300 | 800 |

| UN | 1* | 2 | 3 | 4 | 5 | 6 | 7 |
|---|---|---|---|---|---|---|---|
| 2646 | | 30 | 100 | 100 | 30 | 400 | 500 |
| 2668 | | 30 | 100 | 100 | 30 | 400 | 500 |
| 2676 | | 60 | 400 | 1700 | 500 | 2800 | 7200 |
| 2691 | W | 30 | 100 | 400 | 30 | 400 | 1500 |
| 2692 | L | 30 | 100 | 400 | 60 | 500 | 1000 |
| 2692 | W | 30 | 100 | 600 | 100 | 1000 | 3000 |
| 2740 | | 30 | 200 | 300 | 60 | 700 | 1300 |
| 2742 | | 30 | 100 | 100 | 30 | 400 | 600 |
| 2743 | | 30 | 100 | 100 | 30 | 300 | 500 |
| 2806 | W | 30 | 100 | 400 | 60 | 600 | 2200 |
| 2810 | A | 60 | 800 | 1800 | 300 | 2900 | 5700 |
| 2810 | B | 30 | 100 | 200 | 60 | 500 | 800 |
| 2810[3] | A | 60 | 80 | 1800 | 400 | 4800 | 7400 |
| 2810[3] | B | 30 | 100 | 200 | 60 | 500 | 800 |
| 2826 | | 30 | 100 | 200 | 60 | 500 | 700 |
| 2845[4] | | 30 | 300 | 800 | 150 | 1600 | 2900 |
| 2845[5] | | 30 | 400 | 1200 | 200 | 2600 | 4500 |
| 2901 | | 30 | 200 | 100 | 400 | 2400 | 6500 |
| 2927[6] | | 30 | 100 | 100 | 30 | 200 | 200 |
| 2927[7] | | 30 | 100 | 100 | 30 | 200 | 300 |
| 2927[8] | A | 60 | 800 | 1800 | 300 | 2900 | 5700 |
| 2927[8] | B | 30 | 100 | 200 | 60 | 500 | 800 |
| 2927[9] | A | 100 | 1200 | 2800 | 600 | 7800 | 11+ km |
| 2927 | B | 30 | 100 | 200 | 60 | 500 | 800 |
| 2929 | A | 60 | 700 | 2300 | 400 | 4600 | 8900 |
| 2929 | B | 30 | 100 | 200 | 60 | 500 | 800 |
| 2929[10] | A | 100 | 1100 | 2600 | 600 | 7800 | 11+ km |
| 2929[10] | B | 30 | 100 | 200 | 60 | 500 | 800 |
| 2977 | W | 30 | 100 | 400 | 60 | 500 | 2300 |
| 2978 | W | 30 | 100 | 400 | 60 | 500 | 2200 |
| 2985 | W | 30 | 100 | 200 | 100 | 500 | 1600 |
| 2986 | W | 30 | 100 | 200 | 100 | 500 | 1600 |
| 2987 | W | 30 | 100 | 200 | 100 | 500 | 1600 |
| 2988 | W | 30 | 100 | 200 | 100 | 500 | 1600 |
| 3023 | | 30 | 100 | 200 | 60 | 500 | 700 |
| 3048 | W | 60 | 500 | 1900 | 600 | 5800 | 1100 |
| 3049 | W | 30 | 100 | 200 | 60 | 400 | 1300 |
| 3052 | W | 30 | 100 | 200 | 60 | 400 | 1300 |
| 3057 | | 30 | 200 | 100 | 800 | 4600 | 11+ km |
| 3079 | | 30 | 100 | 200 | 60 | 500 | 900 |
| 3083 | | 30 | 200 | 700 | 500 | 3100 | 8400 |
| 3122 | A | 60 | 800 | 1800 | 300 | 2900 | 5700 |
| 3122 | B | 30 | 100 | 300 | 60 | 600 | 1000 |

[3] Toxic liquid, organic, n.o.s.
[4] Ethyl phosphonous dichloride, anhydrous
[5] Methyl phosphonous dichloride
[6] Ethyl phosphonothioic dichloride, anhydrous
[7] Ethyl phosphorodichloridate
[8] Toxic liquid, corrosive, n.o.s.
[9] Toxic liquid, organic, n.o.s.
[10] Toxic, liquid, flammable, organic n.o.s

Schedule 6

| UN | 1* | 2 | 3 | 4 | 5 | 6 | 7 |
|----|----|---|---|---|---|---|---|
| 3123 | A | 60 | 800 | 1800 | 300 | 2900 | 5700 |
| 3123 | B | 30 | 100 | 200 | 60 | 500 | 800 |
| 3160 | A | 100 | 600 | 2500 | 800 | 4400 | 8900 |
| 3160 | B | 30 | 200 | 800 | 400 | 1900 | 4800 |
| 3160 | C | 30 | 100 | 300 | 300 | 1300 | 4100 |
| 3160 | D | 30 | 100 | 200 | 150 | 700 | 2700 |
| 3162 | A | 100 | 600 | 2500 | 800 | 4400 | 8900 |
| 3162 | B | 30 | 200 | 800 | 400 | 1900 | 4800 |
| 3162 | C | 30 | 100 | 300 | 300 | 1300 | 4100 |
| 3162 | D | 30 | 100 | 200 | 150 | 700 | 2700 |
| 3246 | | 30 | 100 | 100 | 30 | 200 | 200 |
| 3275 | | 30 | 100 | 200 | 60 | 500 | 900 |
| 3276 | | 30 | 100 | 200 | 60 | 500 | 900 |
| 3278 | | 30 | 400 | 1200 | 200 | 2600 | 4500 |
| 3279 | | 30 | 400 | 1200 | 200 | 2600 | 4500 |
| 3280 | | 30 | 200 | 800 | 150 | 200 | 4800 |
| 3281 | | 150 | 1400 | 4900 | 1000 | 11+ km | 11+ km |
| 3287 | A | 60 | 800 | 1800 | 300 | 2900 | 5700 |
| 3287 | B | 30 | 200 | 300 | 150 | 600 | 1100 |
| 3289 | A | 60 | 800 | 1800 | 300 | 2900 | 5700 |
| 3289 | B | 30 | 200 | 300 | 150 | 600 | 1100 |
| 3294 | | 30 | 100 | 300 | 200 | 500 | 1900 |
| 3300 | | 30 | 100 | 200 | 150 | 800 | 2500 |
| 3303 | A | 100 | 500 | 2100 | 800 | 4400 | 8900 |
| 3303 | B | 60 | 200 | 1000 | 500 | 2700 | 7200 |
| 3303 | C | 30 | 100 | 300 | 300 | 1300 | 4100 |
| 3303 | D | 30 | 100 | 200 | 150 | 700 | 2700 |
| 3304 | A | 150 | 700 | 2500 | 800 | 4700 | 10300 |
| 3304 | B | 30 | 200 | 1000 | 400 | 2400 | 6500 |
| 3304 | C | 30 | 100 | 400 | 300 | 1700 | 3600 |
| 3304 | D | 30 | 100 | 200 | 150 | 700 | 2700 |
| 3305 | A | 100 | 700 | 2500 | 800 | 4700 | 10300 |
| 3305 | B | 30 | 200 | 1000 | 800 | 4200 | 10300 |
| 3305 | C | 30 | 100 | 300 | 300 | 1300 | 4100 |
| 3305 | D | 30 | 100 | 200 | 150 | 700 | 2700 |
| 3306 | A | 100 | 600 | 2500 | 800 | 4400 | 8900 |
| 3306 | B | 60 | 200 | 1000 | 500 | 2700 | 7200 |
| 3306 | C | 30 | 100 | 300 | 300 | 1300 | 4100 |
| 3306 | D | 30 | 100 | 200 | 150 | 700 | 2700 |
| 3307 | A | 100 | 500 | 2100 | 800 | 4400 | 8900 |
| 3307 | B | 60 | 200 | 1000 | 500 | 2700 | 7200 |

| UN | 1* | 2 | 3 | 4 | 5 | 6 | 7 |
|----|----|---|---|---|---|---|---|
| 3307 | C | 30 | 100 | 300 | 300 | 1300 | 4100 |
| 3307 | D | 30 | 100 | 200 | 150 | 700 | 2700 |
| 3308 | A | 150 | 700 | 2500 | 800 | 4700 | 10300 |
| 3308 | B | 30 | 200 | 1000 | 400 | 2400 | 6500 |
| 3308 | C | 30 | 100 | 400 | 300 | 1700 | 3600 |
| 3308 | D | 30 | 100 | 200 | 150 | 700 | 2700 |
| 3309 | A | 100 | 700 | 2500 | 800 | 4700 | 10300 |
| 3309 | B | 30 | 200 | 1000 | 800 | 4200 | 10300 |
| 3309 | C | 30 | 100 | 300 | 300 | 1300 | 4100 |
| 3309 | D | 30 | 100 | 200 | 150 | 700 | 2700 |
| 3310 | A | 100 | 600 | 2500 | 800 | 4400 | 8900 |
| 3310 | B | 60 | 200 | 1000 | 500 | 2700 | 7200 |
| 3310 | C | 30 | 100 | 300 | 300 | 1300 | 4100 |
| 3310 | D | 30 | 100 | 200 | 150 | 700 | 2700 |
| 3318 | | 30 | 100 | 200 | 150 | 800 | 2300 |
| 3355 | A | 100 | 600 | 2500 | 800 | 4400 | 8900 |
| 3355 | B | 30 | 200 | 800 | 400 | 1900 | 4800 |
| 3355 | C | 30 | 100 | 300 | 300 | 1300 | 4100 |
| 3355 | D | 30 | 100 | 200 | 150 | 700 | 2700 |
| 3361 | W | 30 | 100 | 200 | 100 | 500 | 1600 |
| 3362 | W | 30 | 100 | 200 | 100 | 500 | 1600 |
| 3381 | A | 60 | 800 | 1800 | 300 | 2900 | 5700 |
| 3382 | B | 30 | 100 | 200 | 60 | 500 | 800 |
| 3383 | A | 60 | 700 | 2300 | 400 | 4600 | 8900 |
| 3384 | B | 30 | 100 | 200 | 60 | 500 | 800 |
| 3385 | A | 60 | 800 | 1800 | 300 | 2900 | 5700 |
| 3386 | B | 30 | 100 | 200 | 60 | 500 | 800 |
| 3387 | A | 60 | 800 | 1800 | 300 | 2900 | 5700 |
| 3388 | B | 30 | 100 | 300 | 60 | 600 | 1000 |
| 3389 | A | 60 | 800 | 1800 | 300 | 2900 | 5700 |
| 3390 | B | 30 | 100 | 200 | 60 | 500 | 800 |
| 3456 | W | 30 | 100 | 500 | 200 | 700 | 2500 |
| 3461 | W | 30 | 100 | 200 | 60 | 400 | 1300 |
| 9191 | W | 30 | 100 | 100 | 30 | 200 | 600 |
| 9192 | | 30 | 100 | 300 | 150 | 800 | 3100 |
| 9202 | | 30 | 100 | 100 | 150 | 700 | 2700 |
| 9206 | | 30 | 100 | 200 | 60 | 500 | 700 |
| 9263 | | 30 | 100 | 100 | 30 | 300 | 400 |
| 9264 | | 30 | 100 | 100 | 30 | 300 | 300 |
| 9269 | | 30 | 200 | 500 | 150 | 100 | 700 |

Schedule 6

# SCHEDULE 7

## Water Reactive Materials that Produce Toxic Gas

The following materials produce gases that are Toxic-by-Inhalation (TIH) when spilled in water. The specific TIH gas(es) produced by each water-reactive material is(are) listed below.

(When a water-reactive TIH producing material is spilled into a river or stream, the source of the toxic gas may move with the current and stretch downstream from the spill point for a substantial distance.)

| UN# | ERG# | TIH Gas | UN# | ERG# | TIH Gas | UN# | ERG# | TIH Gas |
|---|---|---|---|---|---|---|---|---|
| 1162 | 155 | HCl | 1753 | 156 | HCl | 2004 | 135 | $NH_3$ |
| 1183 | 139 | HCl | 1752 | 156 | HCl | 2011 | 139 | $PH_3$ |
| 1196 | 155 | HCl | 1754 | 137 | HCl | 2012 | 139 | $PH_3$ |
| 1242 | 139 | HCl | 1758 | 137 | HCl | 2013 | 139 | $PH_3$ |
| 1250 | 155 | HCl | 1762 | 156 | HCl | 2308 | 157 | $NO_2$ |
| 1295 | 139 | HCl | 1763 | 156 | HCl | 2353 | 132 | HCl |
| 1298 | 155 | HCl | 1765 | 156 | HCl | 2395 | 132 | HCl |
| 1305 | 155P | HCl | 1766 | 156 | HCl | 2434 | 156 | HCl |
| 1340 | 139 | $H_2S$ | 1767 | 155 | HCl | 2435 | 156 | HCl |
| 1360 | 139 | $PH_3$ | 1769 | 156 | HCl | 2437 | 156 | HCl |
| 1384 | 135 | $H_2S$, $SO_2$ | 1771 | 156 | HCl | 2495 | 144 | HF |
| 1397 | 139 | $PH_3$ | 1777 | 137 | HF | 2691 | 137 | HBr |
| 1412 | 139 | $NH_3$ | 1784 | 156 | HCl | 2692 | 157 | HBr |
| 1419 | 139 | $PH_3$ | 1799 | 156 | HCl | 2806 | 138 | $NH_3$ |
| 1432 | 139 | $PH_3$ | 1800 | 156 | HCl | 2977 | 166 | HF |
| 1541 | 155 | HCN | 1801 | 156 | HCl | 2978 | 166 | HF |
| 1680 | 157 | HCN | 1804 | 156 | HCl | 2985 | 155 | HCl |
| 1689 | 157 | HCN | 1806 | 137 | HCl | 2986 | 155 | HCl |
| 1716 | 156 | HBr | 1809 | 137 | HCl | 2987 | 156 | HCl |
| 1717 | 155 | HCl | 1810 | 137 | HCl | 2988 | 139 | HCl |
| 1741 | 125 | HCl | 1816 | 155 | HCl | 3048 | 157 | $PH_3$ |
| 1724 | 155 | HCl | 1818 | 157 | HCl | 3049 | 138 | HCl |
| 1725 | 137 | HBr | 1828 | 137 | HCl, $SO_2$, $H_2S$ | 3052 | 135 | HCl |
| 1726 | 137 | HCl | 1834 | 137 | HCl, $SO_3$ | 3461 | 135 | HCl |
| 1728 | 155 | HCl | 1836 | 137 | HCl, $SO_2$ | 3361 | 156 | HCl |
| 1732 | 157 | HF | 1838 | 137 | HCl | 3362 | 155 | HCl |
| 1745 | 144 | HF, $Br_2$ | 1898 | 156 | HI | 9191 | 143 | $Cl_2$ |
| 1746 | 144 | HF, $Br_2$ | 1923 | 135 | $H_2S$, $SO_2$ | | | |
| 1747 | 155 | HCl | 1931 | 171 | $H_2S$, $SO_2$ | | | |

### Chemical Symbol of TIH Gases

| Symbol | Name of TIH Gas | Symbol | Name of TIH Gas | Symbol | Name of TIH Gas |
|---|---|---|---|---|---|
| $Br_2$ | Bromine | HCN | Hydrogen cyanide | $SO_2$ | Sulphur dioxide |
| $Cl_2$ | Chlorine | HF | Hydrogen fluoride | $SO_3$ | Sulphur trioxide |
| HBr | Hydrogen bromide | HI | Hydrogen iodide | $NH_3$ | Ammonia |
| HCl | Hydrogen chloride | $H_2S$ | Hydrogen sulphide | $PH_3$ | Phosphine |

Notes

**Transporting Dangerous Goods by Truck**

Notes

# CANADIAN EMERGENCY RESPONSE REPORTING REQUIREMENTS

**When dangerous goods are spilled or leaking**, or it seems likely that it may become necessary to transfer dangerous goods from a vehicle, the **driver must immediately notify**:

- the **local police and/or other local authority first**, (See Emergency Contact Numbers below) and then;
- his/her **employer**;
- the **consignor** of the dangerous goods; and
- the **owner or lessee** of the vehicle.

For Class 6.2, Infectious Substances, CANUTEC must also be called at 613 996-6666.

*IMPORTANT: Requirements are now in place (2009) for reporting dangerous goods that are lost or stolen. See 7.11 page 24.*

## EMERGENCY CONTACT NUMBERS

| | |
|---|---|
| Alberta | 800 272-9600 **and** local police |
| British Columbia | 800 663-3456 **and** local police |
| Manitoba | 204 945-4888 **and** local police |
| New Brunswick | 800 565-1633 **or** local police |
| Newfoundland and Labrador | 709 772-2083 **and** local police |
| North West Territories | 867 920-8130 |
| Nova Scotia | 800 565-1633 **or** 902 426-6030 **or** local police |
| Ontario | Local police |
| Nunavut | 867 920-8130 **and** local police |
| Prince Edward Island | 800 565-1633 **or** local police |
| Quebec | Local police |
| Saskatchewan | 800 667-7525 **or** local police |
| Yukon | 867 667-7244 |

## U.S. EMERGENCY RESPONSE REPORTING REQUIREMENTS

An accidental release in the U.S. that must be reported, as described in 12.15 - 12.18, must be reported to the U.S. DOT Response Center which operates a 24-hour service at 800 424-8802.

If an accidental release of a hazardous substance occurs in the U.S.and it exceeds the Reportable Quantity, it must be reported to the U.S. Coast Guard National Response Centre, which operates a 24-hour notification service at 800 424-8802. If there is doubt about the amount of product released, then the accidental release should be reported.

### U.S. EMERGENCY RESPONSE INFORMATION

The following companies operate 24-hour emergency response information systems, and maintain lists of state and federal authorities that will provide emergency information and technical assistance to any caller.

**CHEMTREC**, a service of the Chemical Manufacturers Association
> 800 424-9300 (In the U.S. and Canada) or 703 527-3887

**CHEM-TEL, INC**.
> 800 255-3924 (In the U.S. and Canada) or 813 979-0626

**INFOTRAC**
> 800 535-5053

**3E COMPANY**
> 800 451-8346

For assistance in incidents involving materials being shipped by, for, or to the U.S. Department of Defense (DOD), the following numbers can be called (24 hours):

- for incidents involving explosives and ammunition, U.S. Army Operations Centre at 703 697-0218 (Collect).
- for incidents involving dangerous goods other than explosives and ammunition, Defense Logistics Agency at 800 851-8061.

# PLACARDING REQUIREMENTS FOR LARGE MoC

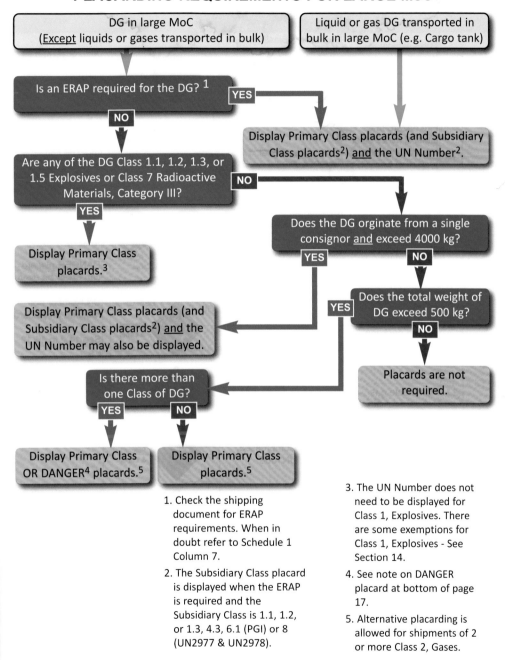

DG in large MoC
(Except liquids or gases transported in bulk)

Liquid or gas DG transported in bulk in large MoC (e.g. Cargo tank)

Is an ERAP required for the DG? [1]

YES

NO

Display Primary Class placards (and Subsidiary Class placards[2]) and the UN Number[2].

Are any of the DG Class 1.1, 1.2, 1.3, or 1.5 Explosives or Class 7 Radioactive Materials, Category III?

NO

YES

Display Primary Class placards.[3]

Does the DG orginate from a single consignor and exceed 4000 kg?

YES

NO

Display Primary Class placards (and Subsidiary Class placards[2]) and the UN Number may also be displayed.

YES

Does the total weight of DG exceed 500 kg?

NO

Is there more than one Class of DG?

Placards are not required.

YES

NO

Display Primary Class OR DANGER[4] placards.[5]

Display Primary Class placards.[5]

1. Check the shipping document for ERAP requirements. When in doubt refer to Schedule 1 Column 7.

2. The Subsidiary Class placard is displayed when the ERAP is required and the Subsidiary Class is 1.1, 1.2, or 1.3, 4.3, 6.1 (PGI) or 8 (UN2977 & UN2978).

3. The UN Number does not need to be displayed for Class 1, Explosives. There are some exemptions for Class 1, Explosives - See Section 14.

4. See note on DANGER placard at bottom of page 17.

5. Alternative placarding is allowed for shipments of 2 or more Class 2, Gases.

# OTHER SYMBOLS USED WITH DANGEROUS GOODS

**Danger Placard**

**Elevated Temperature Sign**

**Class 7 Label Radioactive Materials**

**Marine Pollutant Sign**

**Fumigation Sign**

**Category B Mark**

## Dangerous Goods Routes

**Dangerous Goods Permitted**

**Dangerous Goods Not Permitted**

**1203**

**Options For Displaying UN Number**